CADES 2017-19

Camping, Touring & Mo

Published by
Cade's Guides Limited,
P.O. Box 7568, Milton Keynes, MK11 9GF
Tel: 01908 618320
Email: enquiries@cades.co.uk
Website: www.cades.co.uk

Compiled by
Mary Soper

Advertising Services
Lisa Sherratt

Printed by
Callimedia Limited, Dedham Vale, Essex, CO7 6BL

Distribution (Booktrade)
Kuperard
59 Hutton Grove, London, N12 8DS

(Camping and Caravan Trade)
Cade's Guides Limited (address above)

ISBN 978-1-905963-19-5

Look forward to days away

Save up to
50%*
on 2017 holidays

Find your perfect coastal escape with Haven

- 22 UK touring and camping holiday parks dotted around the coast
- Choice of six pitch types – from basic grass to fully serviced hard-standing
- Modern shower blocks and amenities
- Pets welcome for only £1† a night
- Splash around in our heated pools - some with flumes and slides

- Be adventurous – try out our many activities from Aerial Adventure to learning archery and fencing skills
- Family friendly entertainment and fun packed kids' clubs
- There's plenty of tasty food and drink on the menu at our restaurants
- Most of our parks are right beside the sea – so don't forget your buckets and spades

To find out more, order a brochure and to book visit
haventouring.com/Cades2017

Alternatively, give us a call on **0333 202 1652** Quoting: **Cades2017**

Calls to 0333 numbers are charged at standard UK rates and will be included in any inclusive minute bundles.

Thank you for choosing Cade's to assist with finding the right Touring Holiday Park for you. The internet of course, is full of what you will find in Cade's but unfortunately given the number of similar websites available these days and the different ways in which they work, they do not make it as easy as Cade's to use.

Over 1,500 Touring Holiday Parks are listed in Cade's, each of which has had their information verified or updated for this edition. For those of you intent on web browsing, Cade's makes an excellent website directory as it includes the web address for nearly all the Parks included. Simply shortlist your County, then Town and perhaps Park too and then visit their website. It will save you hours! Of course Cade's have a website too and as easy as it is to use, our printed guide still comes in handy for short listing prior to looking on the internet.

Whether you get away in a tent, a touring caravan, a motorhome or a huge R.V., take care on your travels. Book in advance in peak season and always remember to check directly with the park, that any facilities you particularly require, will be available at the time of you visit.

If you are using a charcoal barbecue, be it a dispoable one or of any other construction, DO NOT take it in to your tent or awning even when it appears to have gone out *(see page 176)*. The poisonous Carbon Monoxide gas which is stll emitted from the charcoal for many, many hours afterwards, is a killer! We have seen this many times unfortunately, as the unnecessary cause of accidental death. We would rather not see it again. Keep your family safe.

Next time you are browsing the internet, why not take a look at our Facebook page at www.facebook.com/cadesguides. Here, as we link with others, you will find valuable information on all sorts of things; it will lead you to deals at dealerships and special offers at Holiday Parks. You can even drop us a line to say what you would like to see or tell us where you have been. So, next time you are on Facebook, visit us and 'Like' our page.

All that remains now is for us to wish you all the very best of touring holidays in 2017.

Cade's

The Cade's Team

SYMBOLS/SYMBOLES FRANCAISE

⋀ Tents	⋀ Tentes
⊟ Motor Caravans	⊟ Auto-Caravanes
⊟ Touring Caravans	⊟ Caravanes
⊟ U.S. R.V.'s	⊟ Auto-Caravanes (Etats Unis)
⇌ Nearest Station	⇌ Gare Locale
♿ Facilities for Disabled	♿ Handicapés
⚍ No Motorcycles	⨍ Branchments Electrique Pour Caravanes
⨍ Electricity Hook-ups	⊟ Emplacement Service Complet
⊟ Fully Serviced Pitches	⊡ Emplacement Surface Dure
⊡ Hard Standings	⚍ Motorcyclettes Non-Admises
⊞ Flush Toilets	⊞ Toilettes
⚲ Water	⚲ Eau
⌂ Showers	⌂ Douches
☉ Shaver Points	☉ Prises Electrique pour Rasoirs
⊿ Washing Facilities	⊿ Bains
▬ Ironing Facilities	▬ Repassage
▣ Launderette	▣ Laverie Automatique
⬤ Chem. Toilet Disposal	⬤ Décharge pour W.C. Chemique
S♄ Site Shop	S♄ Magasin du Terrain
I♄ Local Shop	I♄ Magasin du Quartier
⊘ Gas	⊘ Gaz
✕ Café Restaurant	✕ Café
♈ Licensed Club	♈ Club/Bar Patenté
🖵 T.V.	🖵 Salle de Télévision
✹ Games Room	✹ Salle de Jeux
⋔ Childs Play Area	⋔ Terrain de Jeux Enfants
↘ Outdoor Pool	↘ Piscine du Terrain
⟡ Indoor Pool	⟡ Piscine a l'interieur
♣ Sports Area	♣ Terrain de Sports et de Jeux
⋈ Pets Welcome	⋈ Pêche sur place
✔ Fishing on Site	⊟ Stationment à côté de la caravane permis
⊟ Parking by Unit	⊡ Carte Credit Accepter
⊡ Credit Cards Accepted	⊠ Bon Remise 'Cades' Accepter
⊠ Money-Off Vouchers	A Camping Seulement Adulte
A Adults Only Park	⚜ Emplacements pour La Saison
⚜ Seasonal Pitches	⚓ Gardiennage
⚓ Secure Storage	📶 Wi-Fi
📶 Wi-Fi Access	

Escape to North Devon

Right next to Woolacombe's three miles of golden sandy beach

WOOLACOMBE BAY
Britain's best beach
HOLIDAY PARKS

You won't believe how high I climbed, I could see for miles!

What we've got to offer...

- Sea view camping & touring pitches
- Level pitches with easy access
- 400 all weather pitches
- 16 amp electric hookups
- Modern amenity blocks
- Over 40 **FREE** activities

4 for 1 Stay at one Park and you get to use the facilities on all four of our award winning Holiday Parks...

Golden Coast | Woolacombe Bay | Twitchen House | Easewell Farm

Pitches from just
£6
per night

Call 01271 872 303
or visit woolacombe.com

We're here

WOOLACOMBE BAY
HOLIDAY PARKS

The carbon monoxide from a badly adjusted camping light or stove can kill.

Barbecues in enclosed spaces are lethal, too.

ENGLAND

BERKSHIRE

DORNEY REACH

Amerden Caravan Site, Off Old Marsh Lane, Dorney Reach, Nr Maidenhead, Berkshire, SL6 0EE
Tel: 01628 627461
Email:beverly@amerdencaravanpark.co.uk
www.amerdencaravanpark.webs.com
Pitches For A ⊕ 🚐 **Total** 40
Acreage 3 **Open** Apr to Sept
Access Good **Site** Level
Nearest Bus Stop (Miles) 1¼
Near River Thames.
Facilities ⚓ ♂ 🕮 ⚓ ⌐ ⊙ ⚑ 🔟 🔊 ⚑ ╫ ▣ 🛜
Nearest Town Maidenhead
Directions Leave M4 junc 7, Slough West, then A4 towards Maidenhead. Turn left at second set of traffic lights signposted Dorney Reach and caravan site, then first turn right.
🚆 Taplow

HURLEY

Hurley Riverside Park, Hurley, Nr Maidenhead, Berkshire, SL6 5NE
Tel: 01628 824493
Email: info@hurleyriversidepark.co.uk
www.hurleyriversidepark.co.uk
Pitches For A ⊕ 🚐 🚐
Total 200
Acreage 15
Open Mar to Oct
Access Good **Site** Level
Nearest Bus Stop (Miles) Outside
Alongside river, family run. Peaceful village setting. Nature trail, play area, riverside picnic grounds.
Facilities ⚓ ♂ 🔟 🔊 🕮 ⚓ ⌐ ⊙ ⚑ ▣ 💲 🛜 ⚑ ⊙ ⚙ 🔟 ╫ ▣ 🛒 ✉ 🛜
Nearest Town Henley-on-Thames
Directions From M4 Junc. 8/9, take A404(M), leave on the A4130 to Henley. After 2 miles, turn right.
🚆 Henley/Maidenhead/Twyford

NEWBURY

Oakley Farm Caravan Park, Oakley Farm House, Penwood Road, Wash Water, Newbury, Berkshire, RG20 0LP
Tel: 01635 36581
Email: info@oakleyfarm.co.uk
www.oakleyfarm.co.uk
Pitches For A ⊕ 🚐 **Total** 30
Acreage 3
Open Mar to Oct
Access Good **Site** Gentle Slope
Nearest Bus Stop (Miles) ½
Not suitable for caravans over 22 foot long.
Facilities ♂ 🕮 ⚓ ⌐ ⊙ 🔟 ⚑ ╫ ▣
Nearest Town Newbury
Directions From the A34 south of Newbury take the exit marked Highclere and Wash Common. Turn left onto the A343 towards Newbury, turn right after ¼ mile (by car sales garage) into Penwood Road. Site is then 400 metres on your left.
🚆 Newbury

RISELEY

Wellington Country Park, Odiham Road, Riseley, Berkshire, RG7 1SP
Tel: 01189 326444
Email: info@wellingtoncountrypark.co.uk
www.wellingtoncountrypark.co.uk
Pitches For Å ⊕ ⊟ **Total** 87
Open Mar to Nov
Access Good **Site** Level
Nearest Bus Stop (Miles) ¼
Forest location with free access to country park and facilities.
Facilities ⨍ 🚻 ⬧ ⌂ ⊙ ⌶ ▭ ◲ ☎
🖳 ⓧ ♿ ⊞ ⊟ ⬒
Nearest Town Reading
Directions From the M4 junction 11 follow the A33 south towards Basingstoke.
⇻ Reading

BRISTOL (County of)

BRISTOL

Baltic Wharf Caravan Club Site, Cumberland Road, Bristol, BS1 6XG
Tel: 0117 926 8030
www.caravanclub.co.uk
Pitches For ⊕ ⊟ **Total** 55
Acreage 2½ **Open** All Year
Access Good **Site** Level
Nearest Bus Stop (Miles) Outside
Quiet waterside site ½ mile from the town centre. River ferry service to the city centre in Summer. Near to Bristol Zoo, SS Great Britain and museums. Non members welcome. Booking essential.
Facilities ⬧ ⨍ 🚻 ⬧ ⌂ ⌶ ▭ ◲ ☎
🖳 ⓧ ⊙ ⊟ ⬒
Nearest Town Bristol
Directions Leave M5 at junc. 18 take the A4. After Clifton Suspension Bridge keep in lt lane and follow signs to harbour. At lights stay in rt lane through Hotwells, over the crossing and move to lt lane, go over bridge following signs for SS Great Britain. Site is 500 yds on the lt.
⇻ Bristol Temple Meads

BUCKINGHAMSHIRE

BEACONSFIELD

Highclere Farm Country Touring Park, Newbarn Lane, Seer Green, Nr Beaconsfield, Buckinghamshire, HP9 2QZ
Tel: 01494 874505
Email: highclerepark@aol.com
www.highclerefarmpark.co.uk
Pitches For Å ⊕ ⊟ **Total** 100
Acreage 6 **Open** Mar to Jan
Access Good **Site** Level
Nearest Bus Stop (Miles) Outside
Near to Legoland, Chiltern Air Museum, Miltons Cottage, Odds Farm (Rare Breeds), Bekonscot, Amersham and London.
Facilities ⬧ ⨍ 🚻 ⬧ ⌂ ⊙ ⌶ ▭ ◲ ☎
🖳 🖳 ⓧ ⊙ ⊠ ⚲ ⊞ ⊟ ⬒
Nearest Town Beaconsfield
Directions Leave the M40 at junction 2, go into Beaconsfield and take the A355 towards Amersham. After 1 mile turn right to Seer Green and follow tourist signs.
⇻ Seer Green

MILTON KEYNES

Gulliver's Milton Keynes Camping & Caravanning Club Site, Livingstone Drive, Milton Keynes, Buckinghamshire, MK15 0DT
Tel: 02476 475426
Email: gullivers.site@thefriendlyclub.co.uk
www.campingandcaravanningclub.co.uk/gullivers
Pitches For Å ⊕ ⊟ **Total** 90
Open 14-Mar to 10-Nov
Access Good **Site** Level
Nearest Bus Stop (Miles) ½
Adjacent to Gulliver's Land Theme Park and near a lake. Just a short drive to Central Milton Keynes. Pods for Glamping. Excellent location for footpaths and cycle routes. Non members welcome. You can also call us on 0845 130 7633.
Facilities ⬧ ⨍ 🚻 ▭ 🚻 ⬧ ⌂ ⊙ ⌶ ◲ ☎
🔾 ⊠ ⛰ ⊞ ▭ ⊟ ⬒
Nearest Town Milton Keynes
Directions From the M1 take the A509 towards Central Milton Keynes and follow signs for Gullivers Theme Park (on the V10 Brickhill Street).
⇻ Milton Keynes

MILTON KEYNES

Old Dairy Farm Camping & Caravan Site, Old Dairy Farm, Orchard Mill Lane, Stoke Hammond, Buckinghamshire, MK17 9BF
Tel: 01908 274206
Email: wiblang@aol.com
www.www.theolddairyfarm.co.uk
Pitches For Å ⊕ ⊟ **Total** 30
Acreage 2 **Open** All Year
Access Good **Site** Level
Nearest Bus Stop (Miles) ¼
Ideal for Woburn Abbey & Safari Park, Milton Keynes Bowl, Xscape, MK Dons Stadium, Bletchley Park, Whipsnade Zoo and the Chilterns.
Facilities ⬧ ⨍ 🚻 ⬧ ⌂ ⌶ ⊙ ☎ ▭ ▭ ⬒
Nearest Town Milton Keynes
Directions From A5 take A4146 towards Aylesbury and follow signs to Stoke Hammond.
⇻ Bletchley

CAMBRIDGESHIRE

CAMBRIDGE

Appleacre Park, London Road, Fowlmere, Cambridgeshire, SG8 7RU
Tel: 01763 208354
Email: tony@appleacrepark.co.uk
www.appleacrepark.co.uk
Pitches For Å ⊕ ⊟ **Total** 23
Acreage 3 **Open** All Year
Access Good **Site** Level
Nearest Bus Stop (Miles) Entrance
A small pleasant Park at the southern end of the village. Only 3 miles from Duxford Imperial War Museum. RSPB Nature Reserve just a 20 minute walk away.
Facilities ⨍ 🚻 🚻 ⬧ ⌂ ⊙ ⌶ ◲ 🖳 ⛰ ▭ ⊟
Nearest Town Cambridge
Directions 9 miles south of Cambridge on the B1368 through Fowlmere Village on the left hand side.
⇻ Foxton

CAMBRIDGE

Cambridge Cherry Hinton Caravan Club Site, Lime Kiln Road, Cherry Hinton, Cambridgeshire, CB1 8NQ
Tel: 01223 244088
www.caravanclub.co.uk
Pitches For Å ⊕ ⊟ **Total** 61
Acreage 5½ **Open** All Year
Access Good **Site** Level
Nearest Bus Stop (Miles) ½
Set in old quarry works with imaginative landscaping. Only ½ a mile from Cambridge town centre. Close to the American War Cemetary, Duxford Imperial War Museum, Wicken Fen Nature Reserve, Wimpole Hall and Audley End House & Gardens. Non members welcome. Booking essential.
Facilities ⬧ ⨍ 🚻 🚻 ⬧ ⌂ ⊙ ⌶ ◲ ☎
🖳 🖳 ⓧ ⊙ ⊠ ⊞ ⊟ ⬒
Nearest Town Cambridge
Directions From south west on A10, pass over M11 junc 11 and continue onto A1309 sp Cambridge. At the fifth set of traffic lights turn right into Long Road(A1134) After 1½ miles at the r/about continue to Queen Ediths Way, after 1 mile turn right into Lime Kiln Road.
⇻ Cambridge

CAMBRIDGE

Highfield Farm Touring Park, Highfield Farm, Long Road, Comberton, Cambridge, Cambridgeshire, CB23 7DG
Tel: 01223 262308
Email: enquiries@highfieldfarmtouringpark.co.uk
www.highfieldfarmtouringpark.co.uk
Pitches For Å ⊕ ⊟ **Total** 120
Acreage 8 **Open** Apr to Oct
Access Good **Site** Level
Nearest Bus Stop (Miles) ½
Well maintained, long established family run Touring Park. 1½ miles of farmland walks. Close to the historic University City of Cambridge, and the Imperial War Museum, Duxford. Calor Caravan Park Awards 2002, Best Park in England (Finalist).
Facilities ⨍ 🚻 🚻 ⬧ ⌂ ⊙ ⌶ ▭ ◲ ☎
🖳 🖳 🖳 ⓧ ⊙ ⊠ ⊞ ⊟ ⬒
Nearest Town Cambridge
Directions From Cambridge - Leave A1303/A428 (Bedford) after 3 miles, follow camping signs to Comberton. From M11 - Leave junction 12, take A603 (Sandy) for ½ mile then B1046 to Comberton (2 miles).
⇻ Cambridge

CAMBRIDGE

Roseberry Tourist Park, Earith Road, Willingham, Cambridgeshire, CB24 5LT
Tel: 01954 260346
Email: info@roseberrytouristpark.co.uk
www.roseberrytouristpark.co.uk
Pitches For Å ⊕ ⊟ ⬧ **Total** 90
Acreage 10 **Open** All Year
Access Good **Site** Level
Nearest Bus Stop (Miles) 1
Ideal for touring Cambridge and surrounding Market towns of St. Ives, Huntingdon and Ely.
Facilities ⨍ 🚻 🚻 ⬧ ⌂ ⊙ ⌶ ◲ ☎
⊙ ⛰ ⊞ ⊟ ⬒ ⚭ ⚲
Nearest Town Cambridge

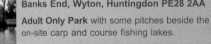

Directions Northwest of Cambridge on A14 Junc 29 Bar Hill, Follow B1050 towards Willingham. Site 1 mile north of Willingham.
⚏ Cambridge/Waterbeach

EARITH

Westview Marina, High Street, Earith, Huntingdon, Cambridgeshire, PE28 3PN
Tel: 01487 841627
Email: elainefidler@homecall.co.uk
Pitches For 🛆 ⚎ ⚎ **Total** 28
Acreage 2 **Open** Mar to Oct
Access Good **Site** Level
Nearest Bus Stop (Miles) Outside
River frontage. Ideal touring.
Facilities ƒ ⬚ ⚑ ↑ 🏳 ⊙ ✦ ◢ ⚆
Nearest Town St. Ives (Cambs)
Directions 5 miles from St. Ives and 12 miles from Cambridge.
⚏ Huntingdon

ELY

Riverside Caravan & Camping Park, 21 New River Bank, Littleport, Ely, Cambridgeshire, CB7 4TA
Tel: 01353 860255
Email: riversideccp@btopenworld.com
www.riversideccp.co.uk
Pitches For 🛆 ⚎ ⚎ **Total** 49
Acreage 4½ **Open** All Year
Access Good **Site** Level
Nearest Bus Stop (Miles) ¼
ADULTS ONLY site alongside the River Ouse for fishing and boating. 5 miles from the historic city and cathedral of Ely.
Facilities ƒ ⬚ ⚑ ↑ 🏳 ⊙ ◣ ⚆
🏫 ⊙ ⚏ ⊟ 🅰 ✦ ⚶ ◆
Nearest Town Ely
Directions On the A10, 5 miles north of Ely, cross the River Ouse and turn right at the roundabout.
⚏ Littleport

GRAFHAM

Grafham Water Caravan Club Site, Church Road, Grafham, Huntingdon, Cambridgeshire, PE28 0BB
Tel: 01480 810264
www.caravanclub.co.uk
Pitches For 🛆 ⚎ ⚎ **Total** 68
Acreage 6 **Open** Mar to Nov
Access Good **Site** Level
Nearest Bus Stop (Miles) ½
Near to Grafham Water. Refurbished amenity block. David Bellamy Gold Award for Conservation 2005. Non members welcome. Booking essential.
Facilities ƒ ⬚ ⚑ ↑ 🏳 ⊙ ◣ ◢ ◻ ⚆
🏫 ⊙ ⚏ ↘ ⊟ ⊟ ◆
Nearest Town Huntingdon
Directions From the A1 at Buckden roundabout follow caravan park signs. From the A14 leave at Ellington and follow caravan park signs from the village.
⚏ Huntingdon

HUNTINGDON

Huntingdon Boathaven & Caravan Park, The Avenue, Godmanchester, Huntingdon, Cambridgeshire, PE18 8AF
Tel: 01480 411977
Email: boathaven.hunts@virgin.net
www.huntingdonboathaven.co.uk
Pitches For 🛆 ⚎ ⚎ **Total** 35
Acreage 2 **Open** All year (subject to weather)
Access Good **Site** Level
Nearest Bus Stop (Miles) ¼
Marina and caravan park situated on the Great River Ouse. Near to many tourist attractions. Limited fishing on site.

Facilities ◔ ƒ ⬚ ⚑ ↑ 🏳 ⊙ ✦ ◆
🏫 ⊙ ⚑ ⬚ ◢ ⚶ ◆
Nearest Town Cambridge
Directions From the A14 turn off to Godmanchester and travel towards Huntingdon. Turn left before the fly-over to Huntingdon Boathaven.
⚏ Huntingdon

HUNTINGDON

Quiet Waters Caravan Park, Hemingford Abbots, Huntingdon, Cambridgeshire, PE28 9AJ
Tel: 01480 463405
Email: quietwaters.park@btopenworld.com
www.quietwaterscaravanpark.co.uk
Pitches For 🛆 ⚎ ⚎ **Total** 20
Acreage ½ **Open** April to October
Access Good **Site** Level
Nearest Bus Stop (Miles) Outside
In the centre of a riverside village, good for fishing and boating.
Facilities ◔ ƒ ⬚ ↑ 🏳 ⊙ ✦ ◣ ◻ ⚆
🏫 ⊙ ⚑ ⊟ ⬚ ◢ ⚶ ◆
Nearest Town St Ives/Huntingdon
Directions Junction 25 off the A14. West of Cambridge on the A14, after 12 miles look for Hemingford Abbots, we are 1 mile into the village. 3 miles east of Huntingdon on the A14.
⚏ Huntingdon

HUNTINGDON

Stroud Hill Park, Fen Road, Pidley, Huntingdon, Cambridgeshire, PE28 3DE
Tel: 01487 741333
Email: stroudhillpark@btconnect.com
www.stroudhillpark.co.uk
Pitches For 🛆 ⚎ ⚎ **Total** 60
Open All Year
Access Good **Site** Lev/Slope
Nearest Bus Stop (Miles) ½
Quiet, attractive, rural, ADULTS ONLY site. Set in ancient bluebell woodland on a 150 acre family farm. Tennis on site. 18 hole golf course next door.
Facilities ◔ ƒ ⬚ ⚑ ↑ 🏳 ⊙ ◣ ◢ ◻ ⚆
🏫 ⊙ ⚆ ✕ ↘ ⊟ ⬚ ◢ 🅰 ◆
Nearest Town St. Ives
Directions Take the A141 signposted March, 4 miles from St Ives and 7 miles from Huntingdon.
⚏ Huntingdon

HUNTINGDON

The Willows Caravan Park, Bromholme Lane, Brampton, Huntingdon, Cambridgeshire, PE18 8NE
Tel: 01480 437566
Email: willows@willows33.freeserve.co.uk
www.willowscaravanpark.com
Pitches For 🛆 ⚎ ⚎ ⚎⚶ **Total** 70
Acreage 4 **Open** All Year
Access Good **Site** Level
Nearest Bus Stop (Miles) ¼
Situated on Ouse Valley Way, attractive walks. Launching area for boats and canoes. Fishing and boating available. Separate tent field. No groundsheets. Heated toilet block. Resident wardens on site. Country park, Grafham Water and sports facilities nearby. Site is Caravan Club, Camping & Caravanning Club and AA Listed.
Facilities ◔ ƒ ⬚ ↑ 🏳 ⊙ ✦ ◻ ⚆
🏫 ✕ ↘ ⊟ ◆
Nearest Town Huntingdon
Directions Brampton is situated between the A1 and the A14 (formerly A604). Follow the B1514 through Brampton towards Huntingdon, taking right hand signposted turning into Bromholme Lane.
⚏ Huntingdon

HUNTINGDON

Wyton Lakes Holiday Park, Banks End, Wyton, Huntingdon, Cambridgeshire, PE28 2AA
Tel: 01480 412715
Email: loupeter@supanet.com
www.wytonlakes.com
Pitches For 🛆 ⚎ ⚎ **Total** 80
Acreage 12½ **Open** Apr to Oct
Access Good **Site** Level
Nearest Bus Stop (Miles) ¼
ADULTS ONLY site situated alongside a river with four fishing lakes on site.
Facilities ◔ ƒ ⬚ ↑ 🏳 ⊙ ◻ ⚆
🏫 ⊙ ⚑ ⊟ ◢ ⚶ ◆
Nearest Town Huntingdon
Directions Leave the A14 at junction 23 and follow signs for the A141 March. On the 4th roundabout take the A1123 for St. Ives, park is approx. 1 mile on the right.
⚏ Huntingdon

PETERBOROUGH

Ferry Meadows Caravan Club Site, Ham Lane, Peterborough, Cambridgeshire, PE2 5UU
Tel: 01733 233526
www.caravanclub.co.uk
Pitches For 🛆 ⚎ ⚎ **Total** 265
Acreage 30 **Open** All Year
Access Good **Site** Level
Nearest Bus Stop (Miles) ½
Set in a country park with plenty of activities available nearby, and a 6 acre shopping complex. Near to Nene Valley Steam Railway. Non members welcome. Booking essential.
Facilities ◔ ƒ ⬚ ↑ 🏳 ◻ ⚆
🏫 ⊙ ⚆ ↘ ⊟ ◆
Nearest Town Peterborough
Directions From South on the A1, do not turn onto the A1139, instead turn left at next junction just past the service station sp Showground. At the T-junction turn left, continue and turn left sp Nene Park, continue and site is on the left.
⚏ Peterborough

ST. NEOTS

Camping & Caravanning Club Site, Hardwick Road, Eynesbury, St. Neots, Cambridgeshire, PE19 2PR
Tel: 01480 474404
Email: stneots.site@thefriendlyclub.co.uk
www.campingandcaravanningclub.co.uk/stneots
Pitches For 🛆 ⚎ ⚎ **Total** 180
Acreage 11 **Open** Apr to 03-Nov
Access Good **Site** Level
Nearest Bus Stop (Miles) ½
On the banks of the River Ouse for boating, fishing and walking. Plenty of sports facilities in the area. Non members welcome. You can also call us on 0845 130 7633.
Facilities ◔ ƒ ⬚ ↑ 🏳 ⊙ ✦ ◣ ◻ ⚆
🏫 ⊙ ⚆ ↘ ⊟ ◢ ◆
Nearest Town Cambridge
Directions From the A1 take the A428 to Cambridge, at the second roundabout turn left to Tesco, go past the sports centre and follow the international signs to the site.
⚏ Cambridge

PLEASE REMEMBER TO MENTION CADE'S WHEN BOOKING

CHANNEL ISLANDS

GUERNSEY

Le Vaugrat Camping, Les Hougues, Route de Vaugrat, St Sampson, Guernsey, Channel Isles, GY2 4TA
Tel: 01481 257468
Email: enquiries@vaugratcampsite.com
www.vaugratcampsite.com
Pitches For Å 🚐 **Total** 150
Acreage 6 **Open** May to Mid Sept
Site Level
Nearest Bus Stop (Miles) Outside
Beautiful garden. 5 mins from the beach.
Facilities ♿ ⨍ 🚿 ♨ ⛽ ⊙ 🚻 🍴 🔯 🛒 🖵 ☎ 🛜
Directions From the harbour turn right at the roundabout heading north. After 2 miles (The Halfway) bear left before filter in turn. At traffic lights turn left towards Llslet, head straight at the traffic lights and through Llslet to the west coast. Campsite is along the coast road from the Peninsular Hotel, turn left into Vaugrat Road.

CHESHIRE

CHESTER

Chester Fairoaks Caravan Club Site, Rake Lane, Little Stanney, Chester, Cheshire, CH2 4HS
Tel: 0151 355 1600
www.caravanclub.co.uk
Pitches For Å 🚐 🚐 **Total** 100
Acreage 8 **Open** All Year
Access Good **Site** Level
Nearest Bus Stop (Miles) ½
Pleasant open and level site with oak tree boundaries. Close to the delightful city of Chester. Non members welcome. Booking essential.
Facilities ♿ ⨍ 🚿 🔯 ♨ ⊙ ⨀ ☎ 🔯 🖵 ⊙ 🛒 🖵 🖵 🛜
Nearest Town Chester
Directions Leave the M53 at junction 10 and take the A5117 signposted Queensferry. After ¼ mile in Little Stanney turn left signposted Chorlton. Site is ¼ mile on the left.
🚌 Chester

CHESTER

Manor Wood Country Caravan Park, Manor Wood, Coddington, Chester, Cheshire, CH3 9EN
Tel: 01829 782990
Email: info@manorwoodcaravans.co.uk
www.manorwoodcaravans.co.uk
Pitches For Å 🚐 🚐 **Total** 25
Acreage 8 **Open** All Year
Access Good **Site** Level
Nearest Bus Stop (Miles) ¼
Excellent views. Only 15 minutes from Chester City. Fishing on site. Fantastic walks and cycleways. Golf courses within 5 minutes drive.
Facilities ♿ ⨍ 🚿 🔯 🚿 ♨ ⊙ ⨀ ♨ 🛒 🖵 ☎
🔯 ⊙ 🍴 🕮 🔯 🍴 🖵 🖵 ✂ 🌿 🛜 ☎ 🛜
Nearest Town Chester
Directions From the A41 Whitchurch to Chester road, at Broxton roundabout take the A534 signposted Wrexham. Turn opposite

the Cock O Barton Pub and the Park is 500 yards on the left.
🚌 Chester

CHESTER

Netherwood Touring Site, Netherwood House, Whitchurch Road, Nr Chester, Cheshire, CH3 6AF
Tel: 01244 335583
Email: netherwood.chester@btinternet.com
www.netherwoodtouringsite.co.uk
Pitches For 🚐 🚐 **Total** 15
Acreage 1½ **Open** Mar to Oct
Access Good **Site** Level
Nearest Bus Stop (Miles) Outside
ADULTS ONLY site on the Shropshire Union Canal. 5 miles from a Zoo.
Facilities ⨍ 🚿 🔯 ♨ ⊙ ⨀ ☎ 🔯 ⊙ 🍴 🖵 ⊿ A
Directions On A41, approx. 1 mile from Chester bypass.
🚌 Chester

KNUTSFORD

Royal Vale Caravan Park, London Road, Allostock, Knutsford, Cheshire, WA16 9JD
Tel: 01565 722355
Email: canistay@royalvale.co.uk
www.royalvale.co.uk
Pitches For Å 🚐 🚐 🚂 ≋ **Total** 52
Access Good **Site** Level
ADULTS ONLY PARK situated in the heart of Cheshire countryside, 3 miles south of the historic market town of Knutsford, which has an excellent shopping centre, fine restaurants and old inns. Country walks direct from the Park. Historic homes nearby including Tatton Park, Gawsworth Hall and Little Moreton Hall.
Facilities ♿ ⨍ 🚿 🔯 🚿 ♨ ⊙ ⨀ ♨ 🛒 🖵 ☎
⊙ 🍴 🖵 🔯 A 🌿 🛜
Nearest Town Knutsford
Directions Just off the A50 midway between Knutsford and Holmes Chapel.
🚌 Knutsford

KNUTSFORD

Woodlands Park, Wash Lane, Allostock, Cheshire, WA16 9LG
Tel: 01565 723429
Email: jane@rongrundy.co.uk
www.rongrundy.co.uk
Pitches For Å 🚐 🚐 **Total** 20
Open Mar to 06-Jan
Access Good **Site** Level
Nearest Bus Stop (Miles) ¼
Facilities ⨍ 🔯 🚿 🔯 ♨ ⊙ ⨀ 🍴 🌿
Directions Take the A50 Knutsford road, Wash Lane is left turn after Boundary Water Park.
🚌 Goostrey

MACCLESFIELD

Strawberry Wood Caravan Park, Home Farm, Farm Lane, Lower Withington, Macclesfield, Cheshire, SK11 9DU
Tel: 01477 571407
Email: info@strawberrywoodcaravanpark.co.uk
www.strawberrywoodcaravanpark.co.uk

Pitches For 🚐 🚐 **Total** 25
Acreage 5 **Open** March to October
Access Good **Site** Level
Nearest Bus Stop (Miles) No buses. Jodrell Bank and several National Trust Properties.
Facilities ⨍ 🔯 🚿 🔯 ♨ ⊙ ⨀ ☎ 🍴 ⊿ 🌿
Nearest Town Congleton
Directions Junction 18 M6 A54 to Holmes Chapel. Follow A535 to Macclesfield, after 4 miles turn right onto the B5392 (Farm Lane). The site entrance is on the right hand side.
🚌 Goostrey

NORTHWICH

Delamere Forest Camping & Caravanning Club Site, Station Road, Delamere, Northwich, Cheshire, CW8 2HZ
Tel: 01606 889231
Email: delamere.forest@thefriendlyclub.co.uk
www.campingandcaravanningclub.co.uk/delamere
Pitches For Å 🚐 🚐 **Total** 80
Acreage 6 **Open** All Year
Access Good **Site** Level
Ideal for walking and cycling (bike hire). Near to Chester Zoo, Go Ape Adventure Playground, Oulton Park Raceway, Railway Age Museum and Beeston Castle. Non members welcome. You can also call us on 0845 130 7633.
Facilities ♿ ⨍ 🔯 🚿 🔯 ♨ ⊙ ⨀ 🛒 🖵 ☎
🔯 ⊙ 🍴 🖵 🔯 🛜
Nearest Town Frodsham
Directions From the A556 in Delamere turn into Station Road and the Site is located on the opposite side of the train tracks.
🚌 Northwich

NORTHWICH

Woodbine Cottage Caravan Park, Warrington Road, Acton Bridge, Northwich, Cheshire, CW8 3QB
Tel: 01606 852319
Email: jjdone@woodbinecottage-caravanpark.co.uk
www.woodbinecottage-caravanpark.co.uk
Pitches For Å 🚐 🚐 **Total** 55
Acreage 2½ **Open** Mar to Oct
Access Good **Site** Lev/Slope
Situated on the banks of the River Weaver. Nearby attractions including Blakemere Crafts and Anderton Boat Lift. Within easy reach of Chester, Liverpool, Manchester and the North Wales coast. Static caravans for hire. You can also contact us on Mobile: 07747 175327.
Facilities ⨍ 🔯 🚿 🔯 ♨ ⊙ ⨀ ☎ 🛒 🖵 ☎
🔯 🖼 🕮 🌿
Nearest Town Northwich
Directions Leave the M56 at Junction 10 and take the A49 towards Whitchurch. Continue across Acton Swing Bridge and the Park entrance is on the left after the Riverside Inn.
🚌 Acton Bridge

WINSFORD

Lamb Cottage Caravan Park, Dalefords Lane, Whitegate, Northwich, Cheshire, CW8 2BN
Tel: 01606 882302
Email: info@lambcottage.co.uk
www.lambcottage.co.uk
Pitches For ⚑ ⛺ **Total** 0
Open Mar **to** Oct
Access Good **Site** Level
Peaceful retreat for Adults only. Ideal for touring the heart of Cheshire.
Facilities ♿ ⚡ ▯ ▣ ▥ ☎ ⌁ ⊙ ↵ ▰ ◻ ☕
◻ ☎ ↵ ▯ ▣ ▢ ☀ ⌃ 📶
Nearest Town Winsford
Directions 1 mile from the A556.
☙ Cuddington

CORNWALL

BODMIN

Lanarth Hotel & Caravan Park, St Kew Highway, Bodmin, Cornwall, PL30 3EE
Tel: 01208 841215
Email: lanarthhotel@live.co.uk
www.lanarthhotel.co.uk
Pitches For ⚑ ⛺ ⛺ **Total** 86
Acreage 10 **Open** April **to** October
Access Good **Site** Level
Beautiful rural setting, conveniently situated for beaches and moors. Ideal for touring Cornwall and Devon.
Facilities ♿ ▣ ☎ ⌁ ↵ ☕
▯ ⊙ ↺ ↳ ↵ ▢ 📶
Nearest Town Wadebridge
Directions On the A39 at St. Kew Highway, approx 4 miles east of Wadebridge and 8 miles west of Camelford.
☙ Bodmin

BODMIN

Ruthern Valley Holidays, Ruthernbridge, Bodmin, Cornwall, PL30 5LU
Tel: 01208 831395
Email: hokidays@ruthernvalley.com
www.ruthernvalley.com
Pitches For ⚑ ⛺ ⛺ **Total** 28
Acreage 9 **Open** All Year
Access Good **Site** Sloping
Nearest Bus Stop (Miles) 3
Quiet, rural, central for all of Cornwall.
Facilities ⚡ ▣ ▥ ☎ ⌁ ⊙ ↵ ▰ ◻ ☕
⅀ ◻ ▯ ▣ ▢ 📶
Nearest Town Bodmin/Wadebridge
Directions From Bodmin to Lanivet A289 turn left to Nanstallon (following brown caravan signs) turn left to Ruthernbridge. In Ruthernbridge, just before Stone Bridge turn left and the Park is 300 metres on the left.
☙ Bodmin Parkway

BODMIN

South Penquite Farm, South Penquite, Blisland, Bodmin, Cornwall, PL30 4LH
Tel: 01208 850491
Email: thefarm@bodminmoor.co.uk
www.southpenquite.co.uk
Pitches For ⚑ ⛺ **Total** 40
Acreage 4 **Open** May **to** Oct
Site Level
Nearest Bus Stop (Miles) 1
South Penquite is a 200 acre organic sheep farm set high on Bodmin Moor. Interesting farm walks and wildlife.
Facilities ♿ ▥ ☎ ⌁ ⊙ ↵ ▢ ⅃ ⚑ ♨ ▯ ◻ ✎
Nearest Town Bodmin
Directions Enter Cornwall on the A30 and drive for approx. 18 miles, take right turn signposted St. Breward, farm lane will be on the right after 3 miles.
☙ Bodmin Parkway

BUDE

Bude Camping & Caravanning Club Site, Gillards Moor, St Gennys, Bude, Cornwall, EX23 0BG
Tel: 01840 230650
Email: bude.site@thefriendlyclub.co.uk
www.campingandcaravanningclub.co.uk/bude
Pitches For ⚑ ⛺ ⛺ **Total** 100
Acreage 6 **Open** 24-Apr **to** Sept
Site Lev/Slope
Nearest Bus Stop (Miles) 1
Near the coastal paths in the heart of King Arthurs Country. Table tennis on site. BTB 4 Star Graded and AA 3 Pennants. Non members welcome. You can also call us on 0845 130 7633.
Facilities ♿ ⚡ ▥ ☎ ⌁ ⊙ ↵ ▰ ◻ ☕
▯ ◻ ☎ ▥ ♨ ↳ ▯ ◻
Directions Going south on the A39 the site is on the right in lay-by 9 miles from Bude. Going north on the A39 the site is on the left in lay-by 9 miles from Camelford, approx. 3 miles from the B3262 junction. Brown camping signs ½ mile either side of the site, also on both ends of the lay-by.
☙ Bodmin

BUDE

Bude Holiday Resort Maer Lane, Bude, Cornwall, EX23 9EE
Tel: 01288 355955
Email: reception@buderesort.co.uk
www.www.buderesort.co.uk
Pitches For ⚑ ⛺ ⛺ **Total** 190
Open All Year
Access Good **Site** Lev/Slope
Nearest Bus Stop (Miles) 1 mile
Near beach, bar café, arcade, entertainment, seasonal summer pool, launderette.

CORNWALL

Facilities ⚅ (facility icons)
(facility icons)

Nearest Town Bude
Directions Follow Maer Lane in to town, head through golf course, follow circular road round if driving.

BUDE

Budemeadows Touring Park, Widemouth Bay, Bude, Cornwall, EX23 0NA
Tel: 01288 361646
Email: holiday@budemeadows.com
www.budemeadows.com
Pitches For Å ⬜ 🚐 **Total** 145
Acreage 9 **Open** All Year
Access Good **Site** Level
Nearest Bus Stop (Miles) Outside
1 mile from sandy beaches, cliff walks and the rolling surf of Widemouth Bay. Spectacular coastal scenery. Licenced Bar and heated pool.(summer months)
Facilities (icons)
(icons)
Nearest Town Bude
Directions From Bude take the A39 south for 3 miles.
⚇ Exeter

BUDE

Cornish Coasts Caravan & Camping Park, Middle Penlean, Poundstock, Bude, Cornwall, EX23 0EE
Tel: 01288 361380
Email: admin@cornishcoasts.co.uk
www.cornishcoasts.co.uk
Pitches For Å ⬜ 🚐 **Total** 66
Acreage 4 **Open** Easter **to** Oct
Access Good **Site** Level
Nearest Bus Stop (Miles) Outside
Near to Widemouth Bay, Bude, Boscastle and Tintagle. Ideal for touring and surfing.
Facilities (icons)
(icons)
Nearest Town Bude
Directions Fokkow the A39 south of Bude, can be foundin a layby on the right, ½ mile after the small cinema.
⚇ Exeter

BUDE

Penhalt Farm Holiday Park, Widemouth Bay, Bude, Cornwall, EX23 0DG
Tel: 01288 361210
Pitches For Å ⬜ 🚐 **Total** 100
Acreage 7 **Open** Easter **to** Oct
Access Good **Site** Lev/Slope
Nearest Bus Stop (Miles) 1
2 miles from Widemouth Bay, ideal for surfing and swimming. 5 miles from Bude.
Facilities (icons)
(icons)
Nearest Town Bude
Directions On the A39 about 4 miles south of Bude, take the second turn right for Widemouth Bay. Turn left by Widemouth Manor Hotel and the site is two thirds of a mile on the left.
⚇ Exeter

BUDE

Upper Lynstone Camping & Caravan Park, Upper Lynstone Farm, Bude, Cornwall, EX23 0LP
Tel: 01288 352017
Email: reception@upperlynstone.co.uk
www.upperlynstone.co.uk
Pitches For Å ⬜ 🚐 **Total** 65
Acreage 5 **Open** Easter **to** Oct
Access Good **Site** Level
Nearest Bus Stop (Miles) ¼

Facilities (icons)
(icons)
Nearest Town Bude
Directions ½ mile south of Bude on the old coast road.
⚇ Exeter

BUDE

Widemouth Bay Caravan Park, John Fowler Holidays, Widemouth Bay, Bude, Cornwall, EX23 0DF
Tel: 01271 866766
Email: bookings@jfhols.co.uk
www.johnfowlerholidays.com
Pitches For Å ⬜ 🚐 **Total** 190
Acreage 6 **Open** Mar 3rd **to** Nov 2nd
Access Good **Site** Sloping
Nearest Bus Stop (Miles) ¼
Close to one of Cornwalls finest surfing beaches. Perfect location for touring both Devon and Cornwall.On the South West Coastal Path.
Facilities (icons)
(icons)
Nearest Town Widemouth Bay
Directions From the M5 junc 31 take the A30 then the A395 then A39 to Bude. Widemouth Bay is 4 miles west of Bude, clearly signposted.
⚇ Exeter St Davids

BUDE

Willow Valley Holiday Park, Dye House, Bush, Bude, Cornwall, EX23 9LB
Tel: 01288 353104
Email: willowvalley@talk21.com
www.willowvalley.co.uk
Pitches For Å ⬜ 🚐 **Total** 40
Open Easter **to** Sept
Access Good **Site** Level
Nearest Bus Stop (Miles) 1
2 miles from beach, river runs through site.
Facilities (icons)
(icons)
Nearest Town Bude
Directions Just off the A39 between Bude and Kilkhampton.

BUDE

Wooda Farm Holiday Park, Poughill, Bude, Cornwall, EX23 9HJ
Tel: 01288 352069
Email: enquiries@wooda.co.uk
www.wooda.co.uk
Pitches For Å ⬜ 🚐 **Total** 200
Acreage 12 **Open** Apr **to** Oct
Access Good **Site** Lev/Slope
Nearest Bus Stop (Miles) Outside
Overlooks sea and coastline. Woodland walks, coarse fishing, large childrens play area, tennis court, badminton court, gym, dog exercise field and short golf course. Sandy beaches 1½ miles. Licensed bar and take-away. Off License on site.
Facilities (icons)
(icons)
Nearest Town Bude
Directions Take road to Poughill 1¼ miles, go through village. At crossroads turn left. Site 200yds along road on right hand side.
⚇ Exeter

BUDE

Woodview Caravan & Camping Park Little Youlstone, Nr Kilkhampton, Bude, Cornwall, EX23 9PU
Tel: 01288 331492
Email: info@woodviewcampsite.co.uk
www.woodviewcampsite.co.uk
Pitches For Å ⬜ 🚐 🚐 **Total** 100
Acreage 4 **Open** All year

Access Good **Site** Sloping
Beach 5 miles. Fishing 5 miles. 100 metres to Woodland walks. Riverside stream on site. Five campfire pits on the riverbank.
Facilities (icons)
(icons)
Nearest Town Bude
Directions Kilkhampton to Bideford A39. Take first right, then first left.
⚇ Exeter/Barnsatple

CAMELFORD

Lakefield Caravan Park, Lower Pendavey Farm, Camelford, Cornwall, PL32 9TX
Tel: 01840 213279
Email:
lakefieldequestriancentre@btconnect.com
www.lakefieldcaravanpark.co.uk
Pitches For Å ⬜ 🚐 **Total** 40
Acreage 5 **Open** Apr **to** Sept
Access Good **Site** Level
Nearest Bus Stop (Miles) ½
3 miles from the beach and 1 mile from local amenities. Full equestrian facilities providing lessons, site rides and hacks for all the family. Close to the Moors and 2 miles form a golf course.
Facilities (icons)
(icons)
Nearest Town Camelford
Directions 1 miles north of Camelford on the B3266 Boscastle road.
⚇ Bodmin

COVERACK

Little Trevothan Caravan Park, Coverack, Helston, Cornwall, TR12 6SD
Tel: 01326 280260
Email: sales@littletrevothan.co.uk
www.littletrevothan.co.uk
Pitches For Å ⬜ 🚐 **Total** 0
Acreage 10½ **Open** Mar **to** Dec
Access Good **Site** Level
Nearest Bus Stop (Miles) 1
¾ miles from the beach in an area of outstanding natural beauty.
Facilities (icons)
(icons)
Nearest Town Helston
Directions Take the A39 to Helston, then follow the B3083 to Culdrose, turn left onto the B3293 signposted Coverack. Go past BT Goonhilly, turn right before Zoar Garage, third turning on the right, site is 300yds on the right.
⚇ Redruth

COVERACK

Penmarth Farm Camp Site, Coverack, Helston, Cornwall,
Tel: 01326 280389
Pitches For Å ⬜ 🚐 **Total** 28
Acreage 2 **Open** Mar **to** Oct
Access Good **Site** Level
Nearest Bus Stop (Miles) ¼
¼ mile woodland walk to the sea and beach.
Facilities (icons)
Nearest Town Helston
Directions From Helston take the B3293 for approx. 10 miles.
⚇ Cambourne

CRANTOCK

Quarryfield Holiday Park, Crantock, Newquay, Cornwall, TR8 5RJ
Tel: 01637 830338/872792
Email: info@quarryfield.co.uk
www.quarryfield.co.uk
Pitches For Å ⬜ 🚐 **Total** 125
Acreage 4½ **Open** Easter **to** Oct
Access Good **Site** Lev/Slope
Nearest Bus Stop (Miles) ¼

Just a 10 minute walk to the village, Crantock beach and the River Gannel.
Facilities ⚅ ⨍ 🗑 🅿 🏠 🍽 🔌 ☎ ⊡ 🅾 ☎
🛱 🅿 🅾 🍴 ♿ 🛒 🔌 🍴 ⊞ 🚲 ☼
Nearest Town Newquay
Directions From the A3075 Newquay to Redruth road, turn off signposted Crantock Village, site is approx. 2½ miles.
🚉 Newquay

CRANTOCK

Treago Farm Caravan & Camping Site,
Treago Farm, Crantock, Nr Newquay, Cornwall, TR8 5QS
Tel: 01637 830277
Email: info@treagofarm.co.uk
www.treagofarm.co.uk
Pitches For ▲ ♙ ⊟ **Total** 81
Open Easter **to** Early Oct
Access Good **Site** Level
Nearest Bus Stop (Miles) ½
Within walking distance to Crantock and two sandy beaches.
Facilities ⚅ ⨍ 🗑 🅿 🏠 🍽 🔌 🍴 🅾 ☎
🛱 🅾 🍴 🛒 🍴 🔌 ⊞ 🍴 ✏
Nearest Town Newquay
Directions 2 miles south west of Newquay. Turn right off the A3075 and follow camping signs.
🚉 Newquay

FALMOUTH

Pennance Mill Farm Touring Park,
Pennance Mill Farm, Maenporth Road, Falmouth, Cornwall, TR11 5HJ
Tel: 01326 317431
Email: jewellshj@bt.internet.com
Pitches For ▲ ♙ ⊟ ⊟ ⟁ **Total** 75
Acreage 8 **Open** Easter **to** Oct
Access Good **Site** Lev/slope
Nearest Bus Stop (Miles) Outside
½ mile to beach, private path to beach.Mountain bike cycle track situated on the site open Saturdays and Sundays.
Facilities ⨍ ⊟ 🍴 🗑 🅿 🍽 🔌 🍴 🅾 ☎
🍴 🅾 🛒 🍴 🔌 ⊞ 🅾 🍴
Nearest Town Falmouth
Directions A390 turn right at Hillhead Roundabout, follow campsite signs 2 miles off roundabout.
🚉 Penmere

FALMOUTH

Retanna Holiday Park, Edgcumbe, Helston, Cornwall, TR13 0EJ
Tel: 01326 340643
Email: retannaholpark@btconnect.com
www.retanna.co.uk
Pitches For ▲ ♙ **Total** 24
Acreage 8 **Open** Mar **to** Nov
Access Good **Site** Lev/Slope
Nearest Bus Stop (Miles) Entrance
Just a short drive to The Flambards Experience, Gweek Seal Sanctuary and Poldark Mine.
Facilities ⚅ ⨍ 🗑 🅿 🍽 🔌 🍴 🅾 ☎
🛱 🅾 🛒 🍴 🅿 ⊞ 🅾 🛜
Nearest Town Falmouth
Directions Midway between Falmouth and Helston on the A394, on the right hand side after passing through Edgcumbe.
🚉 Falmouth/Truro

FALMOUTH

Tregedna Farm Touring Caravan & Camping Park, Maenporth, Falmouth, Cornwall, TR11 5HL
Tel: 01326 250529
www.tregednafarmholidays.co.uk
Pitches For ▲ ♙ ⊟ **Total** 40
Acreage 12 **Open** Easter **to** Sept

Access Good **Site** Sloping
Nearest Bus Stop (Miles) ¼
Situated in the beautiful Maen Valley, just minutes from the beach and surrounded by wooded countryside.
Facilities ⨍ 🗑 🅿 🍽 🔌 🍴 🅾 ☎
🛱 🅾 🛒 🍴 🍽 ⊡
Nearest Town Falmouth
Directions Take the A39 from Truro to Falmouth, 2½ miles to Falmouth on the Maenporth to Mawnan Smith road.
🚉 Penmere

FOWEY

Penhale Caravan & Camping Park,
Fowey, Cornwall, PL23 1JU
Tel: 01726 833425
Email: info@penhale-fowey.co.uk
www.penhale-fowey.co.uk
Pitches For ▲ ♙ ⊟ **Total** 56
Acreage 5 **Open** Apr **to** Oct
Access Good **Site** Lev/Slope
Splendid views, close to sandy beaches with many lovely walks nearby. Central for touring.
Facilities ⨍ 🗑 🗑 🅿 🍽 🔌 🍴 🅾 ☎
🛱 🅿 🅾 🛒 🍴 🔌 ⊞ 🅾 ☼ 🛜
Nearest Town Fowey
Directions 1 mile west of Lostwithiel on the A390, turn left onto the B3269. After 3 miles turn right at the roundabout onto the A3082. Penhale is 500yds on the left.
🚉 Par

FOWEY

Penmarlam Caravan & Camping Park,
BodinnickbyFowey, Fowey, Cornwall, PL23 1LZ
Tel: 01726 870088
Email: info@penmarlampark.co.uk
www.penmarlampark.co.uk
Pitches For ▲ ♙ ⊟ ⟁ **Total** 65
Acreage 4 **Open** Easter **to** Oct
Access Good **Site** Lev/Slope
Quiet site with two areas, one sheltered and one with stunning views. Near the Eden Project. Boat launching and storage.
Facilities ⚅ ⨍ ⊟ 🗑 🅿 🍽 🔌 🍴 🅾 ☎
🛱 🅾 🛒 🍴 ⊞ ☼ 🛜
Nearest Town Fowey
Directions From the A38 eastbound, pass Liskeard and turn left onto the A390 sp St. Austell. In East Taphouse turn left onto the B3359 sp Polperro & Looe. After 5 miles turn right sp Bodinnick. Site is on the right in 5 miles.
🚉 Liskeard/Par/Looe

FOWEY

Polruan Holidays - Camping & Caravanning, Polruan-by-Fowey, Cornwall, PL23 1QH
Tel: 01726 870263
Email: polholiday@aol.com
www.polruanholidays.co.uk
Pitches For ▲ ♙ ⊟ **Total** 35
Acreage 2 **Open** Easter **to** 1st Oct
Access Good **Site** Lev/Slope
Nearest Bus Stop (Miles) Outside
Coastal park surrounded by sea, river and National Trust farmland.
Facilities ⨍ ⊟ 🍴 🗑 🅿 🍽 🔌 🍴 🅾 ☎
🛱 🅾 🍴 ⊞ 🅾 🛜
Nearest Town Fowey
Directions From Plymouth A38 to Dobwalls, left onto A390 to East Taphouse, then left onto B3359. After 4¼ miles turn right signposted Polruan.
🚉 Par

GORRAN HAVEN

Trelispen Caravan & Camping Park,
Gorran Haven, St Austell, Cornwall, PL26 6NR
Tel: 01726 843501
Email: trelispen@care4free.net
www.trelispen.co.uk
Pitches For ▲ ♙ ⊟ **Total** 0
Acreage 1½ **Open** Apr **to** Oct
Access Good **Site** Level
Nearest Bus Stop (Miles) ¼
Within walking distance of Gorran Haven with its beach and fine cliff scenery.
Facilities ⨍ 🗑 🅿 🍽 🔌 🍴 🅾 ☎ 🍽 ⊡
Nearest Town Mevagissey
Directions From St. Austell take the B3273 south following signs for Gorran Haven. Nearing Gorran Haven look for brown tourism signs to Trelispen.
🚉 St. Austell

HAYLE

Beachside Holiday Park, Hayle, Cornwall, TR27 5AW
Tel: 01736 753080
Email: reception@beachside.co.uk
www.beachside.co.uk
Pitches For ▲ ♙ ⊟ **Total** 83
Acreage 20 **Open** Easter **to** Sept
Access Good **Site** Sloping
Right beside a golden sandy beach. Sea fishing from site.
Facilities ⨍ 🗑 🅿 🍽 🔌 🍴 🅾 ☎
🛱 🅿 🅾 🛒 ♿ 🔌 ⊞ 🅾 🍴 🛜
Nearest Town Hayle
Directions Leave the A30 at roundabout signed Hayle, turn right opposite the Jet Petrol Station and the entrance is ½ a mile on the right.
🚉 Hayle

HAYLE

Gwithian Farm Campsite, Gwithian, Hayle, Cornwall, TR27 5BX
Tel: 01736 753127
Email: holidays@gwithianfarm.co.uk
www.gwithianfarm.co.uk
Pitches For ▲ ♙ ⊟ **Total** 130
Acreage 8 **Open** 23-Mar **to** 01-Oct
Access Good **Site** Level
Nearest Bus Stop (Miles) Outside
Just a 10 minute walk from a stunning 3 mile long beach. Friendly, family run site in a village, opposite a good pub.
Facilities ⚅ ⨍ ⊟ 🍴 🗑 🅿 🍽 🔌 🍴 🅾 ☎
🛱 🅾 ♿ 🍴 ⊞ 🅾 🛜
Nearest Town St. Ives
Directions Leave the A30 at Hayle roundabout and turn right onto the B3301 signposted Portreath. After 2 miles the site is on the left opposite the Red River Inn.
🚉 Camborne/Hayle

HAYLE

Higher Trevaskis Caravan & Camping Park, Gwinear Road, Connor Downs, Hayle, Cornwall, TR27 5JQ
Tel: 01209 831736
www.highertrevaskiscaravanpark.co.uk
Pitches For ▲ ♙ ⊟ **Total** 75
Acreage 5¼ **Open** Apr **to** Oct
Access Good **Site** Level
Nearest Bus Stop (Miles) ½
Friendly, secluded, family run, countryside park. Spacious, level pitches in small enclosures. Designated play areas and our renowned spotlessly clean facilities.

CORNWALL

Facilities ♪ ⌂ ⊞ ♒ ⌐ ⊙ ↲ ▭ ▢ ☎
♒ ℞ ☺ ⋔ ✿ ▣ ⚲
Nearest Town Hayle
Directions From the A30 at the Hayle roundabout (McDonalds) take the first exit signposted Connor Downs. After 1 turn take right to Carnhell Green. Park is on the right in ¾ miles.
⇌ Hayle

HAYLE
Lavender Fields Touring Park, Penhale Road, Carnhell Green, Hayle, Cornwall, TR14 0LU
Tel: 01209 832188
Email: info@lavenderfieldstouring.co.uk
www.lavenderfieldstouring.co.uk
Pitches For ▲ ⊞ ♒ ♒ ↟ **Total** 60
Acreage 5 **Open** All Year
Access Good **Site** Level
Nearest Bus Stop (Miles) Outside
10 minutes from Gwithian Beach with excellent surfing. Near to St Ives, Truro and Penzance for all your shopping.
Facilities ♿ ♪ ⌂ ⊞ ⌐ ♒ ⊙ ↲ ▭ ☎
℞ ☺ ⋔ ▣ ▢ ❊ ⚲
Nearest Town Hayle
Directions A30 to campsite 2½ miles. Camborne to campsite 3 miles.
⇌ Camborne

HAYLE
Parbola Holiday Park, Wall, Gwinear, Cornwall, TR27 5LE
Tel: 01209 831503
Email: bookings@parbola.co.uk
www.parbola.co.uk
Pitches For ▲ ⊞ ♒ **Total** 110
Acreage 14 **Open** Apr to Sept
Access Good **Site** Level
Nearest Bus Stop (Miles) Outside
No dogs allowed during July and August. Hair and make-up room.
Facilities ♿ ♪ ⌂ ⊞ ♒ ⌐ ⊙ ↲ ▭ ▢ ☎
♒ ℞ ☺ ♒ ⋔ ⚲ ✿ ▣ ❊ 🛜
Nearest Town Hayle
Directions Travel on A30 to Hayle, at roundabout leave first exit to Connor Downs. At end of village turn right to Carnhell Green, right at T-Junction, Parbola is 1 mile on the left.

HAYLE
Treglisson Touring Park, Wheal Alfred Road, Hayle, Cornwall, TR27 5JT
Tel: 01736 753141
Email: steve@treglisson.co.uk
www.treglisson.co.uk
Pitches For ▲ ⊞ ♒ **Total** 26
Acreage 2½ **Open** Easter to Oct
Access Good **Site** Lev/Slope
Nearest Bus Stop (Miles) 1
Just 5 minutes from the beaches of St Ives Bay. Centrally situated, ideal for touring West Cornwall.
Facilities ♿ ♪ ⌂ ⊞ ♒ ⌐ ⊙ ↲ ▭ ▢ ☎
℞ ☺ ⋔ ▣ ▢ 🛜
Nearest Town Hayle/St. Ives
Directions Take the A30 to roundabout outside Hayle and take the 4th exit to Hayle. At the first mini roundabout turn left, after a mile (past the golf course) theres a sign on the left.
⇌ Hayle

HELSTON
Boscrege Caravan & Camping Park, Ashton, Helston, Cornwall, TR13 9TG
Tel: 01736 762231
Email: boscregecaravanpark@gmail.com
www.caravanparkcornwall.com

Pitches For ▲ ⊞ ♒ **Total** 55
Acreage 12 **Open** Mar to Oct
Access Good **Site** Level
Nearest Bus Stop (Miles) ¼
Praa Sands beach 2 miles, dog friendly, quite. Open for static caravans all year.
Facilities ♪ ⊞ ⌐ ⊙ ↲ ▭ ▢ ☎
♒ ℞ ⋔ ▣ ▢ ❊ 🛜
Nearest Town Helston/Penzance
Directions 1 mile off A394 at Ashton Village.
⇌ Penzance

HELSTON
Gunwalloe Caravan Park, Gunwalloe, Helston, Cornwall, TR12 7QP
Tel: 01326 572668
Pitches For ▲ ⊞ ♒ ♒ **Total** 40
Acreage 3½ **Open** Apr to Oct
Access Good **Site** Level
Nearest Bus Stop (Miles) 1
One mile from the beach. Ideal for touring the Lizard Peninsula.
Facilities ♪ ⊞ ⌐ ⊙ ↲ ☎ ☺ ⋔ ▣
Nearest Town Helston
Directions From Helston take the A3082 towards The Lizard, after 2 miles turn right to Gunwalloe for 1 mile, site is signposted.
⇌ Redruth

HELSTON
Poldown Caravan & Camping Site, Carleen, Breage, Helston, Cornwall, TR13 9NN
Tel: 01326 574560
Email: stay@poldown.co.uk
www.poldown.co.uk
Pitches For ▲ ⊞ ♒ ♒ **Total** 13
Acreage 1¼ **Open** Apr to Sept
Access Good **Site** Level
Nearest Bus Stop (Miles) Outside
Small, secluded, pretty site. 2 hard standings and 6 fully serviced pitches available. Glamzing safari tents, Ideal for touring West Cornwall. ETB 4 Star Graded.
Facilities ♪ ⌂ ⊞ ♒ ⌐ ⊙ ↲ ▭ ▢ ☎
℞ ☺ ▢ ⋔ ▣ ▢ 🛜
Directions Take A394 (signed Penzance) from Helston. At top of the hill on outskirts of Helston take the B3303 signed Hayle/St Ives. Take the second left on this road and we are ¼ mile along.
⇌ Penzance

ISLES OF SCILLY
Bryher Campsite, Bryher, Isles of Scilly, Cornwall, TR23 0PR
Tel: 01720 422886
Email: relax@bryhercampsite.co.uk
www.bryhercampsite.co.uk
Pitches For ▲ **Total** 37
Acreage 1½ **Open** Apr to Oct
Site Level
Near the beach.
Facilities ⊞ ⌐ ⊙ ↲ ☺ ☺ ▢
Nearest Town St Mary's
Directions Can be reached by boat from the main island to St Marys.
⇌ Penzance

ISLES OF SCILLY
Garrison Holidays, Tower Cottage, The Garrison, St Marys, Isles of Scilly, Cornwall, TR21 0LS
Tel: 01720 422670
Email: info@garrisonholidays.com
www.garrisonholidays.com
Pitches For ▲ **Total** 120
Acreage 9½ **Open** Easter to October
Site Level

Small, family orientated campsite. Electric hook-ups (10) on marked pitches, rest of site is not formally marked. Small fields, mostly sheltered. No vehicles on site. Transport for luggage is available from the ferry to the site for a small charge. Childrens play area adjacent to site.New Pre-erected well equiped tents available.
Facilities ♿ ♪ ⊞ ♒ ⌐ ⊙ ↲ ▭ ▢ ℞ ☺ 🛜
Nearest Town St Mary's
Directions From Penzance take a boat, skybus or helicopter to Isles of Scilly. Park is 10 minutes walk from Hugh Town, St Marys.
⇌ Penzance

ISLES OF SCILLY
St. Martins Campsite, Middle Town, St Martins, Isles of Scilly, Cornwall, TR25 0QN
Tel: 01720 422888
Email: camping@stmartinscampsite.co.uk
www.stmartinscampsite.co.uk
Pitches For ▲ **Total** 50
Open Mar to Oct
Site Lev/slope
On own beach,easy walk to shop & pub etc. Sheltered family site.
Facilities ♿ ♪ ⊞ ♒ ⌐ ⊙ ↲ ▭
▢ ℞ ☺ ▢ 🛜
Directions Take a ferry, plane from Penzance to St. Marys. Launch from St. Marys to St. Martins.
⇌ Penzance

LANDS END
Cardinney Caravan & Caravan Park, Main A30, Lands End Road, Crows-an-Wra, Lands End, Cornwall, TR19 6HX
Tel: 01736 810880
Email: cardinney@btinternet.com
www.cardinney-camping-park.co.uk
Pitches For ▲ ⊞ ♒ **Total** 90
Acreage 5 **Open** All Year
Access Good **Site** Level
Nearest Bus Stop (Miles) Outside
Sennen Cove Blue Flag, scenic coastal walks, ancient monuments, scenic flights, Minack Ampitheatre, trips to the Isles of Scilly. Ideal for touring Lands End Peninsula.
Facilities ♪ ⌂ ⊞ ♒ ⌐ ⊙ ↲ ▭ ▢ ☎
℞ ☺ ✕ ▣ ▢ 🛜
Directions From Penzance follow Main A30 to Lands End, approx 5¼ miles. Entrance on right hand side on Main A30, large name board at entrance.
⇌ Penzance

LANDS END
Lower Treave Caravan & Camping Park, Crows-an-Wra, St Buryan, Penzance, Cornwall, TR19 6HZ
Tel: 01736 810559
Email: camping@lowertreave.co.uk
www.lowertreave.co.uk
Pitches For ▲ ⊞ ♒ **Total** 56
Acreage 5 **Open** Apr to Sept
Access Good **Site** Level
Nearest Bus Stop (Miles) Outside
Quiet family site in the heart of Lands End peninsular with panoramic rural views to the sea. Sheltered, level grass terraces. 2 miles from the Blue Flag beach of Sennen Cove, and close to The Minack Theatre and St Michaels Mount.
Facilities ♪ ⊞ ♒ ⌐ ⊙ ↲ ▭ ▢ ☎
℞ ☺ ✕ ▣ ▢ 🛜
Nearest Town Lands End
Directions On A30 midway between Penzance and Lands End, a mile beyond the village of Crows-an-Wra.
⇌ Penzance

LISKEARD

Trenant Chapel House, Trenant Caravan Park, St Neot, Liskeard, Cornwall, PL14 6RZ
Tel: 01579 320896
Pitches For Å ⊕ ⊟ **Total** 8
Acreage 1 **Open** Apr **to** Oct
Site Level
Close to Siblyback and Colliford Reservoirs for fishing, boardsailing and bird watching. Situated in a sheltered corner of Upper Fowey Valley and bounded by tributary of Fowey river. Close to Bodmin moor, ideal for walking and touring.
Facilities
Nearest Town Liskeard
Directions Take St Cleer road off the A38 at Dobwalls, after 1 mile turn left signposted St. Neot, after 1 mile turn right signposted Trenant, ½ mile turn right signposted Trenant.
⇌ Liskeard

LIZARD

Silver Sands Holiday Park, Gwendreath, Nr Kennack Sands, Ruan Minor, Helston, Cornwall, TR12 7LZ
Tel: 01326 290631
Email: stay@silversandsholidaypark.co.uk
www.silversandsholidaypark.co.uk
Pitches For Å ⊕ ⊟ **Total** 36
Acreage 9 **Open** Mid Mar **to** Early Nov
Access Good **Site** Level
Nearest Bus Stop (Miles) 1
Quiet, family site in area of outstanding natural beauty. 800 metres from a sandy beach. Ideal for touring and walking.
Facilities
Nearest Town Helston
Directions From Helston take the A3083 Lizard road, pass RNAS Culdrose then turn left onto the B3293 sp St Keverne. Follow for 4 miles passing Future World @ Goonhilly, turn right at the next crossroads to Kennack Sands. After 1½ miles turn left sp Gwendreath and the Park is 1 mile down the lane.
⇌ Redruth

LOOE

Bay View Farm, St Martins, Looe, Cornwall, PL13 1NZ
Tel: 01503 265922
Email: mike@looebaycaravans.co.uk
www.looebaycaravans.co.uk
Pitches For Å ⊕ ⊟ **Total** 25
Acreage 3 **Open** All Year
Access Good **Site** Lev/Slope
Nearest Bus Stop (Miles) 1
Near to the beach, The Eden Project and many National Trust properties. We have eight shire horses on the farm. You can also contact us on Mobile: 07967 267312. 3 camping snugs available.
Facilities
Nearest Town Looe
Directions From Plymouth or Liskeard take the A38 to Trerulefoot roundabout, then take the (A387) B3253 to No-Mans-Land. Follow signs for the Monkey Sanctuary and Bay View Farm is at the end of the lane.
⇌ Looe

LOOE

Camping Caradon Touring Park, Trelawne, Looe, Cornwall, PL13 2NA
Tel: 01503 272388
Email: enquiries@campingcaradon.co.uk
www.campingcaradon.co.uk

Pitches For Å ⊕ ⊟ **Total** 85
Acreage 3 **Open** All Year
Access Good **Site** Level
Nearest Bus Stop (Miles) Outside
In a rural location, within easy reach of all of Cornwall. The Eden Project is only 20 miles away. 2½ miles from Looe and 2 miles from Polperro. Free Wi-Fi. Family/disabled facilities. On local bus route. November to March by prior booking only.
Facilities
Nearest Town Looe/Polperro
Directions From Looe take the A387 towards Polperro. After 2 miles turn right onto the B3359. Take the next turning right, and Camping Caradon is clearly signposted.
⇌ Looe

LOOE

Polborder House Caravan & Camping Park, Bucklawren Road, St Martin, Looe, Cornwall, PL13 1QS
Tel: 01503 240265
Email: reception@polborderhouse.co.uk
www.polborderhouse.co.uk
Pitches For Å ⊕ ⊟ **Total** 36
Acreage 3 **Open** All Year
Access Good **Site** Level
Nearest Bus Stop (Miles) ½
Small, select, award winning park set in beautiful countryside, 1¼ miles from the sea. Holiday caravans also available for rent. Top 100 UK Parks Regional winner.
Facilities
Nearest Town Looe
Directions 2¼ miles east of Looe off B3253, follow signs for Polborder and Monkey Sanctuary.
⇌ Looe

LOOE

Tencreek Holiday Park, Polperro Road, Looe, Cornwall, PL13 2JR
Tel: 01503 262447
Email: reception@tencreek.co.uk
www.dolphinholidays.co.uk
Pitches For Å ⊕ ⊟ **Total** 0
Acreage 20 **Open** All Year
Access Good **Site** Lev/Slope
Nearest Bus Stop (Miles) ¼
Excellent coastal and countryside views. Good park facilities including indoor pool and a large modern club house with entertainment.
Facilities
Nearest Town Looe
Directions 1¼ miles west of Looe on the A387 Looe to Polperro road.
⇌ Looe

LOOE

Trelay Farmpark, Pelynt, Nr Looe, Cornwall, PL13 2JX
Tel: 01503 220900
Email: stay@trelay.co.uk
www.trelay.co.uk
Pitches For Å ⊕ ⊟ **Total** 70
Acreage 4½ **Open** Apr **to** Oct
Access Good **Site** Sloping
Nearest Bus Stop (Miles) ¼
A small, uncommercialised Park surrounded by farmland, with a friendly, family atmosphere. Good sized grass pitches. 3 miles from Looe and the pretty fishing village of Polperro.
Facilities
Nearest Town Looe

Directions From Looe take the A387 over the bridge towards Polperro. After 2 miles turn right onto the B3359 towards Pelynt and Trelay Farmpark is exactly 1 mile on the right.
⇌ Looe

LOSTWITHIEL

Eden Valley Holiday Park, Lanlivery, Bodmin, Cornwall, PL30 5BU
Tel: 01208 872277
Email:
enquiries@edenvalleyholidaypark.co.uk
www.edenvalleyholidaypark.co.uk
Pitches For Å ⊕ ⊟ **Total** 57
Acreage 12 **Open** Easter **to** Oct
Access Good **Site** Level
Nearest Bus Stop (Miles) 3
Stream runs through the park. Woodland and river walks.
Facilities
Nearest Town Fowey
Directions From Lostwithiel take the A390 for 1½ miles.
⇌ Lostwithiel

MARAZION

Trevair Touring Site, South Treveneague Farm, St Hilary, Penzance, Cornwall, TR20 9BY
Tel: 01736 740647
Email: info@trevairtouringpark.co.uk
www.trevairtouringpark.co.uk
Pitches For Å ⊕ ⊟ **Total** 35
Acreage 3½ **Open** End Mar **to** Oct
Access Good **Site** Level
Nearest Bus Stop (Miles) 1
Everyone is welcome at our clean and friendly site. Set in the peace and quiet of the countryside, yet within 2 to 3 miles of beaches, shops and pubs.
Facilities
Nearest Town Marazion
Directions 3 miles from Marazion, B3280 through Goldsithney signposted South Treveneague.
⇌ St. Erth

MAWGAN PORTH

Magic Cove Touring Park, Mawgan Porth, Newquay, Cornwall, TR8 4BD
Tel: 01637 860263
Email: magic@magiccove.co.uk
www.magiccove.co.uk
Pitches For Å ⊕ ⊟ **Total** 18
Acreage 1 **Open** Easter **to** Sept
Access Good **Site** Level
Nearest Bus Stop (Miles) ¼
300yds from a sandy beach. Ideal centre for North Cornwall coast. Water adjacent to each pitch and TV points.
Facilities
Nearest Town Newquay
Directions Exit the A30 at Highgate Hill Junction (A39) sp Newquay & Airport. Follow Airport signs to Trekenning roundabout and take the first exit. Continue to follow Airport signs, go past the Airport, at the T-Junction turn right to Mawgan Porth. Turn right by Pitch n Putt. Campsite is 300 yards on the left.
⇌ Newquay

MAWGAN PORTH

Marver Touring Park, Marver Chalets, Mawgan Porth, Nr Newquay, Cornwall, TR8 4BB
Tel: 01637 860493
Email: familyholidays@aol.com
www.marverholidaypark.co.uk

CORNWALL

Pitches For ⚑ ⚐ ⚐ **Total** 15
Acreage 2½ **Open** Apr **to** Oct
Access Good **Site** Level
Nearest Bus Stop (Miles) Outside
Peaceful location in a valley with superb views. 300 yards to the beach, excellent coastal walks. Ideal base for touring Cornwall.
Facilities ⚑ ⊞ ⚐ ⚐ ⊙ ⚐ ◻ ⚐ ⚐ ⚐ ⚐ ◻
Nearest Town Newquay
Directions From Newquay take the B3276 coast road to Padstow. After 6 miles, on entering Mawgan Porth, turn right at the Mawgan Porth Stores, park is 300 yards on the left.
⚐ Newquay

MAWGAN PORTH

Sun Haven Valley Holiday Park, Mawgan Porth, Cornwall, TR8 4BQ
Tel: 0800 634 6744
Email: bookings@sunhavenvalley.com
www.sunhavenvalley.com
Pitches For ⚑ ⚐ ⚐ **Total** 109
Open Easter **to** Oct
Access Good **Site** Level
Nearest Bus Stop (Miles) Outside
10 mins walk from sandy beach. Secluded Cornish valley countryside. Families only. 10:30 p.m. silence policy.
Facilities ⚑ ⊞ ⚐ ⚐ ⚐ ◻ ⚐ ◻ ⚐
⚐ ⚐ ⊙ ⊞ ⚐ ⚐ ⚐ ◻ ◻ ⚐ ⚐
Nearest Town Newquay
Directions Head towards Padstow from Newquay on B3276. Tirn right on Mawgan Porth beach front. Site is ¾ mile on left.
⚐ Newquay

MEVAGISSEY

Seaview International, Boswinger, Gorran, St Austell, Cornwall, PL26 6LL
Tel: 01726 843425
Email: holidays@seaviewinternational.com
www.seaviewinternational.com
Pitches For ⚑ ⚐ ⚐ ⚐ **Total** 193
Acreage 36 **Open** Easter **to** Oct
Access Good **Site** Level
Nearest Bus Stop (Miles) 1
Convenient location for lost gardens ofHeligan and the Eden Project.
Facilities ⚑ ⊞ ⚐ ⚐ ⚐ ◻ ⚐ ⚐ ◻ ⚐
⚐ ⚐ ◻ ⚐ ⚐ ⚐ ⚐ ⚐ ⚐ ⚐ ◻ ◻ ⚐ ⚐
Nearest Town Mevagissey/St Austell
Directions From St Austell take the B3273 for approx 4 miles at x-roads turn right and follow signs to Seaview International.
⚐ St Austell

MEVAGISSEY

Tregarton Park, Gorran, Nr Mevagissey, St Austell, Cornwall, PL26 6NF
Tel: 01726 843666
Email: reception@tregarton.co.uk
www.tregarton.co.uk
Pitches For ⚑ ⚐ ⚐ **Total** 125
Acreage 12 **Open** Apr **to** Oct
Access Good **Site** Lev/Terraced
Nearest Bus Stop (Miles) Outside
Beautiful sheltered park with glimpses of the sea through the valley. 1½ miles to the nearest beach, 2½ miles from the Lost Garden of Heligan and 9 miles from The Eden Project.
Facilities ⚐ ⚑ ⊞ ⚐ ⚐ ⚐ ◻ ⚐ ⚐ ◻
⚐ ⚐ ⚐ ◻ ⚐ ⚐ ⚐ ⚐ ◻ ◻ ⚐
Nearest Town St. Austell
Directions From St Austell take the B3273 signposted Mevagissey. After 4 miles, at the top of Pentewan Hill turn right signposted Gorran Haven. Park is 3 miles on the right (signposted).
⚐ St. Austell

MULLION

Franchis, Cury Cross Lanes, Mullion, Helston, Cornwall, TR12 7AZ
Tel: 01326 240301
Email: enquiries@franchis.co.uk
www.franchis.co.uk
Pitches For ⚑ ⚐ ⚐ **Total** 70
Acreage 4 **Open** Easter **to** Oct
Access Good **Site** Lev/Slope
Nearest Bus Stop (Miles) ½
Set in 17 acres of woodland and fields. Near to beaches and Helford River.
Facilities ⚑ ⊞ ⚐ ⚐ ⚐ ⊙ ◻ ⚐ ◻ ⚐
⚐ ⚐ ◻ ⚐ ◻ ⚐
Directions On the A3083, 5 miles south of Helston and 2 miles north of Mullion.
⚐ Redruth

MULLION

Mullion Holiday Park Parkdean, Ruan Minor, Nr Helston, Cornwall, TR12 7LJ
Tel: 0344 3353741
Email: enquiries@parkdeanholidays.co.uk
www.parkdeantouring.com
Pitches For ⚑ ⚐ ⚐ **Total** 103
Open Mar **to** Oct
Access Good **Site** Level
Nearest Bus Stop (Miles) Outside
Very near beach, ideal touring the most southerley point The Lizard
Facilities ⚑ ⊞ ⚐ ⚐ ⚐ ⊙ ◻ ⚐ ⚐ ◻ ⚐
⚐ ⚐ ◻ ⚐ ⚐ ⚐ ⚐ ⚐ ⚐ ⚐ ◻ ◻ ⚐
Nearest Town Helston
Directions From the A30 take the A39 through Truro towards Falmouth. Then take the A394 to Helston then the A3083 for The Lizard. Park is 7 miles on the left.
⚐ Truro

NEWQUAY

Carvynick Country Club Summercourt, Newquay, Cornwall, TR8 5AF
Tel: 01872 510716
Email: info@carvynick.co.uk
www.carvynick.co.uk
Pitches For ⚐ ⚐ ⚐ ⚐ **Total** 0
Open All Year
Nearest Bus Stop (Miles) ¼
Situated in the heart of Cornwall amidst the rolling hills of the beautiful South West, Carvynick Holiday Park in Newquay extends a warm welcome to those seeking tranquil family holidays in Cornwall. Located only 10 minutes from the stunning Newquay beaches, dramatic Cornish coastline and only 14 miles from the world famous Eden Project. Our central location provides easy access to all of Cornwall's many attractions.
Facilities ⚑ ⊞ ⚐ ⚐ ⚐ ◻ ⚐ ◻ ⚐
⚐ ⚐ ⚐ ◻ ⚐ ◻
Nearest Town Newquay
Directions From the A30 heading west, take the Summercourt exit signposted A3058 Newquay. Travel into Summercourt, at the traffic lights turn right and the Park is first on the left.
⚐ Newquay

NEWQUAY

Cottage Farm Touring Park, Treworgans, Cubert, Newquay, Cornwall, TR8 5HH
Tel: 01637 831083
Email: info@cottagefarmpark.co.uk
www.cottagefarmpark.co.uk
Pitches For ⚑ ⚐ ⚐ **Total** 45
Acreage 2 **Open** Apr **to** End Sept
Access Good **Site** Level
Nearest Bus Stop (Miles) ¼
Within easy reach of three National Trust beaches. Small, family site, peaceful and in a rural location.
Facilities ⚑ ⊞ ⚐ ⚐ ⚐ ⊙ ◻ ⚐ ◻ ⚐
⚐ ◻ ⚐
Nearest Town Newquay
Directions Newqauy to Redruth road A3075, turn right onto High Lanes, follow signs to Cubert, at Cubert Village turn right at the mini roundabout sp Crantock-Wesley road. Continue for ½ a mile passing Cubert Primary School on your left, then look for Blue Cottage Farm sign on the left hand side.
⚐ Newquay

NEWQUAY

Crantock Plains Touring Park, Crantock, Newquay, Cornwall, TR8 5PH
Tel: 01637 830955
Email: crantockplainstp@btinternet.co.uk
www.crantock-plains.co.uk
Pitches For ⚑ ⚐ ⚐ **Total** 60
Acreage 4 **Open** Apr **to** Sept

Access Good **Site** Level
Nearest Bus Stop (Miles) ¼
Spacious park set in peaceful countryside.
2½ miles from Newquay.
Facilities ⚲ ⚹ 🄵 🆄🄱 ⇄ ⌂ ⊙ ↲ ⚄ 🆀 🍴
🆂💈 🛝 🛀 🏊 🔗 🔌 🄿 🄳 ✂ ⚘ 🔍
Nearest Town Newquay
Directions Turn off the A30 onto the A392.
Approx. 9 miles past Morrisons turn onto the
A3075, after 1 mile follow signs.
🚋 Newquay

NEWQUAY
Holywell Bay Holiday Park - Parkdean,
Holywell Bay, Cornwall, TR8 5PR
Tel: 0844 335 3741
Email: enquiries@parkdeanholidays.co.uk
www.parkdeantouring.com
Pitches For 🅰 🆋 🚎 **Total** 40
Acreage 40 **Open** Mar **to** Nov
Access Good **Site** Level
Nearest Bus Stop (Miles) 1

Beach is a short stroll from the park, with
Newquay town centre only 5 miles away.
Facilities ⚹ 🆄🄱 ⇄ ⌂ ⊙ ↲ ⚄ 🆀 🍴
🆂💈 ✕ 🍺 🍷 🛀 🔗 🔌 🄿 🄳 🔌 🔗
Nearest Town Newquay
Directions From the A30 follow signs for the
A39 to Newquay. Look for A392 then
continue through Quintrell Downs village and
go straight over the roundabout. At next
roundabout take 1st left signed A3075 and
continue for 2 miles at sign for holywell turn
right.
🚋 Newquay

NEWQUAY
Newquay Holiday Park - Parkdean,
Newquay, Cornwall, TR8 4HS
Tel: 0844 335 3741
Email: enquiries@parkdeanholidays.co.uk
www.parkdeantouring.com
Pitches For 🅰 🆋 🚎 **Total** 55
Acreage 60 **Open** Mar **to** Nov

Access Good **Site** Sloping
Nearest Bus Stop (Miles) Outside
Set in rolling Cornish countryside, only 3
miles from Newquays beautiful beaches.
Facilities ⚹ 🄵 🄷 🆄🄱 ⇄ ⌂ ⊙ ↲ ⚄ 🆀 🍴
🆂💈 ✕ 🍷 🍺 🛀 🔗 🔌 🔗 🄿 🄳 🔗
Nearest Town Newquay
Directions Follow A39 and signs for
Newquay/Wadebridge. At Trekenning
roundabout take the 1st exit A3059
signposted Newquay and Airport. after 4 miles
you will see the park signposted to turn right.
🚋 Newquay

NEWQUAY
Newquay View Resort Trevelgue Road,
Porth, Newquay, Cornwall, TR8 4AS
Tel: 01637 851851
Email: reception@newquayview.co.uk
www.www.newquayview.co.uk
Pitches For 🅰 🆋 🚎 **Total** 0
Open All Year

Access Good **Site** Lev/Slope
Near the beach, entertainment, indoor & seasonal outdoor pools, Sky and BT Sports in venue, steam room.
Facilities ⚐ ⛴ 🚿 ⬜⬜ ☂ 🛈 ☎ 🅿 ⬜ 🐕 💈 ✕ 🍴 🛒 ♨ ⚡ ⬂ ⬕ 🏊 ▣ ⬜ 🚲 ⚡ 📶
Nearest Town Porth/Newquay
Directions Drive up the hill, take the left, follow road to double roundabout, follow signs to town
🚏 Newquay

NEWQUAY
Porth Beach Holiuday Park, Porth, Newquay, Cornwall, TR7 3NH
Tel: 01637 876531
Email: info@porthbeach.co.uk
www.porthbeach.co.uk
Pitches For 🛖 ⛺ 🚐 🚙 **Total** 200
Acreage 7 **Open** March to End Oct
Access Good **Site** Level
Nearest Bus Stop (Miles) Outside
Beach across road, stream running down the side of park. Beautiful coastal walks.
Facilities ⚐ ⛴ 🚿 ⬜ ⬜ ☂ 🛈 ☎ 🅿 ⬜ 🐕 💈 ⚡ ✕ 🍴 🛒 ♨ ⬕ ⬜ 🚲 📶
Nearest Town Newquay
Directions Follow main road W of Newquay towards Padstow. Porth is the first bay.
🚏 Newquay

NEWQUAY
Rosecliston Park, Trevemper, Newquay, Cornwall, TR8 5JT
Tel: 01637 830326
Email: info@rosecliston.co.uk
www.rosecliston.co.uk
Pitches For 🛖 **Total** 126
Acreage 12 **Open** Late May to Sept
Access Good **Site** Lev/Slope
Nearest Bus Stop (Miles) Outside

ADULTS ONLY PARK. 18 to 30s camping site. Close to Newquay with its nightlife, shopping and excellent surfing beaches.
Facilities ⛴ 🛈 ⬜ ☂ 🛈 ☎ ☉ ⬂ ⬜ ⬜ ⬜ ☂ 🛈 ☎ 🏊 ♨ ▣ ⬜ 🅰
Directions On the A3075 Newquay to Redruth road, 1 mile from Newquay Boating Lake.
🚏 Newquay

NEWQUAY
Trebarber Farm, St Columb Minor, Newquay, Cornwall, TR8 4JT
Tel: 01637 873007
Email: trebarber@btinternet.com
www.trebarberfarmholidays.com
Pitches For 🛖 ⛺ 🚐 **Total** 0
Acreage 5 **Open** May to Oct
Access Good **Site** Level
Quiet, ideal family centre for touring and beaches. Within walking distance of Porth Reservoir (coarse fishing) and a golf course.
Facilities ⬜ ☂ 🛈 ☉ ⬂ 🛈 ▣ ⬜ 🚲 📶 ⬜
Nearest Town Newquay
Directions 3 miles from Newquay on A3059, Newquay to St. Columb Major road.
🚏 Newquay

NEWQUAY
Tregurrian Camping & Caravanning Club Site, Tregurrian, Nr Newquay, Cornwall, TR8 4AE
Tel: 01637 860448
Email:
tregurrian.site@thefriendlyclub.co.uk
www.campingandcaravanningclub.co.uk/tregurrian
Pitches For 🛖 ⛺ 🚐 🚙 **Total** 90
Acreage 4½ **Open** 14-Mar to 03-Nov
Access Good **Site** Level
Nearest Bus Stop (Miles) ¼
The glorious sandy beach of Watergate Bay is just ¾ miles away. There is a pretty coastal

walk from the site to the beach. BTB 4 Star Graded, AA 3 Pennants and Loo of the Year Award. Non members welcome. You can also call us on 0845 130 7633.
Facilities ⚐ ⛴ 🚿 ⬜ ⬜ ☂ 🛈 ☉ ⬂ 🛈 ⬜ ▣ 🛒 🅿 ⬜ 🚲 📶
Nearest Town Newquay
Directions Leave the A30 after a prominent railway bridge by turning right signposted Newquay Airport, St Columb Major at roundabout on the A39. Join the A3059 to Newquay, after 1½ miles turn right signposted Newquay Airport and follow signs to Watergate Bay.
🚏 Newquay

NEWQUAY
Trekenning Tourist Park, Trekenning, Newquay, Cornwall, TR8 4JF
Tel: 01637 880462
Email: holidays@trekenning.co.uk
www.trekenning.co.uk
Pitches For 🛖 ⛺ 🚐 **Total** 75
Acreage 6½ **Open** All Year
Access Good **Site** Sloping
Nearest Bus Stop (Miles) ½
Family site, family run. Holiday homes for sale.
Facilities ⛴ 🚿 ⬜ ⬜ ☂ 🛈 ☉ ⬂ 🛈 ▣ 🛈 ⬜ 🐕 ✕ 🍴 🛒 ♨ ⬕ ⬜ 🚲 📶
Nearest Town Newquay
Directions From Newquay take the A3059 to the Trekenning roundabout, site entrance is 20 yards on the right before the roundabout.
🚏 Newquay

NEWQUAY
Trenance Holiday Park, Edgcumbe Avenue, Newquay, Cornwall, TR7 2JY
Tel: 01637 873447
Email: enquiries@trenanceholidaypark.co.uk
www.trenanceholidaypark.co.uk
Pitches For **Total** 134
Acreage 15 **Open** Apr **to** Oct
Access Good **Site** Sloping
Nearest Bus Stop (Miles) Outside
1 mile from Newquay town centre and next door to Newquay Zoo.
Facilities
Nearest Town Newquay
Directions On the main A3075 Newquay to Truro road, approx 1 mile from Newquay town centre.
Newquay

NEWQUAY
Trencreek Holiday Park, Trencreek, Newquay, Cornwall, TR8 4NS
Tel: 01637 874210
Email: trencreek@btconnect.com
www.trencreekholidaypark.co.uk
Pitches For **Total** 150
Acreage 10 **Open** Apr **to** Sept
Access Good **Site** Level
Nearest Bus Stop (Miles) Outside
Coarse fishing on site, 15 minutes footpath walk to Newquay, 1 mile by road.
Facilities
Nearest Town Newquay
Directions A392 to Quintrell Downs, turn right Newquay East/Porth, at Porth crossroads, ¾ miles outside Newquay, turn left to Trencreek.
Newquay

NEWQUAY
Trethiggey Touring Park, Quintrell Downs, Newquay, Cornwall, TR8 4QR
Tel: 01637 877672
Email: enquiries@trethiggey.co.uk
www.trethiggey.co.uk
Pitches For **Total** 157
Acreage 16 **Open** 02-Mar **to** 02-Jan
Access Good **Site** Lev/Slope
Nearest Bus Stop (Miles) ¼
Close to beaches and central for Cornwalls attractions. Licensed Bar on site. Ideal touring.
Facilities
Nearest Town Newquay
Directions 2 miles north west of Newquay on the A3058.
Quintrell Downs

NEWQUAY
Trevella Park, Crantock, Newquay, Cornwall, TR8 5EW
Tel: 01637 830308
Email: holidays@trevella.co.uk
www.trevella.co.uk
Pitches For **Total** 270
Acreage 15 **Open** Easter **to** October
Access Good **Site** Level
mile from the beach, concessionary green fees, own fishing lake. AA 4 Pennants.
Directions 2 miles south of Newquay on the A3075, turn right signposted Crantock.
Newquay

NEWQUAY
Trevornick Holiday Park, Holywell Bay, Newquay, Cornwall, TR8 5PW
Tel: 01637 830531
Email: bookings@trevornick.co.uk
www.trevornick.co.uk
Pitches For **Total** 600
Acreage 30 **Open** 23-Mar **to** 13 Apr Then 18 May - 14 Sept
Access Good **Site** Level
Nearest Bus Stop (Miles) Outside
Right next to the beach with stunning sea views. On site 18 hole golf course and 18 hole pitch n putt. Tourers and static tents.
Limited facilities until 25 May and from 31 Aug.
Facilities
Nearest Town Newquay
Directions Take Newquay to Perrenporth A3075 road. Take turning for Cubert/Holywell.
Newquay

NEWQUAY
Watergate Bay Touring Park, Watergate Bay, Newquay, Cornwall, TR8 4AD
Tel: 01637 860387
Email: email@watergatebaytouringpark.co.uk
www.watergatebaytouringpark.co.uk
Pitches For **Total** 171
Acreage 30 **Open** Mar **to** Oct
Access Good **Site** Level
Nearest Bus Stop (Miles) Outside
½ mile from Watergate Bay in a rural location in an area of outstanding natural beauty.
Facilities
Nearest Town Newquay
Directions 4 miles north of Newquay on the B3276 Coast Road to Padstow. Follow directions shown from Watergate Bay.
Newquay

PADSTOW
Carnevas Farm Holiday Park, Carnevas Farm, St Merryn, Padstow, Cornwall, PL28 8PN
Tel: 01841 520230
Email: carnevascampsite@aol.com
www.carnevasholidaypark.com
Pitches For **Total** 198
Acreage 8 **Open** Apr **to** Oct
Access Good **Site** Lev/Slope
Nearest Bus Stop (Miles) ½
Well run family park in a lovely rural position, near to numerous sandy beaches. Ideal touring. AA 4 Pennants and ETB 4 Star Park.
Facilities
Nearest Town Padstow
Directions From Padstow take the B3726 Newquay coast road, turn right at Tredrea Inn just before getting to Porthcothan Bay. Site ¼ mile up road on right.
Newquay

PADSTOW
Dennis Cove Campsite, Dennis Cove, Padstow, Cornwall, PL28 8DR
Tel: 01841 532349
www.denniscovecampsite.co.uk
Pitches For **Total** 42
Acreage 5 **Open** Apr **to** Sept
Access Fair **Site** Lev/Slope
Nearest Bus Stop (Miles) ¼
Scenic views. Site adjoins Camel Trail cycle track. 10 minute walk to Padstow centre. 6 electric hook-ups. No groups, Reservation essential.
Facilities
Nearest Town Padstow
Directions Signposted off A389 on outskirts of Padstow Town.
Bodmin Parkway

PADSTOW
Dennis Farm, Padstow, Cornwall, PL28 8DR
Tel: 01841 534925
www.wix.com/dennisfarm/campsite
Pitches For **Total** 24
Acreage 1 **Open** Whitsun **to** Sept
Site Lev/Slope
Nearest Bus Stop (Miles) ¼
Tent only site by the River Camel, ten minutes walk to Padstow. Own slipway and moorings.
Facilities
Nearest Town Padstow
Directions Take the A389 to Padstow. Take first turning on the right by Tesco, then turn second right into Dennis Lane, continue to the end of the lane.
Bodmin Parkway

PADSTOW

Mother Ivey's Bay Holiday Park, Trevose Head, Padstow, Cornwall, PL28 8SL
Tel: 01841 520990
Email: info@motheriveysbay.com
www.motheriveysbay.com
Pitches For ▲ ⚏ ⛟ **Total** 100
Acreage 10 **Open** Apr **to** Oct
Access Good **Site** Level
Nearest Bus Stop (Miles) ¼
Own private sandy beach. Beautiful coastal walks.
Facilities ⬚⬚⬚⬚⬚
Nearest Town Padstow
Directions 4 miles from Padstow. Signposted off the B3276 Padstow to Newquay coastal road (Trevose Head).
⚏ Bodmin

PADSTOW

Music Water Touring Park, Rumford, Wadebridge, Cornwall, PL27 7SJ
Tel: 01841 540257
www.wix.com/musicwater/touringpark
Pitches For ▲ ⚏ ⛟ **Total** 140
Acreage 8 **Open** Apr **to** Oct
Access Good **Site** Lev/Slope
5 miles from beaches. Cafe/restaurant nearby. Ideal touring base.We are now on Facebook
Facilities ⬚⬚⬚⬚⬚
Nearest Town Padstow
Directions From Wadebridge take the A39 to Winnards Perch roundabout, then take the B3274. Turn first left and site is on the right.
⚏ Bodmin

PADSTOW

Old MacDonalds Farm, Porthcothan Bay, Padstow, Cornwall, PL28 8LW
Tel: 01841 540829
Email: enquiries@oldmacdonalds.co.uk
www.oldmacdonalds.co.uk
Pitches For ▲ ⚏ ⛟ **Total** 50
Acreage 3 **Open** All Year
Access Good **Site** Level
Nearest Bus Stop (Miles) Outside
½ a mile to the beach. Campers have free access to old MacDonalds Farm Park. Dutch speaking owners.
Facilities ⬚⬚⬚⬚⬚
Nearest Town Padstow
Directions Just off the B3276 coast road. 5 miles south of Padstow and 9 miles north of Newquay.
⚏ Newquay

PADSTOW

Padstow Holiday Park, Cliffdowne, Padstow, Cornwall, PL28 8LB
Tel: 01841 532289
Email: mail@padstowholidaypark.co.uk
www.padstowholidaypark.co.uk
Pitches For ▲ ⛟ **Total** 50
Acreage 7 **Open** Mar **to** Dec
Site Level
Nearest Bus Stop (Miles) Outside
Quiet location in open countryside with no club or bar. Near to several sandy beaches. Footpath to Padstow (1 mile). 1 mile from a Tesco store.
Facilities ⬚⬚⬚⬚⬚
Nearest Town Padstow
Directions From Wadebridge take the A389 to Padstow, site is on the right hand side 1½ miles before Padstow.
⚏ Bodmin

PADSTOW

Padstow Touring Park, Padstow, Cornwall, PL28 8LE
Tel: 01841 532061
Email: bookings@padstowtouringpark.co.uk
www.padstowtouringpark.co.uk
Pitches For ▲ ⚏ ⛟ ⛟⚏ **Total** 180
Acreage 13¼ **Open** All Year
Access Good **Site** Level
Nearest Bus Stop (Miles) Outside
Quiet family park with panoramic views. Several sandy beaches within 3 miles. Footpath to Padstow one mile. Three amenity blocks.
Facilities ⬚⬚⬚⬚⬚
Nearest Town Padstow
Directions On A389 1 mile south south west of Padstow.

PADSTOW

Seagull Tourist Park, St Merryn, Padstow, Cornwall, PL28 8PT
Tel: 01841 520117
Pitches For ▲ ⚏ ⛟ **Total** 100
Acreage 4 **Open** Easter/1 Apr **to** Oct
Access Good **Site** Level
Nearest Bus Stop (Miles) ½
Quiet family site near the fishing port of Padstow, and with seven golden sandy beaches, cliff walks and surfing all within a 15 minute drive.
Facilities ⬚⬚⬚⬚⬚
Nearest Town Padstow
Directions From St.Columb take the B3274 towards Padstow head for St.Merryn and turn into old airfield at seagull sign.
⚏ Bodmin Parkway

PENRYN

Menallack Farm, Treverva, Penryn, Cornwall, TR10 9BP
Tel: 01326 340333
Email: cheese@menallack.co.uk
Pitches For ▲ ⚏ ⛟ **Total** 20
Acreage 1½ **Open** Apr **to** Oct
Access Good **Site** Level
Nearest Bus Stop (Miles) ½
Secluded, simple quiet site. Beautiful views, peaceful countryside. Easy reach of both north and south coasts.
Facilities ⬚⬚⬚⬚⬚
Nearest Town Falmouth
Directions From take the A39 "Asda" roundabout turn right up the hill to Mabe Burnthouse. At the crossroads turn left and follow the road, at crossroads turn right to Gweek, site is signposted 1½ miles.
⚏ Penryn

PENZANCE

Bone Valley Caravan & Camping Park, Heamoor, Penzance, Cornwall, TR20 8UJ
Tel: 01736 360313
www.bonevalleyholidaypark.co.uk
Pitches For ▲ ⛟ **Total** 17
Acreage 1 **Open** All Year
Access Good **Site** Level
Nearest Bus Stop (Miles) Outside
1 mile from Penzance, 3 miles from St Michaels Mount and 10 miles from Lands End. Coastal footpaths.
Facilities ⬚⬚⬚⬚⬚
Nearest Town Penzance
Directions A30 to Penzance to Heamoor signposted approx 1 mile from Penzance
⚏ Penzance

PENZANCE

Garris Farm, Gulval, Penzance, Cornwall, TR20 8XD
Tel: 01736 365806
Pitches For ▲ ⚏ ⛟ **Total** 0
Acreage 8 **Open** May **to** Oct
Access Good **Site** Sloping
Nearest Bus Stop (Miles) ¼
Sailing and water skiing with own equipment
Facilities ⬚⬚⬚⬚⬚
Nearest Town Penzance
Directions Leave A30 turning right at Growlas on road to Luogvan B3309 to Castlegate. Follow road to Chysauster ancient village.
⚏ Penzance

PENZANCE

Kenneggy Cove Holiday Park, Higher Kenneggy, Rosudgeon, Penzance, Cornwall, TR20 9AU
Tel: 01736 763453
Email: enquiries@kenneggycove.co.uk
www.kenneggycove.co.uk
Pitches For ▲ ⚏ ⛟ **Total** 45
Acreage 6 **Open** Mid May **to** End of Sept
Nearest Bus Stop (Miles) ¼
A quiet site which operates a policy of no noise after 10pm. 10 minutes walk to the stunning beach and S.W. Coastal Path. Quality take-away food service.
Facilities ⬚⬚⬚⬚⬚
Nearest Town Penzance
Directions Midway between Penzance and Helston on the A394. Take turn into lane signposted Higher Kenneggy towards the sea.
⚏ Penzance

PENZANCE

Sennen Cove Camping & Caravanning Club Site, Higher Tregiffian Farm, St Buryan, Penzance, Cornwall, TR19 6JB
Tel: 01736 871588
Email:
sennen.covesite@thefriendlyclub.co.uk
www.campingandcaravanningclub.co.uk/sennencove
Pitches For ▲ ⚏ ⛟ **Total** 72
Acreage 4 **Open** Apr **to** 03-Nov
Access Good **Site** Level
Nearest Bus Stop (Miles) ¼
Situated on a farm in peaceful countryside. 2½ miles from the beach at Sennen Cove which has won numerous awards. BTB 4 Star Graded and AA 3 Pennants. Non members welcome. You can also call us on 0845 130 7633.
Facilities ⬚⬚⬚⬚⬚
Nearest Town Penzance
Directions Follow the A30 towards Lands End, turn right onto the A3306 St. to Pendeen road, site is 50 yards on the left.
⚏ Penzance

PENZANCE

Wayfarers Caravan & Camping Park, St Hilary, Penzance, Cornwall, TR20 9EF
Tel: 01736 Penzance 763326
Email: elaine@wayfarerspark.co.uk
www.wayfarerspark.co.uk
Pitches For ▲ ⚏ ⛟ **Total** 39
Acreage 4 **Open** May **to** Sept
Access Good **Site** Level
Nearest Bus Stop (Miles) Outside
ADULTS ONLY PARK. Tranquil, landscaped surroundings. Graded Excellent by the English Tourist Board. Pitches with 16amp hook-ups and awnings from £17 per night Four luxury holiday homes for hire.
Facilities ⬚⬚⬚⬚⬚

22

Nearest Town Marazion
Directions 2 miles east of Marazion on the B3280.
🚂 Penzance

PERRANPORTH

Penrose Holiday Park, Halt Road, Goonhavern, Near Perranporth, Truro, Cornwall, TR4 9QF
Tel: 01872 573185
Email: info@penroseholidaypark.com
www.penroseholidaypark.com
Pitches For ⛺ 🚐 🚍 🏕 **Total** 111
Acreage 10 **Open** Apr **to** Oct
Access Good **Site** Level
Nearest Bus Stop (Miles) ¼
Dog friendly, family site, Take away, 2 miles to Perranporth beach.
Facilities
Nearest Town Perranporth
Directions From the East, take the A30, continue past Bodmin and Indian Queens. Shortly after the wind farm take the B3285 to Perranporth, site is on the left.
🚂 Truro

PERRANPORTH

Perran Springs Holiday Park, Goonhavern, Truro, Cornwall, TR4 9QG
Tel: 01872 540568
Email: info@perransprings.co.uk
www.perransprings.co.uk
Pitches For ⛺ 🚐 🚍 **Total** 0
Acreage 21 **Open** Easter **to** Oct
Access Good **Site** Level
Nearest Bus Stop (Miles) ½
Award winning, friendly, quiet family park offering: Coarse Fishing Lakes, Nature Trail and Pond, Spacious Level Pitches, Electric Hook-ups, Caravan Holiday Homes to buy and hire, Eurotents, Shop, Launderette, Childrens Play Area and Panoramic Countryside Views.
Facilities
Nearest Town Perranporth
Directions Leave the A30 and turn right onto the B3285 signposted Perranporth. Follow the brown tourism signs marked Perran Springs for 1½ miles. Entrance will then be clearly seen.
🚂 Truro

PERRANPORTH

Perranporth Camping & Touring Park, Budnick Road, Perranporth, Cornwall, TR6 0DB
Tel: 01872 572174
Pitches For ⛺ 🚐 🚍 **Total** 150
Acreage 6 **Open** Easter **to** Sept
Access Good **Site** Lev/Slope
Nearest Bus Stop (Miles) ¼
5 to 10 minutes level walk to beach and town. Adjoining a golf course and 300 metres from stables.
Facilities
Nearest Town Perranporth
Directions 10 min walk NE from Perranporth off the B3285 Perranporth to Newquay road.
🚂 Truro

PERRANPORTH

Tollgate Farm Caravan & Camping Park, Budnick Hill, Perranporth, Cornwall, TR6 0AD
Tel: 01872 572130
Email: enquiries@tollgatefarm.co.uk
www.tollgatefarm.co.uk
Pitches For ⛺ 🚐 🚍 🏕 **Total** 106
Acreage 8 **Open** Easter **to** Sept

Access Good **Site** Level
Nearest Bus Stop (Miles) Outside
Near walkable beach, miles of dog walks, animal area,playing field,modern heated showers, new camping pods.
Facilities
Nearest Town Perranporth
Directions From the A30 take the B3285 signposted Perranporth, site is 1½ miles after Goonhavern on the right.
🚂 Truro

POLZEATH

South Winds Camping & Caravan Park, Old Polzeath Road, Polzeath, Nr Wadebridge, Cornwall, PL27 6QU
Tel: 01208 863267
Email: info@southwindscampsite.co.uk
www.polzeathcamping.co.uk
Pitches For ⛺ 🚐 🚍 **Total** 100
Acreage 7 **Open** May **to** Sept
Access Good **Site** Level
Nearest Bus Stop (Miles) ¼
Outstanding views of countryside and sea. ½ a mile from Polzeath Beach.
Facilities
Nearest Town Polzeath
🚂 Bodmin Road

POLZEATH

Valley Caravan Park, Polzeath, Wadebridge, Cornwall, PL27 6SS
Tel: 01208 862391
Email: info@valleycaravanpark.co.uk
www.valleycaravanpark.co.uk
Pitches For ⛺ 🚐 🚍 **Total** 100
Acreage 10 **Open** Apr **to** Oct
Access Good **Site** Level
Nearest Bus Stop (Miles) ¼
Near the beach.
Facilities
Nearest Town Wadebridge
Directions From Wadebridge take the B3314 to Polzeath and enter the village. Entrance is between shops, opposite the beach.
🚂 Bodmin Parkway

PORTHTOWAN

Porthtowan Tourist Park, Mile Hill, Porthtowan, Truro, Cornwall, TR4 8TY
Tel: 01209 890256
Email: admin@porthtowantouristpark.co.uk
www.porthtowantouristpark.co.uk
Pitches For ⛺ 🚐 🚍 **Total** 80
Acreage 5½ **Open** Easter **to** Sept
Access Good **Site** Level
Nearest Bus Stop (Miles) 1
A level site with spacious pitches in an area of outstanding natural beauty. Close to a sandy surfing beach, cycle trail and coastal path. Superb toilet/laundry facilities with free showers and family rooms. Ideal touring base.
Facilities
Nearest Town Porthtowan/Truro
Directions Take signpost off A30 Redruth/Porthtowan. Cross the A30, through north country to T-Junction, right up the hill, park is ½ a mile on the left.
🚂 Redruth

PORTREATH

Cambrose Touring Park, Portreath Road, Redruth, Cornwall, TR16 4HT
Tel: 01209 890747
Email: cambrosetouringpark@supanet.com
www.cambrosetouringpark.co.uk

Pitches For ⛺ 🚐 🚍 **Total** 60
Acreage 7 **Open** Apr **to** Oct
Access Good **Site** Level
Nearest Bus Stop (Miles) ½
1½ miles from the beach. Near to tramway. Ideal for walking and touring.
Facilities
Nearest Town Portreath
Directions From Redruth take the B3300 to Portreath, pass the Treasure Park on the left and after ¼ mile turn right signposted Porthtowan, Cambrose is 100 yards on the left.
🚂 Redruth

PORTREATH

Tehidy Holiday Park, Harris Mill, Illogan, Portreath, Cornwall, TR16 4JQ
Tel: 01209 216489
Email: holiday@tehidy.co.uk
www.tehidy.co.uk
Pitches For ⛺ 🚐 🚍 🏕 **Total** 28
Acreage 4½ **Open** Mar **to** Nov
Access Good **Site** Level
Nearest Bus Stop (Miles) Outside
Voted Best Family Site in UK 2013, Top 3 sites in europe 2012, close to sandy beaches.
Facilities
Nearest Town Portreath
Directions From the A30, exit to Portreath and Porthtowan and follow signs for Portreath. Turn left at the crossroads, go straight over next crossroads, Park is 300 metres after the Cornish Arms.
🚂 Redruth

PORTSCATHO

Treloan Coastal Holidays, Treloan Lane, Portscatho, The Roseland, Truro, Cornwall, TR2 5EF
Tel: 01872 580989
Email: info@treloancoastalholidays.co.uk
www.treloancoastalholidays.co.uk
Pitches For ⛺ 🚐 🚍 **Total** 65
Open All Year
Site Lev/Slope
Nearest Bus Stop (Miles) ¼
3 selcluded beaches/caves. Walking distance of 3 pubs
Facilities
Nearest Town Truro
Directions From Truro take the A390 through Tresillian and the bypass, take second right turn onto the A3078 sp Tregony and St. Mawes. At Trewithian turn left sp Portscatho and follow signs to Gerrans.
🚂 Truro/St. Austell

PORTSCATHO

Trewince Farm Touring Park, Trewince Farm, Portscatho, Truro, Cornwall, TR2 5ET
Tel: 01872 580430
Email: bookings@trewincefarm.co.uk
www.trewincefarm.co.uk
Pitches For ⛺ 🚐 🚍 **Total** 25
Acreage 3 **Open** May **to** Sept
Access Good **Site** Lev/Slope
Nearest Bus Stop (Miles) ½
Near the beach in an area of outstanding natural beauty. Close to village pubs and shops.
Facilities
Nearest Town Truro
Directions From St. Austell take the A390, then turn left onto the B3287 to Tregony, then the A3078 to St. Mawes. Leave at Trewitian and follow the road to St. Anthony.
🚂 Truro

REDRUTH

Globe Vale Holiday Park, Radnor, Redruth, Cornwall, TR16 4BH
Tel: 01209 891183
Email: info@globevale.co.uk
www.globevale.co.uk
Pitches For ▲ ⊞ ⊟ **Total** 138
Acreage 9 Open All Year
Access Good Site Level
Just a 10 minute drive from Portreath and Porthtowan beaches. Good access from the A30, ideal for visiting St. Ives, Penzance and Truro.
Facilities ...
Nearest Town Redruth
Directions From Redruth follow signs to Portreath and Porthtowan from the A30 roundabout. At the double roundabout take the third exit to North Country. At the crossroads turn right signposted Radnor and follow signs. Approx. 4 miles from Redruth.

REDRUTH

Lakeside Camping, The Golden Lion Inn, Stithians Lake, Menherion, Redruth, Cornwall, TR16 6NW
Email: enquiries@goldenlioninn.co.uk
www.goldenlioninn.co.uk
Pitches For ▲ ⊞ ⊟ ⊟ **Total** 14
Open All Year
Access Good Site Level
Nearest Bus Stop (Miles) 1
Set behind the gardens of an award winning pub and restaurant. 50 yards from a lake for windsurfing, sailing and kayaking. Fly fishing permits.
Facilities ...
Nearest Town Redruth
Directions Leave the A30 at Redruth and take the B3297 signposted Four Lanes and Helston. Turn left at signpost for the Golden Lion.
♣ Redruth

REDRUTH

Lanyon Holiday Park, Loscombe Lane, Four Lanes, Redruth, Cornwall, TR16 6LP
Tel: 01209 313474
Email: lanyonadmin@btconnect.com
www.lanyonholidaypark.co.uk
Pitches For ▲ ⊞ ⊟ ⊟ **Total** 50
Acreage 14 Open Apr to Oct
Access Good Site Level
Nearest Bus Stop (Miles) ¼
Surrounded by open countryside. 6 miles to Portreath surfing beach. 3¼ miles from Stithians Lake and close to the Great Flat Lode Trail.
Facilities ...
Nearest Town Redruth/Portreath
Directions Leave the A30 at Camborne/Pool A3047 exit, keep to the left hand lane and drive straight ahead through the next two sets of traffic lights. Pass Tesco Extra (on your left) and turn next right over railway bridge (sp Four Lanes). Follow this road up the hill [approx 1½ miles], at T-Junction turn right then take 2nd right at Pencoys Village Hall. Park is on the left hand side after approx 400 metres.
♣ Redruth

REDRUTH

Wheal Rose Caravan & Camping Park, Wheal Rose, Scorrier, Cornwall, TR16 5DD
Tel: 01209 891496
Email: whealrose@aol.com
www.whealrosecaravanpark.co.uk
Pitches For ▲ ⊞ ⊟ **Total** 50
Acreage 6½ Open Mar to Dec
Access Good Site Level
Nearest Bus Stop (Miles) Outside
Adjacent to a mineral tramway. Cenral for all of West Cornwalls attractions. AA 4 Pennants.
Facilities ...
Nearest Town Redruth
Directions From the A30 take the Scorrier slip road and turn right at the Plume of Feathers, follow signs to park.
♣ Redruth

RUAN MINOR

The Friendly Camp & Caravan Park, Tregullas Farm, Ruan Minor, Helston, Cornwall, TR12 7LJ
Tel: 01326 240387
Email: jbwbennetts@tiscali.co.uk
www.thefriendlycamp.co.uk
Pitches For ▲ ⊞ ⊟ **Total** 8
Open Easter or 1 April to Oct
Access Good Site Level
Nearest Bus Stop (Miles) ¼
Ideal centre for touring the Lizard Peninsula.
Facilities ...
Nearest Town Helston
Directions Take the A3083 Helston to Lizard road, the Park is situated on the left just before the junction of the B3296 to Mullion.
♣ Redruth

SALTASH

Dolbeare Park, Landrake, Saltash, Cornwall, PL12 5AF
Tel: 01752 851332
Email: reception@dolbeare.co.uk
www.dolbeare.co.uk
Pitches For ▲ ⊞ ⊟ ⊟ **Total** 60
Acreage 9 Open All Year
Access Good Site Level
Nearest Bus Stop (Miles) ¾
Centrally located between beaches and the moors, ideal for exploring both Cornwall and Devon. Easy access. Close to Looe, Polperro and Plymouth. Take-away on site.
Facilities ...
Nearest Town Saltash
Directions From Saltash take the A38 west for 4 miles to Landrake. At the footbridge turn right and follow signs to the site. ¾ miles from the A38.
♣ Saltash

ST. AGNES

Beacon Cottage Farm Touring Park, Beacon Drive, St Agnes, Cornwall, TR5 0NU
Tel: 01872 552347
Email: beaconcottagefarm@lineone.net
www.beaconcottagefarmholidays.co.uk

Pitches For ▲ ⊞ ⊟ **Total** 70
Acreage 4 Open Apr to Sept
Access Good Site Level
Nearest Bus Stop (Miles) ½
On a working farm, surrounded by National Trust land. Sandy beach 1 mile, beautiful sea views.
Facilities ...
Nearest Town St Agnes
Directions From the A30, take the B3277 to St. Agnes, take road to the Beacon and follow signs to the site.
♣ Truro

ST. AGNES

Presingoll Farm Caravan & Camping Park, St Agnes, Cornwall, TR5 0PB
Tel: 01872 552333
Email: pam@presingollfarm.co.uk
www.presingollfarm.co.uk
Pitches For ▲ ⊞ ⊟ **Total** 90
Acreage 5 Open Easter to Oct
Access Good Site Level
Nearest Bus Stop (Miles) Outside
Working farm overlooking the North Cornwall coastline. Near the Cornish Coastal Path and surf beaches within 2 miles. Ideal for walking. Dogs must be kept on a lead.
Facilities ...
Nearest Town St. Agnes
Directions Leave the A30 at Chiverton Cross roundabout and take the B3277 for St. Agnes. Site is 3 miles on the right.
♣ Truro

ST. AUSTELL

Little Winnick Touring Park, Pentewan Road, St Austell, Cornwall, PL26 6DL
Tel: 01726 843687
Email: mail@littlewinnick.co.uk
www.littlewinnick.co.uk
Pitches For ▲ ⊞ ⊟ **Total** 90
Acreage 8 Open Easter to Oct
Access Good Site Level
Nearest Bus Stop (Miles) Outside
Ideal for walkers,just 15 minutes walk to beach, centrally situated.
Facilities ...
Nearest Town St Austell
Directions 3 miles south of St Austell on the B3273 Mevagissey road, on left hand side.
♣ St Austell

ST. AUSTELL

Meadow Lakes, Hewas Water, St Austell, Cornwall, PL26 7JG
Tel: 01726 882540
Email: info@meadow-lakes.co.uk
www.meadow-lakes.co.uk
Pitches For ▲ ⊞ ⊟ ⊟ **Total** 200
Acreage 56
Access Good
Nearest Bus Stop (Miles) 1
Close to the Eden Project.
Facilities ...
Nearest Town St Austell

Directions Take the A390 from St Austell towards Truro Approx 4½ miles SW fork left onto B3287 signposted Tregony Meadow Lakes is 1 mile further on left.
⚞ St Austell

ST. AUSTELL

Pensagillas Park, Grampound, Truro, Cornwall, TR2 4SR
Tel: 01872 530808
Email: sales@pensagillaspark.co.uk
www.pensagillaspark.co.uk
Pitches For Å ⬠ ⬠ **Total** 65
Acreage 10 **Open** Mar **to** Oct
Access Good **Site** Level
2 acre course fishing lake, 5 miles from beach, 4 miles from Mevagissey.
Facilities ♿ ⬠ ⬠ ⬠ ⬠ ⬠ ⬠ ⬠ ⬠
⬠ ⬠ ⬠ ⬠ ⬠ ⬠ ⬠ ⬠ ⬠ ⬠ ⬠
Nearest Town Mevagissey
⚞ St Austell

ST. AUSTELL

River Valley Holiday Park, London Apprentice, St Austell, Cornwall, PL26 7AP
Tel: 01726 73533
Email: mail@rivervalleylholidaypark.co.uk
www.rivervalleyholidaypark.co.uk
Pitches For Å ⬠ ⬠ **Total** 40
Acreage 9 **Open** Apr **to** Oct
Access Good **Site** Level
Nearest Bus Stop (Miles) Outside
Alongside a river with woodland walk and cycle trail to the beach.
Facilities ♿ ⬠ ⬠ ⬠ ⬠ ⬠ ⬠ ⬠
⬠ ⬠ ⬠ ⬠ ⬠ ⬠ ⬠ ⬠ ⬠ ⬠ ⬠
Nearest Town St Austell
Directions Take the B3273 from St Austell to Mevagissey, 1 mile to London Apprentice, site is on the left hand side.
⚞ St Austell

ST. AUSTELL

Treveor Farm Caravan & Camping Site, Gorran, St Austell, Cornwall, PL26 6LW
Tel: 01726 842387
Email: info@treveorfarm.co.uk
www.treveorfarm.co.uk
Pitches For Å ⬠ ⬠ **Total** 50
Acreage 4 **Open** April **to** Oct
Access Good **Site** Level
1½ miles to the beach and coastal path. 3 miles from the Lost Gardens of Heligan and only 15 miles from the Eden Project.
Facilities ⬠ ⬠ ⬠ ⬠ ⬠ ⬠ ⬠ ⬠ ⬠ ⬠ ⬠ ⬠
Nearest Town St Austell/Gorran Haven
Directions Take the B3273 from St Austell towards Mevagissey. After Pentewan at top of the hill turn right to Gorran. After approx 4 miles turn right into the park at the signboard.
⚞ St Austell

ST. BURYAN

Tower Park Caravans & Camping, St Buryan, Penzance, Cornwall, TR19 6BZ
Tel: 01736 810286
Email: enquiries@towerparkcamping.co.uk
www.towerparkcamping.co.uk
Pitches For Å ⬠ ⬠ **Total** 102
Acreage 12 **Open** Mar **to** Oct
Access Good **Site** Level
Nearest Bus Stop (Miles) ¼
Peaceful, family run campsite in West Cornwall. Short walk to the village pub and shop. Holiday caravans for hire. Pre erected tents for hire.
Facilities ♿ ⬠ ⬠ ⬠ ⬠ ⬠ ⬠ ⬠
⬠ ⬠ ⬠ ⬠ ⬠ ⬠ ⬠ ⬠ ⬠ ⬠ ⬠ ⬠
Nearest Town Penzance
Directions From the A30 Lands End road turn left onto the B3283 towards St. Buryan. In the village turn right then right again and the park is 300 yards on the right.
⚞ Penzance

ST. BURYAN

Treverven Caravan & Camping Park, St Buryan, Penzance, Cornwall, TR19 6DL
Tel: 01736 810200
Email: info@treverventouringpar.co.uk
www.treverventouringpar.co.uk
Pitches For Å ⬠ ⬠ **Total** 120
Acreage 7 **Open** Easter **to** Oct
Access Good **Site** Level
Nearest Bus Stop (Miles) 1
Situated in an area of outstanding natural beauty with direct access onto the South West Coastal Path. Many sandy beaches and coves in the area.
Facilities ♿ ⬠ ⬠ ⬠ ⬠ ⬠ ⬠ ⬠ ⬠
⬠ ⬠ ⬠ ⬠ ⬠ ⬠ ⬠ ⬠ ⬠ ⬠ ⬠ ⬠
Nearest Town Porthcurno
Directions From Penzance take the A30 Lands End road, after approx 3 miles turn left onto the B3283 1½ miles beyond St Buryan village. Turn left onto the B3315 Lamorna road.
⚞ Penzance

ST. IVES

Balnoon Camping Site, Balnoon, Nr Halsetown, St Ives, Cornwall, TR26 3JA
Tel: 01736 795431
Email: nat@balnoon.fsnet.co.uk
www.balnooncampsite.co.uk
Pitches For Å ⬠ ⬠ **Total** 23
Acreage 1 **Open** Easter **to** Oct
Access Good **Site** Level
Nearest Bus Stop (Miles) Outside
Situated in the countryside with views of adjacent rolling hills. Equidistant from the beautiful beaches of Carbis Bay and St. Ives, approx. 2 miles.
Facilities ⬠ ⬠ ⬠ ⬠ ⬠ ⬠ ⬠ ⬠ ⬠ ⬠
Nearest Town St. Ives

Directions From the A30 take the A3074 for St. Ives, at the second mini-roundabout turn first left signposted Tate St. Ives (B3311), turn second right signposted Balnoon. Approx. 3 miles from the A30.
⚲ St. Ives

ST. IVES

Penderleath Caravan & Camping Park, Towednack, St Ives, Cornwall, TR26 3AF
Tel: 01736 798403
Email: holidays@penderleath.co.uk
www.penderleath.co.uk
Pitches For ▲ ⛺ ⛟ **Total** 75
Acreage 10 **Open** Easter **to** Oct
Access Good **Site** Lev/Slope
Nearest Bus Stop (Miles) Outside
Set in a classified area of outstanding natural beauty, with fabulous views over countryside to the sea. Very peaceful and tranquil. Outside the main season we offer an Adults Only Camping Area. You can also contact us on Mobile: 07840 208542.
Facilities ♿ ☕ 🚿 🅿 📶 ⊙ ⏱ ⛽ 🔲 ♨
🛁 🅿 ⊙ ✗ 🍴 ♨ 🔥 🏧 📮 🔲
Nearest Town St. Ives
Directions From the A30 take the A3074 signposted St. Ives. At the second mini roundabout turn left, at the end of the road turn left then immediately right, turn left at next fork.
⚲ St. Ives

ST. IVES

Polmanter Touring Park, Halsetown, St Ives, Cornwall, TR26 3LX
Tel: 01736 795640
Email: reception@polmanter.co.uk
www.polmanter.co.uk
Pitches For ▲ ⛺ ⛟ **Total** 250
Acreage 20 **Open** 29th Mar **to** 27-Oct
Access Good **Site** Level
Nearest Bus Stop (Miles) Entrance
Within walking distance of St Ives and beaches.
Facilities ♿ ☕ 🚿 🅿 📶 ⊙ ⏱ ⛽ 🔲 ♨
🛁 🅿 ✗ 🍴 ♨ 🔥 🏧 📮 🔲 📶
Nearest Town St Ives
Directions From the A30 take the A3074 to St Ives, turn left at the second mini-roundabout via Halsetown. Turn right at the B3311 and turn right at the Halsetown Inn, then first left.
⚲ St Ives

ST. IVES

St Ives Bay Holiday Park, Upton Towans, Hayle, Cornwall, TR27 5BH
Tel: 01736 752274
Email: enquiries@stivesbay.co.uk
www.stivesbay.co.uk
Pitches For ▲ ⛺ ⛟ **Total** 200
Acreage 12 **Open** Easter **to** 02-Nov
Access Good **Site** Lev/Slope
Nearest Bus Stop (Miles) ¼
Park adjoining own sandy beach, onto St. Ives Bay. Children very welcome. Sea views. Dogs no longer accepted. Dial-a-Brochure 24 hours, Mr R. White. (See our display advertisment).
Facilities 📶 🅿 ⊙ ⏱ ⛽
🔲 🛁 ⊙ ✗ 🍴 🔥 ♨ 🏧 📮 ♪
Nearest Town Hayle
Directions A30 from Camborne to Hayle, at roundabout take Hayle turn-off and then turn right onto B3301, 600yds off left enter park.
⚲ Hayle

ST. JUST

Kelynack Caravan & Camping Park, Kelynack, St Just, Penzance, Cornwall, TR19 7RE
Tel: 01736 787633
Email: enquiries@kelynackholidays.co.uk
www.kelynackholidays.co.uk
Pitches For ▲ ⛺ ⛟ **Total** 30
Acreage 2 **Open** All Year
Access Good **Site** Level
Nearest Bus Stop (Miles) ¼
Small and secluded site nestling alongside a stream. Just 1 mile from the coast in the beautiful Cot Valley.
Facilities ♿ ☕ 🔲 📶 🅿 ⊙ ⏱ ⛽ 🔲 ♨
🛁 ⊙ ♨ 🔥 🔲 🖥 📶
Nearest Town Penzance
Directions From Penzance take the A3071 to St Just. Just before reaching St Just turn left onto the B3306, follow road down the hill for 1 mile then turn left, after 200 yards turn left again.
⚲ Penzance

ST. JUST

Roselands Caravan Park, Dowran, St Just, Penzance, Cornwall, TR19 7RS
Tel: 01736 788571
Email: info@roselands.co.uk
www.roselands.co.uk
Pitches For ▲ ⛺ ⛟ **Total** 38
Acreage 3 **Open** Mar **to** Oct
Nearest Bus Stop (Miles) ¼
Nr Lands End, South West Coast Path near Sennen Cove surf beach, in an area of Outstanding natural beauty.
Facilities ☕ 📶 🅿 ⊙ ⏱ ⛽ 🔲 ♨
🛁 ⊙ ♨ 🔥 ♨ 🔲 📶
Nearest Town St Just
Directions From the A30 Penzance by-pass take the A3071 to St Just for 5 miles, turn left at sign and park is 800 yards.
⚲ Penzance

ST. JUST

Secret Garden Caravan Park, Bosavern House, St Just, Penzance, Cornwall, TR19 7RD
Tel: 01736 788301
Email: mail@bosavern.com
www.secretbosavern.com
Pitches For ▲ ⛺ ⛟ **Total** 12
Acreage 1 **Open** March **to** October
Access Good **Site** Level
Nearest Bus Stop (Miles) ½
Walled garden site surrounded by trees and flowers. Excellent walking country, good beaches nearby. Local authorities licensed site.
Facilities ☕ 🔲 📶 🅿 ⊙ ⏱ ⛽ 🔲 ♨
🏧 ✗ 🔲 📮 🔲 📶
Nearest Town St Just/Penzance
Directions Take the A3071 from Penzance towards St. Just. Approximately 550yds before St. Just turn left onto the B3306 signposted Lands End and airport. Secret Garden Caravan Park is 500yds from the turn off, behind Bosavern House.
⚲ Penzance

ST. MAWES

Trethem Mill Touring Park, St Just-in-Roseland, Truro, Cornwall, TR2 5JF
Tel: 01872 580504
Email: reception@trethem.com
www.trethem.com
Pitches For ▲ ⛺ ⛟ **Total** 84
Acreage 4 **Open** Apr **to** Mid Oct
Access Good **Site** Lev/Slope
Nearest Bus Stop (Miles) ¼

Discover the unexplored Roseland, staying on the only 5 Star Park on the Peninsula. Family owned and run, we offer a relaxing and tranquil setting. Ideally located for for walking, sailing, beaches and gardens. National Caravan Park of the Year 2010, England in Excellence Awards.
Facilities ♿ ☕ 🔲 📶 🅿 ⊙ ⏱ ⛽ 🔲 ♨
🛁 ⊙ ♨ 🔲 📮 🔲 📶
Nearest Town St Mawes
Directions From Tregony follow the A3078 to St. Mawes. Approx. 2 miles after passing through Trewithian look out for caravan and camping sign.
⚲ Truro

ST. MERRYN

Tregavone Farm Touring Park, St Merryn, Padstow, Cornwall, PL28 8JZ
Tel: 01841 520148
Email: info@tregavone.co.uk
www.tregavonefarm.co.uk
Pitches For ▲ ⛺ ⛟ **Total** 40
Acreage 4 **Open** Mar **to** Oct
Access Good **Site** Level
Quiet family run site situated near sandy surfing beaches, country views, well maintained and grassy. AA 2 Pennants.
Facilities ♿ ☕ 📶 🅿 ⊙ ⏱ ⛽ 🔲 ♨ 🖥 📮
Nearest Town Padstow
Directions Turn right off A39 (Wadebridge-St. Columb) onto A389 (Padstow) come to a T-junction and turn right, in 1 mile turn left, entrance on left after 1 mile.
⚲ Newquay

ST. MERRYN

Trethias Farm Caravan Park, St Merryn, Padstow, Cornwall, PL28 8PL
Tel: 01841 520323
Email: trethiasfarm@btconnect.com
Pitches For ▲ ⛺ ⛟ **Total** 63
Acreage 12 **Open** Apr **to** Sept
Access Good **Site** Level
Nearest Bus Stop (Miles) 1
Near beach, scenic views. Couples and family groups only. ETB 3 Star Graded and David Bellamy Gold Award for Conservation 2012.
Facilities ☕ 🔲 🅿 ⊙ ⏱ ⛽ 🔲 ♨
🛁 🏧 ⊙ 📮 🔲 📶
Nearest Town Padstow
Directions From Wadebridge follow signs to St. Merryn, go past Farmers Arms, third turning right (our signs from here).
⚲ Bodmin Parkway

ST. MERRYN

Trevean Farm Caravan & Camping Park, St Merryn, Padstow, Cornwall, PL28 8PR
Tel: 01841 520772
Email: trevean.info@virgin.net
www.treveancaravanandcamping.net
Pitches For ▲ ⛺ ⛟ **Total** 68
Acreage 2 **Open** Apr **to** Oct
Access Good **Site** Level
Nearest Bus Stop (Miles) ½
Situated near several sandy, surfing beaches. ETC 4 Star Grading.
Facilities ♿ ☕ 🔲 📶 🅿 ⊙ ⏱ ⛽ 🔲 ♨
🛁 🏧 ⊙ 🔲 🔥 📮 ☀ 📶
Nearest Town Padstow
Directions From St. Merryn village take the B3276 Newquay road for 1 mile. Turn left for Rumford, site ¼ mile on the right.
⚲ Newquay

TINTAGEL
The Headland Caravan & Camping Park, Atlantic Road, Tintagel, Cornwall, PL34 0DE
Tel: 01840 770239
Email: headland.caravan@unicomemail.co.uk
www.headlandcaravanpark.co.uk
Pitches For A ⊕ ⊟ ⊟ ⊰ **Total** 60
Acreage 4 **Open** Easter **to** Oct
Access Good **Site** Lev/Slope
Nearest Bus Stop (Miles) ¼
Three beaches within walking distance. Scenic views. Ideal touring centre.
Facilities ⌇ ⬚⬚⬚⬚⬚⬚⬚⬚⬚ ⬚⬚⬚⬚⬚⬚⬚
Nearest Town Tintagel
Directions Follow camping/caravan signs from B3263 through village to Headland.
⚆ Bodmin Parkway

TINTAGEL
Trewethett Farm Caravan Club Site, Trethevy, Tintagel, Cornwall, PL34 0BQ
Tel: 01840 770222
www.caravanclub.co.uk
Pitches For A ⊕ ⊟ **Total** 122
Acreage 15 **Open** Mar **to** Nov
Access Good **Site** Level
Breathtaking views overlooking Bossiney Cove. ½ a mile from a sandy beach. Spectacular clifftop walks. Near Tintagel Castle, picturesque ports and harbours. Non members welcome. Booking essential.
Facilities ⬚ ⌇ ⬚⬚⬚⬚⬚⬚⬚⬚⬚⬚⬚
Nearest Town Tintagel
Directions From NE on the A30, t onto the A395 via slip road. After 11 miles at the T-junc t onto the A39, after 1 mile just before the transmitter t lt, at T-junc t rt onto the B3266. After 2½ miles at the junc on the bend turn left onto the B3263, site is on the right.
⚆ Tintagel

TORPOINT
Whitsand Bay Holiday Park, Millbrook, Torpoint, Cornwall, PL10 1JZ
Tel: 01752 822597
Email: enquiries@whitsandbayholidays.co.uk
www.whitsandbayholidays.co.uk
Pitches For A ⊕ ⊟ ⊰ **Total** 50
Acreage 24 **Open** All Year
Access Good **Site** Sloping
Nearest Bus Stop (Miles) Outside
Near beach.
Facilities ⌇ ⬚⬚⬚⬚⬚⬚⬚⬚⬚⬚⬚⬚⬚⬚⬚
Nearest Town Torpoint
Directions Follow signs for Antony take left turn by Ring o Bells at t junc turn left and take next right and follow signs.
⚆ Plymouth/St Germans

TRURO
Carnon Downs Caravan & Camping Park, Carnon Downs, Truro, Cornwall, TR3 6JJ
Tel: 01872 862283
Email: info@carnondownscaravanpark.co.uk
www.carnondownscaravanpark.co.uk
Pitches For A ⊕ ⊟ **Total** 150
Acreage 30 **Open** All Year
Access Good **Site** Level
Idea touring
Facilities ⬚ ⌇ ⬚⬚⬚⬚⬚⬚⬚⬚⬚⬚⬚⬚⬚⬚
Nearest Town Truro
Directions On the A390 Falmouth road, 3 miles South of Truro.
⚆ Truro

TRURO
Chacewater Camping & Caravan Park, Coxhill, Chacewater, Truro, Cornwall, TR4 8LY
Tel: 01209 820762
Email: chacewaterpark@hotmail.com
www.chacewaterpark.co.uk
Pitches For ⊕ ⊟ **Total** 100
Acreage 6 **Open** May **to** Sept
Access Good **Site** Level
Nearest Bus Stop (Miles) Outside
Exclusively for Adults. Special discounts for the over 50's
Facilities ⬚ ⌇ ⬚⬚⬚⬚⬚⬚⬚⬚⬚⬚⬚⬚
Nearest Town Truro
Directions From A30 take the A3047 to Scorrier. Turn left at Crossroads Hotel onto the B3298. 1½ miles turn left to Chacewater, ½ mile sign directs you to the park.
⚆ Truro

TRURO
Killiwerris Touring Park, Penstraze, Truro, Cornwall, TR4 8PF
Tel: 01872 561356
Email: killiwerris@aol.com
www.killiwerris.co.uk
Pitches For ⊕ ⊟ **Total** 20
Acreage 1 **Open** All year
Access Good **Site** Level
ADULTS ONLY site. 4 miles from beach, countryside, ideal central location for exploring Cornwall.
Facilities ⬚ ⌇ ⬚⬚⬚⬚⬚⬚⬚⬚⬚⬚⬚⬚
Nearest Town Truro
Directions Chacewater village 1 mile, Truro 4 miles.
⚆ Truro

TRURO
Summer Valley Touring Park, Shortlanesend, Truro, Cornwall, TR4 9DW
Tel: 01872 277878
Email: james@summervalley.co.uk
www.summervalley.co.uk
Pitches For A ⊕ ⊟ **Total** 50
Acreage 3 **Open** Apr **to** Oct
Access Good **Site** Sloping
Nearest Bus Stop (Miles) ¼
Ideal touring centre for all of Cornwall.
Facilities ⌇ ⬚⬚⬚⬚⬚⬚⬚⬚⬚⬚⬚⬚⬚
Nearest Town Truro
Directions 2½ miles north of Truro on the B3284 Perranporth road.
⚆ Truro

TRURO
Trevarth Holiday Park, Blackwater, Truro, Cornwall, TR4 8HR
Tel: 01872 560266
Email: trevarth@btconnect.com
www.trevarth.co.uk
Pitches For A ⊕ ⊟ **Total** 30
Acreage 4 **Open** Apr **to** Mid Oct
Access Good **Site** Level
Nearest Bus Stop (Miles) Outside
Rural park, centrally situated for touring Cornwall.
Facilities ⌇ ⬚⬚⬚⬚⬚⬚⬚⬚⬚⬚⬚⬚⬚
Nearest Town St Agnes
Directions Take the A30 to Chiverton roundabout, take the exit for the B3277 to St Agnes. At the next roundabout take the Blackwater exit and the park is 200 yards on the right.
⚆ Truro

TRURO
Veryan Camping & Caravanning Club Site, Tretheake Manor, Veryan, Truro, Cornwall, TR2 5PP
Tel: 01872 501658
Email: veryan.site@thefriendlyclub.co.uk
www.campingandcaravanningclub.co.uk/veryan
Pitches For A ⊕ ⊟ **Total** 150
Acreage 9 **Open** 15-Mar **to** 04-Nov
Access Good **Site** Sloping
Nearest Bus Stop (Miles) ¼
Ideal for exploring the beaches and coves of the Cornish Coast. BTB 4 Star Graded and AA 3 Pennants. Non members welcome. You can also call us on 0845 130 7633.
Facilities ⬚ ⌇ ⬚⬚⬚⬚⬚⬚⬚⬚⬚⬚⬚⬚⬚⬚⬚⬚
Nearest Town Veryan
Directions Take the A390 from St. Austell, leave at the A3078 sign on the left, turn left at the filling station and follow international signs.
⚆ Truro

WADEBRIDGE
Gunvenna Caravan & Camping Park, St Minver, Wadebridge, Cornwall, PL27 6QN
Tel: 01208 862405
Email: gunvenna.bookings@gmail.com
www.gunvenna.co.uk
Pitches For A ⊕ ⊟ ⊰ **Total** 63
Acreage 11 **Open** Easter **to** 2nd week in Oct
Access Good **Site** Level
Nearest Bus Stop (Miles) ½
Polzeath and rock beaches. Good sandy beaches.
Facilities ⬚ ⌇ ⬚⬚⬚⬚⬚⬚⬚⬚⬚⬚⬚⬚⬚⬚⬚⬚
Nearest Town Wadebridge
Directions From Wadebridge follow the signs for Polzeath. Gunvenna Caravan Park is on the right hand side.
⚆ Bodmin

WADEBRIDGE
Little Bodieve Holiday Park, Bodieve Road, Wadebridge, Cornwall, PL27 6EG
Tel: 01208 812323
Email: info@littlebodieve.co.uk
www.littlebodieve.co.uk
Pitches For A ⊕ ⊟ ⊟ **Total** 195
Acreage 22
Access Good **Site** Lev/Slope
Nearest Bus Stop (Miles) Outside
Just a few minutes from superb beaches and golf courses. 5 minutes from The Camel Trail, 10 minutes from Padstow and Crealy Adventure Park and 25 minutes from The Eden Project.
Facilities ⌇ ⬚⬚⬚⬚⬚⬚⬚⬚⬚⬚⬚⬚⬚⬚⬚⬚
Nearest Town Wadebridge
Directions 1 mile north of Wadebridge Town centre turn off the A39 take the B3314 towards Rock, Portreath and Port Isaac.
⚆ Bodmin Parkway

WADEBRIDGE
Lundynant Caravan Site, Polzeath, Nr Wadebridge, Cornwall, PL27 6QX
Tel: 01208 862268
www.lundynant@btconnect.com
Pitches For A ⊕ ⊟ **Total** 33
Open Easter **to** Oct
Access Good **Site** Level
Nearest Bus Stop (Miles) ¼
Public footpath to the beach and village.
Facilities ⌇ ⬚⬚⬚⬚⬚⬚⬚⬚⬚⬚⬚
Nearest Town Wadebridge
Directions From Wadebridge take the B3314 to Polzeath, 7 miles.
⚆ Bodmin

WADEBRIDGE
Ponderosa Caravan Park, St Issey, Wadebridge, Cornwall, PL27 7QA
Tel: 01841 540359
Pitches For ▲ ⬛ ⬛ **Total** 40
Acreage 3½ **Open** Easter **to** Oct
Access Good **Site** Level
Nearest Bus Stop (Miles) ¼
Seven beaches within 4 miles. Close to the Camel Trail, Creely Adventre Park and the Eden Project.
Facilities ⬛ ⬛ ⬛ ⬛ ⬛ ⬛ ⬛ ⬛ ⬛ ⬛ ⬛ ⬛
Directions On main Wadebridge to Padstow road.
� Bodmin Parkway

WADEBRIDGE
St. Mabyn Holiday Park, Longstone Road, St Mabyn, Nr Wadebridge, Cornwall, PL30 3BY
Tel: 01208 841677
Email: info@stmabyn.co.uk
www.stmabynholidaypark.co.uk
Pitches For ▲ ⬛ ⬛ **Total** 120
Acreage 12 **Open** 15-Mar **to** 03-Nov
Access Good **Site** Level/Sloping
Nearest Bus Stop (Miles) ¼
Situated near Bodmin Moor. Ideal for exploring the whole of Cornwall. Easy access to Eden Project, Truro, Wadebridge, Padstow and many other places of interest.
Facilities ⬛
Nearest Town Wadebridge
Directions Take the B3266 from either Camelford or Bodmin. Site is at Longstone crossroads. From Wadebridge take the A389 to Bodmin then the B3266.
� Bodmin Parkway

WADEBRIDGE
The Laurels Holiday Park, Padstow Road, Whitecross, Wadebridge, Cornwall, PL27 7JQ
Tel: 01209 313474
Email: lanyonadmin@btconnect.com
www.thelaurelsholidaypark.co.uk
Pitches For ▲ ⬛ ⬛ **Total** 35
Acreage 2 **Open** Apr **to** Oct
Access Good **Site** Level
Nearest Bus Stop (Miles) Outside
6 miles from Padstow, and close to Rock and Port Isaac. Ideal for touring north and south Cornwall.
Facilities ⬛ ⬛ ⬛ ⬛ ⬛ ⬛ ⬛ ⬛ ⬛ ⬛ ⬛ ⬛
Nearest Town Padstow
Directions On the crossroads of the A39 and the A389 Wadebridge/Padstow junction, close to the Royal Cornwall Showground.
🚩 Bodmin

WADEBRIDGE
Trewince Farm Holiday Park, St Issey, Wadebridge, Cornwall, PL27 7RL
Tel: 01208 812830
Email: enquiries@trewincefarm-holidaypark.co.uk
www.trewincefarm-holidaypark.co.uk
Pitches For ▲ ⬛ ⬛ **Total** 120
Acreage 15 **Open** Easter **to** Oct
Access Good **Site** Level
Nearest Bus Stop (Miles) ¼
Only 4 miles from picturesque Padstow and the Camel Trail. Ideal for cycling and walking.
Facilities ⬛
Nearest Town Padstow
Directions Take the A39 from Wadebridge towards Padstow, turn right onto the A389, site is signposted 1 mile on the left.
🚩 Bodmin Parkway

CUMBRIA
AMBLESIDE
Baysbrown Farm, Great Langdale, Ambleside, Cumbria, LA22 9JZ
Tel: 01539 437150
Email: baysbrowninfo@gmail.com
www.baysbrownfarmcampsite.co.uk
Pitches For ▲ **Total** 150
Open Mar **to** Nov
Access Poor **Site** Lev/Slope
Nearest Bus Stop (Miles) ¼
Ideal for walking climbing and other adventures.
Facilities ⬛ ⬛ ⬛ ⬛ ⬛ ⬛
Nearest Town Ambleside
Directions From Ambleside take the A593 to Skelwith Bridge. Turn right onto B5343 Follow to Chapel Stile. 2nd leftafter Wainwright pub
🚩 Windermere

APPLEBY
Hawkrigg Farm, Colby, ApplebyinWestmorland, Cumbria, CA16 6BB
Pitches For ▲ ⬛ ⬛ **Total** 0
Open All Year
Access Good **Site** Level
Nearest Bus Stop (Miles) 1½
Quiet site with beautiful views. Ideal for touring the Eden Valley.
Facilities ⬛ ⬛ ⬛ ⬛ ⬛ ⬛ ⬛ ⬛
Directions From Appleby take the B6260, turn west onto the Colby road. In Colby turn left onto Kings Meaburn Road, take the first turning right.
🚩 Appleby

APPLEBY
Silverband Park, Silverband, Knock, Nr Appleby, Cumbria, CA16 6DL
Tel: 01768 361218
Pitches For ⬛ ⬛ **Total** 12
Acreage ½ **Open** All Year
Access Good **Site** Sloping
Nearest Bus Stop (Miles) Outside
Ideal for touring the Lakes and Fells. Two fully serviced pitches available. Bus service only once a week.
Facilities ⬛ ⬛ ⬛ ⬛ ⬛ ⬛ ⬛ ⬛ ⬛ ⬛
Nearest Town Appleby/Penrith
Directions Turn left off the A66 Penrith to Scotch Corner road at Kirkby Thore. After 2 miles at T-Junction turn left, after 100 yards take the first turn right, site is 1 mile on the right.
🚩 Appleby/Penrith

ARNSIDE/SILVERDALE
Fell End Caravan Park, Slackhead Road, Hale, Nr Milnthorpe, Cumbria, LA7 7BS
Tel: 01524 889192
Email: enquiries@pureleisuregroup.com
www.fellendcaravanpark.co.uk
Pitches For ⬛ ⬛ **Total** 85
Acreage 28 **Open** All Year
Access Good **Site** Lev/Slope
Nearest Bus Stop (Miles) Outside
Located in the Arnside/Silverdale area of outstanding natural beauty in the Southern Lake District.
Facilities ⬛
Nearest Town Arnside/Silverdale
Directions From Milnthorpe follow A6 South. Turn right at Wildlife Oasis and follow sign posts. From Carnforth, follow A6 North.
🚩 Arnside

ARNSIDE/SILVERDALE
Hall More Caravan Park, Hale, Nr Milnthorpe, Cumbria, LA7 7BP
Tel: 01524 889192
Email: enquiries@pureleisure.com
www.pureleisuregroup.com
Pitches For ▲ ⬛ ⬛ **Total** 64
Acreage 10 **Open** 1st March **to** 5th January
Access Good **Site** Level
Located in the Arnside/Silverdale area of outstanding natural beauty in the Southern Lake District.
Facilities ⬛ ⬛ ⬛ ⬛ ⬛ ⬛ ⬛ ⬛ ⬛ ⬛ ⬛ ⬛ ⬛ ⬛ ⬛ ⬛ ⬛ ⬛
Nearest Town Arnside/Milnthorpe
Directions North from Carnforth follow A6. Turn left at Wildlife Oasis Park or follow A6 from Milnthorpe.
🚩 Arnside

ARNSIDE/SILVERDALE
Silverdale Caravan Park, Cove Road, Silverdale, Nr Carnforth, Lancashire, LA5 0SH
Tel: 01524 701508
Email: reception@holgates.co.uk
www.holgates.co.uk
Pitches For ▲ ⬛ ⬛ **Total** 70
Acreage 10 **Open** All year
Access Good **Site** Lev/Slope
Nearest Bus Stop (Miles) Outside
On Morecambe Bay. In area of outstanding natural beauty. Indoor swimming pool, gym, spa bath, sauna and steam room. Restaurant and bar. Multi award winning park.
Facilities ⬛
Nearest Town Morecambe
Directions 5 miles northwest of Carnforth, between Silverdale and Arnside.
🚩 Silverdale

BASSENTHWAITE
Herdwick Croft Caravan Park, Herdwick Croft, Ousebridge, Bassenthwaite, Keswick, Cumbria, CA12 4RD
Tel: 017687 76241
Email: info@herdwickcroft.co.uk
www.herdwickcroft.co.uk
Pitches For ▲ ⬛ ⬛ ⬛ **Total** 20
Acreage 10 **Open** Apr **to** 01-Nov
Access Good **Site** Level
Nearest Bus Stop (Miles) Outside
Lake District
Facilities ⬛ ⬛ ⬛ ⬛ ⬛ ⬛ ⬛ ⬛ ⬛ ⬛ ⬛ ⬛
Nearest Town Keswick
Directions From the A66 take the B5291 at Dubwath and follow signs for Castle Inn. Site is on the left hand side after crossing the bridge.
🚩 Penrith

CARLISLE
Dalston Hall Caravan Park, Dalston, Carlisle, Cumbria, CA5 7JX
Tel: 01228 710165
Email: info@dalstonholidaypark.com
www.dalstonhallholidaypark.com
Pitches For ▲ ⬛ ⬛ ⬛ **Total** 71
Acreage 3½ **Open** Mar **to** Jan
Access Good **Site** Level
Nearest Bus Stop (Miles) Outside
Adjacent to a golf course (same ownership). Fishing rights on the adjacent river.
Facilities ⬛
Nearest Town Carlisle

A picturesque
countryside retreat

Fell End Holiday Park is an award winning, secluded, 28 acre, beautiful woodland park.

The park is set in the Arnside & Silverdale Area of Outstanding Beauty, in the Southern Lake District and with easy motorway access.

Touring Pitches
from £20
per night

Camping Pods
from £42
per night

A perfect
relaxing break

Hall More Holiday Park is a peaceful retreat, situated amongst 10 acres of picturesque meadow and woodland.

Hall More holidaymakers can enjoy the stunning surrounding countryside and access to the cafe, bar & leisure facilities at neighbouring Fell End Holiday Park.

Touring Pitches
from £18
per night

Tent Pitches
from £17
per night

Camping Pods
from £42
per night

Call us 01524 889192 *or Visit* pure-leisure.co.uk

FELL END, SLACKHEAD ROAD, HALE, MILNTHORPE LA7 7BS

Directions Leave the M6 at junction 42 and take the road to Dalston. At Dalston take the B5299 towards Carlisle, site is on the right after 1 mile.
⚐ Dalston

CARLISLE

Dandy Dinmont Caravan & Camping Site, Blackford, Carlisle, Cumbria, CA6 4EA
Tel: 01228 674611
Email: dandydinmont@btopenworld.com
www.caravan-camping-carlisle.co.uk
Pitches For Å ⬔ ⬕ **Total** 47
Acreage 4 **Open** Mar to Oct
Access Good **Site** Level
Nearest Bus Stop (Miles) ¼
Now a mainly Adult Park, children are accepted, but there are no ball games or play area. Ideal for historic Carlisle Castle, Cathedral, Roman Wall, Border Country, and only 45 minutes from the Lake District.
Facilities ⌨ ⊡ ⬚ ⬔ ⌇ ⊙ ▣ 🖾
⊙ ⬒⬕⬓ ▣
Nearest Town Carlisle
Directions On A7 at Blackford, 4¼ miles north of Carlisle. Leave M6 at intersection 44, and take the A7 north (Galashiels road), site approx 1½ miles on the right. After Blackford sign, follow road directional signs to site.
⚐ Carlisle

CARLISLE

Englethwaite Hall Caravan Club Site, Armathwaite, Carlisle, Cumbria, CA4 9SY
Tel: 01228 560202
www.caravanclub.co.uk
Pitches For ⬔ ⬕ **Total** 63
Acreage 15 **Open** Mar to Nov
Access Good **Site** Lev/Slope
Tranquil 15 acre estate in the Eden Valley with lovely views and Inglewood Forest as a backdrop. Riverside walks. Near the Lake District, Yorkshire Dales and Hadrians Wall. Own sanitation required. Non members welcome. Booking essential.
Facilities ⌇ ⊡ ⊞ 🖾 ⬚⬓ ⊙⬕⊡
Nearest Town Carlisle
Directions Leave the M6 or A6 at junction 42 and take the B6263 signposted Wetheral, after 1¾ miles turn right signposted Armathwaite. Site is approx. 2¾ miles on the right. Warning! - Bumpy road, recommended max speed 35mph.
⚐ Carlisle

CARLISLE

Green Acres Caravan Park, High Knells, Houghton, Carlisle, Cumbria, CA6 4JW
Tel: 01228 675418
Email: info@caravanpark-cumbria.com
www.caravanpark-cumbria.com
Pitches For Å ⬔ ⬕ **Total** 30
Acreage 3 **Open** Easter to October
Access Good **Site** Level
ADULT ONLY PARK. Ideal touring base for Hadrians Wall, Carlisle City, the Lake District and the Scottish Borders. AA 4 Pennant Graded.
Facilities ⌇ ⊡ ⊞ 🖾 ⬚ ⌇ ⊙⊙ 🖾⬕⬓A⬗⬕
⬚
Nearest Town Carlisle
Directions Leave the M6 at junction 44 (North Carlisle). Take the A689 east for 1 mile, turn left signposted Scaleby. Site is 1 mile on the left.
⚐ Carlisle

COCKERMOUTH

Wheatsheaf Inn, Low Lorton, Cockermouth, Cumbria, CA13 9UW
Tel: 01900 85199
Email: j.williams53@sky.com
www.wheatsheafinnlorton.co.uk
Pitches For Å ⬔ ⬕ **Total** 40
Open Mar to 15-Nov
Access Good **Site** Level
Nearest Bus Stop (Miles) ¼
In the town of Cockermouth (Wordsworth) and close to five lakes (osprey), Whinlatter and Go Ape.
Facilities ⌇ ⊡ ⬚ ⬔ ⌇ ⊙ ⬓ 🖾
⊙ ⬕ ⬓ ⊙ ✕⬕⬓ ⬗⬕
Nearest Town Cockermouth
Directions From Keswick take the A66, turn left at Embleton sign onto the B5292, then take the B5289.
⚐ Workington

COCKERMOUTH

Whinfell Camping, Lorton, Nr Cockermouth, Cumbria, CA13 0RQ
Tel: 01900 85260
Email: whinfell.campsite@gmail.com
Pitches For Å ⬔ ⬕ **Total** 30
Acreage 3 **Open** Easter to Oct
Access Good **Site** Level
Nearest Bus Stop (Miles) ½
Ideal touring and walking. Near to many attractions including Whinlatter Visitor Centre, Sellafield Visitor Centre, Ravenglass Miniature Steam Railway, Muncaster Castle & Gardens and an Owl centre.
Facilities ⌇ ⬚⬓ ⬔ ⌇ ⊙⬕ ⬚⬓⬔⬕
Nearest Town Cockermouth
Directions From Cockermouth take B5292 to Low Lorton, then B5289 through village. Signed from B5289.
⚐ Workington

CONISTON

Birchbank Farm, Birchbank, Blawith, Ulverston, Cumbria, LA12 8EW
Tel: 01229 885277
Email: info@birchbank.co.uk
www.birchbank.co.uk
Pitches For Å ⬔ ⬕ **Total** 25
Acreage 1 **Open** May to Oct
Access Good **Site** Mostly Level
Small farm site. Next to open Fell, good walking area.
Facilities ⌇ ⊡ ⬚⬓ ⬔ ⌇ ⊙ ⬓ 🖾 ⬕ ▣ ⬓
Nearest Town Coniston Water
Directions A5092 ¼ mile west of Gawthwaite turn for Woodland. Site is 2 miles on the right along an unfenced road.
⚐ Kirkby in Furness

CONISTON

Coniston Hall Camping Site, Coniston, Cumbria, LA21 8AS
Tel: 015394 41223
Pitches For Å ⬔ ⬕ **Total** 0
Acreage 200 **Open** Mar to Oct
Site Level
Nearest Bus Stop (Miles) ½
Lake access. Dogs to be kept on leads.
Facilities ⬚⬓ ⬔ ⌇ ⊙ ⬓ 🖾 🖾
⬕⬓ ⬕⬓ ⊙⬕▣ 🖾
Nearest Town Coniston
Directions 1 mile south of Coniston.
⚐ Windermere

CONISTON

Coniston Park Coppice Caravan Club Site, Coniston, Cumbria, LA21 8LA
Tel: 01539 441555
www.caravanclub.co.uk
Pitches For Å ⬔ ⬕ **Total** 280

Acreage 20 **Open** All year
Access Poor **Site** Lev/Slope
Nearest Bus Stop (Miles) ½
Situated between Coniston Water and mountains in 63 acres of National Trust woodland. Ideal for walking and bird watching, especially in Grizedale Forest. Post Office, junior orienteering course and Red Squirrel Nature Trail on site. Non members welcome. Booking essential.
Facilities ⬚ ⌇ ⊡ ⬚⬓ ⬔ ⌇ ⬓ 🖾 ▣ ⬕
⬕⬓ ⬕⬓ ⊙⬕▣ ⬓ 🖾
Nearest Town Coniston
Directions On the A593, 1 miles south of Coniston Village, just past the A5084 junction in Torver. NB: Approach is narrow in places.
⚐ Windermere

CONISTON

Pier Cottage Caravan Park, Pier Cottage, Coniston, Cumbria, LA21 8AJ
Tel: 01539 441252
www.piercottageconiston.co.uk
Pitches For ⬔ ⬕ **Total** 10
Acreage 1 **Open** Mar to Oct
Access Good **Site** Level
Nearest Bus Stop (Miles) ¼
Lakeside site with boating, fishing and fellwalking.
Facilities ⬚⬓ ⬔ ⌇ ⊙ 🖾 ⬕⬓⬕⬓ ⬓
Nearest Town Coniston
Directions 1 mile east of Coniston off the B5285 Hawkshead road.
⚐ Windermere

CUMWHITTON

Cairndale Caravan Park, Cumwhitton, Headsnook, Brampton, Nr Carlisle, Cumbria, CA8 9BZ
Tel: 01768 896280
Pitches For ⬔ ⬕ **Total** 5
Acreage 2 **Open** Mar to Oct
Access Good **Site** Level
Scenic views, ideal touring, quiet site, water and electricity to individual touring sites. Windsurfing nearby.
Facilities ⌇ ⊡ ⬚⬓ ⬔ ⌇ ⊙ 🖾 ⬓⬕▣
Nearest Town Carlisle
Directions Follow A69 to Warwick Bridge and then follow unclassified road through Great Corby to Cumwhitton, approx. 9 miles.
⚐ Carlisle

DENT

Conder Farm Campsite, Deepdale Road, Dent, Sedbergh, Cumbria, LA10 5QT
Tel: 015396 25277
Email: conderfarm@aol.com
Pitches For Å ⬕ **Total** 47
Acreage 1½ **Open** Mar to Oct
Site Sloping
Nearest Bus Stop (Miles) ¼
Facilities ⌇ ⬚⬓ ⬔ ⌇ ⊙
Nearest Town Kendal
Directions Leave the M6 at junction 37 and take the road for Sedbergh following signs for Dent for approx. 10 miles. At the George & Dragon take the right hand fork to Dent.
⚐ Dent

DENT

Ewegales Farm, Dent, Sedbergh, Cumbria, LA10 5RH
Tel: 01539 625440
Pitches For Å ⬔ ⬕ **Total** 60
Acreage 5½ **Open** All Year
Access Good **Site** Level
Nearest Bus Stop (Miles) Outside
Alongside a river for fishing.
Facilities ⬕⬓ ⬚⬓ ⌇ 🖾 ⬕⬓▣ ⬓
Nearest Town Dent

Directions Leave the M6 at junction 37 and head towards Sedbergh then Dent, park is 3½ miles east of Dent Village.
≉ Dent

EGREMONT

Tarnside Caravan Park, Braystones, Egremont, Cumbria, CA21 2YL
Tel: 01946 822777
Email: reception@seacote.com
www.tarnsidepark.co.uk
Pitches For **Total** 20
Acreage 2 **Open** Mar **to** Oct
Access Good **Site** Level
Nearest Bus Stop (Miles) Outside
Beside a lovely beach and tarn. Ideal for walking.
Facilities
Nearest Town Egremont
Directions From the A595 3 miles south of Egremont, take the B5345 and follow signs for Tarnside Park.
≉ Braystones

ESKDALE

Eskdale Camping & Caravanning Club Site, Boot, Holmrook, Cumbria, CA19 1TH
Tel: 01946 723253
Email: eskdale2@thefriendlyclub.co.uk
www.campingandcaravanningclub.co.uk/eskdale
Pitches For **Total** 80
Acreage 8 **Open** Mar **to** 14-Jan
Access Good **Site** Level
Close to Scafell Pike, Wastwater, the River Esk, Hardknott Fort, Eskdale Mill and Muncaster Castle. Camping Pods available for hire. Camping barn available. Non members welcome. You can also call us on 0845 130 7633.
Facilities
Nearest Town Ravenglass
Directions From the A595 turn right onto local road signposted Birkby, continue on to Eskdale.
≉ Dalegarth

ESKDALE

Fisherground Campsite, Fisherground, Eskdale, Cumbria, CA19 1TF
Tel: 01946 723349
Email: camping@fishergroundcampsite.co.uk
www.fishergroundcampsite.co.uk
Pitches For **Total** 215
Acreage 12 **Open** Mar **to** Oct
Site Level/Sloping
Quiet family site in the heart of the Lake District. Near the beach, a river and a waterfall. Plenty of good walks in the area. 7 mile miniature railway with our own private station. Childrens adventure play area.We allow campfires.
Facilities
Nearest Town Eskdale
Directions Turn right ¾ miles past Broughton on A595 and go up Duddon Valley (signed Ulpha). 4 miles to Ulpha, then turn left (sp Eskdale). 6 miles over Birker Moor, descend to Eskdale and turn right at the King George IV Inn, Site is the first turning on the left.
≉ Ravenglass

GOSFORTH

Seven Acres Caravan Park & Camping Site, Holmrook, Cumbria, CA19 1YD
Tel: 019467 25480
Email: enquiries@southlakelandcaravans.co.uk
www.southlakelandcaravans.co.uk
Pitches For **Total** 59
Acreage 3 **Open** Mar **to** Oct
Access Good **Site** Level
At the foot of Wasdale Valley, 3 miles from the coast. Ideal for touring the Western Lake District, walking, golf, fishing, riding and relaxing.
Facilities
Nearest Town Egremont
Directions Half way between Gosforth and Holmrook on the A595 (BroughtoninFurness to Workington road) west coast road.
≉ Seascale

GRANGEOVERSANDS

Greaves Farm Caravan Park, c/o Prospect House, Barber Green, GrangeoverSands, Cumbria, LA11 6HU
Tel: 015395 36329/36587
www.greavesfarmcaravanpark.co.uk
Pitches For **Total** 20
Acreage 3 **Open** Mar **to** Oct
Access Good **Site** Level
Quiet, select, family run park. Ideal base for exploring the Lake District.
Facilities
Nearest Town Grange-over-Sands
Directions Come off the A590 approx 1 mile south of Newby Bridge at the sign "Cartmel 4 miles". Proceed 1½ miles to sign for caravan park.
≉ Grange-over-Sands

GRANGEOVERSANDS

Meathop Fell Caravan Club Site, GrangeoverSands, Cumbria, LA11 6RB
Tel: 01539 532912
www.caravanclub.co.uk
Pitches For **Total** 129
Acreage 10 **Open** All Year
Access Good **Site** Lev/Slope
Peaceful site. Ideal base to explore North Lancashire and Southern Lake District. Close to Brockhole National Park Visitor Centre. Non members welcome. Booking essential.
Facilities
Nearest Town Grange-over-Sands
Directions Leave M6 at junc 36 take the A590 sp South Lakes. After 3¼ mls t lt via slip rd sp Barrow, at r/about t lt on the B5277 and immediately t lt sp Meathop. Within ¾ miles t rt up incline and keep rt at the top, in 200 yds fork lt at green notice board, site on lt in 150 yds. NB: Steep approach.

KENDAL

Ashes Exclusively Adult Caravan Park, The Ashes, New Hutton, Kendal, Cumbria, LA8 0AS
Tel: 01539 731833
Email: info@ashescaravanpark.co.uk
www.ashescaravanpark.co.uk
Pitches For **Total** 25
Acreage 1½ **Open** Mar **to** 07-Nov
Access Good **Site** Lev/Slope
Nearest Bus Stop (Miles) ½
ADULTS ONLY SITE in a countryside setting with views of the Cumbrian Fells. Popular with walkers and ideal for visiting many local attractions. Close to the Lakes and the Yorkshire Dales.
Facilities
Nearest Town Kendal
Directions Leave the M6 at junction 37 and take the A684 towards Kendal. In 2 miles at the crossroads turn left signposted New Hutton, site is in ¾ miles on the right.
≉ Oxenholme

KENDAL

Kendal Camping & Caravanning Club Site, Millcrest, Shap Road, Kendal, Cumbria, LA9 6NY
Tel: 01539 741363
Email: kendal.site@thefriendlyclub
www.campingandcaravanningclub.co.uk/kendal
Pitches For **Total** 50
Acreage 3 **Open** 14-Mar **to** 04-Nov
Site Lev/Slope
Nearest Bus Stop (Miles) ½
Right in the middle of the Lake District. Tumble drier and spin drier on site. BTB 4 Star Graded and AA 3 Pennants. Non members welcome. You can also call us on 0845 130 7633.
Facilities
Directions On the A6, 1½ miles north of Kendal, site entrance is 100 yards north of the nameplate Skelsmergh.
≉ Kendal

KENDAL

Kendal Caravan Club Site, Sedgwick, Kendal, Cumbria, LA8 0JZ
Tel: 01539 560186
www.caravanclub.co.uk
Pitches For **Total** 141
Acreage 20 **Open** Mar **to** Nov
Nearest Bus Stop (Miles) ½
Peaceful site with varied bird life and wild flowers. River fishing. Non members welcome. Booking essential.
Facilities
Nearest Town Kendal
Directions M6 junc 36 take the A590 sp South Lakes, after 3¼ mls leave via slip rd sp Barrow. At r/about follow brown signs t into rd sp Sedgwick, After 150 yds t lt onto road running parallel with the river. Fork rt at the junc, site on lt in ½ a mile.
≉ Kendal

KENDAL

Waters Edge Caravan Park, Crooklands, Nr Kendal, Cumbria, LA7 7NN
Tel: 015395 67708
Email: info@watersedgecaravanpark.co.uk
www.watersedgecaravanpark.co.uk
Pitches For **Total** 32
Acreage 3 **Open** Mar **to** Nov
Access Good **Site** Level
Nearest Bus Stop (Miles) ¼
Set in quiet and pleasant countryside. Lakes, Yorkshire Dales and Morecambe Bay within easy reach.
Facilities
Nearest Town Kendal
Directions A65 Crooklands, ¾ mile from M6 motorway junction 36.
≉ Oxenholme

KESWICK

Borrowdale Caravan Club Site, Manesty, Keswick, Cumbria, CA12 5UG
Tel: 01768 777275
www.caravanclub.co.uk
Pitches For **Total** 60

Acreage 12 Open Mar to Nov
Access Good Site Level
Set in National Trust woodland, close to Derwentwater. Numerous walks from the site. Many visitor attractions within easy reach. Own sanitation required. Non members welcome. Booking essential.
Facilities ♪ ☐ ⚊ ℞ ℠ ⓪ ⓦ ▢ ⓒ
Nearest Town Keswick
Directions M6 at junc 40 take A66, on the outskirts of Keswick keep right onto bypass. At r/about within 1½ mls t lt sp A5271 Keswick, follow signs onto the B5289. After 4¼ mls t rt over the bridge (care required), site on the rt in 1 mile.
⚏ Keswick

KESWICK

Bridge End Camp & Caravan Site, Bridge End Farm, Thirlmere, Keswick, Cumbria, CA12 4TG
Tel: 01768 772166
Pitches For ⋏ ⚏ ⚌ Total 15
Acreage 2 Open Mar to Nov
Access Good Site Lev/Slope
Nearest Bus Stop (Miles) Outside
Central for the Lake District and all its attractions. Fishing on Thirlmere Lake 200 yards away.
Facilities ♪ ☐ ⓦ ℞ ℮ ⊙ ⚑ ♥ ⓪ ⚌ ▢
Nearest Town Keswick
Directions 4 miles from Keswick on the A591 or 16 miles from Penrith on the A66.
⚏ Penrith

KESWICK

Burns Farm Caravan Site, St Johns-in-the-Vale, Keswick, Cumbria, CA12 4RR
Tel: 01768 79225
Email: linda@burns-farm.co.uk
www.burns-farm.co.uk
Pitches For ⋏ ⚏ ⚌ Total 40
Acreage 1¼ Open Easter to Oct
Access Good Site Level
Nearest Bus Stop (Miles) Outside
Quiet family site with beautiful views. Small charge for use of WiFi. Ideal touring, walking and climbing. AA Graded.
Facilities ⅙ ♪ ⓦ ℞ ℮ ⊙ ⚑ ▢ ♥
⊙ ⚌ ▢ ⚊ ⚐ ❧
Nearest Town Keswick
Directions Turn left off the A66 (Penrith to Keswick road) ½ mile past B5322 junction signposted Castlerigg Stone Circle and Burns Farm. Site is on the right, farm is on the left. 2¼ miles from Keswick.
⚏ Penrith

KESWICK

Castlerigg Farm Camping & Caravan Site, Keswick, Cumbria, CA12 4TE
Tel: 01768 72479
Email: info@castleriggfarm.com
www.castleriggfarm.com
Pitches For ⋏ ⚏ ⚌ ⚏≶ Total 80
Acreage 4½ Open Mar to Nov
Access Good Site Sloping
Nearest Bus Stop (Miles) ¼
Panoramic views quite site for familes, singles or couples. Ideal base for walking. On site Hayloft cafe.
Facilities ℠ ⚑ ☐ ⓪ ⚊ ✕ ▢ ⓒ ❧ ❧
Nearest Town Keswick
Directions From Keswick take the A591 towards Windermere, after approx. 1½ miles turn right at the top of the hill following camping sign and the Site is on the left.
⚏ Penrith

KESWICK

Derwentwater Camping & Caravanning Club Site, Crow Park Road, Keswick, Cumbria, CA12 5EN
Tel: 01768 772579
Email: linda.watson@thefriendlyclub.co
www.campingandcaravanningclub.co.uk/derwentwater
Pitches For ⋏ ⚏ ⚌ Total 44
Acreage 16 Open 28-Feb to 05-Jan
Access Good Site Level
Nearest Bus Stop (Miles) ½
Within the heart of the Lake District National Park. BTB 4 Star Graded, David Bellamy Gold Award and AA 3 Pennants. Non members welcome. You can also call us on 0845 130 7633.
Facilities ⅙ ♪ ⓦ ℞ ℮ ⊙ ⚑ ⚌ ⓪ ⚊
⚊ ▢ ✕ ❧
Nearest Town Keswick
Directions Leave the M6 at junction 40 and take the A66 signposted Keswick and Workington for 13 miles. Do not take the A591, stay on the A66. At the roundabout turn left signposted Keswick Town Centre, follow signs for caravan park to Derwentwater.
⚏ Penrith

KESWICK

Gill Head Farm Caravan & Camping Park, Troutbeck, Penrith, Cumbria, CA11 0ST
Tel: 017687 79652
Email: enquiries@gillheadfarm.co.uk
www.gillheadfarm.co.uk
Pitches For ⋏ ⚏ ⚌ Total 40
Acreage 10 Open Mar to Nov
Access Good Site Sloping
Nearest Bus Stop (Miles) ¼
Situated on a working hill farm in a great location within the Lake District National Park providing superb views. Ideal for families and walkers.
Facilities ♪ ⓦ ℞ ℮ ⊙ ⚑ ♥ ⊙
℠ ⚑ ⓪ ⚊ ⓣ ⚊ ✕ ▢ ⓒ ❧ ❧ ❧
Nearest Town Keswick
Directions Leave the M6 at junction 40 (Penrith), take the A66 west for 9 miles. Then take the A5091 (left) and after 100 yards turn first right.
⚏ Penrith

KESWICK

Keswick Camping & Caravanning Club Site, Crow Park Road, Keswick, Cumbria, CA12 5EP
Tel: 01768 772392
Email: keswick.site@thefriendlyclub.co.uk
www.campingandcaravanningclub.co.uk/keswick
Pitches For ⋏ ⚏ ⚌ Total 250
Acreage 14 Open 20-Feb to 04-Jan
Access Good Site Level
Nearest Bus Stop (Miles) ½
Situated on the banks of Derwentwater, ideal for fishing and water sports. Boat launching for small boats. Good hillwalking area. Close to the centre of Keswick. All units must have towing vehicle on site overnight. One vehicle per pitch. BTB 4 Star Graded, David Bellamy Gold Award and AA 3 Pennants. Non members welcome. You can also call us on 0845 130 7633.
Facilities ♪ ☐ ⓦ ℞ ℮ ⊙ ⚑ ⚌ ⓪ ⚊
℠ ⓪ ⓣ ⚊ ▢ ⓒ ❧
Nearest Town Keswick
Directions From Penrith take the A5271, turn left into Main Street (Keswick), turn right to pass Lakes Bus Station, pass the rugby club and turn right, site is on the right.
⚏ Penrith

KESWICK

Thirlspot Farm Caravan Park, Thirlspot Farm, Thirlmere, Keswick, Cumbria, CA12 4TN
Tel: 017687 72551
Pitches For ⋏ Total 25
Acreage 4 Open Mar to Nov
Site Level
Nearest Bus Stop (Miles) Outside
Facilities ⓦ ℞ ℮ ⊙
Nearest Town Keswick
Directions Situated on the A591, 6 miles from Keswick and 6 miles from Grasmere.
⚏ Windermere

KIRKBY LONSDALE

New House Caravan Park, Kirkby Lonsdale, Cumbria, LA6 2HR
Tel: 015242 71590
Email: colinpreece9@aol.com
Pitches For ⚏ ⚌ Total 50
Acreage 3½ Open All year
Access Good Site Lev/Slope
Situated near to the historic town of Kirkby Lonsdale and Devils Bridge. An ideal location to visit lakes and Yorkshire Dales.
Facilities ⅙ ♪ ☐ ⓦ ℞ ℮ ⊙ ⚑ ⚊ ⓪ ♥
℠ ⓪ ⚊ ⚌ ▢ ⓒ ❧
Nearest Town Kirkby Lonsdale/Kendal
Directions From Kirkby Lonsdale take the A65 towards Settle, after approx. 1½ miles site is on the right 300 yards past Whoop Hall Inn.
⚏ Carnforth

KIRKBY LONSDALE

Woodclose Caravan Park, High Casterton, Kirkby Lonsdale, Cumbria, LA6 2SE
Tel: 015242 71597
Email: info@woodclosepark.com
www.woodclosepark.com
Pitches For ⋏ ⚏ ⚌ Total 17
Acreage 9 Open Mar to 14-Nov
Access Good Site Lev/Slope
An award winning Park set within the beautiful valley of the River Lune between the Yorkshire Dales and the Lake District National Park. Nine acres providing a unique holiday base in an area of outstanding natural beauty. Offering Wigwams, touring and camping holidays.
Facilities ⅙ ♪ ☐ ⓦ ℞ ℮ ⊙ ⚑ ⚊ ⓪ ♥
℠ ⓪ ⓣ ⚊ ✕ ▢ ⓒ ❧ ❧
Nearest Town Kirkby Lonsdale
Directions Leave the M6 at junction 36 and take the A65 for approx. 6 miles. Woodclose entrance is past Devils Bridge on the left hand side.

KIRKBY STEPHEN

Pennine View Caravan & Camping Park, Station Road, Kirkby Stephen, Cumbria, CA17 4SZ
Tel: 01768 371717
Pitches For ⋏ ⚏ ⚌ Total 58
Acreage 2½ Open Early Mar to Oct
Access Good Site Level
Nearest Bus Stop (Miles) ½
On the edge of the River Eden and on the outskirts of the small market town of Kirkby Stephen. Ideal for walking and touring the Yorkshire Dales and the Lake District, Teesdale and Durham.
Facilities ⅙ ♪ ☐ ⓦ ℞ ℮ ⊙ ⚑ ⚊ ⓪ ♥
⓪ ⓣ ⚊ ▢ ⓒ ❧
Nearest Town Kirkby Stephen
Directions Just off the A685 approx 1 mile from Kirkby Stephen town centre. 11 miles from the M6 junction 38, and 5 miles from the A66 at Brough.
⚏ Kirkby Stephen

LAMPLUGH

Dockray Meadow Caravan Club Site,
Lamplugh, Cumbria, CA14 4SH
Tel: 01946 861357
www.caravanclub.co.uk
Pitches For ⬜ ⬜ **Total** 53
Acreage 4½ **Open** Mar **to** Nov
Access Good **Site** Lev/Slope
Nearest Bus Stop (Miles) ½
Sheltered site alongside a stream with fell scenery. Ideal for walkers. Own sanitation required. Non members welcome. Booking essential.
Facilities ƒ 🄷 🞉 ⬛ ⬤ ⬛⭢⬛
Nearest Town Lamplugh
Directions From the A66 Cockermouth bypass turn onto the A5086 sp Egremont. After 6½ miles (300yds past Lamplugh Tip Pub) turn left at signpost for Loweswater. Within ¾ miles turn right signposted Croasdale, site is 50 yards on the left.

LONGTOWN

Camelot Caravan Park, Sandysike, Longtown, Carlisle, Cumbria, CA6 5SZ
Tel: 01228 791248
Pitches For ⅄ ⬜ ⬜ **Total** 20
Acreage 1¼ **Open** Mar **to** Oct
Access Good **Site** Level
Nearest Bus Stop (Miles) ¼
Ideal base for the Solway coast, Carlisle Settle Railway, Carlisle Castle, romantic Gretna Green, Hadrians Wall and Border towns. AA 2 Pennants. Waiting List for Secure Storage.
Facilities ƒ ⬛⬛⬛⬤⭢⬛ 🞉 ⬤⭢⬛⬛
Nearest Town Longtown
Directions On the A7, 1¼ miles south of Longtown on the left. Leave the M6 northbound at junction 44 and take the A7 (Longtown), Park is on the right in 4 miles.
🚶 Carlisle

LONGTOWN

High Gaitle Caravan Park, Gaitle Bridge, Longtown, Carlisle, Cumbria, CA6 5LU
Tel: 01228 791819
Pitches For ⅄ ⬜ ⬜ **Total** 30
Acreage 6 **Open** All Year
Access Good **Site** Level
Nearest Bus Stop (Miles) Outside
Ideal touring location for the Lake District, South Scotland, Borders, Gretna Green and Hadrians Wall. Great for fishing on the world famous River Esk.
Facilities ⬛⬛ ƒ 🄷⬛⭢⬛⬤⭢⬛⬛ ⬛ ⬛⭢⬛⬛
Nearest Town Longtown
Directions Leave the M6 at junction 44 and take the A7 for 6 miles through Longtown, then take the A6071 towards Gretna, Site is 1¼ miles on the left.
🚶 Carlisle

MARYPORT

Spring Lea Caravan Park, Allonby, Maryport, Cumbria, CA15 6QF
Tel: 01900 881331
Email: mail@springlea.co.uk
www.springlea.co.uk
Pitches For ⅄ ⬜ ⬜ **Total** 35
Acreage 5 **Open** Mar **to** Oct
Access Good **Site** Level
Nearest Bus Stop (Miles) ¼
300 yards from the beach with views of Lakeland and Scottish hills. Leisure centre for sauna etc.. Bar/restaurant on site.
Facilities ƒ 🄷⬛⬛⭢⬛⬤⭢⬛⬛ ⬛
⬛⬤⬛⬛⬛⭢⬛⬛⭢
Nearest Town Maryport
Directions 5 miles north of Maryport on the B5300 coast road.
🚶 Maryport

MEALSGATE

The Larches Caravan Park, Mealsgate, Wigton, Cumbria, CA7 1LQ
Tel: 016973 71379 / 71803
Email: thelarches@hotmail.co.uk
www.thelarchescaravanpark.co.uk
Pitches For ⅄ ⬜ ⬜ **Total** 45
Acreage 19 **Open** Mar **to** Oct
Access Good **Site** Lev/slope
ADULTS ONLY SITE. Ideal for couples, peace and quiet in the countryside with beautiful views. Excellent toilets.
Facilities ⬛ ƒ ⬛🄷⬛⭢⬛⬤⭢⬛ ⬛⬛ ⬛
🞉 ⬛⬤⭢⬛⬛⬛
Nearest Town Wigton
Directions From the north take the A57/A74/A7/A69 to Carlisle, follow the A595 to Mealsgate. From the south leave the M6 at junction 41, take the B5305 Wigton road as far as the A595. Turn left and follow the A595 to Mealsgate.
🚶 Wigton

PENRITH

Cross Dormont Camp Site, Cross Dormont, Howtown, Penrith, Cumbria, CA10 2NA
Tel: 01768 486537
Email: crossdormont@gmail.com
Pitches For ⅄ ⬜ ⬜ ⬛ **Total** 100
Acreage 7 **Open** Mar **to** Nov
Access Good **Site** Lev/slope
Nearest Bus Stop (Miles) 1
Close by - pony trekking, bike hire, boat hire, steamers on lake, shops and pubs.
Facilities 🄷⬛⭢⬛⬤⭢⬛ ⬛⭢⬛⬛⭢⬛
Nearest Town Penrith
Directions From Penrith follow Dale main Road for approx. 4 miles, turn left at the T-Junction and go through Pooley Bridge and turn right.
🚶 Penrith

PENRITH

Flusco Wood Caravan Park, Flusco, Penrith, Cumbria, CA11 0JB
Tel: 017684 80020
Email: peter@fluscowood.co.uk
www.fluscowood.co.uk
Pitches For ⬜ ⬜ **Total** 36
Acreage 24 **Open** Mar **to** Oct
Access Good **Site** level
Nearest Bus Stop (Miles) 1
Only 4 miles from Ullswater, half an hour from major centres of the Lake District.
Facilities ⬛⬛ ƒ ⬛🄷⬛⭢⬛⬤⭢⬛ ⬛
⬛⬛🞉⬛⬤⭢⬛⬛⬛⭢ ⬛
Nearest Town Penrith
Directions Leave the M6 at junction 40 and travel west on the A66 following brown caravan signsfor Flusco.
🚶 Penrith

PENRITH

Gillside Caravan & Camping Site, Glenridding, Penrith, Cumbria, CA11 0QQ
Tel: 017684 82346
Email: gillside@btconnect.com
www.gillsidecaravanandcampingsite.co.uk
Pitches For ⅄ ⬜ ⬜ **Total** 65
Acreage 8 **Open** Mar **to** Mid Nov
Access Good **Site** Level
Nearest Bus Stop (Miles) ½
Foot of Helvellyn, 5 minutes walk from Lake Ullswater.
Facilities ƒ 🄷⬛⬛⭢⬛⬤⭢⬛⬛ ⬛
⬛⬛ ⬤⬛⭢⬛⬛
Nearest Town Penrith
Directions A592 signposted Ullswater, 14 miles from Penrith. In Glenridding turn right, follow sign for Gillside.
🚶 Penrith

PENRITH

Lowther Holiday Park, Eamont Bridge, Penrith, Cumbria, CA10 2JB
Tel: 01768 863631
Email: alan@lowtherholidaypark.co.uk
www.lowtherholidaypark.co.uk
Pitches For ⅄ ⬜ ⬜ **Total** 150
Acreage 50 **Open** Mar **to** Nov
Access Good **Site** Level
Nearest Bus Stop (Miles) 1
Set in 50 acres of wooded parkland on the banks of the River Lowther. Home of the rare and fascinating Red Squirrel.
Facilities ⬛ ƒ 🄷⬛⬛⭢⬛⬤⭢ ⬛⬤ ⬛
🞉 ⬛⬤⬛☓⬛⬛⬛⬛ ⬛⬛⬛⭢⬛⬛⬛⭢ ⭢
⬛
Nearest Town Penrith
Directions On the A6 just south of Penrith in the village of Eamont Bridge.
🚶 Penrith

PENRITH

Park Foot Caravan & Camping Park, Howtown Road, Pooley Bridge, Penrith, Cumbria, CA10 2NA
Tel: 017684 86309
Email: holidays@parkfoottullswater.co.uk
www.parkfoottullswater.co.uk
Pitches For ⅄ ⬜ ⬜ ⬛ ⎓ **Total** 332
Acreage 40 **Open** Mar **to** Oct
Access Good **Site** Lev/Slope
Nearest Bus Stop (Miles) ½
Family run park beside Lake Ullswater with boat launching access. Licensed bar, restaurant and takeaway. Childrens Club during the summer school holidays and two play areas. Pony trekking, mountain bike hire, tennis and table tennis on site. Own access to the lake where customers can fish using their own equipment.
Facilities ⬛ ƒ 🄷⬛⬛⭢⬛⬤⭢ ⬛⬤ ⬛
🞉 ⬛⬤⬛☓⬛⬛⬛⬛ ⬛⬛⬛⭢⬛⬛⬛⭢⭢⬛
Nearest Town Pooley Bridge
Directions 5 miles SW of Penrith. Leave M6 at junc 40, then take A66 for Ullswater, next roundabout take A592 then road for Pooley Bridge and 1 mile on Howtown Road to site.
🚶 Penrith

PENRITH

Thacka Lea Caravan Site, Thacka Lea, Penrith, Cumbria, CA11 9HX
Tel: 01768 863319
Pitches For ⬜ ⬜ **Total** 25
Acreage 1 **Open** Mar **to** Oct
Access Good **Site** Lev/Slope
Nearest Bus Stop (Miles) ¼
Just a 10 minute walk from the town centre. Good touring.
Facilities ⭢ ƒ 🄷⬛⭢⬛⬤⭢⬛ ⬤⭢⬛
Nearest Town Penrith
Directions From south, turn left off the A6, go past the Esso Station at the north end of town. From north, turn right at the Esso Station.
🚶 Penrith

PENRITH

Troutbeck Head Caravan Club Site, Troutbeck, Penrith, Cumbria, CA11 0SS
Tel: 01768 483521
www.caravanclub.co.uk
Pitches For ⬜ ⬜ **Total** 150
Acreage 25 **Open** Mar **to** Nov
Access Good **Site** Level
Set in countryside, alongside a brook with fabulous views. Only 4 miles from Ullswater. Ideal for walkers and nature lovers. Rookin House Farm Centre adjacent offering go-karting, quad bikes, archery, horse riding and much more. Non members welcome. Booking essential.

33

CUMBRIA

Facilities ♿ ♨ 🚻 🅿 ↑ 🛁 ⚡ 🛒
🔥 🍽 🐕 🔌 💧 📞

Nearest Town Penrith
Directions Leave M6 at junc 40 and take A66 sp Keswick. Go straight on at the roundabout and after approx. 7 miles turn left onto A5091. Site is 1¼ miles on the right. NB: No arrivals before 12 noon.
🚉 Penrith

PENRITH

Waterside House Campsite, Waterside Farm, Howtown Road, Pooley Bridge, Penrith, Cumbria, CA10 2NA
Tel: 01768 486332
Email: enquire@watersidefarm-campsite.co.uk
www.watersidefarm-campsite.co.uk
Pitches For ⛺ 🚐 **Total** 120
Acreage 10 **Open** Mar **to** Oct
Site Lev/Slope
Nearest Bus Stop (Miles) 1
Alongside the lake shore of Ullswater with beautiful views of the lake and fells. Footpath from the site to the local village. Boat and bike hire available. Tipi tent hire (furnished) or glamping.
Facilities ♿ ♨ 🚻 🅿 ↑ 😊 🛁 ⚡ 🛒
🔥 📞 🔌 🛒 💧 🍽

Nearest Town Pooley Bridge/Penrith
Directions +Leave the M6 at junction 40 and take the A66 sp Keswick. After 1 mile turn left onto the A592 for Ullswater. Turn left by the lake and go over the bridge, turn first right along Howtown Road. Waterside House is the second campsite on the right (approx. 1
🚉 Penrith

RAVENGLASS

Ravenglass Camping & Caravanning Club Site, Ravenglass, Cumbria, CA18 1SR
Tel: 01229 717250
www.campingandcaravanningclub.co.uk/ravenglass
Pitches For ⛺ 🚐 🚐 **Total** 75
Acreage 6 **Open** Feb **to** Nov
Access Good **Site** Lev/Slope
Set in 5 acres of mature woodland, this is a walkers paradise on Cumbrias Western Coast, where the Lake District National Park meets the sea. Non members welcome. You can also call us on 0845 130 7633.
Facilities ♨ 🚻 🅿 ↑ 😊 🛁 ⚡ 🛒
🔥 🔌 🍽 🐕 📞 🛒

Nearest Town Egremont
Directions From the A595 turn west for Ravenglass, before village turn left to site.
🚉 Ravenglass

SEDBERGH

Yore House Farm Caravan Park, Yore House Farm, Lunds, Sedbergh, Cumbria, LA10 5PX
Tel: 01969 667358
Email: j.pedley@btinternet.com
Pitches For ⛺ 🚐 **Total** 7
Open Easter **to** Sept
Access Good **Site** Level
Quiet, farm site beside the River Ure. In sight of the famous Settle to Carlisle railway.
Facilities 🚻 🛒 🐕

Nearest Town Hawes
Directions On the A684 10 miles from Sedbergh and 6 miles from Hawes, near the Moorcock Pub. On the North Yorkshire and Cumbria border.
🚉 Garsdale

SILLOTH

Hylton Caravan Park, Eden Street, Silloth, Cumbria, CA7 4AY
Tel: 016973 31707
Email: enquiries@stanwix.com
www.stanwix@stanwix.com
Pitches For ⛺ 🚐 🚐 **Total** 90
Acreage 18 **Open** Mar **to** 15-Nov
Access Good **Site** Level
Nearest Bus Stop (Miles) ¼
Silloth is on the Solway coast. Beach ½ mile. Base to explore Lakes and Roman Wall.
Facilities ♿ ♨ 🚻 🅿 ↑ 😊 🛁 ⚡ 🛒
🔥 📞 🔌 🍽 🐕 🛒

Nearest Town Silloth
Directions From the east on entering town follow signs ½ mile
🚉 Carlisle

SILLOTH

Stanwix Park Holiday Centre, Silloth (West), Cumbria, CA7 4HH
Tel: 016973 32666
Email: enquiries@stanwix.com
www.www.stanwix.com
Pitches For ⛺ 🚐 🚐 🚐 **Total** 121
Acreage 18 **Open** All Year
Access Good **Site** Level
Nearest Bus Stop (Miles) Outside
Silloth is on the Solway coast sandy beaches stretching 13 miles to Maryport. Base to explore Lakes and Roman wall.
Facilities ♿ ♨ 🚻 🅿 ↑ 😊 🛁 ⚡ 🛒
🔥 📞 🔥 ✕ 🍽 🐕 🔌 🛒 💧 🍴 🐕 🔌 📞 🛒 ♨
📶

Nearest Town Silloth
Directions entering Silloth from east follow signs 1 mile. from west entering Silloth site on left.
🚉 Carlisle

SILLOTH

Tanglewood Caravan Park,
Causewayhead, Silloth, Wigton, Cumbria, CA7 4PE
Tel: 016973 31253
Email:
tanglewoodcaravanpark@hotmail.com
www.tanglewoodcaravanpark.co.uk
Pitches For ⛺ 🚐 🚐 **Total** 31
Acreage 7 **Open** Mar **to** Jan
Access Good **Site** Level
Enjoy the promenade at Silloth, the sandy west beach and beautiful sunsets over the Solway Firth. Excellent golf courses. Seasonal tourers welcome. bus stop 100yds.
Facilities ♨ 🚻 🅿 ↑ 😊 🛁 ⚡ 🛒
🔥 📞 🔥 🍽 🐕 🔌 📞 🛒 ♨ 📶

Nearest Town Silloth
Directions On B5302 on left, 4 miles from Abbeytown.
🚉 Wigton

ST. BEES

Seacote Park, St Bees, Cumbria, CA27 0ET
Tel: 01946 822777
Email: reception@seacote.com
www.seacote.com
Pitches For ⛺ 🚐 🚐 🚐 **Total** 32
Acreage 4 **Open** Mar **to** Oct
Access Good **Site** Level
Nearest Bus Stop (Miles) Outside
Beside a lovely beach in a historic village. Golf links and walks locally. Hotel adjacent which is owned by the Park.
Facilities ♿ ♨ 🚻 🅿 ↑ 😊 🛁 ⚡ 🛒
🔥 📞 ✕ 🍽 🔥 🛒 🐕 🔌 📞 🛒 ♨

Nearest Town Whitehaven
Directions Leave the A595 near Whitehaven or Egremont and take the B5345 following signs to St Bees, then to the beach.
🚉 St. Bees

TEBAY

Westmorland Caravan Site Tebay, Tebay Services, M6 Northbound, Cumbria, CA10 3SB
Tel: 01539 711322
Email: caravans@westmorland.com
www.westmorland.com/caravans
Pitches For 🚐 🚐 🚐 **Total** 80
Open Mid-Mar **to** Oct
Access Good
Nearest Bus Stop (Miles) 2
Ideal base for the Lake District and the Yorkshire Dales.
Facilities ♨ 🚻 🅿 ↑ 🛒 📞
🔥 📞 🔥 🔌 📞 🛒 ♨

Nearest Town Penrith
Directions Situated 1 mile north of junc 38, M6 near orton, reached via Tebay services.
🚉 Penrith/Oxenholme

TROUTBECK

Troutbeck Camping & Caravanning Club Site, Hutton Moor End, Troutbeck, Penrith, Cumbria, CA11 0SX
Tel: 01768 779149
Email: troutbeck@thefriendlyclub.co.uk
www.campingandcaravanningclub.co.uk/troutbeck
Pitches For Å ⌂ ⌂ **Total** 54
Open 07-Mar **to** Nov
Access Good **Site** Level
Nearest Bus Stop (Miles) ½
Superb location in unbeatable walking country with fantastic views. Close to both Keswick and Penrith. 70 main tourist attractions in the district. Non members welcome. You can also call us on 0845 130 7633.
Facilities ⌂ ⌿ ⌂⌂⌂⌿ ⌂ ⊙⌿ ⌂ ⌂ ⌂
⌂⌂ ⌂ ⌂ ⌂ ⌂⌂⌂⌂⌂⌂⌂ ⌂
Nearest Town Keswick
Directions Leave the M6 at junction 40 and take the A66 towards Keswick. After 8 miles take a sharp left at signpost Wallthwaite, site is on the left.
⇌ Penrith

ULLSWATER

Cove Caravan & Camping Park, Watermillock, Ullswater, Penrith, Cumbria, CA11 0LS
Tel: 01768 486549
Email: info@cove-park.co.uk
www.cove-park.co.uk
Pitches For Å ⌂ ⌂ **Total** 50
Acreage 3 **Open** 15-Mar **to** Oct
Small, quiet and peaceful Park, 400 ft above Ullswater. Ideal for touring Ullswater & Helvellyn Range, Keswick and Windermere.
Facilities ⌂ ⌿ ⌂ ⌂ ⌂⌂⌿⌂ ⊙⌿ ⌂ ⌂ ⌂
⌂ ⌂⌂⌂⌂⌂ ⌂⌂⌂
Nearest Town Penrith
Directions Leave M6 at junction 40 and take A66 west to Rheged roundabout, take A592 to Ullswater. After approx. 4 miles at the T-Junction by the lake turn right onto the A592. After 2 miles turn right at Brackenrigg Inn, Park is 1½ miles on the left.
⇌ Penrith

ULLSWATER

Sykeside Camping Park, Hartsop, Brotherswater, Patterdale, Cumbria, CA11 0NZ
Tel: 01768 482239
Email: info@sykeside.co.uk
www.sykeside.co.uk
Pitches For Å ⌂ ⌂ ⌂⌂ **Total** 80
Acreage 15 **Open** All Year
Access Good **Site** Level/Sloping
Nearest Bus Stop (Miles) Entrance
At the foot of Kirkstone Pass with many walks. ¼ of a mile from Brotherswater for fishing. Pub on site.
Facilities ⌿ ⌂ ⌂ ⌂⌂⌿⌂ ⊙⌿ ⌂ ⌂
⌂⌂ ⌂ ⌂ ⌂⌂⌂⌂⌂⌂⌂
Nearest Town Ambleside
Directions On the A592 between Windermere and Glenridding (Ullswater).
⇌ Windermere

ULLSWATER

The Quiet Site, Ullswater, Penrith, Cumbria, CA11 0LS
Tel: 07768 727016
Email: info@thequietsite.co.uk
www.thequietsite.co.uk
Pitches For Å ⌂ ⌂ **Total** 90
Acreage 10 **Open** All Year
Access Fair **Site** level
Nearest Bus Stop (Miles) 1½

Family site set in the idyllic Ullswater Valley. Ideal for walking. The best campsite bar in Britain!. Excellent showers and family bathrooms. Large play field. Carbon neutral.
Facilities ⌂ ⌿ ⌂ ⌂ ⌂⌂⌿⌂ ⊙⌿ ⌂ ⌂ ⌂
⌂⌂ ⌂ ⌂ ⌂ ⌂⌂ ⌂ ⌂⌂⌂⌂⌂⌂⌂ ⌂ ⌂
Nearest Town Ullswater
Directions Take A592 from Penrith, turn right at lake and right again at Brackenrigg Hotel follow road for 1½ miles, site on right hand side of road.
⇌ Penrith

ULLSWATER

Ullswater Caravan Camping & Marine Park, Watermillock, Penrith, Cumbria, CA11 0LR
Tel: 00176 84 86666
Email: info@ullswatercaravanpark.co.uk
www.ullswatercaravanpark.co.uk
Pitches For Å ⌂ ⌂ **Total** 160
Acreage 13 **Open** Mar **to** 14-Nov
Access Good **Site** Level
Nearest Bus Stop (Miles) ½
1 mile up from Lake Ullswater.
Facilities ⌂ ⌿ ⌂ ⌂ ⌂⌂⌿⌂ ⊙⌿ ⌂ ⌂ ⌂
⌂⌂ ⌂ ⌂ ⌂⌂⌂⌂⌂ ⌂ ⌂
Nearest Town Ullswater
Directions A592 to Ullswater, reach lakeside road after 5 miles turn right. 2 miles later turn right by telephone box, park situated ½ mile up hill.
⇌ Penrith

ULLSWATER

Waterfoot Caravan Park, Pooley Bridge, Penrith, Cumbria, CA11 0JF
Tel: 017684 86302
Email: enquiries@waterfootpark.co.uk
www.waterfootpark.co.uk
Pitches For ⌂ ⌂ **Total** 34
Acreage 22 **Open** Mar **to** 14-Nov
Access Good **Site** Lev/Slope
Waterfoot Park is located in one of the most beautiful locations within the Lake District National Park. Nestled in the grounds of a Georgian mansion, overlooking Ullswater, the Park is an idyllic location for touring vans, motor homes and privately owned holiday homes.
Facilities ⌂ ⌿ ⌂ ⌂ ⌂⌂⌿⌂ ⊙⌿ ⌂ ⌂ ⌂
⌂⌂ ⌂ ⌂ ⌂⌂⌂⌂⌂ ⌂⌂ ⌂⌂⌂ ⌿ ⌂ ⌂
Nearest Town Penrith
Directions Leave the M6 at junction 40 and take the A66 for approx. 1 mile. Then take the A592 and Waterfoot can be found on the right hand side. Do not leave the A592 until the Park entrance. NB: SatNav is not compatible in this area.
⇌ Penrith

ULVERSTON

Bardsea Leisure, Priory Road, Ulverston, Cumbria, LA12 9QE
Tel: 01229 584712
Email: reception@bardsealeisure.co.uk
www.bardsealeisure.co.uk
Pitches For ⌂ ⌂ ⌂⌂ **Total** 84
Acreage 10 **Open** All Year
Access Good **Site** Lev/Slope
Nearest Bus Stop (Miles) ¼
Ideal for touring.
Facilities ⌂ ⌿ ⌂ ⌂ ⌂⌂⌿⌂ ⊙⌿ ⌂ ⌂ ⌂
⌂⌂ ⌂ ⌂ ⌂⌂⌂⌂⌂ ⌂ ⌂
Nearest Town Ulverston
Directions Leave the M6 at junction 36 and take the A590 then the A5087.
⇌ Ulverston

ULVERSTON

Crake Valley Holiday Park, Water Yeat, Blawith, Nr Ulverston, Cumbria, LA12 8DL
Tel: 01229 885203
Email: info@crakevalley.co.uk
www.crakevalley.co.uk
Pitches For Å **Total** 6
Acreage ¼ **Open** May **to** Sept
Site Level
Nearest Bus Stop (Miles) ½
Opposite Coniston Water. Ideal base for touring the Lakes.
Facilities ⌂⌂⌿⌂ ⌂ ⊙ ⌂ ⌂
Nearest Town Ulverston
Directions Take the A590 Barrow road, turn right at Greenodd onto the A5092. Within 2 miles fork right for Coniston onto the A5084, the Park is 3 miles along on the left hand side.
⇌ Ulverston

WINDERMERE

Braithwaite Fold Camping & Caravanning Club Site, Glebe Road, Bowness-on-Windermere, Windermere, Cumbria, LA23 3HB
Tel: 01539 442177
Email: enquires@thefriendlyclub.co.uk
www.campingandcaravanningclub.co.uk/braithwaitefold
Pitches For Å ⌂ ⌂ **Total** 65
Acreage 4 **Open** 14-Mar **to** 05-Nov
Access Good
Beattrix Potter Gallery, Lakes Aquarium, Lakeland Motor Museum, Lake District National Park.
Facilities ⌂ ⌿ ⌂ ⌂ ⌂⌂⌿⌂ ⊙⌿ ⌂ ⌂ ⌂
⌂ ⌂⌂⌂⌂ ⌂
Nearest Town Windermere
Directions Turn left onto A592, at roundabout take 1st exit onto A591, turn right onto A593, take left onto Campston Road and keep right.
⇌ Windermere

WINDERMERE

Hill of Oaks Caravan Estate, Windermere, Cumbria, LA12 8NR
Tel: 015395 31578
Email: enquiries@hillofoaks.co.uk
www.hillofoaks.co.uk
Pitches For ⌂ ⌂ **Total** 43
Acreage 31 **Open** Mar **to** 14-Nov
Access Good **Site** Lev/Slope
Nearest Bus Stop (Miles) Outside
Nestling on the slopes of ancient woodland, Hill of Oaks offers exclusive lake frontage for more than one kilometre along the shore of Lake Windermere with private jetties. The Park is family orientated, with well laid out nature walks where intrepid explorers can seek out the wildlife.
Facilities ⌂ ⌿ ⌂ ⌂ ⌂⌂⌿⌂ ⊙⌿ ⌂ ⌂ ⌂
⌂⌂ ⌂ ⌂ ⌂⌂⌂⌂⌂ ⌿ ⌂ ⌂
Nearest Town Windermere
Directions Leave the M6 at junction 36 and take the A590 to Newby Bridge. Turn right onto the A592 and the site is 3 miles on the left hand side.
⇌ Windermere

WINDERMERE

Park Cliffe Camping & Caravan Estate, Birks Road, Tower Wood, Windermere, Cumbria, LA23 3PG
Tel: 015395 31344
Email: info@parkcliffe.co.uk
www.parkcliffe.co.uk
Pitches For Å ⌂ ⌂ **Total** 170
Acreage 25 **Open** Mar **to** Mid Nov
Access Good **Site** Lev/Slope
Nearest Bus Stop (Miles) ¼

Near to Lake Windermere with outstanding views of lakes and mountains, ideal touring. AA 5 Pennants, Cumbria Tourism Winner 2011, AA Northwest Campsite of the Year 2009 and England for Excellence Highly comended 2012.
Facilities
Nearest Town Windermere
Directions M6 junction 36, A590 to Newby Bridge. Turn right onto A592, in 3½ miles turn right into Birks Road. Park is roughly ½ mile on the right.
Windermere

DERBYSHIRE
ASHBOURNE
Ashbourne Camping & Caravanning Club Site, Belper Road (A517), Bradley, Near Ashbourne, Derbyshire, DE6 3EN
Tel: 01335 370855
Email: ashbourne.site@thefriendlyclub.co.uk
www.campingandcaravanning.co.uk/ ashbourne
Pitches For Å ♏ ♐ **Total** 70
Open 14-Mar to 10-Nov
Access Good **Site** Level
Nearest Bus Stop (Miles) Outside
Ideal for exploring the Derbyshire Peaks and Dales. Also Open 9th-26th February 2012. Non members welcome. You can also call us on 0845 130 7633.
Facilities
Nearest Town Ashbourne
Directions From Ashbourne take the A517 Belper road, pass Bradley and site is signposted ½ a mile on the right.
Belper

ASHBOURNE
Bank Top Caravan & Camping, Bank Top Farm, Fenny Bentley, Ashbourne, Derbyshire, DE6 1LF
Tel: 01335 350250
Pitches For Å ♏ ♐ **Total** 51
Acreage 3 **Open** Apr to 01-Oct
Access Good **Site** Lev/Slope
Nearest Bus Stop (Miles) ¼
Working farm with scenic views from the site. Ideal for touring Dovedale and other Dales, also pretty little villages.
Facilities
Nearest Town Ashbourne
Directions From Ashbourne take the A515 north, then take the B5056 and the site is 200 yards on the right.
Derby

ASHBOURNE
Callow Top Holiday Park, Buxton Road, Ashbourne, Derbyshire, DE6 2AQ
Tel: 01335 344020
Email: enquiries@callowtop.co.uk
www.callowtop.co.uk
Pitches For Å ♏ ♐ **Total** 200
Acreage 15 **Open** Easter to Nov
Access Good **Site** Level
Nearest Bus Stop (Miles) 1
Alton Towers only 20 minutes away, Tissington Trail cycle path is adjacent. On site coarse fishing, Carsington Reservoir 5 miles. Many footpaths. Ideal location for exploring the Peak District.
Facilities
Nearest Town Ashbourne

Directions The access to Callow Top is only ¼ mile from Ashbourne on the A515 Buxton road. The entrance is directly opposite Sandybrook Garage, follow the private road for ½ mile to the end.
Derby

ASHBOURNE
Carsington Water Caravan Club Site, Kirk Ireton, Ashbourne, Derbyshire, DE6 3JL
Tel: 01335 370903
www.caravanclub.co.uk
Pitches For ♏ ♐ **Total** 130
Acreage 25 **Open** Mar to Nov
Access Good **Site** Level
Set in a beautifully landscaped pine plantation. Adjacent to Carsington Reservoir for fishing and sailing. BBQs allowed with wardens permission. Non members welcome. Booking essential.
Facilities
Nearest Town Ashbourne
Directions Take the A517 from Ashbourne, turn left after 4½ miles at signpost Carsington Water, after ¾ miles at crossroads turn right, site is 1 mile on the right.
Ashbourne

ASHBOURNE
Newton Grange Caravan Site, Newton Grange, Ashbourne, Derbyshire, DE6 1NJ
Tel: 01335 310214
Pitches For Å ♏ ♐ **Total** 15
Acreage 1 **Open** Mid Mar to Oct
Access Good **Site** Level
Nearest Bus Stop (Miles) ½
Close to Buxton, Matlock and Alton Towers. Tissington Trail adjacent for cycling and walking. Ideal touring.
Facilities
Nearest Town Ashbourne
Directions On the A515 4½ miles north of Ashbourne.
Derby

ASHBOURNE
Peak Gateway Ltd., Moor Lane, Osmaston, Ashbourne, Derbyshire, DE6 1NA
Tel: 01335 344643
Email: info@peakgateway.com
www.peakgateway.com
Pitches For Å ♏ ♐ **Total** 150
Open 22-Jan to 14-Dec
Access Good **Site** Level
Nearest Bus Stop (Miles) Outside
On the door step of the market town of Ashbourne. Ideal for walking in the Peak District. Only a 20 minute drive to Alton Towers.
Facilities
Nearest Town Ashbourne
Directions From Derby take the A52 to Ashbourne, turn left at second sign for Osmaston, site entrance is 100 yards on the right.
Derby

ASHBOURNE
Rivendale Caravan & Leisure Park, Buxton Road, Alsop-en-le-Dale, Ashbourne, Derbyshire, DE6 1QU
Tel: 01335 310311
Email: cades@rivendalecaravanpark.co.uk
www.www.rivendalecaravanpark.co.uk
Pitches For Å ♏ ♐ **Total** 80
Acreage 35 **Open** Feb to Jan
Access Good **Site** Level
Nearest Bus Stop (Miles) ¼

Surrounded by scenic countryside, ideal for walking, cycling and outdoor hobbies. Convenient for Chatsworth, Alton Towers and many other attractions. Yurts and Camping Pods for glamping! Holiday caravans/lodges for hire and sale luxurious B&B rooms.
Facilities
Nearest Town Hartington
Directions 6½ miles north of Ashbourne, directly accessed from the A515 (Buxton road).
Buxton

BAKEWELL
Bakewell Camping & Caravanning Club Site, Hopping Lane, Youlgreave, Bakewell, Derbyshire, DE45 1NA
Tel: 01629 636555
Email: bakewell.site@thefriendlyclub.co.uk
www.campingandcaravanningclub.co.uk/bakewell
Pitches For Å ♏ ♐ **Total** 100
Acreage 14 **Open** 21-Mar to 04-Nov
Site Sloping
Nearest Bus Stop (Miles) 1
Ideally situated for the Peak District. Near to Haddon Hall and Chatsworth House. BTB 3 Star Graded and AA 1 Pennant. Non members welcome. You can also call us on 0845 130 7633.
Facilities
Directions Take the A6 Bakewell to Matlock road, turn onto the B5056 Ashbourne road. After ½ mile take the right hand branch to Youlgreave, turn sharp left after the church into Bradford Lane opposite The George Hotel. Continue ½ mile to club sign then turn right into Farmers Lane for ¼ mile.
Matlock

BAKEWELL
Chatsworth Park Caravan Club Site, Chatsworth, Bakewell, Derbyshire, DE45 1PN
Tel: 01246 582226
www.caravanclub.co.uk
Pitches For ♏ ♐ **Total** 120
Acreage 6½ **Open** All Year
Access Good **Site** Level
Nearest Bus Stop (Miles) ½
Situated in the old walled garden on the Chatsworth Estate with beautiful countryside views. Visit Chatsworth House, 1000 acre park and farm. Non members welcome. Booking essential.
Facilities
Nearest Town Bakewell
Directions From Bakewell take the A619, after 3¼ miles (on the outskirts of Baslow) at the mini roundabout turn right signposted Sheffield. Site is 150 yards on the right.
Bakewell

BAKEWELL
Greenhills Holiday Park, Crowhill Lane, Bakewell, Derbyshire, DE45 1PX
Tel: 01629 813052/813467
Email: info@greenhillsholidaypark.co.uk
www.greenhillsholidaypark.co.uk
Pitches For Å ♏ ♐ **Total** 233
Acreage 8 **Open** Mar to Oct
Access Good **Site** Lev/Slope
Nearest Bus Stop (Miles) ¼
In the heart of the Peak District. Close to Chatsworth House and Haddon Hall.
Facilities
Nearest Town Bakewell

Directions 1 mile north west of Bakewell turn left into Crow Hill Lane, turn first right over the cattle grid.
➜ Matlock

BAKEWELL

Haddon Grove Farm, Bakewell, Derbyshire, DE45 1JF
Tel: 01629 812343
Pitches For Å ⚏ ⊟ **Total** 0
Acreage 3 **Open** Mar **to** Oct
Access Good **Site** Level
Nearest Bus Stop (Miles) ½
Close to Lathkil Dale.
Facilities ⎓ 🔟 ⇌ ⊙ ⌐ 🍴 ☎ ⊙ ✦ ⊡
Nearest Town Bakewell
Directions From Bakewell take the B5055 towards Monyash. Travel for 3 miles then turn left into lane sp Haddon Grove.
➜ Buxton

BAKEWELL

The Grouse & Claret, Rowsley, Matlock, Derbyshire, DE4 2EB
Tel: 01629 733233
Email: grouseandclaretmatlockmarstons.co.uk
Pitches For Å ⚏ ⊟ **Total** 28
Acreage 27 **Open** All Year
Access Good **Site** Level
Nearest Bus Stop (Miles) ¼
Facilities ⌐ 🔟 ⇌ ⌐ ⌐ ☎ ✕ ⋔ ✦ ⊡ ⎙
Nearest Town Bakewell
Directions 3 miles from Bakewell on the A6 towards Matlock.
➜ Matlock

BAMFORD

Swallowholme Camping & Caravan Park, Station Road, Bamford, Hope Valley, Derbyshire, S33 0BN
Tel: 01433 650981
Email: swallowholmecamping@btconnect.com
www.swallowholmecampingandcaravanpark.co.uk
Pitches For Å ⚏ ⊟ **Total** 65
Acreage 3½ **Open** Mar **to** Oct
Access Good **Site** Level
Nearest Bus Stop (Miles) Outside
Alongside the River Derwent and close to Derwent Dam. 5 minutes from Hathersage. Outdoor swimming pool nearby. Ideal for walking. Sorry no dogs.
Facilities ⌐ 🔟 ⇌ ⊙ 🍴 ☎ ⌐ ✗ ⋌
Nearest Town Buxton/Bakewell
Directions On the A6013 on the edge of Bamford Village. 12 miles west of Sheffield off the A525.
➜ Bamford

BRADWELL

Eden Tree Caravan Park, Eccles Lane, Bradwell, Hope Valley, Derbyshire, S33 9JT
Tel: 01433 623444
Email: edentreecaravanpark@fsmail.net
www.edentreecaravanpark.co.uk
Pitches For Å ⚏ ⊟ **Total** 20
Open Mar **to** Oct
Access Good **Site** Sloping
Nearest Bus Stop (Miles) ¼
In the heart of the Peak District National Park. Close to Chatsworth House, Castleton, Buxton and many other attractions.
Facilities ⌐ 🔟 ⇌ ⌐ ⊙ ⌐ ☎ ⌐ ⊡ ✕
Nearest Town Bakewell
Directions On the outskirts of the village of Bradwell, 10 miles from Bakewell.
➜ Hope

BUXTON

Beech Croft Farm, Blackwell in the Peak, Nr Buxton, Derbyshire, SK17 9TQ
Tel: 01298 85330
Email: mail@beechcroftfarm.co.uk
www.beechcroftfarm.co.uk
Pitches For Å ⚏ ⊟ **Total** 30
Acreage 3 **Open** All Year
Access Good **Site** Level
Nearest Bus Stop (Miles) ¼
In the centre of a National Park, ideal for walking and touring. Hardstandings have 16 amp hook-up, water tap and TV aerial socket. Hotel and restaurant in 1 mile.
Facilities ⎓ ☼ ⌐ 🔟 🐶 ⌐ ⊙ ⌐ ⌐ ⊡ ☎
🕿 ⊙ ✦ ⊡ ⊡ ⎙
Nearest Town Buxton
Directions Turn off the A6 midway between Buxton and Bakewell, signposted.
➜ Buxton

BUXTON

Buxton Caravan Club Site, Grin Low Road, Ladmanlow, Buxton, Derbyshire, SK17 6UJ
Tel: 01298 77735
www.caravanclub.co.uk
Pitches For Å ⚏ ⊟ **Total** 117
Acreage 11 **Open** Mar **to** Nov
Access Good **Site** Level
Situated in the Peak District National Park. Ideal for walking and cycling. Near to many historic houses. No late night arrivals. Non members welcome. Booking essential.
Facilities ⎓ ⌐ 🔟 🐶 ⌐ ⌐ ⊙ ⎅ ⊙ ⌐ ⋔ ✦ ⊡ ⎙
Nearest Town Buxton
Directions From Buxton take the A53 Leek road, after 1½ miles turn left signposted Grin Low. After 300 yards turn left into site road, entrance is ¼ mile.
➜ Buxton

BUXTON

Lime Tree Park, Dukes Drive, Buxton, Derbyshire, SK17 9RP
Tel: 01298 22988
Email: info@limetreeparkbuxton.co.uk
Pitches For Å ⚏ ⊟ **Total** 100
Acreage 17 **Open** Mar **to** Nov
Access Good **Site** Lev/slope
Nearest Bus Stop (Miles) ½
Surrounded by farmland with old viaduct backdrop.
Facilities ⎓ ⌐ 🔟 ⌐ 🐶 ⌐ ⌐ ⊙ ⊡ ☎
🕿 ⊙ 🐶 ⋔ ✦ ⊡ ⊡ ✕ ⋌
Nearest Town Buxton
Directions From A515 towards Buxton turn right across the carriageway to Dukes Drive, site on right 1 mile from Buxton.
➜ Buxton

BUXTON

Newhaven Caravan & Camping Park, Newhaven, Nr Buxton, Derbyshire, SK17 0DT
Tel: 01298 84300
Email: newhavencaravanpark@btconnect.com
www.newhavencaravanpark.co.uk
Pitches For Å ⚏ ⊟ **Total** 125
Acreage 27 **Open** Mar **to** Oct
Access Good **Site** Lev/Slope
Ideal centre for touring Peak District, National Park and Derbyshire Dales. Cafe/restaurant opposite site.
Facilities ⌐ 🔟 ⇌ ⌐ ⌐ ⊙ ⊡ ☎
🕿 ⊙ 🐶 ⋔ ✦ ⊡ ⊡ ✕
Nearest Town Buxton
Directions Midway between Ashbourne and Buxton on A515. At the junction with A5012.
➜ Buxton

BUXTON

Pomeroy Caravan & Camping Park, Street House Farm, Pomeroy, Nr Flagg, Buxton, Derbyshire, SK17 9QG
Tel: 01298 83259
Email: pomeroycandc@gmail.com
Pitches For Å ⚏ ⊟ **Total** 30
Acreage 2 **Open** Apr **to** Oct
Access Good **Site** Level
Nearest Bus Stop (Miles) 1
Peaceful site adjoining the High Peak Trail. Tarmac road to all pitches. Separate site for campers. 16 miles north of Ashbourne. You can also call us on Mobile: 07980 585545.
Facilities ⌐ 🔟 ⇌ ⌐ ⌐ ⊙ ⎅ ⌐ ⊡ ☎
⊙ ✦ ⊡ ⊡
Nearest Town Buxton
Directions 5 miles south of Buxton on the A515, site is on the right opposite corner sign. Go over the cattle grid and up a 200 yard tarmac drive to the site.
➜ Buxton

BUXTON

Shallow Grange, Chelmorton, Nr Buxton, Derbyshire, SK17 9SG
Tel: 01298 23578
Email: info@shallowgrange.com
www.shallowgrange.com
Pitches For Å ⚏ ⊟ **Total** 48
Acreage 3 **Open** Mar **to** Oct
Access Good **Site** Level
Nearest Bus Stop (Miles) 1
Walking in the SSSI Dale. Chatsworth House, Haddon Hall and Bakewell nearby.
Facilities ⎓ ⌐ 🔟 ⇌ ⌐ ⊙ ⎅ ⌐ ⊡ ☎
⋔ ⊡ ✗ ⋌ ⋌ ⚲
Nearest Town Buxton
Directions From Buxton take the A515 Ashbourne road and travel for 2 to 3 miles. Turn left onto the A5270 and Shallow Grange is mile on the left.
➜ Buxton

BUXTON

Thornheyes Farm Caravan & Camping Site, Longridge Lane, Peak Dale, Buxton, Derbyshire, SK17 8AD
Tel: 01298 26421
Pitches For Å ⚏ ⊟ **Total** 18
Acreage 1½ **Open** Easter **to** Oct
Access Poor **Site** Sloping
Nearest Bus Stop (Miles) ¼
ADULTS ONLY. Ideal for touring the Peak District.
Facilities ⌐ 🔟 ⌐ ⎅ ☎ ✦ ⊡ A
Nearest Town Buxton
Directions A6 Towards Manchester 2½ miles turn right Batham Gate turn right site on right.
➜ Buxton

CASTLETON

Castleton Caravan Club Site, Castleton, Hope Valley, Derbyshire, S33 8WB
Tel: 01433 620636
www.caravanclub.co.uk
Pitches For ⚏ ⊟ **Total** 93
Acreage 6½ **Open** All Year
Access Good **Site** Level
Nearest Bus Stop (Miles) ½
Set in the heart of the Peak National Park with panoramic views. Ideal for outdoor activities such as walking, cycling, potholing, etc.. ½ mile from Peveril Castle. Non members welcome. Booking essential.
Facilities ⎓ ⌐ 🔟 ⇌ ⌐ ⌐ ⊙ ⊡ ☎
🕿 ⌐ ⊙ ☎ ✦ ⊡ ⊡
Directions M1,junc 29 take the A617. In C/field t onto the A619, after 8¾ mls in Baslow t rt at mini r/about onto A623. In Calver t rt onto B6001, in G/ford t lt at sp Hathersage. After 2½ mls t lt onto A6187, site 5 mls on rt.

37

CASTLETON

Rowter Farm, Castleton, Hope Valley, Derbyshire, S33 8WA
Tel: 01433 620271
www.peakdistrictsnationalpark.com
Pitches For Å ⚑ ⚑ **Total** 30
Acreage 4 **Open** End Mar **to** End Oct
Access Good **Site** Level
One static caravan available for hire.
Facilities 🏠♿️⌂ 🏪🍴🅿️
Nearest Town Castleton
Directions From Castleton take the B6061 Winnats Pass road, go to the top and continue for 200 yards, turn left through the gate.
⚏ Hope

CHESTERFIELD

Millfield Camping & Touring Park, Mill Lane, Old Tupton, Chesterfield, Derbyshire, S42 6AE
Tel: 01246 861082
Pitches For Å ⚑ ⚑ **Total** 30
Acreage 2½ **Open** All Year
Access Good **Site** Level
Nearest Bus Stop (Miles) ½
The Peak District.
Facilities ♿️ ⌂ 🏠🅿️🏪⌂☉🛒🔲♨️
🍴☉✕🍴🅿️🔲⚑ ♿️♿️
Nearest Town Chesterfield
⚏ Chesterfield

DERBY

Beechwood Park, Main Road, Elvaston, Thulston, Derby, Derbyshire, DE72 3EQ
Tel: 01332 751938
Email: colinbeech@btconnect.com
www.beechwoodparkleisure.co.uk
Pitches For Å ⚑ ⚑ ⚑ **Total** 200
Acreage 25 **Open** All Year
Access Good **Site** Level
Nearest Bus Stop (Miles) ½
On the edge of the Peak District with fishing lakes and a childrens go-karting track. Opposite Elvaston Castle & Country Park. Cafe and tackle shop on site. Pub in the village.
Facilities ♿️ ⌂ 🏠🅿️⌂☉🛒🔲♨️
🍴☉✕🍴🔲♨️✎
Nearest Town Derby
Directions From Derby take the A6 towards Loughborough and turn left onto the B5010. Beechwood Park is 1 mile on the right hand side.
⚏ Derby

DOVERIDGE

Cavendish Caravan Site, 1 Old Marston Lane, Doveridge, Ashbourne, Derbyshire, DE6 5JS
Tel: 01889 563487
Pitches For Å ⚑ ⚑ **Total** 15
Acreage 2 **Open** All Year
Access Good **Site** Level
Nearest Bus Stop (Miles) Outside
Ideal for Alton Towers, Dovedale, Sudbury Hall and many pleasant walks.
Facilities 🍴 🏠 🏪🍴
Nearest Town Uttoxeter
Directions 2 miles esst of Uttoxeter on the A50.
⚏ Uttoxeter

EDALE

Fieldhead Campsite, Edale, Hope Valley, Derbyshire, S33 7ZA
Tel: 01433 670386
Email: bookings@fieldhead-campsite.co.uk
www.fieldhead-campsite.co.uk
Pitches For Å **Total** 45
Acreage 3 **Open** All Year
Site Level
Alongside a river, next to Peak District Visitor Centre. 6 fields, 2 of which are by the river. All superb views of Mamtor Ridge and Kinder Scout. At the start of Pennine Way.
Facilities ♿️🏠♿️⌂☉🛒♨️🍴🏪
Nearest Town Castleton
Directions 4½ miles from Castleton.
⚏ Edale

EDALE

Highfield Farm, Upper Booth, Edale, Hope Valley, Derbyshire, S33 7ZJ
Tel: 01433 670245
Pitches For Å ⚑ ⚑ **Total** 0
Acreage 10 **Open** Easter **to** Oct
Access Good **Site** Sloping
Good walking country, near the start of Pennine Way.
Facilities 🏠 🏪🍴🅿️
Nearest Town Buxton
Directions Turn right off the A6187 opposite Hope Church, take minor road to Edale. Follow the road up the valley, pass the turning for Edale Village, at bottom of the hill turn right, go past the viaduct and pass picnic area, round the corner and the house is up ahead.
⚏ Edale

GLOSSOP

Crowden Camping & Caravanning Club Site, Woodhead Road, Crowden, Glossop, Derbyshire, SK13 1HZ
Tel: 01457 866057
Email: crowden.site@thefriendlyclub.co.uk
www.campingandcaravanningclub.co.uk/crowden
Pitches For Å ⚑ ⚑ **Total** 45
Acreage 2½ **Open** 21-Mar **to** 04-Nov
Site Level
Nearest Bus Stop (Miles) 100 metres
In the heart of the Peak District National Park, close to the Pennine Way. BTB 3 Star Graded and AA 2 Pennants. Non members welcome. You can also call us on 0845 130 7633.
Facilities 🏠🏪⌂☉🛒♨️🍴 🏪 🏪🍴🔲♨️
Directions On the A628 Manchester to Barnsley road, in Crowden follow signs for car park, Youth Hostel and camp site. Camp site is approx. 300 yards from the main road.
⚏ Hadfield/Glossop

HARTINGTON

Barracks Farm Caravan & Camping Site, Beresford Dale, Hartington, Buxton, Derbyshire, SK17 0HQ
Tel: 01298 84261
Pitches For Å ⚑ ⚑ **Total** 40
Acreage 5 **Open** Easter **to** Oct
Access Good **Site** Level
Alongside river, scenic views and ideal touring.
Facilities 🏠♿️⌂ 🏪🍴 🏪🍴🔲
Nearest Town Buxton
Directions Buxton A515 approx 10 miles. After leaving Buxton go on for 7 miles, turn right for Hartington B5054. Go through village for 1½ miles, turn left for Beresford Dale, continue for ¼ mile then turn left again signposted Beresford Dale. The site is second on the left.
⚏ Buxton

HAYFIELD

Hayfield Camping & Caravanning Club Site, Kinder Road, Hayfield, High Peak, Derbyshire, SK22 2LE
Tel: 01663 745394
Email: hayfield.site@thefriendlyclub.co.uk
www.campingandcaravanningclub.co.uk/hayfield
Pitches For Å ⚑ **Total** 90
Acreage 6 **Open** 21-Mar **to** 01-Nov
Access Difficult **Site** Level
Nearest Bus Stop (Miles) 1
On the banks of the River Sett. Ideal for fell and moorland walkers. 6 miles from a Victorian style swimming pool. 12 miles from Granada Studios. BTB 3 Star Graded and AA 2 Pennants. Non members welcome (no caravans). You can also call us on 0845 130 7633.
Facilities 🏠♿️⌂☉🛒 🍴
🍴☉🏪🍴🔲♨️🏪🛜
Directions On the A624 Glossop to Chapel-en-le-Frith road, the Hayfield by-pass. Well signed to the village, follow wooden carved signs to the site.
⚏ New Mills

HOPE

Hardhurst Farm, Parsons Lane, Hope, Hope Valley, Derbyshire, S33 6RB
Tel: 01433 620001
Email: hardhurstcamping@hotmail.co.uk
Pitches For Å ⚑ ⚑ **Total** 52
Acreage 5 **Open** All Year
Access Good **Site** Level
Nearest Bus Stop (Miles) ¼
Climbing, walking, mountain biking popular in area.
Facilities ♿️🍴🏠🏪♿️⌂☉🛒♨️🍴
✕🏪🍴🔲
Nearest Town Castleton
⚏ Hope

HOPE

Laneside Caravan Park, Laneside Farm, Station Road, Hope, Hope Valley, Derbyshire, S33 6RR
Tel: 01433 620215
Email: laneside@lineone.net
www.lanesidecaravanpark.co.uk
Pitches For Å ⚑ ⚑ **Total** 85
Acreage 5 **Open** Mar **to** Nov
Access Good **Site** Level
Nearest Bus Stop (Miles) Outside
Sheltered riverside setting adjacent to to Hope Village. Wonderful central location for walking and touring the Peak District.

Facilities   🅿 ∮ ▣ 🆎 🎣 ⌂ ☉ ↵ 🚃 ▣ 🛉
🆘 🅿 👁 🛇 🖈 ▣ ▣ 🎿 ☼
Nearest Town Bakewell
🚃 Hope

HOPE

Pindale Farm Camp Site, Pindale Farm,
Pindale Road, Hope, Hope Valley,
Derbyshire, S33 6RN
Tel: 01433 620111
Email: pindalefarm@btconnect.com
www.pindalefarm.co.uk
Pitches For ⛺   **Total** 30
Acreage 2 **Open** Mar **to** Oct
Site Level
Pindale farm is situated at the west end of
the Hope Valley, the heart of the Derbyshire
Peak District. AA 3 Pennant site separate
camping area for D of E expeditions,
bunkhouse available.
Facilities ∮ ▣ 🆎 🎣 ⌂ ☉ ↵ ▣ 🅟 ▣ ☼
Nearest Town Hope
Directions Follow signs from church 1 mile.
🚃 Hope

MATLOCK

Birchwood Farm Caravan Park,
Wirksworth Road, Whatstandwell, Nr
Matlock, Derbyshire, DE4 5HS
Tel: 01629 822200
www.birchwoodfcp.co.uk
Pitches For ⛺ ⛟ 🚐 🚍 **Total** 66
Acreage 4 **Open** 25-Mar **to** Oct
Access Good **Site** Sloping
Nearest Bus Stop (Miles) ½
Situated off Midshires Way which leads to
High Peak Trail or the Cromford Canal.
Facilities & 🛆 ∮ ▣ 🆎 🎣 ⌂ ☉ ↵ 🚃
▣ 🆘 🅿 ⌂ 🖈 ▣ ▣ 🎿
Nearest Town Wirksworth
Directions Leave the A6 at Whatstandwell
Bridge (look for our sign by the telephone
box) and take the B5035 towards Wirksworth,
after 1 mile turn right down our drive.
🚃 Whatstandwell

MATLOCK

Lickpenny Caravan Park, Lickpenny
Lane, Tansley, Nr Matlock, Derbyshire,
DE4 5GF
Tel: 01629 583040
Email: lickpennycp@btinternet.com
www.lickpennycaravanpark.co.uk
Pitches For ⛟ 🚐 🚍 **Total** 100
Acreage 16 **Open** All Year
Nearest Bus Stop (Miles) ¼
Located in the heart of the Peak District.
Garden centre and cafe nearby.
Facilities & ∮ ▣ 🆎 🆎 🎣 ⌂ ☉ ↵ 🚃 ▣ 🛉
🆘 🅿 👁 🛇 ⌂ 🖈 ▣ ▣ 🎿 ☼
Nearest Town Matlock
Directions From Matlock take the A615
towards the M1 for 3 miles, site is signposted
on the left. 8 miles from the M1.
🚃 Matlock

MATLOCK

Packhorse Farm Bungalow, Packhorse
Farm, Tansley, Matlock, Derbyshire, DE4
5LF
Tel: 01629 582781
Pitches For ⛺ ⛟ 🚐 **Total** 20
Acreage 3 **Open** All Year
Access Good **Site** Level
ADULTS ONLY. Ideal for touring the
countryside.
Facilities ∮ ▣ 🆎 🎣 ⌂ ☉ ↵ 🛉 🖈 ▣ A 🎿
Nearest Town Matlock
Directions Take the A615 to Tansley Village,
1½ miles to the site. 4½ miles from Matlock.
🚃 Matlock

MATLOCK

Pinegroves Caravan Park, High Lane,
Tansley, Matlock, Derbyshire, DE4 5BG
Tel: 01629 534815
Pitches For ⛟ 🚐 **Total** 20
Acreage 7 **Open** Apr **to** Oct
Access Good **Site** Level
Peaceful countryside site. Near to many
attractions including Tramway Museum,
Chatsworth House, Matlock Bath Cable Cars
and Lea Rhododendron Gardens.
Facilities & 🛆 ∮ 🆎 🎣 ⌂ ☉ ↵ ▣ 🅟 ▣
🖈 ▣ ▣ 🎿
Nearest Town Matlock
Directions Leave the M1 at junction 28, take
the A38 to Alfreton then take the A615
towards Matlock. 2 miles after Wessington
turn left at the crossroads into High Lane,
site is on the left.
🚃 Matlock

SWADLINCOTE

**Conkers Camping & Caravanning Club
Site,** Bath Lane, Moira, Swadlincote,
Derbyshire, DE12 6BD
Tel: 01283 224925
Email: conkers.site@thefriendlyclub.co.uk
www.campingandcaravanningclub.co.uk/
conkers
Pitches For ⛺ ⛟ 🚐 **Total** 90
Acreage 4 **Open** All Year
Access Good **Site** Level
Nearest Bus Stop (Miles) 1
Close to Corrs Visitor Centre, Donnington
Park, Grangewood Zoo, Calke Abbey and
Twycross Zoo. Non members welcome. You
can also call us on 0845 130 7633.
Facilities & ∮ ▣ 🅟 👁 🛇 🖈 ▣ ▣ 🎿 ☼
Nearest Town Swadlincote
Directions From Burton-on-Trent take the
A444 towards Overseal. Turn into Moira road
and take the fourth exit on the left, site is
immediately on the right.
🚃 Burton-on-Trent

DEVON
ASHBURTON

Parkers Farm Holiday Park, Higher Mead
Farm, Ashburton, Devon, TQ13 7LJ
Tel: 01364 654869
Email: parkersfarm@btconnect.com
www.parkersfarmholidays.co.uk
Pitches For ⛺ ⛟ 🚐 **Total** 100
Acreage 25 **Open** Easter **to** Oct
Access Good **Site** Level Terrace
Nearest Bus Stop (Miles) ¼
Friendly, family run, site with spectacular
views. Children and pets paradise. Static
caravans also for hire. Farm animals to see
and feed.
Facilities & ∮ ▣ 🆎 🎣 ⌂ ☉ ↵ 🚃 ▣ 🛉
🆘 🅿 👁 🛇 🛇 ✕ 🛇 🖈 ⌂ 🖈 ▣ ▣ 🎿 ☼
Nearest Town Ashburton
Directions Take the A38 to Plymouth, when
you see the sign 29 miles Plymouth take
second left marked Woodland - Denbury.
🚃 Newton Abbot

ASHBURTON

River Dart Country Park, Holne Park,
Ashburton, Newton Abbot, Devon, TQ13
7NP
Tel: 01364 652511
Email: info@riverdart.co.uk
www.riverdart.co.uk
Pitches For ⛺ ⛟ 🚐 **Total** 185
Acreage 90 **Open** Apr **to** Sept
Access Good

River Dart Adventures, free access for
duration of stay, dare devils not included.
Facilities & ∮ ▣ 🆎 🎣 ⌂ ☉ ↵ 🚃 ▣ 🛉
🆘 🅟 👁 🛇 ✕ 🛇 ⌂ 🖈 ▣ ▣ 🛇 🎿 ☼
Nearest Town Ashburton
Directions From the M5 at Exeter take the
A38 towards Plymouth. Exit at Peartree
Junction in Ashburton and follow brown
tourism signs.
🚃 Newton Abbot

AXMINSTER

Andrewshayes Holiday Park, Dalwood,
Axminster, Devon, EX13 7DY
Tel: 01404 831225
Email: info@andrewshayes.co.uk
www.andrewshayes.co.uk
Pitches For ⛺ ⛟ 🚐 **Total** 150
Acreage 12 **Open** Easter **to** Oct
Access Good **Site** Lev/Terraced
Nearest Bus Stop (Miles) ¼
Close to the Jurassic coast. Outdoor heated
pool, bar and take-away food.
Facilities & ∮ ▣ 🆎 🎣 ⌂ ☉ ↵ 🚃 ▣ 🛉
🆘 🅿 👁 🛇 🛇 ⌂ 🖈 ⌂ ✕ 🖈 ▣ ▣ 🎿
🛇 ☼
Nearest Town Axminster
Directions From Axminster take the A35, site
is 3 miles on the right.
🚃 Axminster

BARNSTAPLE

Greenacres Farm Touring Caravan Park,
Bratton Fleming, Barnstaple, North Devon,
EX31 4SG
Tel: 01598 763334
Pitches For ⛟ 🚐 **Total** 30
Acreage 4 **Open** Apr **to** Oct
Access Good **Site** Level
Nearest Bus Stop (Miles) ¼
Peaceful, secluded park with scenic views.
5 miles from moors and coast, 10 miles from
towns. Ideal for touring, walking and cycling.
Facilities & ∮ ▣ 🆎 🎣 ⌂ ☉ ↵ 🚃 ▣
🛉 🅟 👁 🛇 ⌂ ✕ 🖈 ▣ ▣ ☼
Nearest Town Barnstaple
Directions From North Devon link road
(A361), turn right at Northaller roundabout.
Take the A399 to Blackmoor Gate, approx
10 miles. Park signed (300yds from the
A399).
🚃 Barnstaple

BRAUNTON

Lobb Fields Caravan & Camping Park,
Saunton Road, Braunton, Devon, EX33 1HG
Tel: 01271 812090
Email: info@lobbfields.com
www.lobbfields.com
Pitches For ⛺ ⛟ 🚐 **Total** 180
Acreage 14 **Open** 28-Mar **to** 02-Nov
Access Good **Site** Gentle Slope
Nearest Bus Stop (Miles) Outside
1½ miles from the beach. 1 mile from the
Tarka Trail. Disabled toilet and shower.
Facilities & ∮ ▣ 🆎 🎣 ⌂ ☉ ↵ 🚃 ▣ 🛉
🛉 🅟 👁 🛇 ⌂ ✕ 🖈 ▣ ▣ ☼
Nearest Town Braunton
Directions Take the A361 to Braunton, then
take the B3231. The park entrance is 1 mile
from Braunton centre on the right.
🚃 Barnstaple

BRIXHAM

Hillhead Caravan Club Site, Hillhead,
Brixham, Devon, TQ5 0HH
Tel: 01803 853204
www.caravanclub.co.uk
Pitches For ⛺ ⛟ 🚐 **Total** 241
Acreage 20 **Open** Mar **to** Jan
Access Good **Site** Lev/Slope

In a great location with many pitches affording stunning views of the sea, South Devon and parts of Dorset. Ideal site for families. Kingswear-Paignton Steam Railway and Paignton Zoo nearby. Non members welcome. Booking essential.
Facilities ⚫ 🅗 🆆🄱 ♿ 🄿 ⊙🔥 ▣ 🍴
🍴 🄾 🔒 ✗ 🎱 🎡 🔔 🛒 ⚡🚐🔌 🄳 🛜
Nearest Town Brixham
Directions From A380 3 miles south of Newton Abbot t rt onto the ring road sp Brixham. After 7 miles at traffic lights t rt onto A3022, just past Churston Golf Course t rt onto A379. At mini r/bout t rt and immediately fork lt onto B3205. Site is ¼ of a mile on the lt.
🚉 Paignton

BRIXHAM

Upton Manor Farm Camping & Touring, Upton Manor Farm, St Marys Road, Brixham, Devon, TQ5 9QH
Tel: 01803 882384
Email: uptoncamp@aol.com
www.uptonmanorfarm.co.uk
Pitches For 🅰 ⛺ �caravan **Total** 200
Acreage 7½ **Open** End May **to** Sept
Access Good **Site** Lev/Slope
Nearest Bus Stop (Miles) Outside
Close to St Marys Bay with its sandy beach, and under a mile from the picturesque fishing town of Brixham.
Facilities ⚫ 🅗 🆆🄱 ♿ 🄿 ⊙🔥 ▣ 🎱 🄶 🄿 🔌
Nearest Town Brixham
Directions In Brixham town centre turn right into Bolton Street, at the traffic lights go straight on, then turn left into Castor Road which leads to St. Marys Road. Well signposted.
🚉 Paignton

BUCKFAST

Churchill Farm, Buckfastleigh, Devon, TQ11 0EZ
Tel: 01364 642844/07977113175
Email: apedrick@btinternet.com
www.churchillfarmcampsite.com
Pitches For 🅰 ⛺ �caravan **Total** 25
Acreage 2 **Open** Apr **to** Oct
Access Good **Site** Lev/Slope
Nearest Bus Stop (Miles) ½
Stunning views of Dartmoor and Buckfast Abbey, the latter being within easy walking distance as are the Steam Railway, Butterfly Farm, Otter Sanctuary and local inns. Seaside resort 10 miles.
Facilities 🔥 🆆🄱 🄿 ⊙🔥 🍴 🔔 🄳
Nearest Town Buckfastleigh/Buckfast
Directions Exit A38 at Dartbridge, follow signs for Buckfast Abbey, proceed up hill to crossroads. Turn left into no-through road towards church. Farm entrance is opposite the church 1½ miles from the A38.
🚉 Totnes

BUCKFASTLEIGH

Beara Farm Camping Site, Colston Road, Buckfastleigh, Devon, TQ11 0LW
Tel: 01364 642234
Pitches For 🅰 ⛺ �caravan **Total** 30
Acreage 3¼ **Open** All Year
Access Good **Site** Level
Quiet, select, sheltered site adjoining River Dart. Within easy reach of sea and moors and 1½ miles southeast of Buckfastleigh.
Facilities ✗ 🅗 🆆🄱 🄿 ⊙🔥 🔔🛒 🄳
Nearest Town Buckfastleigh
Directions Coming from Exeter take first left after passing South Devon Steam Railway and Butterfly Centre at Buckfastleigh, signpost marked Beara, fork right at next turning then 1 mile to site, signposted on roadside and junctions.
🚉 Totnes

BUCKFASTLEIGH

Bowden Farm Campsite, Bowden Farm, Buckfastleigh, Devon, TQ11 0JG
Tel: 01364 643955
www.www.holidaydevon.co.uk
Pitches For 🅰 ⛺ �caravan **Total** 40
Acreage 20 **Open** All Year
Access Good **Site** Level
Magnificent scenic location overlooking Dartmoor & South Devon.
Facilities 🔔🄳
Nearest Town Buckfastleigh
Directions 3 milesfrom Buckfastleigh, A38 Devon Expressway
🚉 Totnes

BUDLEIGH SALTERTON

Ladram Bay Holiday Park, Otterton, Budleigh Salterton, Devon, EX9 7BX
Tel: 01395 568398
Email: info@ladrambay.co.uk
www.ladrambay.co.uk
Pitches For 🅰 ⛺ �caravan **Total** 750
Open 14-Mar **to** 02-Nov
Access Good **Site** Sloping
Nearest Bus Stop (Miles) ½
Private beach, stunning views from pitches, lots of facilities.
Facilities ⚫ 🅗 🆆🄱 🄿 ⊙🔥 🍴 🄾 🄳 🔔🛒
🄾 🔒 🎱 ✗ 🎱 🎡 🔔 🛒 🍴 🄳 🔌 ☀
🛜
Nearest Town Budleigh Salterton
Directions Leave the M5 at junction 30 and take the A3052, Newton Poppleford, signs then to Ladram Bay.
🚉 Exmouth

CHAGFORD

Woodland Springs Adult Touring Park, Venton, Drewsteignton, Devon, EX6 6PG
Tel: 01647 231695
Email: enquiries@woodlandsprings.co.uk
www.woodlandsprings.co.uk
Pitches For 🅰 ⛺ �caravan **Total** 81
Acreage 4 **Open** All Year
Access Good **Site** Level
ADULTS ONLY. Quiet, secluded site within the Dartmoor National Park, surrounded by wood and farmland. Good access for the larger units and large all-weather pitches. Off season breaks.
Facilities ⚫ 🅗 🆆🄱 🄿 ⊙🔥 🔔🛒 🄳
🍴 🄾 🔌 🄳 ☀
Nearest Town Okehampton
Directions From Exeter take the A30, after 17 miles turn left at Whiddon Down Junction onto the A382 towards Moretonhampstead, after ½ a mile turn left at the roundabout, site is 1 mile on the left signpost Venton.
🚉 Exeter

CHUDLEIGH

Holmans Wood Holiday Park, Harcombe, Cross, Chudleigh, Devon, TQ13 0DZ
Tel: 01626 853785
Email: enquiries@holmanswood.co.uk
www.holmanswood.co.uk
Pitches For 🅰 ⛺ �caravan **Total** 100
Acreage 11 **Open** Mar **to** Oct
Access Good **Site** Level
Picturesque setting. Ideal touring for Dartmoor, Haldon Forest, Exeter and Torbay. Holiday homes for sale.
Facilities ⚫ 🅗 🆆🄱 🄿 ⊙🔥 🔔🛒 🄳
🄾 🎱 🎡 🔔 🔌 🄳 ☀ 🍴 🛜
Nearest Town Chudleigh
Directions From Exeter take the A38 Towards Plymouth. Go past the racecourse and after 1 mile take the B3344 for Chudleigh. We are on the left at the end of the sliproad.
🚉 Newton Abbot

COMBE MARTIN

Newberry Valley Park, Woodlands, Combe Martin, Devon, EX34 0AT
Tel: 01271 882334
Email: relax@newberryvalleypark.co.uk
www.newberryvalleypark.co.uk
Pitches For 🅰 ⛺ �caravan **Total** 110
Acreage 20 **Open** Mar **to** Oct
Access Good **Site** Level
Near beach and village, adjacent to Wolf Centre.
Facilities ⚫ 🔥 🅗 🆆🄱 🄿 ⊙🔥 🔔🛒 🄳 🛒
🎱 🎡 ✗ 🎱 🎡 🔔 🔌 🄳 🍴 ☀ 🔌 🛜
Nearest Town Combe Martin/Ilfracombe
Directions A399 from Aller Cross to Combe Martin. Site at seaside end of village.
🚉 Barnstaple

COMBE MARTIN

Sandaway Beach Holiday Park, John Fowler Holidays, Sandaway, Nr Combe Martin, North Devon, EX34 9ST
Tel: 01271 866766
Email: booking@jfhols.co.uk
www.johnfowlerholidays.com
Pitches For 🅰 ⛺ �caravan **Total** 18
Acreage 1½ **Open** 03-Mar **to** 02-Nov
Access Good **Site** Sloping
Nearest Bus Stop (Miles) ¼
Own private beach. Fantastic walks and scenery. Close to all major holiday attractions.
Facilities ⚫ 🔥 🅗 🄿 ⊙🔥 🔔🛒 🄳 🛒
🎱 🎡 ✗ 🎱 🎡 🔔 🔌 🄳 🍴 ☀ 🔌 🛜
Nearest Town Ilfracombe/Combe Martin
Directions From the M5 junc 27 take the A361 towards Barnstaple, then take the A399 to Combe Martin. Sandaway is on the right at the far end of the village. 5 miles from Ilfracombe.
🚉 Barnstaple

COMBE MARTIN

Stowford Farm Meadows, Combe Martin, Devon, EX34 0PW
Tel: 01271 882476
Email: enquiries@stowford.co.uk
www.stowford.co.uk
Pitches For 🅰 ⛺ �caravan **Total** 700
Acreage 140 **Open** All Year
Access Good **Site** Lev/Slope
Nearest Bus Stop (Miles) 1
Set in 450 acres of beautiful countryside. Ideal touring site at the heart of North Devon. Renowned for our extensive range of facilities at excellent value. Horse riding on site. Caravan repair workshop, caravan accessories shop and caravan sales.
Facilities ⚫ 🔥 🅗 🆆🄱 🄿 ⊙🔥 🔔🛒 🄳
🎱 🄾 🔒 ✗ 🎱 🎡 🔔 🄳 🍴 ☀ 🛒 🛜
Nearest Town Combe Martin
Directions Situated on the A3123 Combe Martin/Woolacombe road at Berry Down.
🚉 Barnstaple

CREDITON

Yeatheridge Farm Caravan & Camping Park, East Worlington, Crediton, Devon, EX17 4TN
Tel: 01884 860330
Email: yeatheridge@talk21.com
www.yeatheridge.co.uk
Pitches For 🅰 ⛺ �caravan **Total** 85
Open 01-Apr **to** 01-Oct
Access Good **Site** Lev/Slope
2½ mile woodland walk. Fishing and horse riding on site.
Facilities ⚫ 🔥 🆆🄱 🄿 ⊙🔥 🔔🛒 🄳 🛒
🎱 🄾 🔒 ✗ 🎱 🎡 🔔 🄳 🍴 ☀ 🔌 🛜
Directions From Tiverton take the B3137 to Witheridge, turn left onto the B3042 and Yeatheridge is 3½ miles on the left.
🚉 Eggesford

CROYDE BAY
Bay View Farm Holidays, Croyde, Devon, EX33 1PN
Tel: 01271 890501
www.bayviewfarm.co.uk
Pitches For ⋏ ⊞ ⊟ **Total** 0
Acreage 10 **Open** Easter **to** Sept
Site Level
Nearest Bus Stop (Miles) Outside
Scenic views. Just a five minute walk to the beach. Ideal touring. Booking is advisable during peak season. Limited statics available. Please send SAE for further information.
Facilities ⚫ ⚫ ⚫ ⚫ ⚫ ⚫ ⚫ ⚫ ⚫ ⚫ ⚫ ⚫ ⚫ ⚫ ⚫ ⚫ ⚫ ⚫ ⚫
Directions At Braunton on A361 turn west on main road B3231 towards Croyde Village
🚆 Barnstaple

CROYDE BAY
Ruda Holiday Park - Parkdean, Croyde Bay, Devon, EX33 1NY
Tel: 0344 335 3741
Email: enquiries@parkdeanholidays.co.uk
www.parkdeantouring.com
Pitches For ⋏ ⊞ ⊟ **Total** 312
Acreage 220 **Open** Mar **to** Nov
Access Good **Site** Level
Nearest Bus Stop (Miles) 1
Our own beach, Croyde Bay is immediately adjacent to camping and touring pitches. Excellent surfing and walking.
Facilities ⚫
Nearest Town Croyde
Directions From Barnstaple take the A361 to Braunton. In the centre of Braunton at the traffic lights turn left onto the B3231 and follow signs to Croyde.
🚆 Barnstaple

CULLOMPTON
Forest Glade Holiday Park, Cullompton, Devon, EX15 2DT
Tel: 01404 841381
Email: enquiries@forest-glade.co.uk
www.forest-glade.co.uk
Pitches For ⋏ ⊞ ⊟ ⊟ **Total** 135
Acreage 16 **Open** Mid Mar **to** Oct
Access Good **Site** Level
Central for southwest twixt coast and moors. Large flat sheltered camping pitches. Caravans for hire. Free heated indoor swimming pool and Paddling pool. Riding and gliding nearby. Tennis on site.

Facilities ⚼ ∤ 🖃 🇭 📧 🈺 📶 ⊙ ↩ 🅿 ⊡ ☎ 🏧 🇮🇴 🎣 🛁 🕭 🍴 🇵 🇨 ⌨ ☀ ⚒ ⚓ 🛜
Nearest Town Cullompton
Directions 5 miles from M5 junc 28 A373 Cullompton/Honiton, turn for Sheldon at Keepers Cottage Inn, 2½ miles east of Cullompton. Touring caravans via Dunkeswell Road only.
⇛ Honiton

DARTMOUTH

Dartmouth Camping & Caravanning Club Site, Stoke Fleming, Dartmouth, Devon, TQ6 0RF
Tel: 01803 770253
Email:
dartmouth.site@thefriendlyclub.co.uk
www.campingandcaravanningclub.co.uk/dartmouth
Pitches For ⚐ ⊡ 🚐 **Total** 90
Acreage 6 **Open** 14-Mar to 16-Nov
Access Good **Site** Lev/Slope
Nearest Bus Stop (Miles) Outside
A pretty site in an area of outstanding natural beauty. Just a few minutes from the award winning beach of Blackpool Sands and the south west coastal path. 1½ miles from Dartmouth with its historic and royal connections, cobbled streets, bistros and excellent restaurants and pubs. You can also call us on 0845 130 7633.
Facilities ⚼ ∤ 🖃 🇭 📧 🈺 ⊙ ↩ 🅿 ☎ 🏧 🇮🇴 🎣 🛁 🇵 🇨 ☀ 🛜
Nearest Town Dartmouth
Directions From Totnes take the A381 Turn left onto the A3122 left onto A379. Right at Deer Park Inn.
⇛ Totnes

DARTMOUTH

Little Cotton Caravan Park, Dartmouth, Devon, TQ6 0LB
Tel: 01803 832558
Email: enquiries@littlecotton.co.uk
www.littlecotton.co.uk
Pitches For ⚐ ⊡ 🚐 **Total** 117
Acreage 7 **Open** Mid Mar to End Oct
Access Good **Site** Lev/Slope
Nearest Bus Stop (Miles) Outside
River Tripps, Steam Trains, Beaches, ideal touring.
Facilities ⚼ ∤ 🖃 🇭 📧 🈺 ⊙ ↩ 🅿 ⊡ ☎ 🏧 🇮🇴 🎣 🛁 🇵 🇨 🛜
Nearest Town Dartmouth
Directions Leave A38 onto A384 sign for Dartmouth. Follow directions to Dartmouth we are opposite Sainsburys.
⇛ Totnes

DARTMOUTH

Woodlands Grove Caravan & Camping Park, Blackawton, Totnes, Devon, TQ9 7DQ
Tel: 01803 712598
Email: holiday@woodlandsgrove.com
www.woodlandsgrove.com
Pitches For ⚐ ⊡ 🚐 **Total** 210
Acreage 16 **Open** 28-Mar to 02-Nov
Access Good **Site** Mostly Level
Nearest Bus Stop (Miles) Outside
Combining fantastic facilities with personal supervision. Spacious pitches in beautiful countryside. 4 miles from Dartmouth coast. Excellent bathrooms, laundry and Free hot showers. Two nights stay gives FREE entrance to our 90 acre Leisure Park. 3 watercoasters, 500m Toboggan Run and Arctic Gliders. All weather fun guaranteed - perfect family holiday! Also 'Adults Only Midweek Special', the perfect rural break for adults.

Facilities ⚼ ∤ 🇭 📧 🈺 📶 ⊙ ↩ 🅿 ⊡ ☎ 🏧 🇮🇴 🎣 🛁 🕭 🇵 🇨 ⌨ 🛜
Nearest Town Dartmouth
Directions 4 miles from Dartmouth on main road A3122 (formally B3207).
⇛ Totnes

DAWLISH

Cofton Country Holidays, Starcross, Nr Dawlish, Devon, EX6 8RP
Tel: 01626 890111
Email: info@coftonholidays.co.uk
www.coftonholidays.co.uk
Pitches For ⚐ ⊡ 🚐 🚐 **Total** 450
Acreage 45 **Open** All Year
Access Good **Site** Level
Nearest Bus Stop (Miles) Outside
Near Dawlish Warren Blue flag beach, good location for touring South Devon.
Facilities ⚼ ∤ 🖃 🇭 📧 🈺 📶 ⊙ ↩ 🅿 ⊡ ☎ 🏧 🇮🇴 🎣 ✕ 🛁 🇵 🇨 🎾 ☀ 🛜
Nearest Town Dawlish
Directions On the A379 Exeter to Dawlish road, ½ mile past Cockwood Harbour on the left.
⇛ Starcross

DAWLISH

Lady's Mile Holiday Park, Exeter Road, Dawlish, Devon, EX7 0LX
Tel: 01626 863411
Email: info@ladysmile.co.uk
www.ladysmile.co.uk
Pitches For ⚐ ⊡ 🚐 **Total** 486
Acreage 16 **Open** Mid Mar to End Oct
Access Good **Site** Lev/Slope
Nearest Bus Stop (Miles) Outside

Lady's Mile
HOLIDAY PARK

Dawlish, Devon EX7 0LX
www.ladysmile.co.uk

Lady's Mile is the perfect family holiday with two free swimming pools, waterslides, Oceans Bar & Restaurant, entertainment nightly, takeaway, piano bar, adventure play area, gym and a great choice of holiday accommodation with new touring pitches and holiday homes.

Electric hook-ups, plenty of hard standing for caravans, motorhomes and tents with FREE hot water and showers.

even more to enjoy...
Steam Room & Sauna
Licensed Shop • Splash Zone
Takeaway, Pizzeria & Café
Multi Sports • Themed Soft Play Area
Launderettes • Piano Bar

AWARD WINNING HOLIDAYS
for all the family...

OPEN ALL YEAR

Luxury Holiday Homes for Sale
Arrange a visit: 01626 862030

Oceans
RESTAURANT & BAR

Call us now on
01626 863411
or visit our website to receive our free brochure.

DEVON

Very close to a Blue Flag beach and near to Dartmoor National Park. Ideal base for exploring Devon. Gym and sauna on site.
Facilities ♿ ⅃ 🏠 📖 🚿 🛁 📻 ⊙ 🍴 🛒 📶 🛜
Nearest Town Dawlish
Directions On the A379, 1 mile north of Dawlish and 10 miles south of Exeter.
⚏ Dawlish

DAWLISH

Leadstone Camping, Warren Road, Dawlish, Devon, EX7 0NG
Tel: 01626 864411
Email: post@leadstonecamping.co.uk
www.leadstonecamping.co.uk
Pitches For ▲ 🚐 🚗 **Total** 137
Acreage 7 **Open** 23-May **to** 01-Sep
Access Good **Site** Lev/Slope
Nearest Bus Stop (Miles) Outside
Rolling grassland in a natural secluded bowl within ½ mile of Dawlish Warrens Blue Flag Beach and nature reserve. Ideally situated for discovering Devon.
Facilities ⅃ 🏠 📖 ⊙ 🛒 📻 📶 🛜
Nearest Town Dawlish
Directions Leave the M5 at junction 30 and take signposted road A379 to Dawlish. As you approach Dawlish, turn left on brow of hill, signposted Dawlish Warren. Our site is ½ mile on the RIGHT.
⚏ Dawlish Warren

EXETER

Exeter Racecourse Caravan Club Site, Kennford, Exeter, Devon, EX6 7XS
Tel: 01392 832107
www.caravanclub.co.uk
Pitches For ▲ 🚐 🚗 **Total** 103
Acreage 10 **Open** Mar **to** Nov
Access Good **Site** Level
Access to racing. Large late night arrivals area. Near to Exeter Cathedral, Dartmoor National Park and Trago Mills Shopping Complex. Non members welcome. Booking essential.
Facilities ⅃ 🏠 📖 ⊙ 🍴 📻
Nearest Town Exeter
Directions At the top of Haldon Hill turn left sp Exeter Racecourse then immediately right, follow signs to the site.
⚏ Exeter

EXETER

Kennford International Caravan Park, Kennford, Exeter, Devon, EX6 7YN
Tel: 01392 833046
Email: ian@kennfordinternational.com
www.kennfordinternational.co.uk
Pitches For ▲ 🚐 🚗 **Total** 32
Acreage 15 **Open** All Year
Access Good **Site** Level
Nearest Bus Stop (Miles) Outside
Kennford International is a family run park close to beaches and the city of Exeter. Fishing and the villages of Kenn and Kennford nearby. 10% discount for the over 50s (not available July & August). 7 Night Special available from Sept to Nov.
Facilities ♿ ⅃ 🏠 📖 ⊙ 🛒 📻 🍴
Nearest Town Exeter
Directions From the M5 join the A38 towards Plymouth and Torquay. Exit at Kennford Services, pass the garage, go over the bridge and we are on the left. Approx. 10 minutes from Exeter.
⚏ Exeter

EXETER

Springfield Holiday Park, Tedburn St Mary, Exeter, Devon, EX6 6EW
Tel: 01647 24242
Email: enquiries@springfieldholidaypark.co.uk
www.springfieldholidaypark.co.uk
Pitches For ▲ 🚐 🚗 **Total** 100
Acreage 9 **Open** 15-Mar **to** 15-Nov
Access Good **Site** Lev/Slope
Nearest Bus Stop (Miles) Outside
Central location for the Moors or the coast, north or south Devon. 20 minutes from the seaside.
Facilities ⅃ 🏠 📖 ⊙ 🛒 📻 🍴
Directions Leave the M5 at junction 31 (Okehampton) and take the A30. Leave at left exit signposted Cheriton Bishop and follow brown tourism signs. For SAT-NAV purposes, please use Postcode EX6 6JN.
⚏ Exeter

EXETER

Teign Valley, Barley Meadow Camping & Caravanning Club Site, Crockernwell, Exeter, Devon, EX6 6NR
Tel: 01647 281629
Email: dartmoor.site@thefriendlyclub.co.uk
www.campingandcaravanningclub.co.uk/dartmoor
Pitches For ▲ 🚐 🚗 **Total** 63
Acreage 4 **Open** 14-Mar **to** 04-Nov
Access Good **Site** Level
Nearest Bus Stop (Miles) Outside
Set towards the east of the Dartmoor National Park in the heart of Devon. Non members welcome. You can also call us on 0845 130 7633.
Facilities ♿ ⅃ 🏠 📖 ⊙ 🛒 📻 🍴
Nearest Town Okehampton
Directions From Okehampton take the A30. Leave at the A382 and turn onto Hask Lane. Site is on the right before Hopperton Lane.
⚏ Exeter

EXMOUTH

St Johns Caravan & Camping Park, St Johns Road, Exmouth, Devon, EX8 5EG
Tel: 01395 263170
Email: stjohns.farm@virgin.net
www.stjohnsfarm.co.uk
Pitches For ▲ 🚐 🚗 **Total** 45
Acreage 6 **Open** Mar **to** Mid Jan
Access Good **Site** Sloping
Nearest Bus Stop (Miles) ¼
Quiet location near lovely common land with ponds and a reservoir for fishing. 2 miles to the town and beach.
Facilities ♿ ⅃ 🏠 📖 ⊙ 🛒 📻 🍴
Nearest Town Exmouth
Directions Heading towards Exmouth go through Woodbury Village and head for Budleigh Salterton and take the B3180, site is a turning off this road.
⚏ Exmouth

EXMOUTH

Webbers Park, Castle Lane, Woodbury, Exeter, Devon, EX5 1EA
Tel: 01395 232276
Email: reception@webberspark.co.uk
www.webberspark.co.uk
Pitches For ▲ 🚐 🚗 **Total** 150
Acreage 15 **Open** Mid Mar **to** End Oct
Access Good **Site** Lev/Slope
Nearest Bus Stop (Miles) ¼
Crealy Adventure Park and Exmouths sandy beach nearby.

Facilities ♿ ⅃ 🏠 📖 ⊙ 🛒 📻 🍴
Nearest Town Exmouth
Directions Leave the M5 at junction 30 and take the A376 to Exmouth. Then take the B3179 to Woodbury and follow brown tourism signs.
⚏ Exeter

GREAT TORRINGTON

Smytham Manor, Little Torrington, Devon, EX38 8PU
Tel: 01805 622110
Email: info@smytham.co.uk
www.smytham.co.uk
Pitches For ▲ 🚐 🚗 **Total** 45
Acreage 23 **Open** Mar **to** Oct
Access Good **Site** Lev/Slope
Nearest Bus Stop (Miles) Outside
Direct access to the Tarka Trail.
Facilities ♿ ⅃ 🏠 📖 ⊙ 🛒 📻 🍴
Nearest Town Great Torrington
Directions 2 miles south of Great Torrington on the A386.
⚏ Barnstaple

HOLSWORTHY

Noteworthy Caravan & Campsite, Bude Road, Holsworthy, Devon, EX22 7JB
Tel: 01409 253731
Email: enquiries@noteworthy-devon.co.uk
www.noteworthy-devon.co.uk
Pitches For ▲ 🚐 🚗 **Total** 30
Acreage 5 **Open** All Year
Access Good **Site** Slight Slope
Nearest Bus Stop (Miles) Outside
Set on a working Angora goat farm on the Devon/Cornwall border.
Facilities ⅃ 📖 ⊙ 🛒 📻 🍴
Nearest Town Holsworthy/Bude
Directions From Holsworthy take the A3072 towards Bude. The site is 2.7 miles on the right hand side.
⚏ Barnstaple

ILFRACOMBE

Ilfrcombe Caravan Club Site, West Down, Ilfracombe, Devon, EX34 8NE
Tel: 01271 862848
www.caravanclub.co.uk
Pitches For 🚐 🚗 **Total** 103
Acreage 9 **Open** Mar **to** Oct
Access Good **Site** Lev/Slope
Nearest Bus Stop (Miles) ½
Elevated position with superb views and a woodland walkway. 5 miles from a sandy beach and near to Exmoor National Park and Tarka Trail Cycle Track. Own sanitation required. Non members welcome. Booking essential.
Facilities ⅃ 🏠 📖 ⊙ 🛒 📻 🍴
Nearest Town Ilfracombe
Directions From Barnstaple take the A361, at Mullacott Cross roundabout turn right onto the A3123. Turn right at caravan sign signposted West Down, site is 1 mile on the left.
⚏ Ilfracombe

ILFRACOMBE

Napps Touring Holidays, Napps, Old Coast Road, Berrynarbor, Ilfracombe, Devon, EX34 9SW
Tel: 01271 882557
Email: enquiries@napps.fsnet.co.uk
www.napps.co.uk
Pitches For ▲ 🚐 🚗 **Total** 250
Acreage 11 **Open** Mar **to** Nov
Access Good **Site** Level
Nearest Bus Stop (Miles) Outside

Probably the most beautiful coastal setting you will see. 200 yards from the beach. Popular family site with woodland and coastal walks. Heated swimming pool, tennis, coffee shop, breakfasts, Devon cream teas and your own local pub on site.
Facilities ✦ ⌑ ▥⚷ℓ ⌐ ⏍ ☺ ⛱ ➠ ⌸ ☕
⛬ ▨ ⊘ ✕ ⛁ ♠ ⋀ ⤳ ✿⤙☂ ⛊ ✹
Directions On A399, 1¼ miles west of Combe Martin, turn right onto Old Coast Road (signposted). Site 400yds along Old Coast Road.
⇌ Barnstaple

ILFRACOMBE

Watermouth Cove Holiday Park,
Berrynarbor, Nr Ilfracombe, North Devon, EX34 9SJ
Tel: 01271 862504
Email: info@watermouthcoveholidays.co.uk
www.watermouthcoveholidays.co.uk
Pitches For ⅄ ⊕ ⇔ **Total** 90
Acreage 27 **Open** Apr **to** Oct
Access Good **Site** Lev/Slope
Nearest Bus Stop (Miles) Outside
On the headlands with stunning views across the Channel. Own cove with rock pools and caves. Adjacent to Watermouth Harbour.
Facilities ✦ ⌑ ▥⚷ℓ ⌐ ⏍ ☺ ⛱ ➠ ⌸ ☕
⛬ ▨ ⊘ ✕ ⛁ ♠ ⋀ ⤳ ✿⤙☂ ⛊ ✹
Nearest Town Ilfracombe
Directions From Barnstaple tale the A361 through to Ilfracombe and on to Watermouth Cove.
⇌ Barnstaple

ILFRACOMBE

Watermouth Valley Camping Park,
Watermouth, Ilfracombe, North Devon, EX34 9SJ
Tel: 01271 862282
Email: watermouthvalley@hotmail.co.uk
www.watermouthpark.co.uk
Pitches For ⅄ ⊕ ⇔ **Total** 155
Acreage 30 **Open** Easter **to** Mid Sept
Access Good **Site** Level
Nearest Bus Stop (Miles) Outside
Just a 5 minute walk to Watermouth Castle and harbour. Near beaches, Ilfracombe, Combe Martin and Woolacombe.
Facilities ✦ ℓ ▥⚷ ⌐ ⏍ ☺ ⛱ ➠ ⌸ ☕
⛬ ▨ ⊘ ⊘ ✕ ⛁ ♠ ⋀⤙➠
Nearest Town Ilfracombe
Directions Situated on the A399 Ilfracombe to Combe Martin road, near to Watermouth Harbour.
⇌ Barnstaple

IVYBRIDGE

Cheston Caravan & Camping Park, Folly Cross, Wrangaton Road, South Brent, Devon, TQ10 9HF
Tel: 01364 72586
Email: enquiries@chestoncaravanpark.co.uk
www.chestoncaravanpark.co.uk
Pitches For ⅄ ⊕ ⇔ **Total** 24
Acreage 1¾ **Open** 15-Mar **to** Oct
Access Good **Site** Level
Nearest Bus Stop (Miles) ¼
Set in Dartmoor National Park. Close to lots of major attractions located in Torquay, Paignton and Plymouth. Ideal for a family holiday, perfect for walking and sightseeing.
Facilities ✦ ℓ ▥⚷ℓ ⌐ ⏍ ☺ ⛱ ➠ ⌸ ✹
Nearest Town Ivybridge
Directions From Exeter, after by-passing South Brent, turn left at Wrangaton Cross slip road then right A38. From Plymouth take South Brent (Woodpecker) turn, at end of slip road turn right, go under A38 and rejoin A38 and follow directions from Exeter.

KINGSBRIDGE

Karrageen Caravan & Camping Site,
Bolberry, Malborough, Kingsbridge, Devon, TQ7 3EN
Tel: 01548 561230
Email: phil@karrageen.co.uk
www.karrageen.co.uk
Pitches For ⅄ ⊕ ⇔ **Total** 70
Acreage 7½ **Open** Easter **to** Sept
Access Good **Site** Lev/slope
Nearest Bus Stop (Miles) 1
Nearest and best park to Hope Cove, beaches 1 mile away. Situated in beautiful, scenic countryside and surrounded by superb National Trust coastline. Terraced, level, tree lined pitches. Family shower room. Hot take-away food. Superb cliff top walking. A site with a view. Caravans for hire. See our advertisement under Salcombe.
Facilities ⚷✦ℓ ▥⚷ℓ ⌐ ⏍ ☺ ➠ ⌸ ☕
⛬ ▨ ⊘ ✕⤙➠ ✹
Nearest Town Salcombe
Directions Take the A381 Kingsbridge to Salcombe road, turn sharp right into Malborough Village. In 0.6 miles turn right, after 0.9 miles the site is on the right and reception is at the house on the left.
⇌ Totnes

KINGSBRIDGE

Parkland, Sorley Green Cross, Kingsbridge, Devon, TQ7 4AF
Tel: 01548 852723
Email: enquiries@parklandsite.co.uk
www.parklandsite.co.uk
Pitches For ⅄ ⊕ ⇔ ⇔≤ **Total** 50
Acreage 3 **Open** All Year
Access Good **Site** Level
Nearest Bus Stop (Miles) ¼
Parkland, the premier AA 5 Pennant site, near Kingsbridge offers you something special in South Devon. Set in 3 acres of mature grounds, stunning views towards Salcombe and Dartmoor.
Facilities ⚷✦ℓ ▥⚷ ⌐ ⏍ ☺ ⛱ ➠ ⌸ ☕
⛬ ▨ ⊘ ⋀⤙➠ ⛁ ♠ ✹
Nearest Town Kingsbridge/Salcombe
Directions From Totnes follow the A381, main Kingsbridge road, to Sorley Green Cross. Go straight ahead and the site is 100 yards on the left.

KINGSBRIDGE

Slapton Sands Camping & Caravanning Club Site, Middle Grounds, Slapton, Kingsbridge, Devon, TQ7 2QW
Tel: 01548 580538
Email:
slapton.sandssite@thefriendlyclub.co.uk
www.campingandcaravanningclub.co.uk/slaptonsands
Pitches For ⅄ ⇔ **Total** 115
Acreage 5½ **Open** 10-Apr **to** 10-Nov
Access Good **Site** Lev/Slope
Nearest Bus Stop (Miles) ¼
Overlooking Start Bay, just a few minutes from the beach. BTB 4 Star Graded and AA 3 Pennants. Club Member Caravans Only. Non-members welcome. You can also call us on 0845 130 7633.
Facilities ⚷✦ℓ ▥⚷ℓ ⌐ ⏍ ☺ ⛱ ➠ ⌸ ☕
⛬ ⊘ ⋀⤙➠ ⛁ ♠ ✹
Nearest Town Dartmouth
Directions From Kingsbridge take the A379, site entrance is ¼ mile from the A379, beyond the brow of the hill approaching Slapton Village.
⇌ Totnes

LYDFORD

Lydford Caravan & Camping Park,
Lydford, Nr Okehampton, Devon, EX20 4BE
Tel: 01822 820497
Email: info@lydfordsite.co.uk
www.lydfordsite.co.uk
Pitches For ⅄ ⊕ ⇔ **Total** 80
Acreage 7 **Open** 15-Mar **to** 04-Nov
Access Good **Site** Level
Nearest Bus Stop (Miles) ½
Quiet beautiful park in Dartmoor National Park with beautiful views. Lydford has the deepest gorge in the South West. Ideal for visiting National Trust properties.
Facilities ⚷✦ℓ ▥⚷ℓ ⌐ ⏍ ☺ ⛱ ➠ ⌸ ☕
⛬ ⊘ ⊘⤙➠ ⛁ ♠ ⋀ ✹
Nearest Town Okehampton
Directions From the A30 (DO NOT follow SatNav) take the A386 sp Tavistock and Plymouth. After 5 miles turn right to Lydford. At the war memorial turn right, right fork, site is on the left.
⇌ Gunnislake

LYNTON

Channel View Caravan & Camping Park,
Manor Farm, Barbrook, Lynton, Devon, EX35 6LD
Tel: 01598 753349
Email: relax@channel-view.co.uk
www.channel-view.co.uk
Pitches For ⅄ ⊕ ⇔ **Total** 70
Acreage 6 **Open** 15-Mar **to** 15-Nov
Access Good **Site** Lev/Slope
Nearest Bus Stop (Miles) ½
On the edge of Exmoor overlooking Lynton and Lynmouth for panormanic views.
Facilities ⚷✦ℓ ▥⚷ℓ ⌐ ⏍ ☺ ⛱ ➠ ⌸ ☕
⛬ ⊘ ⊘ ⋀⤙➠ ⛁ ♠ ✹
Nearest Town Lynton/Lynmouth
Directions On the A39 ½ a mile from Barbrook.
⇌ Barnstaple

LYNTON

Lynton Camping & Caravanning Club Site, Caffyns Cross, Lynton, Devon, EX35 6JS
Tel: 01598 752379
Email: lynton.site@thefriendlyclub.co.uk
www.campingandcaravanningclub.co.uk/lynton
Pitches For ⅄ ⊕ ⇔ **Total** 105
Acreage 5½ **Open** 10-Apr **to** Sept
Access Good **Site** Lev/Slope
Nearest Bus Stop (Miles) ½
Overlooking the Bristol Channel. 2 miles from Lynton and Lynmouth. ETB 4 Star Graded and AA 3 Pennants. Non members welcome. You can also call us on 0845 130 7633.
Facilities ⚷✦ℓ ▥⚷ℓ ⌐ ⏍ ☺ ⛱ ➠ ⌸ ☕
⊘ ⊘ ⋀ ✿⤙➠ ⛁ ♠ ✹
Nearest Town Lynton
Directions Leave the M5 and take the A361 to Barnstaple. At South Molton turn right to Blackmoor Gate sp Lynmouth and Lynton. After 5 miles turn left at the bus shelter, turn first left then first right to camp site.
⇌ Barnstaple

MODBURY

California Cross Camping & Caravanning Club Site, California Cross, Modbury, Ivybridge, Devon, PL21 0SG
Tel: 01548 821297
Email:
california.crosssite@thefriendlyclub.co.uk
www.campingandcaravanningclub.co.uk/californiacross
Pitches For ⅄ ⊕ ⇔ **Total** 80

Acreage 2.9 **Open** 30-Apr **to** 05-Oct
Access Good **Site** Lev/Slope
Nearest Bus Stop (Miles) 3
Rural setting centrally situated in the South Hams. Close to the beaches of Salcombe and Torbay. Take-away food available two nights a week. 5 miles from Sorley Tunnel Childrens Adventure Park. Chocks needed on some pitches. BTB 4 Star Graded and AA 3 Pennants. Non members welcome. You can also call us on 0845 130 7633.
Facilities ⬥ ⟊ 🏠 ⬚ 🏪 🍴 ⊙ ⊒ 🔌 ▣ 🍽
🈂 🐕 🛒 🔥 🗑 🏗 🍴 🎤 🤟
Nearest Town Ivybridge
Directions On the A38 travelling south west take the A3121 to the crossroads, straight across to the B3196 to California Cross Hamlet. Turn left after California Cross Hamlet sign but before the petrol station, site is on the right.
� Ivybridge

MODBURY
Modbury Caravan Club Site, Higher East Leigh, Modbury, Ivybridge, Devon, PL21 0SH
Tel: 01548 830714
www.caravanclub.co.uk
Pitches For ⬚ 🚐 **Total** 113
Open Mar to Nov
Access Poor **Site** Level
Situated between moors and sea, this makes a splendid base from which to explore South Devon. Local attractions include Dart Valley Steamer Trips, Dartmoor Wildlife Park and Miniature Pony Centre. Non members welcome. Booking essential.
Facilities ⬥ ⟊ 🏠 ⬚ 🏪 🍴 ⊙ ⊒ 🔌 ▣ 🍽
🈂 🐕 🛒 🔥 🗑 🏗 🍴 🎤 🤟
Nearest Town Ivybridge
Directions From Exeter SW on A38, after 30 miles pass the Woodpecker Inn and after ½ a mile take the A3121. At the top of the slip road t lt following Broad Park sign, at Xroads go straight across, after 2½ miles continue rt just past California Cross onto B3207. Site on lt in 1 mile.
� Ivybridge

MORTEHOE
North Morte Farm Caravan & Camping Park, North Morte Road, Mortehoe, Woolacombe, Devon, EX34 7EG
Tel: 01271 870381
Email: info@northmortefarm.co.uk
www.northmortefarm.co.uk
Pitches For ⬚ 🚐 **Total** 175
Open Apr to Oct
Access Narrow **Site** Lev/Slope
Nearest Bus Stop (Miles) ¼
500 yards from Rockham Beach. Adjoining National Trust land. Ideal walking country.
Facilities ⬥ ⟊ 🏠 ⬚ 🏪 🍴 ⊙ ⊒ 🔌 ▣ 🍽
🈂 🐕 🛒 🔥 🗑 🏗 🍴 🎤 🤟
Nearest Town Woolacombe
Directions 14 miles from Barnstaple on the A361 take the B3343 and follow signs to Mortehoe. In the village turn right at the Post Office, park is 500 yards on the left.
� Barnstaple

NEWTON ABBOT
Dornafield Touring Park, Two Mile Oak, Newton Abbot, Devon, TQ12 6DD
Tel: 01803 812732
Email: enquiries@dornafield.com
www.dornafield.com
Pitches For ⋀ ⬚ 🚐 **Total** 135
Acreage 30 **Open** 13-Mar **to** 03-Jan
Access Good **Site** Level
Nearest Bus Stop (Miles) ½
Beautiful 14th Century farmhouse location with superb facilities to suit discerning caravanners and campers. Tennis court on site. Booking essential.
Facilities ⬥ ⟊ 🏠 ⬚ 🏪 🍴 ⊙ ⊒ 🔌 ▣ 🍽
🈂 🐕 🛒 🔥 🗑 🏗 🍴 🎤 🤟
Directions Take the A381 (Newton Abbott to Totnes), in 2 miles at Two Mile Oak Inn turn right. In ½ mile turn first left, site is 200 yards on the right.
� Newton Abbot

NEWTON ABBOT
Lemonford Caravan Park, Bickington, Newton Abbot, Devon, TQ12 6JR
Tel: 01626 821242
Email: info@lemonford.co.uk
www.lemonford.co.uk
Pitches For ⋀ ⬚ 🚐 🚐 **Total** 85
Acreage 7 **Open** All Year
Access Good **Site** Level
Nearest Bus Stop (Miles) Outside
In a beautiful setting and scrupulously clean. Close to Torbay and tDartmoor National Park.
Facilities ⬥ ⟊ 🏠 ⬚ 🏪 🍴 ⊙ ⊒ 🔌 ▣ 🍽
🈂 🐕 🛒 🔥 🗑 🏗 🍴 🎤 🤟
Nearest Town Ashburton
Directions From Exeter along A38 take A382 turnoff, on roundabout take 3rd exit and follow site signs to Bickington. From Plymouth take A383 turnoff, follow road for ¼ mile and turn left into site.
� Newton Abbot

NEWTON ABBOT
Woodville Caravan Park, Totnes Road, Ipplepen, Newton Abbot, Devon, TQ12 5TN
Tel: 01803 812240
Email: jo@woodvillepark.co.uk
www.woodvillepark.co.uk
Pitches For ⬚ 🚐 **Total** 26
Acreage 3½ **Open** 01-Mar **to** 02-Jan
Access Good **Site** Level
Nearest Bus Stop (Miles) Outside
Good location for touring south Devon.
Facilities ⬥ ⟊ 🏠 ⬚ 🏪 🍴 ⊙ ⊒ 🔌 ▣ 🍽
🈂 🐕 🛒 🔥 🗑 🏗 🍴 🎤 🤟
Directions From Newton Abbot take the A381 towards Totnes we are next to Fermoys Garden Centre.
� Newton Abbot

OKEHAMPTON
Bridestowe Caravan Park, Bridestowe, Nr Okehampton, Devon, EX20 4ER
Tel: 01837 861261
www.glebepark.co.uk
Pitches For ⋀ ⬚ 🚐 **Total** 53
Open Mar to Dec **Access** Good **Site** Level
Nearest Bus Stop (Miles) ½

Dartmoor National Park 2 miles, ideal for walking, cycling, horse riding, fishing and touring Devon and Cornwall. Within easy reach of coastal resorts.
Facilities ⟊ 🏠 ⬚ 🏪 🍴 ⊙ ⊒ 🔌 ▣ 🍽
🈂 🐕 🛒 🔥 🗑 🏗 🎤
Nearest Town Bude
Directions Leave M5 for A30 to Okehampton 3 miles west of Okehampton turn off A30 to Bridestowe village, follow camping signs to site.

OKEHAMPTON
Bundu Camping & Caravan Park, Sourton Down, Okehampton, Devon, EX20 4HT
Tel: 01837 861747
Email: bundu@btconect.com
www.bundu.co.uk
Pitches For ⋀ ⬚ 🚐 **Total** 38
Acreage 4½ **Open** All Year
Access Good **Site** Level
Nearest Bus Stop (Miles) ¼
Situated with access to Dartmoor and adjacent to National Cycleway Route 27. Ideal for touring Devon and Cornwall.
Facilities ⬥ ⟊ 🏠 ⬚ 🏪 🍴 ⊙ ⊒ 🔌 ▣ 🍽
🈂 🐕 🛒 ✕ 🔥 🗑 🏗 🍴 🎤
Nearest Town Okehampton
Directions On the A30 west, turn off at first slip road taking the A386 to Tavistock. Take first turn left to Sourton Down, site is at the end of the lane.
� Okehampton

PAIGNTON
Beverley Park Holiday Centre, Goodrington Road, Paignton, Devon, TQ4 7JE
Tel: 01803 661973
Email: info@beverley-holidays.co.uk
www.beverley-holidays.co.uk
Pitches For ⋀ ⬚ 🚐 **Total** 180
Acreage 9½ **Open** Feb **to** Dec
Access Good **Site** Level
Nearest Bus Stop (Miles) ¼
Views across Torbay. Indoor heated swimming pool, tennis court and sauna on site.
Facilities ⬥ ⟊ 🏠 ⬚ 🏪 🍴 ⊙ ⊒ 🔌 ▣ 🍽
🈂 🐕 🛒 ✕ 🍷 🍴 ♣ 🏗 🔥 ⚓ 🎤 🏊 🤟
🤟
Nearest Town Paignton
Directions 2 miles south of Paignton (ring road) A3022. Turn left into Goodrington Road.
� Paignton

PAIGNTON
Higher Well Farm Holiday Park, Stoke Gabriel, Totnes, Devon, TQ9 6RN
Tel: 01803 782289
www.higherwellfarmholidaypark.co.uk
Pitches For ⋀ ⬚ 🚐 **Total** 80
Acreage 8 **Open** Easter **to** Oct
Access Good **Site** Lev/Slope
Nearest Bus Stop (Miles) ¼
Within 4 miles of Torbays beaches, 1 mile from the village of Stoke Gabriel and the River Dart.
Facilities ⬥ ✖ ⟊ 🏠 ⬚ 🏪 🍴 ⊙ ⊒ 🔌 ▣ 🍽
🈂 🐕 🛒 🔥 🗑 🏗
Nearest Town Paignton

Directions From Paignton take A385 towards Totnes, turn off left at Parkers Arms. Go 1½ miles then turn left again, site is 200 yards down road.
⇥ Paignton

PAIGNTON

Hoburne Torbay, Grange Road, Goodrington, Paignton, Devon, TQ4 7JP
Tel: 01803 558010
Email: enquiries@hoburne.com
www.hoburne.com
Pitches For 🚐 🚙 **Total** 139
Acreage 65 **Open** 26-Feb **to** 30-Jan
Access Good **Site** Lev/Slope
Nearest Bus Stop (Miles) 0.25
Park with many facilities. Panoramic views over Torbay and within walking distance of Goodrington beach. Just a short drive to Dartmoor.
Facilities ⨍ 🎏 🖩 🏠 ⌗ ☉ ⤵ 🅰 🔲 🛝
🏪 🈂 🅿 ✕ ⛾ 🎪 🔥 ⚡ ☂ 🐾 🔌 ☽ ☎
Nearest Town Paignton

Directions From junc 31 of M5, travel south for approx 20 miles on A380 to junction with A385. Continue south on A380 (Paignton Ring Road) for 1 mile, turn left into Goodrington Road by Esso Filling Station. After ¾ miles turn left into Grange Road and follow signs to park.
⇥ Paignton

PUTSBOROUGH

Putsborough Sands Caravan Park, Manor Farm, Putsborough, Braunton, North Devon, EX33 1LB
Tel: 01271 890230
Email: rob@putsborough.com
www.putsborough.com
Pitches For 🚐 **Total** 25
Acreage 2 **Open** 01-Apr **to** 10-Oct
Access Poor **Site** Level
Nearest Bus Stop (Miles) 1
Adjacent to the multi award winning Putsborough Sands. Unrivalled views over the Atlantic. Booking is essential. single carriageway road for last mile.

Facilities ⛵ ⨍ 🎏 🖩 🏠 ⌗ ☉ ⤵ 🅰 🔲 🛝
🏪 🈂 🅿 ✕ ☂ 🔲 🔲 ⚡ 📶
Nearest Town Croyde
Directions From Braunton take the B3231 Croyde road and follow signs.
⇥ Barnstaple

SALCOMBE

Alston Farm Camping & Caravan Site, Nr Salcombe, Kingsbridge, Devon, TQ7 3BJ
Tel: 01548 561260
Email: info@alstoncampsite.co.uk
www.alstoncampsite.co.uk
Pitches For ⛺ 🚐 🚙 **Total** 200
Acreage 15 **Open** Easter **to** Oct
Access Good **Site** Level
Nearest Bus Stop (Miles) 1
Secluded, sheltered site. Dish washing facilities. You can also contact us on Mobile: 07808 030921.
Facilities ⛵ ⨍ 🎏 🖩 🏠 ⌗ ☉ ⤵ 🅰 🔲 🛝
🏪 🈂 🅿 🔲 ⤵ 🔲 ☽ ☂ ⚡ 📶
Nearest Town Salcombe

Family Camping on the Coast
www.leadstonecamping.co.uk
www.dawlishwarren.com

Directions Signposted on left of A381 between Kingsbridge and Salcombe towards Salcombe.
⇌ Totnes

SALCOMBE

Higher Rew Touring Caravan & Camping Park, Rew, Malborough, Kingsbridge, South Devon, TQ7 3BW
Tel: 01548 842681
Email: enquiries@higherrew.co.uk
www.higherrew.co.uk
Pitches For ⋀ ⊕ ⊟ **Total** 90
Acreage 6 **Open** Easter **to** Oct
Access Fair **Site** Lev/Slope
Sloping Park with level pitches. Only 1 mile from the coastal path and Salcombe Estuary.
Facilities ⨍ 🕮 ♿ ⌂ ☺ ⊿ ☎ 🖸 ☎
🕮 🅾 🌢 ⚲ ⊞
Nearest Town Salcombe
Directions From Kingsbridge take the A381 towards Salcombe. Im Malborough turn sharp right through the village towards Soar, after 1 mile turn left.
⇌ Totnes

SEATON

Ashdown Caravan Park, Colyton Hill, Colyton, Devon, EX24 6HY
Tel: 01297 20292
Email:
ashdowncaravanpark@btinternet.com
Pitches For ⊕ ⊟ **Total** 80
Acreage 7 **Open** Apr **to** Nov
Access Good **Site** Level
Nearest Bus Stop (Miles) 1
Pecorama, beach, Seaton Tramway.Dog walking area nearest village Beer.
Facilities ⨍ ⌂ 🕮 🕮 ♿ ⌂ ☺ ☎
🕮 🅾 ⊞ 🌢 🖸
Nearest Town Seaton
Directions A3052 north of Seaton.
⇌ Axminster

SEATON

Berry Barton Caravan & Camping Park, Berry Barton, Branscombe, Seaton, Devon, EX12 3BD
Tel: 01297 680208
Email: tmandaewhite@btconnect.com
www.berrybarton.co.uk
Pitches For ⋀ ⊕ ⊟ **Total** 0
Acreage 16 **Open** 15-Mar **to** 15-Nov
Access Good **Site** Level
Nearest Bus Stop (Miles) ¼
Situated on a working farm in an area of outstanding natural beauty, with our land finishing at the top of the pebble beach at Littlecombe Shute. 1 mile of coastline and the Jurassic Coast for good walks. New washing up room.
Facilities ⨍ 🕮 ♿ ⌂ ☺ ⊿ ☎ 🖸 ☎ ⊞ ⊞
Nearest Town Seaton/Sidmouth
Directions From the M5 at Exeter take the A3052 to Branscombe turning and turn off right following brown tourism signs. At the T-Junction turn left, after 10 metres turn right, at the next T-Junction turn left and the site is on the right after ½ a mile, Berry Barton.
⇌ Honiton

SIDMOUTH

Kings Down Tail Caravan & Camping Park, Salcombe Regis, Sidmouth, Devon, EX10 0PD
Tel: 01297 680313
Email: info@kingsdowntail.co.uk
www.kingsdowntail.co.uk
Pitches For ⋀ ⊕ ⊟ **Total** 100
Acreage 5 **Open** 15-Mar **to** 15-Nov
Access Good **Site** Level
Nearest Bus Stop (Miles) Outside
Heated shower block. Local fishermen are happy to take people out on boat trips. Ideal centre for East Devon and West Dorset. Pets are welcome if kept on a lead.
Facilities ⨍ 🕮 🕮 ♿ ⌂ ☺ ⊿ ☎ 🖸 ☎
🕮 🅾 🌢 ⚲ ⊞
Nearest Town Sidmouth
Directions On the A3052 3 miles east of Sidmouth, opposite Branscombe Water Tower. Please note that we are NOT in Salcombe Regis Village.
⇌ Honiton

SEATON

Leacroft Touring Park, Colyton Hill, Colyton, Devon, EX24 6HY
Tel: 01297 552823
www.leacrofttouringpark.co.uk
Pitches For ⋀ ⊕ ⊟ **Total** 138
Acreage 10 **Open** Apr **to** Sept
Access Good **Site** Sloping
Nearest Bus Stop (Miles) 2
Quiet, peaceful site in open countryside. Picturesque villages to explore and woodland walks nearby.
Facilities ⨍ ⨍ 🕮 🕮 ♿ ⌂ ☺ ⊿ ☎ 🖸 ☎
🕮 🅾 🌢 ⚲ ⊞ 🌢 ⚲ 🛜
Nearest Town Colyton
Directions A3052 Sidmouth to Lyme Regis road, 2 miles west of Seaton. Turn left at Stafford Cross international caravan sign, site is 1 mile on the right.
⇌ Axminster

SIDMOUTH

Oakdown Country Holiday Park, Weston, Sidmouth, Devon, EX10 0PT
Tel: 01297 680387
Email: enquiries@oakdown.co.uk
www.oakdown.co.uk
Pitches For ⋀ ⊕ ⊟ ⊟ ⊱ **Total** 150
Acreage 16 **Open** Apr **to** Oct
Access Good **Site** Level
Nearest Bus Stop (Miles) ¼
Welcome to Oakdown, a Caravan Holiday Park of the Year Winner - SIDMOUTHS MULTI AWARD WINNING PARK near the Jurassic Coast World Heritage Site and beautiful Weston Valley - lovely cliff walks. Oakmead Par 3 Golf Course. Field trail to nearby world famous Donkey Sanctuary. Luxurious Holiday Caravans to let. Awards for 2012/13: ETB 5 Star Grading, AA 5 Pennant De-Luxe Park, David Bellamy Gold.
Facilities ⨍ ⨍ 🕮 🕮 ♿ ⌂ ☺ ⊿ ☎ 🖸 ☎
🕮 🅾 🍴 📺 🌢 🛒 ♿ ⊞ 🖸 🖸 🌢 ⚲ 🌢
Directions 1½ miles east of Sidford on A3052, take the second Weston turning at the Oakdown sign. Site 50 yards on left. Also sp with international Caravan/Camping signs.
⇌ Honiton

SIDMOUTH
Putts Corner Caravan Club Site, Sidbury, Sidmouth, Devon, EX10 0QQ
Tel: 01404 42875
www.caravanclub.co.uk
Pitches For ⬠ 🚐 **Total** 118
Acreage 7 **Open** Mar **to** Nov
Access Good **Site** Lev/Slope
Nearest Bus Stop (Miles) ¼
Quiet site in pretty surroundings where wildlife and flowers abound. Plenty of walks from the site. Boules pitch, water softening plant and water supply from borehole. 200 yards from a pub. Near the Donkey Sanctuary. Non members welcome. Booking essential.
Facilities 🛁 ✆ 🖤 ⊞ 🚻 🕭 ☻
🕃 🅟 ⊙ 🈯 ➔ 🚮 ⊟ 🛈 🛜
Nearest Town Sidmouth
Directions From east on A30 Honiton bypass, turn off via slip road at sp Sidmouth A375, at end of slip road turn left then 100 yards and turn left again, after 350 yards turn right onto A375. At Hare & Hounds Inn turn right onto B3174, site is ¼ mile on the right.
⚓ Sidmouth

SIDMOUTH
Salcombe Regis Camping & Caravan Park, Salcombe Regis, Sidmouth, Devon, EX10 0JH
Tel: 01395 514303
Email: contact@salcombe-regis.co.uk
www.salcombe-regis.co.uk
Pitches For ⚑ ⬠ 🚐 **Total** 100
Acreage 16 **Open** 11-Mar **to** 02-Nov
Access Good **Site** Level
A park with peace and quiet. Just a 5 minute walk from the Jurassic Coastal Path, and a 5-10 minute drive from Select Sidmouth. Ideally based for touring East Devon. Static caravans for hire.
Facilities ✆ ⊞ 🖤 ⊞ 🚻 🕭 ⊙ 🍴 🚮 🛈 🕆
🕃 🅟 ⊙ 🄰 ➔ 🚮 ⊟ 🛜 🕭 🛜
Nearest Town Sidmouth
Directions From Exeter M5 take the A3052 through Sidford towards Lyme Regis. Take second turning to Salcombe Regis, on the left after Golf Range.
⚓ Honiton or Exeter

SLAPTON
Sea View Campsite, Newlands Farm, Slapton, Nr Dartmouth, Devon, TQ7 2RB
Tel: 01548 580366
Email: cades@devon-camping.co.uk
www.camping-devon.com
Pitches For ⚑ ⬠ 🚐 **Total** 45
Acreage 10 **Open** 23-May **to** Sept
Access Good **Site** Level
Nearest Bus Stop (Miles) ½
We have a friendly, uncommercialised, quiet site overlooking beautiful countryside and sea. Within 1 mile of glorious beaches, cliff walks and a nature reserve. Woodlands Leisure Centre is close by with fun for all the family.
Facilities ✆ 🖤 ⊞ 🕭 ⊙ 🍴 🄰 🚮 ⊟
Nearest Town Dartmouth

Directions From Totnes take the A381 towards Kingsbridge, after Halwell Village take the fourth left signposted Slapton. Go 4 miles to Buckland Cross, proceed for ¼ mile, site is on the left hand side.

SOUTH MOLTON
Riverside Caravan & Camping Park, Marsh Lane, North Molton Road, South Molton, Devon, EX36 3HQ
Tel: 01769 579269
Email: relax@exmoorriverside.co.uk
www.www.exmoorriverside.co.uk
Pitches For ⚑ ⬠ 🚐 🚐⌁ **Total** 100
Acreage 70 **Open** All Year
Access Good **Site** Level
Nearest Bus Stop (Miles) Outside
Lakes - rivers on site, woodland - valley walks on and from site, ideal touring.
Facilities 🛁 ✆ 🖤 ⊞ 🖤 🕭 🕆 ⊙ 🍴 🚮 🛈 🛁
🕃 🕃 🅟 ⊙ 🈯 🕆 🍴 🄰 🔅 ➔ 🚮 ⊟ 🛈 🖋 🕭
🕭 🛜
Nearest Town South Molton
⚓ Barnstaple

SOUTH MOLTON
Riverside Caravan and Camping Park. Marsh Lane, North Molton Road, South Molton, Devon, EX36 3HQ
Tel: 01769 579269
Email: relax@exmoorriverside..co.uk
www.www.exmoorriverside..co.uk
Pitches For ⚑ ⬠ 🚐 🚐⌁ **Total** 100
Acreage 70 **Open** All year
Access Good **Site** Level
Nearest Bus Stop (Miles) Outside
River, fishing lakes, woods, ideal touring, valley walks.
Facilities 🛁 ✆ 🖤 ⊞ 🖤 🕭 🕆 ⊙ 🍴 🚮
🕃 🕃 🅟 ⊙ 🈯 🕆 🍴 🄰 🔅 ➔ 🚮 ⊟ 🛈 🖋 🕭
🕭 🛜
Nearest Town South Moulton
Directions M5 turn off at junc. 27 onto A361 stay on this road until you see the sign North Moulton and Riverside Caravan and Camping Park.
⚓ Barnstaple

SOUTH MOLTON
Romansleigh Holiday Park, Odam Hill, South Molton, Devon, EX36 4NB
Tel: 01769 550259
Email: romhols@btconnect.com
www.romansleigh.com
Pitches For ⚑ ⬠ 🚐 **Total** 20
Acreage 14 **Open** 15-Mar **to** 31-Oct
Access poor **Site** Lev/slope
Nearest Bus Stop (Miles) outside
Ideal for touring,countryside site 35 minites from the North Devon Coast.
Facilities ✆ 🖤⌁ 🕭 🕆 ⊙ 🍴 🛈 🕭
🕃 🅟 ⊙ 🈯 🕆 🍴 🄰 🔅 ➔ 🚮 ⊟ 🛜
Nearest Town South Moulton
Directions Take the B3137 South Molton to Witheridge road. Site is signposted right approximately 4 miles.
⚓ Kings Nympton

TAVISTOCK
Langstone Manor Caravan & Camping Park, Langstone Manor, Moortown, Tavistock, Devon, PL19 9JZ
Tel: 01822 613371
Email: web@langstone-manor.co.uk
www.langstone-manor.co.uk
Pitches For ⚑ ⬠ 🚐 **Total** 40
Acreage 5½ **Open** 15-Mar **to** 15-Nov
Access Good **Site** Level
Nearest Bus Stop (Miles) 1½
Direct access onto Dartmoor. Quiet, friendly park with views over moor and farmland. Bar and evening meals. Dogs welcome. ETB 5 Star Graded and AA 4 Pennants.
Facilities 🛁 ✆ 🖤 ⊞ 🖤 🕭 🕆 ⊙ 🍴 🚮 🛈 🕭
🕃 🅟 ⊙ 🈯 🕆 🍴 🄰 ➔ 🚮 ⊟ 🛈 🕭 🔅 🛜
Directions Take the B3357 from Tavistock towards Princetown, after approx. 2 miles turn right at crossroads, pass over the cattle grid, continue up the hill then turn left following signs for Langstone Manor. We are ½ mile on the right.
⚓ Plymouth

TAVISTOCK
Tavistock Camping & Caravanning Club Site, Higher Longford, Moorshop, Tavistock, Devon, PL19 9LQ
Tel: 01822 618672
Email: tavistock.site@thefriendlyclub.co.uk
www.campingandcaravanningclub.co.uk/tavistock
Pitches For ⚑ ⬠ 🚐 **Total** 80
Acreage 6 **Open** All Year
Access Good **Site** Level
Nearest Bus Stop (Miles) Outside
Lying on the west side of the Dartmoor National Park, ideal for walkers and cyclists. Non members welcome. You can also call us on 0845 130 7633.
Facilities 🛁 ✆ 🖤 ⊞ 🖤 🕭 🕆 ⊙ 🍴 🚮 🛈 🕭
🕃 🅟 ⊙ 🈯 🕆 🍴 🄰 ➔ 🚮 ⊟ 🛈 🔅 🛜
Nearest Town Tavistock
Directions From Tavistock take the B3357 towards the National Park, site is approx. 2 miles on the right, signposted.
⚓ Plymouth

TAVISTOCK
Woodovis Park, Gulworthy, Tavistock, Devon, PL19 8NY
Tel: 01822 832968
Email: info@woodovis.com
www.woodovis.com
Pitches For ⚑ ⬠ 🚐 **Total** 50
Acreage 14 **Open** Apr **to** Oct
Access Good **Site** Level
Nearest Bus Stop (Miles) ½
5 Star BTB Graded Park. Quiet, rural site with outstanding views. Near to Dartmoor, coasts and Cornwall. Excellent facilities, free showers, laundry/washing-up room. Shop, off-license, farm produce, bread/croissants baked on site. Heated indoor pool, Infrared therapy, sauna and jacuzzi. Petanque court. Outdoor table tennis
Facilities 🛁 ✆ 🖤 ⊞ 🖤 🕭 🕆 ⊙ 🍴 🚮 🛈 🕭
🕃 🅟 ⊙ 🈯 🕆 🍴 🄰 🔅 ➔ 🚮 ⊟ 🛈 🔅 🛜
Nearest Town Tavistock

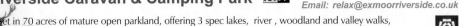

Directions Take A390 Liskeard road from Tavistock, after 3 miles turn right at the roundabout.
≠ Plymouth/Gunnislake

TEIGNMOUTH

Coast View Holiday Park, Torquay Road, Shaldon, Teignmouth, South Devon, TQ14 0BG
Tel: 01626 818350
Email: holidays@coastview.co.uk
www.coastview.co.uk
Pitches For ⚏ ⚏ Total 250
Acreage 18 **Open** 18-Mar
Access Good **Site** Lev/Slope
Nearest Bus Stop (Miles) Outside
Near the beach with fantastic views.
Facilities ƒ ⛒ ⬚ ⌂ ⊙ ⊡ ⚏ ♔
⚒ ⬚ ⊟ ⚑ ✕ ⊽ ⬚ ♠ ⚒ ⌇ ⟶ ⊡ ⬚
Nearest Town Teignmouth
Directions On the A379 between Teignmouth and Torquay.
≠ Teignmouth

TIVERTON

Minnows Touring Park, Sampford Peverell, Tiverton, Devon, EX16 7EN
Tel: 01884 821770
www.minnowstouringpark.co.uk
Pitches For ⚏ ⚏ ⚏ ⚏⚹ Total 60
Acreage 5½ **Open** 05-Mar **to** 29-Oct
Access Good **Site** Level

Nearest Bus Stop (Miles) ¼
Alongside the Grand Western Canal and National Cycle Way, ideal for walking, cycling, fishing, canoeing and bird watching. Centrally placed for coasts, Exmoor and Dartmoor.
Facilities ⚏ ⚹ ƒ ⬚ ⬚ ⬚⌂ ⌂ ⊙ ⊟ ⚏
⊡ ⬚ ⚒ ⚏ ⬚ ⬚ ♠ ⟶ ⬚ ⬚ ⚏ ⟁
Nearest Town Tiverton
Directions Leave the M5 at junction 27 and take the A361 signposted Tiverton and Barnstaple. After 500 yards take the slip road signposted Sampford Peverell, turn right at the mini roundabout, site is ¼ of a mile ahead.
≠ Tiverton Parkway

TIVERTON

West Middlewick Farm Caravans & Camping, West Middlewick Farm, Nomansland, Tiverton, Devon, EX16 8NP
Tel: 01884 861235
Email: stay@westmiddlewick.co.uk
www.westmiddlewick.co.uk
Pitches For ⚏ ⚏ ⚏ Total 25
Acreage 3½ **Open** All Year
Access Good **Site** Level
Nearest Bus Stop (Miles) Outside
Working family farm with lovely walks. Fishing ½ mile. Ideal touring. Log cabins B&B.
Facilities ⚏ ƒ ⬚ ⬚⌂ ⌂ ⊙ ⬚ ⚏
⚒ ⟶ ⬚ ⚏ ⟁

Nearest Town Tiverton
Directions Leave the A361 at junction 27 for Tiverton, then take the B3137 to Witheridge. 9 miles from Tiverton.
≠ Tiverton Parkway

TORQUAY

Widdicombe Farm Touring Park, The Ring Road (A380), Paignton, Torquay, Devon, TQ3 1ST
Tel: 01803 558325
Email: info@widdicombefarm.co.uk
www.widdicombefarm.co.uk
Pitches For ⚏ ⚏ ⚏ ⚏⚹ Total 200
Acreage 8 **Open** Mid Mar **to** Mid Oct
Access Good **Site** Level
Nearest Bus Stop (Miles) Park Entrance
Near beaches. Ideal for touring Torquay, Paignton, Brixham and Dartmoor.
Facilities ⚏ ƒ ⬚ ⬚ ⬚⌂ ⌂ ⊙ ⊟ ⚏ ♔
⚒ ⚏ ⊟ ✕ ⟶ ⬚ ⬚ ⬚⚹ ⚏ ⟁
Nearest Town Torquay
Directions Follow A380 towards Torquay on the new South Devon Link Road. Follow signs Paignton, Brixham and Totnes. T 2nd roundabout, take 4th exit and follow signs to Widdicombe Farm.
≠ Torquay

Escape to North Devon

Right next to Woolacombe's three miles of golden sandy beach

WOOLACOMBE BAY
Britain's best beach
HOLIDAY PARKS

You won't believe how high I climbed, I could see for miles!

What we've got to offer...

- Sea view camping & touring pitches
- Level pitches with easy access
- 400 all weather pitches
- 16 amp electric hookups
- Modern amenity blocks
- Over 40 **FREE** activities

 Stay at one Park and you get to use the facilities on all four of our award winning Holiday Parks...

Golden Coast | Woolacombe Bay | Twitchen House | Easewell Farm

Pitches from just £6 per night

Call 01271 872 303
or visit woolacombe.com

We're here

WOOLACOMBE BAY
HOLIDAY PARKS

DEVON

TOTNES

Steamer Quay Caravan Club Site,
Steamer Quay Road, Totnes, Devon, TQ9 5AL
Tel: 01803 862738
www.caravanclub.co.uk
Pitches For ⚐ ⛺ **Total** 43
Acreage 3 **Open** Mar **to** Oct
Access Good **Site** Level
Nearest Bus Stop (Miles) Outside
Quiet site with lovely views, just a short walk from Totnes centre. Close to Paignton Zoo, Dart River Cruises and South Devon Railway. Non members welcome. Booking essential.
Facilities
Nearest Town Totnes
Directions From A38 take either A384 at Buckfastleigh or A385 at South Brent, both roads become A385 at Dartington. In Totnes cross the railway bridge and t rt at r/about, in 300 yds t lt over the bridge, t rt into Seymour Road, t rt into Steamer Quay Road.
➤ Totnes

UFFCULME

Waterloo Cross Caravan Park, Uffculme, Devon, EX15 3ES
Tel: 01884 841342
Pitches For ⚐ ⛺ **Total** 50
Acreage 50 **Open** Mar **to** Feb
Access Good **Site** Level
Nearest Bus Stop (Miles) Outside
Ideal for touring.
Facilities
Nearest Town Tiverton
Directions 6 miles from Tiverton and Cullompton.
➤ Tiverton Parkway

UMBERLEIGH

Umberleigh Camping & Caravanning Club Site, Over Weir, Umberleigh, Devon, EX37 9DU
Tel: 01769 560009
Email:
umberleigh.site@thefriendlyclub.co.uk
www.campingandcaravanningclub.co.uk/umberleigh
Pitches For ⚐ ⛺ **Total** 60
Acreage 3 **Open** 10-Apr **to** 10-Nov
Access Good **Site** Lev/Slope
Nearest Bus Stop (Miles) Entrance
The site enjoys a peaceful and relaxing atmosphere, situated between Exmoor and Dartmoor National Park. Superb golden beaches nearby. BTB 4 Star Graded and AA 3 Pennants. Non members welcome. You can also call us on 0845 130 7633.
Facilities
Nearest Town Barnstaple
Directions From Barnstaple take the A377 and turn right at Umberleigh nameplate.
➤ Umberleigh

WOOLACOMBE

Damage Barton, Mortehoe, Woolacombe, Devon, EX34 7EJ
Tel: 01271 870502
Email: info@damagebarton.co.uk
www.damagebarton.co.uk
Pitches For ⚐ ⛺ **Total** 155
Acreage 16 **Open** 15-Mar **to** 05-Nov
Access Good **Site** Lev/Slope
Nearest Bus Stop (Miles) Outside
Peaceful site with good views, wild flowers and birds. Access to a network of footpaths including the coastal path.
Facilities

Nearest Town Woolacombe
Directions Take the A361 from Barnstaple and turn left at the Mullacott Cross roundabout onto the B3343 signposted Woolacombe and Mortehoe. After 1¾ miles turn right signposted Mortehoe, site is on the right after approx. 1 mile.
➤ Barnstaple

WOOLACOMBE

Easewell Farm Holiday Village & Golf Club Station Road, Mortehoe, Woolacombe, Devon, EX34 7EH
Tel: 0844 7700 367
Email: goodtimes@woolacombe.com
www.woolacombe.com/cades
Pitches For ⚐ ⛺ **Total** 318
Open 24-Mar **to** 30-Oct
Access Good **Site** Level
Nearest Bus Stop (Miles) Outside
A haven of peace and tranquillity with unforgettable views over the surrounding countryside and coastline. Close to **"Britain's best beach"** voted by TripAdvisor in 2015 & 2016. There are all-weather pitches and heated shower block, big private showers, disabled shower, washing up areas and launderette. Plus indoor heated pool, sports bar, adventure play area, professional golf course and lots more!
Facilities
Nearest Town Woolacombe
Directions From Barnstaple take the A361 Ilfracombe road to the junction with the B3343 at Mullacott Cross. Turn first left signposted Woolacombe, after 1¾ miles turn right to Mortehoe. Park is 1¼ miles on the right.
➤ Barnstaple

WOOLACOMBE

Golden Coast Holiday Village, Station Road, Woolacombe, Devon, EX34 7HW
Tel: 01271 872303
Email: goodtimes@woolacombe.com
www.woolacombe.com
Pitches For ⚐ ⛺ **Total** 89
Open 10-Feb **to** 30-Oct
Access Good **Site** Lev/Slope
Nearest Bus Stop (Miles) Outside
Award winning Park situated next to **"Britain's best beach"** voted by Trip Advisor in 2015 & 2016. Also voted as **"Britain's Best Holiday Park"** in 2015! Family owned Park has fantastic entertainment, excellent facilities and all-weather activities, many of them FREE! There's a Sports Complex, surfing simulator and more! Pitches are all-weather, have heated shower blocks, launderettes and chemical disposal facilities.
Facilities
Directions Take the A361 to Barnstaple and follow signs for Ilfracombe, take the Woolacombe junction from Mullacott Cross.

➤ Barnstaple

WOOLACOMBE

Little Roadway Farm, Woolacombe, Devon, EX34 7HL
Tel: 01271 870313
Email: enquiries@littleroadway.co.uk
www.littleroadway.co.uk
Pitches For ⚐ ⛺ ⛺ **Total** 180
Acreage 15 **Open** Mar **to** 01-Nov
Access Good **Site** Level
Nearest Bus Stop (Miles) 1
Within 1 mile of Woolacombe beach, which is perfect for families and surfing.
Facilities

Nearest Town Woolacombe
Directions Woolacombe is off the main road to Ilfracombe via Braunton.
➤ Barnstaple

WOOLACOMBE

Twitchen House Holiday Village, Station Road, Mortehoe, Woolacombe, North Devon, EX34 7ES
Tel: 01271 872303
Email: goodtimes@woolacombe.com
www.woolacombe.com
Pitches For ⚐ ⛺ ⛺ **Total** 333
Acreage 20 **Open** 24-Mar **to** 30-Oct
Access Good **Site** Sloping
Nearest Bus Stop (Miles) Outside
Located next to **"Britain's best beach"** voted by Trip Advisor in 2015 & 2016. Footpath to the sea, excellent facilities and activities, many FREE! All-weather pitches, sea views, sauna, steam room, shower block, hairdryers, fully equipped launderettes, easy access, restaurant, bars, heated pools, flume and SplashPad, shop, surf lessons and more! Recently invested £2.5 million in a family all-weather entertainment centre.
Facilities
Nearest Town Woolacombe
Directions From Barnstaple/Ilfracombe road (A361) to junction with B3343 at Mullacott Cross, first left signposted Woolacombe for 1¾ miles, then right signposted Mortehoe. Park is 1¼ miles on left.
➤ Barnstaple

WOOLACOMBE

Woolacombe Bay Holiday Village, Sandy Lane, Woolacombe, Devon, EX34 7AH
Tel: 01271 872303
Email: goodtimes@woolacombe.com
www.woolacombe.com
Pitches For ⚐ **Total** 119
Open 24-Mar **to** 10-Sep
Nearest Bus Stop (Miles) Outside
Stunning sea views next to **"Britain's best beach"** voted by TripAdvisor in 2015 & 2016. All-weather activities, many of them FREE! Invested £4 million in 2016 with a **NEW** entertainment complex, sea view terrace, cinema, fitness gym, craft centre, soft play area and indoor fun pool. Shower block has under floor heating, hairdryers, fully equipped launderettes and spotless washing up areas
Facilities
Nearest Town Woolacombe
Directions From Barnstaple take the A361 Ilfracombe road to the junction of the B3343 at Mullacott Cross. Turn first left signposted Woolacombe, after 1¾ miles turn right to Mortehoe, Park is 1 mile on the left.

➤ Barnstaple

WOOLACOMBE

Woolacombe Sands Holiday Park, Beach Road, Woolacombe, Devon, EX34 7AF
Tel: 01271 870569
Email:
lifesabeach@woolacombesands.co.uk
www.woolacombesands.co.uk
Pitches For ⚐ ⛺ ⛺ **Total** 147
Open Mar **to** Nov
Access Good **Site** Lev/Slope
Nearest Bus Stop (Miles) Outside
Woolacombes beach.
Facilities
Nearest Town Woolacombe
Directions On main A361 road.
➤ Barnstaple

DORSET

BLANDFORD

The Inside Park, Blandford, Dorset, DT11 9AD
Tel: 01258 453719
Email: mail@theinsidepark.co.uk
www.theinsidepark.co.uk
Pitches For Å ⏢ 🚐 **Total** 100
Acreage 13 **Open** Easter **to** Oct
Access Good **Site** Lev/Slope
Rural environment with extensive wildlife. Ideal for touring.
Facilities ♿ �ℹ ⊞🛉♠🖭 ⊙ ⛽ 🔲 ☎
♨ ⌨ 🖸 🏪 🔥 ✿🍴🖃 🖳 ⚓
Nearest Town Blandford Forum
Directions 1¼ miles south west of Blandford on the road to Winterborne Stickland. Signposted from junction of A350 and A354 on Blandford bypass.

BOURNEMOUTH

Charris Camping & Caravan Park, Candys Lane, Corfe Mullen, Wimborne, Dorset, BH21 3EF
Tel: 01202 885970
Email: bookings@charris.co.uk
www.charris.co.uk
Pitches For Å ⏢ 🚐 **Total** 45
Acreage 3 **Open** All Year
Access Good **Site** Lev/Slope
Nearest Bus Stop (Miles) ¼
AA 3 Pennants and Caravan & Camping Club listed. Good central site convienient for the coast and New Forest. Poole 7½ miles and Bournemouth 8¼ miles. Cafe/restaurant close by.
Facilities ℹ 🖭🖺🖀🖼 ⊙⊣🖭 🔲 ☎
♨ ⌨ 🖸 🏪 🖃 🖳
Nearest Town Wimborne
Directions A31 Wimborne bypass 1 mile west of Wimborne. Signs for entrance.
🚆 Poole

BOURNEMOUTH

St Leonards Farm, Ringwood Road, West Moors, Ferndown, Dorset, BH22 0AQ
Tel: 01202 872637
Email: enquiries_stleonards@yahoo.co.uk
www.stleonardsfarm.biz
Pitches For Å ⏢ 🚐 **Total** 120
Acreage 12 **Open** Apr **to** Oct
Access Good **Site** Level
Nearest Bus Stop (Miles) Outside
AA 3 Pennants.
Facilities ♿ ℹ 🖭🖺🖀🖼 ⊙⊣🖭 🔲 ☎
♨ 🖸 🏪 ✿🖃 🖳 ⚓ ✿ ⚓
Nearest Town Bournemouth
Directions On the A31 4 miles west of Ringwood, opposite the Murco Garage.
🚆 Bournemouth Central

BRIDPORT

Bingham Grange Touring Camping Park, Binghams Farm, Melplash, Bridport, Dorset, DT6 3TT
Tel: 01308 488234
Email: enquiries@binghamgrange.co.uk
www.binghamgrange.co.uk
Pitches For Å ⏢ 🚐 🚐≤ **Total** 111
Acreage 5 **Open** Mar **to** Nov
Access Good **Site** Lev/Slope
Nearest Bus Stop (Miles) Outside
EXCLUSIVELY FOR ADULTS. An Award Winning Park set in an area of outstanding natural beauty yet only 4½ miles from the coast. An ideal base to explore Dorset. All modern heated facilities.
Facilities ℹ 🖭🖺🖀🖼 ⊙⊣🖭 🔲 ☎
♨ ⌨ 🖸 🖀🖳 ✿🖃 🖳🖃⚓✿ 🛜
Directions Turn off A35 in Bridport at the roundabout onto A3066, signposted Beaminster. In 1¼ miles turn left into Farm Road.
🚆 Dorchester/Crewkerne

BRIDPORT

Britt Valley Campground, West Bay, Bridport, Dorset, DT6 4SU
Tel: 01308 897232
Email: enq@brittvalley.co.uk
www.brittvalley.co.uk
Pitches For Å ⏢ 🚐 **Total** 100
Acreage 13 **Open** 06-Jul **to** 03-Sep
Access Good **Site** Level
Nearest Bus Stop (Miles) ¼
Alongside the River Britt and near the beach.
Facilities 🖭🖺🖀 ⊣ 🖭 🖳🖃🔲 🖃 ✎
Directions From Bridport Crown roundabout on the A35, take the exit for West Bay and the entrance is approx 1 mile on the right.
🚆 Dorchester

BRIDPORT

Eype House Caravan Park, Eype, Bridport, Dorset, DT6 6AL
Tel: 01308 424903
Email: enquiries@eypehouse.co.uk
www.eypehouse.co.uk
Pitches For Å ⏢ **Total** 20
Acreage 4 **Open** Easter **to** Sept
On the Dorset coastal path and only 200 yards from the beach. Pitches are levelled into hill. NO electric hook-ups. Sorry, NO touring caravans.
Facilities 🖭🖺🖀 ⊙⊣ 🔲 ♨ 🖸🖀✖🖃🖳
Directions Signposted Eype off the A35, follow signs to the sea.
🚆 Dorchester/Crewkerne

BRIDPORT

Freshwater Beach Holiday Park, Burton Bradstock, Bridport, Dorset, DT6 4PT
Tel: 01308 897317
Email: office@freshwaterbeach.co.uk
www.freshwaterbeach.co.uk
Pitches For Å ⏢ 🚐 **Total** 500
Acreage 40 **Open** Mid Mar **to** Mid Nov

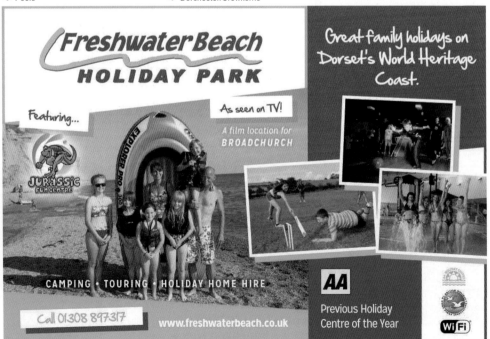

DORSET

Access Good **Site** Level
Nearest Bus Stop (Miles) Outside
Own private beach. Free family entertainment (SBH to Mid Sept). Good cliff walks. Leisure complex with 10 pin bowling, indoor water play, sauna, steam room and hot tub. Golf course adjoining park. Pitch price includes 6 people and free club membership.
Facilities ♿ ⚡ ⌷ ⓦ ☏ ⌂ ☺ ◔ ⊿ ■ ◎ ☎
♨ ☺ ⚙ ✗ ▽ ♠ ⌂ ⚘ ✈ ⊡ ☐ ■ ✗ ☂
Nearest Town Bridport
Directions From Bridport take B3157 towards Weymouth, Park is 2 miles on the right.
⚏ Dorchester

BRIDPORT

Graston Copse Holiday Park, Annings Lane, Burton Bradstock, Bridport, Dorset, DT6 4QP
Tel: 01308 426947
Email: enquiries@wdlh.co.uk
www.grastoncopseholidaypark.co.uk
Pitches For ▲ ⚑ ⊕ **Total** 48
Open 26-Apr to 08-Sep
Access Average **Site** Level
Nearest Bus Stop (Miles) ½
Peaceful location in the Dorset countryside. 25 minutes walk to the beach. Online booking available or call our Bookings Hotline: 01308 426947.
Facilities ⚡ ⓦ ☏ ⌂ ☺ ◔ ⊿ ■ ◎ ☎
♨ ✈ ⊡ ☐ ☂
Nearest Town Bridport
Directions From Bridport take the B3157 coastal road towards Weymouth. When in Burton Bradstock turn left at the Anchor Pub, then turn second right into Annings Lane.
⚏ Dorchester

BRIDPORT

Highlands End Holiday Park, Eype, Bridport, Dorset, DT6 6AR
Tel: 01308 422139
Email: holidays@wdlh.co.uk
www.highlandsendholidaypark.co.uk
Pitches For ▲ ⚑ ⊕ **Total** 195
Acreage 8 **Open** 21-Mar to 02-Nov
Access Good **Site** Level
Nearest Bus Stop (Miles) ½
Exceptional views across Lyme Bay, 500 metres from the beach. Heated swimming pool, steam room and sauna. Tennis and Pitch & Putt on site. All weather awning areas. Online booking available or call our Bookings Hotline: 01308 426947.
Facilities ♿ ⚡ ⌷ ⓦ ☏ ⌂ ☺ ◔ ⊿ ■ ◎ ☎
♨ ☺ ⚙ ✗ ▽ ♠ ⌂ ⚘ ✈ ⊡ ☐ ☂
Nearest Town Bridport
Directions On approach to Bridport from east

(Dorchester) on A35 turn left at roundabout, follow Bridport By-pass. Second roundabout take third exit signposted A35 West 1 mile turn left to Eype and follow signposts.
⚏ Axminster

BRIDPORT

West Bay Holiday Park - Parkdean, West Bay, Bridport, Dorset, DT6 4HB
Tel: 0844 335 3741
Email: enquiries@parkdeanholidays.co.uk
www.parkdeantouring.com
Pitches For ▲ ⚑ ⊕ **Total** 116
Acreage 30 **Open** Mar **to** Nov
Access Good **Site** Level
Nearest Bus Stop (Miles) 2
Set on the stunning Jurassic Coast.
Facilities ♿ ⚡ ⌷ ⓦ ☏ ⌂ ☺ ◔ ⊿ ■ ◎ ☎
♨ ☺ ✗ ▽ ♠ ⌂ ⚘ ✈ ⊡ ☐ ☂
Nearest Town Bridport
Directions Take the M3 towards Winchester, then follow the M27 then the A31. Join the A35 to Dorchester and head west to Bridport, then head into West Bay.
⚏ Dorchester

CHARMOUTH

Charmouth Camping & Caravanning Club Site, Monkton Wylde Farm, Scotts Lane, Nr Charmouth, Dorset, DT6 6DB
Tel: 01297 32965
Email: charmouth.site@thefriendlyclub.co.uk
www.campingandcaravanningclub.co.uk/charmouth
Pitches For ▲ ⚑ ⊕ **Total** 150
Acreage 23 **Open** 08-Mar **to** 04-Nov
Access Good **Site** Level
Nearest Bus Stop (Miles) 1
3 miles from Forde Abbey and Charmouths fossil beach. 7 miles from Cricket St. Thomas Wildlife Park. Motorhome service point. Non members welcome. You can also call us on 0845 130 7633.
Facilities ♿ ⚡ ⌷ ⓦ ☏ ⌂ ☺ ◔ ⊿ ■ ◎ ☎
♨ ☺ ⚙ ♠ ⌂ ⚘ ✈ ⊡ ☐
Nearest Town Charmouth
Directions From Dorchester take the A35, turn right onto the B3165 signposted Marshwood, site is on the left within ¼ of a mile.
⚏ Axminster

CHARMOUTH

Manor Farm Holiday Centre, Manor Farm, Charmouth, Bridport, Dorset, DT6 6QL
Tel: 01297 560226
Email:
enquiries@manorfarmholidaycentre.co.uk
www.manorfarmholidaycentre.co.uk
Pitches For ▲ ⚑ ⊕ ⚑ **Total** 345

Acreage 30 **Open** All Year
Access Good **Site** Lev/Slope
Nearest Bus Stop (Miles) Outside
Ten minutes level walk to beach, alongside river. In area of outstanding natural beauty. Ideal touring.
Facilities ♿ ⚡ ⌷ ⓦ ☏ ⌂ ☺ ◔ ⊿ ■ ◎ ☎
♨ ☺ ⚙ ✗ ▽ ♠ ⌂ ⚘ ✈ ⊡ ☐ ☂ ✗ ⚡
Nearest Town Charmouth
Directions Come off the Charmouth bypass at east end Manor Farm is ¾ miles on the right, in Charmouth.
⚏ Axminster

CHARMOUTH

Monkton Wyld Farm, Charmouth, Dorset, DT6 6DB
Tel: 01297 631131
Email: holidays@monktonwyld.co.uk
www.www.monktonwyld.co.uk
Pitches For ▲ ⚑ ⊕ **Total** 130
Acreage 20 **Open** Mid Mar **to** End Oct
Access Good **Site** Level
Nearest Bus Stop (Miles) 1
Beautifully landscaped pitches with room to relax, and space for children to play. Friendly, helpful wardens offer every assistance. Spotless shower block. Self catering houses sleeping between 2 and 10 persons available to rent on farm.
Facilities ♿ ⚡ ⌷ ⌂ ⓦ ☏ ⌂ ☺ ◔ ⊿ ■ ◎ ☎
Directions Take the A35 from Axminster towards Charmouth, cross the county boundary into Dorset and almost immediately turn left down an unmarked lane. Brown tourist sign only.
⚏ Axminster

CHARMOUTH

Newlands Holiday Park, Charmouth, Nr. Bridport, Dorset, DT6 6RB
Tel: 01297 560259
Email: enq@newlandsholidays.co.uk
www.www.newlandsholidays.co.uk
Pitches For ▲ ⚑ ⊕ **Total** 200
Acreage 23
Access Good **Site** Terraced
Nearest Bus Stop (Miles) Outside
Situated in the Heritage Coast village of Charmouth, near Lyme Regis. Wonderful views and walks through National Trust land. A short stroll to the village centre and safe beach.
Facilities ♿ ⚡ ⌷ ⓦ ☏ ⌂ ☺ ◔ ⊿ ■ ◎ ☎
♨ ☺ ⚙ ✗ ▽ ♠ ⌂ ⚘ ✈ ⊡ ☐ ☂
Nearest Town Lyme Regis
Directions Turn off the A35 at the eastern exit for Charmouth, Newlands is situated a short distance on the left hand side.
⚏ Axminster

CHIDEOCK

Golden Cap Holiday Park, Seatown, Chideock, Nr Bridport, Dorset, DT6 6JX
Tel: 01308 426947
Email: enquiries@wdlh.co.uk
www.goldencapholidaypark.co.uk
Pitches For Å 🏕 🚐 **Total** 260
Acreage 12 **Open** 21-Mar **to** 02-Nov
Site Level/Sloping
Nearest Bus Stop (Miles) ¼
100 metres from beach, overlooked by the famous Golden Cap cliff top. All weather awning areas. Unique location on the Jurassic Coast, ideal for Lyme Regis and Weymouth. Online booking available or call our Bookings Hotline: 01308 426947.
Facilities 🚿 🕭 🏠 🖾 ♠ ⅍ ⊙ ⌕ 🖙 🛒 ⛲
⛲ 🛒 🖾 🚿 ♿ 🖰 🖲 ✂ ⚡ 🚑 ⏣
Directions Follow the A35 to Chideock, once in the village turn opposite the church into Duck Street signposted Seatown. Follow the lane to the beach and turn left.
⇌ Axminster/Dorchester

CHRISTCHURCH

Holmsley Caravan & Camping Site, Forest Road, Thorney Hill, Bransgore, Christchurch, Dorset, BH23 7EQ
Tel: 02476 423008
Email: enquiries@campingintheforestd.co.uk
www.campingintheforest.co.uk
Pitches For Å 🏕 🚐 **Total** 600
Open 10-Apr **to** 03-Nov
Access Good **Site** Level
Just a short drive from the beaches at Bournemouth and Christchurch.
Facilities 🚿 🕭 🖾 🏠 🖙 ⅌ ⊙ ⊙ 🖲 🖰 ➴
Nearest Town Bransgore
Directions Located off the A35 Lyndhurst to Christchurch road, 8 miles south west of Lyndhurst.
⇌ Hinton Admiral

CHRISTCHURCH

Longfield Caravan Park, Matchams Lane, Hurn, Christchurch, Dorset, BH23 6AW
Tel: 01202 485214
www.longfieldcaravanpark.co.uk
Pitches For 🏕 🚐 **Total** 20
Acreage 2½ **Open** All Year
Access Good **Site** Level
Dry ski slope within walking distance, with bar and food available. Swimming pool on site. Near to the New Forest and within easy reach of Christchurch and Bournemouth.
Facilities 🕭 🖾 🖙 🖰 ⅌ ⊙ ⌕ 🖾 🖲 ♠ ➴ ➳
Nearest Town Christchurch
Directions From the A338 follow signs for Bournemouth International Airport. At Hurn bare right and then left into Matchams Lane. After approx 3 miles Longfield is on the left.

⇌ Christchurch

CHRISTCHURCH

Meadowbank Holidays, Stour Way, Christchurch, Dorset, BH23 2PQ
Tel: 01202 483597
Email:
enquiries@meadowbankholidays.co.uk
www.meadowbankholidays.co.uk
Pitches For 🏕 🚐 **Total** 41
Acreage 2 **Open** Mar **to** Oct
Access Good **Site** Level
Riverside setting. Close to Bournemouth, Christchurch and the New Forest.
Facilities 🚿 🕭 🖾 🖙 🖰 ⅌ ⊙ ⌕ 🖾 🖲 ⛲
🛒 🖰 🖾 ♠ 🖰 🖲 ✂ 🚿 ⛲
Nearest Town Bournemouth
Directions From Ringwood take the A338 towards Bournemouth and turn off for Christchurch, follow caravan signs.
⇌ Christchurch

CHRISTCHURCH

Mount Pleasant Touring Park, 91 Matchams Lane, Hurn, Christchurch, Dorset, BH23 6AW
Tel: 01202 475474
Email: enq@mountpleasantcc.co.uk
www.mountpleasantcc.co.uk
Pitches For 🏕 🚐 **Total** 150
Acreage 8 **Open** All Year
Access Good **Site** Level
Nearest Bus Stop (Miles) 1
Close to the beach, a river for fishing, a dry ski slope and the Wonderland Complex.
Facilities 🚿 🕭 🖾 🖙 🖰 ⅌ 🖰 🖲 🖾 🖲 ⛲
🛒 🖰 🖾 🖂 🖲 ✂ 🚿 ⛲
Nearest Town Christchurch/Bournemouth
Directions From Christchurch go straight through for 4 miles to Hurn. Then Matchams lane. From Bournemouth take the A338.
⇌ Bournemouth

CORFE CASTLE

Corfe Castle Camping & Caravanning Club Site, Bucknowle, Wareham, Dorset, BH20 5PQ
Tel: 01929 480280
www.campingandcaravanningclub.co.uk/corfecastle
Pitches For Å 🏕 🚐 **Total** 80
Open Mar **to** 02-Nov
Access Good **Site** Lev/Slope
Nearest Bus Stop (Miles) ½
Very close to the historic thousand year old Corfe Castle, which survived the English Civil War, rising above the Isle of Purbeck. Chocks may be required on some pitches. You can also call us on 0845 130 7633.
Facilities 🚿 🕭 🖾 🖙 🖰 ⅌ ⊙ ⌕ 🖾 🖲 ⛲
🛒 🖰 🖾 ♠ 🖲 🖲

Nearest Town Wareham
Directions From Wareham head south along A351, turn right at foot of castle, after ¾ mile turn right at first brown camping sign.
⇌ Wareham

CORFE CASTLE

Knitson Farm Tourers Site, Knitson Farm, Corfe Castle, Dorset, BH20 5JB
Tel: 01929 425121
www.knitsonfarm.co.uk
Pitches For Å 🏕 🚐 **Total** 60
Acreage 5½ **Open** See web site
Site Lev/Slope
Set in very beautiful countryside with many walks radiating from the field, including Swanage and Studland beaches.
Facilities 🕭 🖙 ♿ ♠ ➴ 🖾 🚿
Directions Take the A351 to Swanage outskirts, turn first left into Wash Pond Lane. Continue until the lane finishes at a T-Junction turn left. Site is approx. ½ mile further on, on the left hand side.
⇌ Wareham

DORCHESTER

Crossways Caravan Club Site, Crossways, Dorchester, Dorset, DT2 8BE
Tel: 01305 852032
www.caravanclub.co.uk
Pitches For 🏕 🚐 **Total** 95
Acreage 35 **Open** 22-Mar **to** 14-Oct
Access Good **Site** Level
Nearest Bus Stop (Miles) ½
Landscaped site set in 35 acres of woodland. So much to see and do in the local area. 8½ miles from Weymouth beach and attractions. Non members welcome. Booking essential.
Facilities 🚿 🕭 🖾 🖙 🖰 ⌕ 🖾 🚿
🖰 🖲 🖾 🖰 🖲
Nearest Town Dorchester
Directions From NE on A31, at the roundabout on the outskirts of Bere Regis turn right onto A35. At Tolpuddle Ball junction turn left onto slip road sp Warmwell, at T-junction turn left, at next T-junction turn right, site is 4 miles down.
⇌ Dorchester

DORCHESTER

Giants Head Caravan & Camping Park, Old Sherborne Road, Dorchester, Dorset, DT2 7TR
Tel: 01300 341242
Email: holidays@giantshead.co.uk
www.giantshead.co.uk
Pitches For Å 🏕 🚐 🚐⅊ **Total** 50
Acreage 3½ **Open** Easter **to** Oct
Access Good **Site** Lev/Slope
Nearest Bus Stop (Miles) 1

Rural, Beautiful countryside, peaceful surroundings.
Facilities
Nearest Town Dorchester
Directions 8 miles from Dorchester, 10 miles from Sherborne, 2 miles from Cerne Abbas.
⇌ Dorchester

LULWORTH COVE
Durdle Door Holiday Park, Lulworth Cove, Wareham, Dorset, BH20 5PU
Tel: 01929 400200
Email: durdle.door@lulworth.com
www.lulworth.com
Pitches For Å ⊕ ⊜ **Total** 104
Acreage 45 **Open** Mar **to** Oct
Access Good **Site** Lev/Slope
Unique cliff top position overlooking the famous landmark of Durdle Door. Sea view hook-ups for motor homes and touring caravans only, and pitches for tents with electric hook-ups.
Facilities
Nearest Town Wareham
Directions Take the B3077 Wool to West Lulworth road, fork right in West Lulworth Village, entrance is at the top of the hill.

⇌ Wool

OWERMOIGNE
Sandyholme Holiday Park, Moreton Road, Owermoigne, Dorchester, Dorset, DT2 8HZ
Tel: 01308 426947
Email: holidays@wdlh.co.uk
www.sandyholmeholidaypark.co.uk
Pitches For Å ⊕ ⊜ **Total** 143
Acreage 6 **Open** 21-Mar **to** 02-Nov

Access Good **Site** Level
Nearest Bus Stop (Miles) ½
Near to Lulworth Cove, Durdle Door and Ringstead Bay. The nearby towns of Dorchester and Weymouth provide plenty of attractions and sights. Online booking available or call our Bookings Hotline: 01308 426947.
Facilities
Directions Take the A35 to Dorchester then take the A352 to Broadmayne. Continue for 4 miles, at the roundabout take second exit, take left hand turning onto Moreton Road, Park can be found on the left hand side.
⇌ Moreton

POOLE
Huntick Farm Caravan Park, Huntick Road, Lytchett Matravers, Poole, Dorset, BH16 6BB
Tel: 01202 622222
Email: huntickcaravans@btconnect.com
www.huntick.co.uk
Pitches For Å ⊕ ⊜ **Total** 30
Acreage 4 **Open** Apr **to** Oct
Access Good **Site** Level
Nearest Bus Stop (Miles) 1
Very spacious site which is quiet and friendly.
Facilities
Directions Turn right off the A350 or left off the A35 and follow signs to Lytchett Matravers. At the Rose & Crown turn into Huntick Road.

POOLE
Sandford Holiday Park - Parkdean, Holton Heath, Poole, Dorset, BH16 6JZ
Tel: 0344 335 3741
Email: enquiries@parkdeanholidays.co.uk
www.parkdeantouring.com

Pitches For Å ⊕ ⊜ **Total** 353
Acreage 22 **Open** Mar **to** Nov
Access Good **Site** Level
A lively park in a glorious countryside setting.
Facilities
Nearest Town Poole
Directions Located on the A351 (signposted Wareham) which branches off the A35 approx. 5 miles west of Poole. Turn right at Holton Heath traffic lights, park is on the left.
⇌ Wareham

POOLE
South Lytchett Manor Caravan & Camping Park, Dorchester Road, Lytchett Minster, Poole, Dorset, BH16 6JB
Tel: 01202 622577
Email: info@southlytchettmanor.co.uk
www.southlytchettmanor.co.uk
Pitches For Å ⊕ ⊜ **Total** 150
Acreage 22 **Open** Mar **to** 02-Jan
Access Good **Site** Level
Nearest Bus Stop (Miles) Outside
Close to Sandbanks, Poole and Bournemouth, set in 22 acres of parkland.
Facilities
Nearest Town Poole
Directions From Poole take A35 dual carriageway. At Bakers Arms Island take the third exit to Lytchett Minster, go through Lytchett Minster and the site is situated on the left 400 yards out of the village.
⇌ Hamworthy

SHAFTESBURY
Blackmore Vale Caravan & Camping Park, Sherborne Causeway, Shaftesbury, Dorset, SP7 9PX
Tel: 01747 851523

Email: mike_farrow@btconnect.com
www.blackmorevalecaravanpark.co.uk
Pitches For 𝗔 ⚏ ⚏ ⚏ **Total** 0
Acreage 5 **Open** All Year
Access Good **Site** Level
Friendly, family run Park in the heart of Hardy country. Gym and a lake for fishing.
Facilities 𝒇 ⬛️ ⬛️ ⚏ ⚏ ⊙ ⬛️ ⬛️ ⬛️ ⬛️ ⬛️ ⬛️ ⬛️ ✓
Nearest Town Shaftesbury
Directions 2 miles west of Shaftesbury on the A30.
⊁ Gillingham

SIXPENNY HANDLEY

Church Farm Caravan & Camping Park, The Bungalow, Church Farm, High Street, Sixpenny Handley, Salisbury, Dorset, SP5 5ND
Tel: 01725 552563
Email: churchfarmcandcpark@yahoo.co.uk
www.churchfarmcandcpark.co.uk
Pitches For 𝗔 ⚏ ⚏ ⚏ **Total** 35
Acreage 100 **Open** All Year
Access Good **Site** Level
Nearest Bus Stop (Miles) Outside
In an area of outstanding natural beauty on the Cranborne Chase and West Wiltshire Downs. Ideal for walking ,touring.
Facilities ⬛️ 𝒇 ⬛️ ⬛️ ⚏ ⚏ ⊙ ⚏ ⬛️ ⬛️ ⬛️
⬛️ ⬛️ ✗ ⬛️ ⬛️ ⬛️ ⬛️ ⬛️ ⬛️ ⚥ ⬛️
Nearest Town Poole/Bournemouth
Directions From Salisbury on the A354 to Handley Cross then B3081 by church.
⊁ Salisbury

ST. LEONARDS

Back-of-Beyond Touring Park, 234 Ringwood Road, St Leonards, Dorset, BH24 2SB
Tel: 01202 876968

Email: melandsuepike@aol.com
www.backofbeyondtouringpark.co.uk
Pitches For 𝗔 ⚏ ⚏ **Total** 80
Acreage 28 **Open** Mar **to** Oct
Access Good **Site** Level
Nearest Bus Stop (Miles) ½
Quiet 4 Star ADULTS ONLY country and woodland site with good facilities. Golf and fishing on site. Central for the New Forest, Bournemouth and the World Heritage coast.
Facilities ⬛️ 𝒇 ⬛️ ⚏ ⚏ ⊙ ⚏ ⬛️ ⬛️ ⬛️
⬛️ ⬛️ ⬛️ ⬛️ ⬛️ ✓ ⬛️ ⚥ ⚥ ⬛️
Nearest Town Ringwood
Directions Off the A31 at Boundary Lane roundabout in St. Leonards.
⊁ Bournemouth

ST. LEONARDS

Shamba Holidays, 230 Ringwood Road, St Leonards, Ringwood, Hampshire, BH24 2SB
Tel: 01202 873302
Email: enquiries@shambaholidays.co.uk
www.shambaholidays.co.uk
Pitches For 𝗔 ⚏ ⚏ ⚏ **Total** 150
Acreage 7 **Open** March **to** October
Access Good **Site** Level
Nearest Bus Stop (Miles) 0.5
Close to Bournemouth and the New Forest. AA 4 Pennants, 4 Star Rose Award, David Bellamy Gold Award for Conservation and 5 Star Loo of the Year Award.
Facilities ⬛️ 𝒇 ⬛️ ⬛️ ⚏ ⊙ ⚏ ⬛️ ⬛️ ⬛️
⬛️ ⬛️ ⬛️ ✗ ⬛️ ⬛️ ⬛️ ⬛️ ⬛️ ⬛️ ⬛️ ⬛️ ⬛️ ⚥
⬛️
Nearest Town Ringwood
Directions Just off the A31 midway between Ringwood and Wimborne.
⊁ Bournemouth

SWANAGE

Haycraft Caravan Club Site, Haycrafts Lane, Swanage, Dorset, BH19 3EB
Tel: 01929 480572
www.caravanclub.co.uk
Pitches For ⚏ ⚏ **Total** 53
Acreage 6 **Open** Mar **to** Nov
Access Good **Site** Level
Nearest Bus Stop (Miles) ½
Tranquil site set in the heart of Purbeck countryside, 5 miles from the beach. Ideal for walkers. Just a few minutes walk from the Swanage Light Railway. Members only. Booking essential.
Facilities ⬛️ 𝒇 ⬛️ ⬛️ ⚏ ⚏ ⊙ ⚏ ⬛️ ⬛️
⬛️ ⬛️ ⬛️ ⬛️ ⬛️ ⬛️ ⚥ ⬛️ 🛜
Nearest Town Swanage
Directions From A352, at the mini roundabout on the outskirts of Wareham turn onto A351 sp Swanage. After 6¾ miles at Harmans Cross, just before the petrol station, turn right into Haycrafts Lane, site is ½ mile on the left.
⊁ Swanage

SWANAGE

Tom's Field Camping & Shop, Tom's Field Road, Langton Matravers, Swanage, Dorset, BH19 3HN
Tel: 01929 427110
Email: tomsfield@hotmail.com
www.tomsfieldcamping.co.uk
Pitches For 𝗔 ⚏ **Total** 100
Acreage 4½ **Open** Mid Mar **to** Oct
Site Lev/Slope
Nearest Bus Stop (Miles) ¼
Set in beautiful countryside, an area of outstanding natural beauty. Coastal walk can be reached in 20 minutes.
Facilities 𝒇 ⬛️ ⚏ ⚏ ⊙ ⚏ ⬛️ ⬛️ ⬛️ ⬛️

Directions A351 from Swanage,then B3069 to Langton Matravers, campsite at end of Tom's Field
Road.
≠ Wareham

SWANAGE

Ulwell Cottage Caravan Park, Ulwell, Swanage, Dorset, BH19 3DG
Tel: 01929 422823
Email: enq@ulwellcottagepark.co.uk
www.ulwellcottagepark.co.uk
Pitches For Å ⊕ ➡ **Total** 77
Acreage 13 **Open** Mar **to** 07-Jan
Access Good **Site** Lev/Slope
Nearest Bus Stop (Miles) Outside
Adjoining the Purbeck Hills for scenic walks. Near sandy beaches.
Facilities & ƒ 🖫 🕮 🖺 ⌐ ⊙⌐ 🝗 🖵 🖸 🝙
ℝ 🛇 🗙 ♈ 🕅 🕈 ⊌ 🖵 🖸 🛜
Nearest Town Swanage
Directions 1½ miles from Swanage on Studland Road. Turn left by telephone box (left hand side) on side of road.
≠ Wareham

WAREHAM

Birchwood Tourist Park, Bere Road, Coldharbour, Wareham, Dorset, BH20 7PA
Tel: 01929 554763
Email: birchwoodtouristpark@hotmail.com
www.birchwoodtouristpark.co.uk
Pitches For Å ⊕ ➡ **Total** 175
Acreage 28 **Open** All year
Access Good **Site** Sloping
Situated in Wareham Forest with direct access to forest walks. Ideal for touring the whole of Dorset.
Facilities ƒ 🖫 🕮 🖺 ⌐ ⊙⌐ 🖵 🝙
ℝ 🛇 ♈ 🕅 🖵 🖸 🔆 🝙 🛜
Directions Located 2¼ miles north-west of Wareham on the Bere road (unclassified) in Wareham Forest.
≠ Wareham

WAREHAM

East Creech Caravan & Camping Site, East Creech Farm, East Creech, Wareham, Dorset, BH20 5AP
Tel: 01929 480519/481312
Email: east.creech@virgin.net
www.eastcreechfarm.co.uk
Pitches For Å ⊕ ➡ **Total** 80
Acreage 5 **Open** Apr **to** Oct
Access Good **Site** Lev/Slope
Nearest Bus Stop (Miles) 2
Free fishing at the Farm.
Facilities ƒ 🕮 ⌐ ⊙⊙ 🝙 🛆 ♈ 🖵 ✍
Nearest Town Wareham
Directions From Wareham bypass A351, turn right at the roundabout signposted Blue Pool. Site is on the right ½ a miles past Blue Pool.
≠ Wareham

WAREHAM

Lookout Holiday Park, Stoborough, Wareham, Dorset, BH20 5AZ
Tel: 01929 552546
Email: enquiries@caravan-sites.co.uk
www.caravan-sites.co.uk
Pitches For Å ⊕ ➡ **Total** 150
Acreage 15 **Open** Mar **to** Jan
Access Good **Site** Level
Nearest Bus Stop (Miles) Outside
Ideal for touring the Purbecks and Studland Bay. Static caravans available all year.
Facilities ƒ 🖫 🕮 🖺 ⌐ ⊙⌐ 🝗 🖵 🖸 🝙
ℝ 🛇 🖸 🕅 ♈ 🖵 🖸 🔆 🝙 🛜
Nearest Town Wareham
Directions 1 mile south of Wareham on the Swanage road.

WAREHAM

Manor Farm Caravan & Camping Park, Church Lane, East Stoke, Wareham, Dorset, BH20 6AW
Tel: 01929 462870
Email: info@manorfarmcp.co.uk
www.manorfarmcp.co.uk
Pitches For Å ⊕ ➡ **Total** 60
Acreage 2½ **Open** All Year
Access Good **Site** Level
Nearest Bus Stop (Miles) ½
Flat, grass touring park in a rural area of outstanding natural beauty, central for most of Dorset. Family run park with clean facilities. Close to Monkey World, Bovington Tank Museum and the World Heritage Coast on Pirbeck Cycle Way. Winter storage available. rallies wellcome, No groups and No commercial vans.
Facilities & ✗ ƒ 🕮 🖺 ⌐ ⊙⌐ 🝙
ℝ 🛇 🕅 🖸 🔆 🝙 🛜
Directions From Wareham take A352 then B3070. Turn into Holme Lane, at the crossroads turn right sp Manor Farm CP. Or from Wool sp down Bindon Lane, at the crossroads turn left sp Manor Farm CP, site is 300 yards on the left.
≠ Wool/Wareham

WAREHAM

Wareham Forest Tourist Park, North Trigon, Wareham, Dorset, BH20 7NZ
Tel: 01929 551393
Email: holiday@warehamforest.co.uk
www.warehamforest.co.uk
Pitches For Å ⊕ ➡ ⋹ **Total** 200
Acreage 55 **Open** All Year
Access Good **Site** Level
Tranquil, family owned park set in the forest. Ideal for relaxing and walking. Central location for exploring East Dorset and the Purbeck coastline.
Facilities & ƒ 🖫 🕮 🖺 ⌐ ⊙⌐ 🝗 🖵 🖸 🝙
ℝ 🛇 🖸 ♈ 🕅 ⋟ ♻ ♈ 🖵 🖸 🔆 🝙 🛜

Nearest Town Wareham
Directions Located midway between Wareham and Bere Regis in Wareham Forest.
≠ Wareham

WEYMOUTH

Bagwell Farm Touring Park, Knights in the Bottom, Chickerell, Weymouth, Dorset, DT3 4EA
Tel: 01305 782575
Email: cab@bagwellfarm.co.uk
www.bagwellfarm.co.uk
Pitches For Å ⊕ ➡ ⋹ **Total** 320
Acreage 14 **Open** All Year
Access Good **Site** Level
Nearest Bus Stop (Miles) ½
A friendly welcome awaits you. 5 miles from Weymouth's sandy beach. Close to The Fleet Lagoon and the World Heritage Coast. Access to the coastal path. Seasonal bar, restaurant and take-away on the Park. Ideal location for discovering Dorset and exploring Dorsets Jurassic Coastline. Wheelchair friendly
Facilities & ƒ 🖫 🕮 🖺 ⌐ ⊙⌐ 🝗 🖵 🖸 🝙
ℝ 🛇 🖸 🗙 ♈ 🕅 🖵 🖸 🔆 🝙 🛜
Nearest Town Weymouth
Directions From A354 follow signs for Weymouth town centre and Portland until you see signs for Chickerell, Abbotsbury B3157 We are 1 mile west of Chickerell.
≠ Weymouth

WEYMOUTH

Sea Barn Farm Camping Park, Fleet, Weymouth, Dorset, DT3 4ED
Tel: 01305 782218
Email: enquiries@seabarnfarm.co.uk
www.seabarnfarm.co.uk
Pitches For Å ➡ **Total** 250
Acreage 12 **Open** 16-Mar **to** Oct
Site Lev/slope
Nearest Bus Stop (Miles) 1
Fabulous views of the coast and Dorset countryside. Access to a coastal footpath. Ideal location for discovering Dorset.
Facilities & ƒ 🕮 ⌐ ⊙⌐ 🝗 🖵 🖸 🝙
ℝ 🛇 🕅 🖵 🖸 🛜
Nearest Town Weymouth
Directions From Weymouth take the B3157 towards Abbotsbury. After 2½ miles at the mini roundabout turn left into Fleet road. site is 1 mile on the left.
≠ Weymouth

WEYMOUTH

West Fleet Holiday Farm, Fleet, Weymouth, Dorset, DT3 4EF
Tel: 01305 782218
Email: ca@westfleetholidays.co.uk
www.westfleetholidays.co.uk

Pitches For ⋏ 🚐 **Total** 250
Acreage 12 **Open** Easter **to** Sept
Site Level
Nearest Bus Stop (Miles) 1
Kids love camping at West Fleet. Outdoor pool, family clubhouse and lots of space to play. Ideal location for discovering Dorset.
Facilities 🏃 ⅃ 🚾 🅿 ⊙ ↻ 🔌 ▣ 🍴
🏵 🛒 ✗ 🍼 🛍 ⚲ ↻ 🅿 🖃 🖻 🛝 🤸 🛜
Nearest Town Weymouth
Directions From Weymouth take the B3157 towards Abbotsbury. After 2½ miles at the mini roundabout turn left into Fleet Road. site is 1 mile on the right.
⚓ Weymouth

WIMBORNE

Gundrys Farm Caravan & Camping Park, School Lane, Three Legged Cross, Wimborne, Dorset, BH21 6RU
Tel: 01202 826322
Email: gundrysfarm@gmail.com
Pitches For ⋏ 🚐 🚐 **Total** 50
Acreage 8 **Open** Mar **to** Oct
Access Good **Site** Level
Nearest Bus Stop (Miles) ¼
Friendly, family run park in a beautiful secluded location. All pitches are flat and level. 5 mins from a country park for fishing, golf and walking. 15 mins from Bournemouth and Poole with their sandy beaches, and the New Forest. 15 minute off-road walk to Moors Valley Country Park.
Facilities ⅃ 🚾 🅿 ⊙ ↻ 🔌 ▣ 🍴
Nearest Town Ringwood
Directions Take the A31 west 1 mile past Ringwood, follow the slip road and turn right at the roundabout signposted Three Legged Cross and Moors Valley Country Park, site is 1½ miles past Moors Valley on the left.
⚓ Bournemouth

WIMBORNE

Springfield Touring Park, Candys Lane, Corfe Mullen, Wimborne, Dorset, BH21 3EF
Tel: 01202 881719
Email: john.clark18@btconnect.com
www.springfieldtouringpark.co.uk
Pitches For ⋏ 🚐 🚐 **Total** 45
Acreage 3½ **Open** Apr **to** Oct
Access Good **Site** Lev/Slope
Nearest Bus Stop (Miles) ¼
Family run park, overlooking the Stour Valley. Free showers and awnings. Convenient for the coast, New Forest, also ferry. Low Season Offers - £85, any 7 days for 2 adults including electric. Practical Caravan Top 100 Parks 2008/09/10/11.
Facilities 🏃 ⅃ 🚾 🅿 ↻ 🔌 ▣ 🍴
🏵 🛍 ⚲ 🤸 🖃 🖻
Nearest Town Wimborne
Directions 1¼ miles west of Wimborne just off main A31.
⚓ Poole

WIMBORNE

Verwood Camping & Caravanning Club Site, Sutton Hill, Woodlands, Wimborne, Dorset, BH21 8NQ
Tel: 01202 822763
Email: verwood.site@thefriendlyclub.co.uk
www.campingandcaravanningclub.co.uk/
verwood
Pitches For ⋏ 🚐 🚐 **Total** 150
Acreage 12 **Open** 14-Mar **to** 10-Nov
Access Good **Site** Gentle Slope
Beautifully situated next to Ringwood Forest. Miles of safe, sandy beaches at Poole and Bournemouth are a reasonable distance. BTB 4 Star Graded and AA 3 Pennants. Non members welcome. You can also call us on 0845 130 7633.

Facilities 🏃 ⅃ 🚾 🅿 ⊙ ↻ 🔌 ▣ 🍴 🖻
🏵 🛍 ⚲ 🤸 🖃 🖻 🛝 🤸 🛜
Nearest Town Ringwood
Directions From Salisbury take the A354, after 13 miles turn left onto the B3081, site is 1½ miles west of Verwood.
⚓ Bournemouth

WOOL

Whitemead Caravan Park, East Burton Road, Wool, Dorset, BH20 6HG
Tel: 01929 462241
Email: whitemeadcp@aol.com
www.whitemeadcaravanpark.co.uk
Pitches For ⋏ 🚐 🚐 **Total** 95
Acreage 5 **Open** Mid Mar **to** Oct
Access Good **Site** Level
Nearest Bus Stop (Miles) ¼
Woodland site with several secluded pitches. Off licence on site.
Facilities ⅃ 🚾 🅿 ⊙ ↻ 🔌 ▣ 🍴
🏵 🛍 🛒 ⚲ 🤸 🖃 🖻 🛝 🛜
Nearest Town Wareham
Directions Off the A352 Wareham to Weymouth road. 5 miles west of Wareham and 5 miles north of Lulworth Cove.
⚓ Wool

DURHAM

BARNARD CASTLE

Barnard castle Camping & Caravanning Club Site, Dockenflatts Lane, Lartington, Barnard Castle, Durham, DL12 9DG
Tel: 01833 630228
Email:
barnard.castlesite@thefriendlyclub.co.uk
www.campingandcaravanningclub.co.uk/
barnardcastle
Pitches For ⋏ 🚐 🚐 **Total** 90
Acreage 10 **Open** 10-Apr **to** 10-Nov
Site Level
Nearest Bus Stop (Miles) ½
Well placed for exploring the Pennines and the city of Durham. BTB 5 Star Graded, AA 4 Pennants and Loo of the Year Award. Non members welcome. You can also call us on 0845 130 7633.
Facilities 🏃 ⅃ 🚾 🅿 ⊙ ↻ 🔌 ▣ 🍴
🏵 🛍 ⚲ 🤸 🖃 🖻 🛝 🛜
Directions On approach from Scotch Corner take the second turn right for Middleton in Teesdale and Barnard Castle. On approach from Penrith take the B6277 to Middleton in Teesdale. In approx 1 mile take turn off left signposted Raygill Riding Stables. The site is 500 metres on the left.
⚓ Darlington

BARNARD CASTLE

Hetherick Caravan Park, Marwood, Barnard Castle, Durham, DL12 8QX
Tel: 01388 488384
Email: info@hetherickcaravanpark.co.uk
www.hetherickcaravanpark.co.uk
Pitches For ⋏ 🚐 🚐 **Total** 41
Acreage 15 **Open** Mar **to** Oct
Access Good **Site** Level
Nearest Bus Stop (Miles) ½
Pleasant park situated on a working farm in open countryside, in the heart of beautiful Teesdale. 3 miles from the pretty market town of Barnard Castle.
Facilities 🏃 ⅃ 🚾 🅿 ⊙ ↻ 🔌 ▣ 🍴
🏵 🛍 🛒 🤸 🖃
Nearest Town Barnard Castle
Directions Take the B6278 from Barnard Castle towards Eggleston, once past the golf course take the second right turn towards Kinninvie and Woodland.
⚓ Darlington

BARNARD CASTLE

Pecknell Farm Caravan Site, Pecknell Farm, Lartington, Barnard Castle, Co. Durham, DL12 9DF
Tel: 01833 638357
Pitches For 🚐 🚐 **Total** 20
Acreage 1½ **Open** Apr **to** Oct
Access Good **Site** Level
Nearest Bus Stop (Miles) ¼
Ideal walking area, very attractive walk into historic Barnard Castle. Within easy reach of many attractions.
Facilities ⅃ 🚾 🅿 ⊙ ↻ 🔌 ▣ 🍴 🐾
Nearest Town Barnard Castle
Directions 1½ miles from Barnard Castle on the B6277 to Lartington, we are the first farm on the right.
⚓ Darlington

BARNARD CASTLE

Winston Caravan Park, The Old Forge, Winston, Darlington, Durham, DL2 3RH
Tel: 01325 730228
Email: m.willetts@ic24.net
www.touristnetuk.com/ne/winston
Pitches For ⋏ 🚐 🚐 **Total** 21
Open Mar **to** Oct
Access Good **Site** Level
Nearest Bus Stop (Miles) Outside
Ideally situated for exploring the many attractions in County Durham. Caravan for the disabled available for hire.
Facilities ⅃ 🚾 🅿 ⊙ ↻ 🔌 ▣ 🍴
🖻 🤸 🖃 🖻
Nearest Town Darlington
Directions From Darlington take the A67 west for 10 miles, turn left onto the B6274 into Winston Village, site is 400 yards on the right hand side.
⚓ Darlington

CONSETT

Manor Park Caravan & Camping Park, Manor Park Limited, Broadmeadows, Near Castleside, Consett, Durham, DH8 9HD
Tel: 01207 501000
Pitches For 🚐 🚐 **Total** 20
Open May **to** Aug
Access Good **Site** Sloping
Ideal base for visiting Durham with its cathedral and castle, Northumberland, Beamish Museum and the Angel of the North.
Facilities 🚾 🅿 ⊙ ↻ 🛒
Nearest Town Consett
Directions From A68, Castleside Tow Law turn east onto Eliza Lane site ¾ mile on right.
⚓ Durham

DURHAM

Durham Grange Caravan Club Site, Meadow Lane, Durham, Co. Durham, DH1 1TL
Tel: 0191 384 4778
www.caravanclub.co.uk
Pitches For 🚐 🚐 **Total** 76
Acreage 12 **Open** All Year
Access Good **Site** Level
Nearest Bus Stop (Miles) ½
Only 3 miles from the city of Durham with its castle and cathedral. Beamish Open Air Museum nearby. Non members welcome. Booking essential.
Facilities
⅃ 🏃 🚾 🅿 ⊙ 🏵 🛍 🖻 ⚲ 🤸 🛒 ⚲ 🛜
Nearest Town Durham
Directions Leave the A1(M) via slip road onto the A690 signposted Durham. Immediately move to the outside lane to turn right in 50 yards at brown caravan sign into Meadow Lane, site entrance is ahead.
⚓ Durham

DURHAM

Finchale Abbey Caravan Park, Finchale Abbey Farm, Durham, DH1 5SH
Tel: 0191 386 6528
Email: godricawatson@hotmail.com
www.finchaleabbey.co.uk
Pitches For ⬛ ⬛ ⬛ Total 40
Acreage 6 **Open** All Year
Access Good **Site** Level
Nearest Bus Stop (Miles) 1
ADULTS ONLY PARK set in the meander of the River Wear. Ideally situated to visit most of the North Easts highlights.
Facilities 🚿🚽 ♿ 🕭 🖂 🛒 ♒ ⊙ 🍴
🛢 🗜 🏊 ✕ ➡ ⛏ 🛒 ⬛ 🌳 ⚓
Nearest Town Durham City
Directions Leave the A1M at junction 63 and head south on the A167. At Arnson roundabout follow signs for Finchale Priory, site is at the same place.
🚉 Durham City

DURHAM

Strawberry Hill Farm Caravan & Camping Park, Old Cassop, Durham, Durham, DH6 4QA
Tel: 0191 372 3457
Email: info@strawberryhf.co.uk
www.strawberry-hill-farm.co.uk
Pitches For ⛺ ⬛ ⬛ Total 30
Acreage 6 **Open** Mar to Dec
Access Good **Site** Terraced
Nearest Bus Stop (Miles) ¼
Approx. 4 miles from Durham City, World Heritage Site, Castle and Cathedral. Caravan holiday homes for hire.
Facilities 🚿 ♿ 🖂 🛒 ♒ ⊙ 🍴 ⬛ 🍴
🛢 ⊙➡ ⬛ 🍴
Nearest Town Durham City
Directions From junction 61 of the A1M take exit sp Bowburn A177. Travel to the second set of traffic lights (2.6 miles) and turn right sp A19 Peterlee and Hartlepool. The Park is 3½ miles on the left.
🚉 Durham City

ESSEX

BRENTWOOD

Kelvedon Hatch Camping & Caravanning Club Site, Warren Lane, Doddinghurst, Brentwood, Essex, CM15 0JG
Tel: 01277 372773
Email:
kelvedon.hatch@thefriendlyclub.co.uk
www.campingandcaravanningclub.co.uk/kelvedonhatch
Pitches For ⛺ ⬛ ⬛ Total 90
Acreage 12 **Open** Apr to 03-Nov
Access Fair **Site** Level
Nearest Bus Stop (Miles) ½

Peaceful site, good for country walks. 20 miles from the centre of London. Plenty of sporting activities within easy reach. Non members welcome. You can also call us on 0845 130 7633, to book.
Facilities ♿ 🕭 🖂 🛒 ♒ ♒ ⊙ 🍴 ⬛ 🍴
🗜 ⬛ 🏊 🛆 ➡ 🖂 ⬛ 🌳 ⚓ 🌐
Directions Leave the M25 at junction 28 and take the A1023 towards Brentwood. Turn left onto the A128 to Ongar, the site is 3 miles on the right, signposted.
🚉 Brentwood

BRIGHTLINGSEA

Lakeside Caravan Park, Promenade Way, Brightlingsea, Nr Colchester, Essex, CO7 0HJ
Tel: 01206 303421
Pitches For ⛺ ⬛ ⬛ Total 50
Open Mar to Oct
Access Good **Site** Level
Nearest Bus Stop (Miles) Outside
Near the beach and shops. 5 minute walk to a swimming pool.
Facilities 🕭 🛒 ♒ ♒ ⊙ 🍴 🛒 ➡ 🖂 🌳
Nearest Town Brightlingsea
🚉 Colchester

CLACTONONSEA

Silver Dawn Touring Park, Jaywick Lane, ClactononSea, Essex, CO16 8BB
Tel: 01255 421856
www.silverdawntouringpark.co.uk
Pitches For ⬛ ⬛ Total 38
Acreage 3 **Open** Apr to Oct
Access Good **Site** Level
Nearest Bus Stop (Miles) ¼
Sky TV. David Bellamy Silver Award for Conservation. You can also contact us on Mobile: 07906 222353.
Facilities 🕭 ♒ ♒ ⊙ 🍴 🍴
🗜 ⊙ 🏊 ⬛ 🛆 ⚓ 🌳
Directions Take the A12 then the A120 to Clacton.
🚉 Clacton-on-Sea

HARWICH

Dovercourt Caravan Park, Low Road, Harwich, Essex, CO12 3TZ
Tel: 01255 243433
Email: enquiries@dovercourtcp.com
www.dovercourtcp.com
Pitches For ⬛ ⬛ Total 60
Acreage 8 **Open** Apr to Oct
Access Good **Site** Level
Nearest Bus Stop (Miles) Outside
Near the beach, Harwich ferries and Constable Country.
Facilities 🚿 🕭 🖂 🛒 ♒ ⊙ 🍴 🍴 ⬛ 🍴
🛢 ⊙ 🏊 ✕ ➡ 🛆 ⬛ 🍴 🌳 ⚓ 🖂 🍴 🌐
Nearest Town Dovercourt

Directions From Colchester take the A120 towards Harwich and follow brown tourism signs from Ramsey roundabout.
🚉 Dovercourt/Harwich

HARWICH

Greenacres Caravan Park, Low Road, Dovercourt, Harwich, Essex, CO12 3TS
Tel: 01255 502657
www.www.greenacres@dovercourt.co.uk
Pitches For ⬛ ⬛ ⬛ Total 93
Open Mar to Oct
Access Good **Site** Level
Nearest Bus Stop (Miles) outside
Next to beach, open air skating rink, 2 miles from Port of Harwich.
Facilities 🕭 🖂 🛒 ♒ ♒ ⊙ 🍴 ⬛ 🍴
🗜 ⊙ 🍴 ➡ 🖂 🌳 ⚓
Nearest Town Harwich

MERSEA ISLAND

Fen Farm Caravan & Camping Site, Moore Lane, East Mersea, Colchester, Essex, CO5 8FE
Tel: 01206 383275
Email: hfnefun@fenfarm.co.uk
www.fenfarm.co.uk
Pitches For ⛺ ⬛ ⬛ ⬛ Total 90
Acreage 5 **Open** Mid Mar to Oct
Access Good **Site** Level
Quiet, rural, family run site just a 2 minute walk to the beach and on an estuary. Close to a country park.
Facilities 🚿 🕭 🖂 🛒 ♒ ♒ ⊙ 🍴 ⬛ 🍴
🛢 🗜 ⊙ 🏊 ✕ ➡ 🖂 🌳 ⚓ 🌐
Nearest Town Colchester
Directions Take the B1025 from Colchester to Mersea, take the left fork to East Mersea. Moore Lane is the first left turn after the Dog & Pheasant Public House.

MERSEA ISLAND

Waldegraves Holiday & Leisure Park, Mersea Island, Colchester, Essex, CO5 8SE
Tel: 01206 382898
Email: holidays@waldegraves.co.uk
www.waldegraves.co.uk
Pitches For ⛺ ⬛ ⬛ Total 60
Acreage 45 **Open** Mar to Nov
Access Good **Site** Level
Nearest Bus Stop (Miles) ½
Ideal family park, surrounded by trees and lakes. Safe private beach. Licensed bar and restaurant, swimming pool, undercover golf driving range, pitch & putt, Crazy golf, Foot Golf, Family entertainment, play areas and games room, fishing and boating lake. Luxury holiday homes for hire and sale. Discover Mersea Island & see for yourself why it is one of the most sought after destinations on
the beautiful Essex coast.

Facilities ⚠ ♿ 🚻 🚿 🔌 🔥 ☕ 🛒 💧 📮 ☎
📶 🛁 📶 🔌

Nearest Town Colchester
Directions From Colchester take B1025, 10 miles to West Mersea. Take left fork to East Mersea, second road to right.
🚆 Colchester

SOUTHEND-ON-SEA
Riverside Village Holiday Park, Creeksea Ferry Road, Wallasea Island, Rochford, Essex, SS4 2EY
Tel: 01702 258297
Email: riversidevillage@tiscali.co.uk
www.riversidevillageholidaypark.co.uk
Pitches For ⛺ 🚐 🚍 **Total** 60
Acreage 25 **Open** Mar **to** 01-Nov
Access Good **Site** Level
Open countryside walks,cycling,wildlife (RSPB) top notch pubs/resturants. Easy access to London. Bus stop on site.
Facilities ⚠ ♿ 🚻 🔌 🔥 ☕ 🛒 💧 📮 ☎
🛁 🔌 🚿 🔌 🛒 📮 📶 🔌
Nearest Town SouthendonSea
Directions A127 to Tesco roundabout to B1013 Rochford follow signs for Wallasea Island.
🚆 Rochford

ST. OSYTH
Hutleys Touring Park, St Osyth Beach, St Osyth, Essex, CO16 8TB
Tel: 01255 820712
Pitches For 🚐 🚍 **Total** 18
Acreage 1 **Open** Mar **to** Oct
Access Good **Site** Level
Nearest Bus Stop (Miles) Outside
Adjacent to the beach. Naturist beach nearby.
Facilities ⚠ ♿ 🚻 🔌 🔥 ☕ 💧 📮 ☎
🛁 🔌 🚿 🍴 🛒 📮 🔌 📶 🔌
Nearest Town St. Osyth
Directions Take the A12 from Colchester, then the A133 to Clacton, then the B1027 to St. Osyth. Crossroads - to St Osyth Beach (2 miles).
🚆 Clacton-on-Sea.

GLOUCESTERSHIRE
CHELTENHAM
Briarfields Motel & Touring Park, Gloucester Road, Cheltenham, Gloucestershire, GL51 0SX
Tel: 01242 235324
Email: briarfields@hotmail.co.uk
www.briarfields.net
Pitches For ⛺ 🚐 🚍 **Total** 72
Acreage 6 **Open** All Year
Access Good **Site** Level
Nearest Bus Stop (Miles) Outside
Excellent bus service to Cheltenham and Gloucester from outside our park.
Facilities ⚠ ♿ 🚻 🔌 🔥 ☕ 💧 📮 ☎
🛁 🔌 📮 🔌 🛒 📶
Nearest Town Cheltenham
Directions Leave the M5 at junction 11 and take the A40 for Cheltenham. At the first roundabout take the first exit onto the B4063, Briarfields is 200 metres on the left.
🚆 Cheltenham Spa

CHELTENHAM
Cheltenham Racecourse Caravan Club Site, Prestbury Park, Cheltenham, Gloucestershire, GL50 4SH
Tel: 01242 523102
www.caravanclub.co.uk
Pitches For ⛺ 🚐 **Total** 80
Acreage 7 **Open** Apr **to** Oct
Access Good **Site** Lev/Slope
Nearest Bus Stop (Miles) ¼
Set on the edge of elegant Cheltenham with panoramic views of the Cleeve Hills. Free racing, putting course adjacent (small charge). Non members welcome. Booking essential.
Facilities ⚠ ♿ 🚻 🔌 🔥 ☕ ☎
🛁 🔌 📮 🔌 📮 🔌
Nearest Town Cheltenham
Directions From west on the A40, 1½ miles past M5 junc at Benhall r/about t lt into Princess Elizabeth Way. At the r/about continue straight into Kingsditch Industrial Estate, after ½ mile turn right, at r/about turn left into racecourse and follow signs.
🚆 Cheltenham

CIRENCESTER
Mayfield Touring Park, Cheltenham Road, Perrotts Brook, Cirencester, Gloucestershire, GL7 7BH
Tel: 01285 831301
Email: mayfield-park@cirencester.fsbusiness.co.uk
www.mayfieldpark.co.uk
Pitches For ⛺ 🚐 🚍 **Total** 76
Acreage 10 **Open** All Year
Access Good **Site** Lev/Slope

Nearest Bus Stop (Miles) Outside
In a position central to the Cotswolds with pleasant views and a warm welcome. This site benefits from having a variety of pitch types with something to suit every need. Disabled toilet/shower and baby changing facilities.
Facilities ⚠ ♿ 🚻 🔌 🔥 ☕ 💧 📮 ☎
🛁 🔌 📮 🔌 📮 📶 🔌 📶
Directions On A435, 13 miles from Cheltenham and 2 miles from Cirencester. From Cirencester by-pass A419/A417 take the Burford Road exit then follow camping and caravan signs.
🚆 Kemble

CIRENCESTER
Hoburne Cotswold, Broadway Lane, South Cerney, Cirencester, Gloucestershire, GL7 5UQ
Tel: 01285 860216
Email: enquiries@hoburne.com
www.hoburne.com
Pitches For ⛺ 🚐 🚍 **Total** 189
Acreage 70 **Open** March **to** October
Access Good **Site** Level
Nearest Bus Stop (Miles) 0.25
In the centre of the Cotswold Water Park and built around five lakes, this Park is the perfect base for watersports and sightseeing.
Facilities ♿ 🚻 🔌 🔥 ☕ ☎
🛁 🔌 📮 🍴 🔌 🛒 🔥 🔌 📶 📶
Nearest Town South Cerney
Directions 4 miles south of Cirencester on the A419, follow signs to Cotswold Hoburne, in the Cotswold Water Park.

CIRENCESTER
Second Chance Caravan Park, Nr Marston Meysey, Wiltshire, SN6 6SZ
Tel: 01285 810675/810939
www.secondchancetouring.co.uk
Pitches For ⛺ 🚍 **Total** 26
Acreage 2 **Open** Mar **to** Nov
Access Good **Site** Level
Nearest Bus Stop (Miles) ¼
Riverside location with private fishing. The first camping/caravan park on the Thames Path, great for exploring the upper reaches of the Thames. Excellent opportunity to visit the old Roman capital of Cirencester and the many attractions of the Cotswolds. AA 2 Pennants.
Facilities ♿ 🚻 🔌 🔥 ☕ 💧 📮 ☎
🔌 📮 🔌 📶
Nearest Town Castle Eaton/Fairford

The Red Lion
Riverside Inn &
Caravan & Camping Park
Wainlode Hill, Norton,
Gloucester GL2 9LW
01452 731810/01299 400787

Idyllic country location on the banks of the River Severn, ideal for fishing and walking. Close to The Cotswolds, Forest of Dean and Cheltenham. Our 26 acre site welcomes touring caravans, tents and motor caravans, and is OPEN ALL YEAR. Electric hook-ups, full toilet and shower facilities and launderette. Seasonal pitches are available. All year round holiday homes for sale. Our own country inn serves a wide range of hot and cold food & beverages. Site shop offers fresh milk, groceries and ice cream.

www.redlioninn-caravancampingpark.co.uk

Directions Between Swindon and Cirencester on the A419. Turn off at the Fairford/Marston Meysey exit and follow the caravan park signs. Proceed approx. 3 miles then turn right at the brown caravan/camping signpost. We are on the right.
≠ Swindon

COLEFORD

Bracelands Caravan & Camping Site, Bracelands Drive, Christchurch, Coleford, Gloucestershire, GL16 7NN
Tel: 02476 423008
Email: enquiries@campingintheforest.co.uk
www.campingintheforest.co.uk
Pitches For **Total** 520
Open Mar **to** 03-Nov
Access Good **Site** Sloping
Panoramic views over the magnificent countryside of the Wye Valley. Near to Symonds Yat.
Facilities
Nearest Town Coleford
Directions From Coleford take the B4432, after approx. a mile turn right into Bracelands Drive.
≠ Lydney

DURSLEY

Hogsdown Farm Caravan & Camping, Hogsdown Farm, Lower Wick, Dursley, Gloucestershire, GL11 6DD
Tel: 01453 810224
www.hogsdownfarm.co.uk
Pitches For **Total** 0
Acreage 5 **Open** All Year
Access Good **Site** Level
Nearest Bus Stop (Miles) 1
Great for visiting Berkeley Castle, Jenner Museum, Wild Fowl Trust, Weston Birt Arboretum, and the hills and valleys of the Cotswolds.
Facilities
Nearest Town Berkeley
Directions Between junctions 13 and 14 of the M5, off the A38.
≠ Cam

GLOUCESTER

The Red Lion Inn Caravan & Camping Park, Wainlode Hill, Norton, Gloucestershire, GL2 9LW
Tel: 01452 730251
www.redlioninncaravancampingpark.co.uk
Pitches For **Total** 109
Acreage 10 **Open** All Year
Access Good **Site** Level
Nearest Bus Stop (Miles) ½
On the banks of the River Severn with a riverside pub.
Facilities
Nearest Town Gloucester/Tewkesbury
Directions From Tewkesbury take the A38 south for 3 miles, turn right onto the B4213. After 3 miles turn left to Wainlode Hill, 350 yards alongside the River Severn, park is on the left.
≠ Gloucester

LECHLADE

Bridge House Campsite, Bridge House, Thames Street, Lechlade, Gloucestershire, GL7 3AG
Tel: 01367 252348
www.bridgehousecampsite.co.uk
Pitches For **Total** 75
Acreage 3½ **Open** Apr **to** Oct
Access Good **Site** Level
Nearest Bus Stop (Miles) ¼
Set on the edge of the Cotswolds, near to Lechlade with its local shops, pubs and resturants.
Facilities
Nearest Town Lechlade
Directions Site is on the A361 to Swindon, approximately 500yds from River Thames. r
≠ Swindon

MORETON VALENCE

Gables Farm Caravan & Camping Site, Moreton Valence, Gloucestershire, GL2 7ND
Tel: 01452 720331
Pitches For 𝗔 ⬛ ⬛ **Total** 30
Acreage 3 **Open** Mar **to** Nov
Access Good **Site** Level
Nearest Bus Stop (Miles) Outside
Facilities ⚡ ⬛ 🅟 ⊙ ⬛ ⬛ ⬛ ⬛ ⬛ ⬛
Nearest Town Gloucester
Directions Leave the M5 at junction 13 and take the A38 north for 2 miles. Or leave the M5 at junction 12 and take the A38 south for 1½ miles.
⬆ Gloucester

MORETONINMARSH

MoretonInMarsh Caravan Club Site, Bourton Road, MoretoninMarsh, Gloucestershire, GL56 0BT
Tel: 01608 650519
www.caravanclub.co.uk
Pitches For ⬛ ⬛ **Total** 183
Acreage 21 **Open** All Year
Access Good **Site** Level
Nearest Bus Stop (Miles) ¼
Attractive, wooded site offering crazy golf, 5-a-side football, volleyball and a boules pitch. Near Batsford Arboretum & Falconry Centre and Sleepy Hollow Farm Park. Non members welcome. Booking essential.
Facilities ⬛ ⚡ ⬛ ⬛ 🅟 ⊙ ⬛ ⬛
⬛ ⬛ ⬛ ⬛ ⬛ ⬛ ⬛ ⬛ 🛜
Nearest Town Moreton-in-Marsh
Directions Leave Evesham on the A44, site entrance is on the left approx. 1¼ miles past Bourton-on-the-Hill and 150 yards before Moreton-in-Marsh sign. NB: No arrivals before 1pm at weekends and in peak periods.

SLIMBRIDGE

Tudor Caravanning & Camping Park, Shepherds Patch, Slimbridge, Gloucestershire, GL2 7BP
Tel: 01453 890483
Email: cades@tudorcaravanpark.co.uk
www.tudorcaravanpark.com
Pitches For 𝗔 ⬛ ⬛ ⬛ **Total** 75
Acreage 7¼ **Open** All Year
Access Good **Site** Level
Sharpness Canal alongside, Slimbridge Wetlands Centre 800 metres, Cotswold Way 5 miles. Pub on our doorstep. NEW toilet and shower block. AA 4 Pennants. Visit Britain 4*.
Facilities ⬛ ⚡ ⬛ ⬛ 🅟 ⊙ ⬛ ⬛ ⬛
⬛ ⬛ ⬛ ⬛ ⬛ ⬛
Nearest Town Dursley/Gloucester
Directions Leave the M5 at junction 13 and follow signs for WWT Wetlands Centre, Slimbridge. 1½ miles off the A38 at the rear of the Tudor Arms Pub.
⬆ Dursley

TEWKESBURY

Croft Farm Leisure & Water Park, Bredons Hardwick, Tewkesbury, Gloucestershire, GL20 7EE
Tel: 01684 772321
Email: alan@croftfarmleisure.co.uk
www.croftfarmleisure.co.uk
Pitches For 𝗔 ⬛ ⬛ ⬛ **Total** 60
Acreage 10 **Open** Mar **to** Oct
Access Good **Site** Level
Nearest Bus Stop (Miles) ¼
Lakeside location with own watersports centre and lake for sailing, windsurfing and canoeing. River Avon close by. Gym and Clubhouse on site.
Facilities ⬛ ⚡ ⬛ ⬛ 🅟 ⊙ ⬛ ⬛ ⬛ ⬛
⬛ ⬛ ⬛ ⬛ ⬛ ⬛ ⬛ ⬛ ⬛ ⬛ ⬛

Nearest Town Tewkesbury
Directions 1½ miles north-east of Tewkesbury on the B4080.
⬆ Ashchurch

TEWKESBURY

Dawleys Caravan Park, Owls Lane, Shuthonger, Tewkesbury, Gloucestershire, GL20 6EQ
Tel: 01684 292622
Email: enquiries@dawleyscaravanpark.co.uk
www.ukparks.co.uk/dawleys
Pitches For 𝗔 ⬛ ⬛ **Total** 20
Acreage 3 **Open** Apr **to** Sept
Access Fair **Site** Sloping
Nearest Bus Stop (Miles) ½
Secluded rural site, near a river. Close to the M5 and M50.
Facilities ⬛ ⚡ ⬛ ⬛ 🅟 ⊙ ⬛ ⬛
⬛ ⬛ ⬛ ⬛
Nearest Town Tewkesbury
Directions A38 north from Tewkesbury, approimately 2 miles on the left hand side. Or 1¼ miles south on A38 from M50 junction 1.
⬆ Tewkesbury

TEWKESBURY

Mill Avon Holiday Park, Gloucester Road, Tewkesbury, Gloucestershire, GL20 5SW
Tel: 01684 296876
Email: millavon@btconnect.com
www.millavon.com
Pitches For ⬛ ⬛ **Total** 24
Open Mar **to** Dec
Access Good **Site** Level
Nearest Bus Stop (Miles) ¼
Alongside river, close to town centre.
Facilities ⬛ ⚡ ⬛ ⬛ 🅟 ⊙ ⬛ ⬛ ⬛
⬛ ⬛ ⬛ ⬛ ⬛ ⬛ ⬛ ⬛
Nearest Town Tewkesbury
Directions ¼ of a mile from the town centre.
⬆ Ashchurch

TEWKESBURY

Sunset View Park, Church End Lane, Twyning, Nr Tewkesbury, Gloucestershire, GL20 6DA
Tel: 01684 292145
Email: info@hollandparks.com
www.hollandparks.com
Pitches For 𝗔 ⬛ ⬛ **Total** 80
Acreage 7½ **Open** All Year
Access Good **Site** Level
Nearest Bus Stop (Miles) ¼
Facilities ⚡ ⬛ ⬛ ⬛ 🅟 ⬛ ⬛ ⬛ ⬛ 🛜
Nearest Town Tewkesbury
Directions From Tewkesbury take the A38 towards Worcester. Park is signposted on the right, approx. 1 mile.
⬆ Ashchurch/Tewkesbury

TEWKESBURY

Tewkesbury Abbey Caravan Club Site, Gander Lane, Tewkesbury, Gloucestershire, GL20 5PG
Tel: 01684 294035
www.caravanclub.co.uk
Pitches For 𝗔 ⬛ ⬛ **Total** 145
Acreage 9 **Open** Mar **to** Nov
Access Good **Site** Lev/Slope
Nearest Bus Stop (Miles) ½
Situated adjacent to the ancient Abbey. Many interesting walks, historic buildings and museums locally. Near the Battle Trail and Royal Worcester Factory. Non members welcome. Booking essential.
Facilities ⬛ ⚡ ⬛ ⬛ 🅟 ⊙ ⬛ ⬛
⬛ ⬛ ⬛ ⬛ ⬛ ⬛ ⬛ 🛜
Nearest Town Tewkesbury

Directions Leave the M5 at junc 9 and take the A438 sp Tewkesbury. At the traffic lights by Morrisons go straight on, at the town centre crossroads keep left and after 200 yards turn left into Gander Lane, site is on the left.
⬆ Tewkesbury

TEWKESBURY

Winchcombe Camping & Caravanning Club Site, Brooklands Farm, Alderton, Nr Tewkesbury, Gloucestershire, GL20 8NX
Tel: 01242 620259
Email:
winchcombe.site@thefriendlyclub.co.uk
www.campingandcaravanningclub.co.uk/winchcombe
Pitches For 𝗔 ⬛ ⬛ **Total** 84
Acreage 20 **Open** Mar **to** 11-Jan
Access Good **Site** Level
Nearest Bus Stop (Miles) 1
Set amidst the lovely Cotswold countryside, with its own fishing lake. Lodges available for hire. Non members welcome. You can also call us on 0845 130 7633 to book.
Facilities ⬛ ⚡ ⬛ ⬛ 🅟 ⊙ ⬛ ⬛ ⬛
⬛ ⬛ ⬛ ⬛ ⬛ ⬛ ⬛ ⬛ ⬛ 🛜
Nearest Town Tewkesbury
Directions From Tewkesbury take the A46, at the roundabout go straight over then take the B4077 to Stow-on-the-Wold, site is on the right in 3 miles.
⬆ Tewkesbury

HAMPSHIRE

ASHURST

Ashurst Caravan & Camping Site, Lyndhurst Road, Ashurst, Hampshire, SO42 7AR
Tel: 02476 423008
Email:
enquiries@campingintheforest.co.uk
www.campingintheforest.co.uk
Pitches For 𝗔 ⬛ ⬛ **Total** 280
Open 10-Apr **to** 29-Sep
Access Good **Site** Level
Just a 5 minute walk to the shops, pub and railway station of Ashurst Village.
Facilities ⬛ ⚡ 🅟 ⊙ ⬛ ⬛ ⬛ ⬛
Nearest Town Ashurst
Directions 2 miles northeast of Lyndhurst on the A35. Pass through Ashurst Village with the train station to the left, continue over the railway bridge and Ashurst Site is sp left.
⬆ Ashurst

BRANSGORE

Harrow Wood Farm Caravan Park, Poplar Lane, Bransgore, Nr Christchurch, Hampshire, BH23 8JE
Tel: 01425 672487
Email: harrowwood@caravan-sites.co.uk
www.caravan-sites.co.uk
Pitches For ⬛ ⬛ **Total** 60
Open Mar **to** 06-Jan
Access Good **Site** Level
Nearest Bus Stop (Miles) ½
Set in 80 acres of farmland. Within easy reach of the New Forest and the sea.
Facilities ⬛ ⚡ ⬛ 🅟 ⊙ ⬛ ⬛ ⬛
⬛ ⬛ ⬛ ⬛ 🛜
Nearest Town Christchurch
Directions 4 miles from Christchurch on the A35, in Bransgore turn first right after the school into Poplar Lane.
⬆ Hinton Admiral

63

BROCKENHURST

Aldridge Hill Caravan & Camping Site,
Brockenhurst, Hampshire, SO42 7QD
Tel: 02476 423008
Email:
enquiries@campingintheforest.co.uk
www.campingintheforest.co.uk
Pitches For ⚊ ⚊ ⚊ **Total** 170
Open 22 May2 Jun **to** 26 Jun 8 Sept
Access Poor **Site** Level
The site borders Obar Water where you can follow the Obar Water Trail. No toilet on site chemical toilet required.
Facilities ⚊⚊⚊
Nearest Town Brockenhurst
Directions From Lyndhurst take the A337 towards Brockenhurst, turn right onto the B3055 and turn first right into The Rise. At the end of the road turn right, after 1 miles turn right into Beachem Wood Car Park.
⚊ Brockenhurst

BROCKENHURST

Hollands Wood Caravan & Camping Site, Lyndhurst Road, Brockenhurst, Hampshire, SO42 7QH
Tel: 02476 423008
Email:
enquiries@campingintheforest.co.uk
www.campingintheforest.co.uk
Pitches For ⚊ ⚊ ⚊ **Total** 600
Open 10-Apr **to** 29-Sep
Access Good **Site** Level
set in 22 hectacres of woodland, 10 minute stroll to Brockenhurst Village, numerous walking and cycling paths, Lymington River.
Facilities ⚊⚊⚊⚊⚊⚊⚊
Nearest Town Brockenhurst
Directions From the A337 at the TJunction turn left onto the A35 (one way) sp All Traffic. Turn right onto the A35 (one way) sp Lymington and Brockenhurst, keep in left hand lane and continue onto the A337, turn left at sign for Hollands Wood.
⚊ Brockenhurst

BROCKENHURST

Roundhill Caravan & Camping Site,
Beaulieu Road, Brockenhurst, Hampshire, SO42 7QL
Tel: 02476 423008
Email:
enquiries@campingintheforest.co.uk
www.campingintheforest.co.uk
Pitches For ⚊ ⚊ ⚊ **Total** 500
Open 10-Apr **to** 29-Sep
Access Good **Site** Sloping
Nearby at Beaulieu youll find the National Motor Museum. New Forest Ponies roamin free.
Facilities ⚊⚊⚊⚊⚊⚊⚊⚊

Nearest Town Brockenhurst
Directions From Lyndhurst take the A337 towards Lymington. At Brockenhurst turn left onto the B3055 towards Beaulieu, after approx. 1½ miles turn right into the Site.
⚊ Brockenhurst

CADNAM

Ocknell Caravan & Camping Site,
Fritham, Hampshire, SO43 7HH
Tel: 02476 423008
Email:
enquiries@campingintheforest.co.uk
www.campingintheforest.co.uk
Pitches For ⚊ ⚊ ⚊ **Total** 280
Open 10-Apr **to** 29-Sep
Access Good **Site** Level
Only 16 miles from the Roman town of Salisbury with its magnificent cathedral.
Facilities ⚊⚊⚊⚊⚊⚊
Nearest Town Cadnam
Directions From west eastbound on A31, approx 8 miles from Ringwood, site is signposted on your left (if you reachj1 of M27 you have missed turning)
⚊ Brockenhurst

FAREHAM

Dibles Park, Dibles Road, Warsash, Southampton, Hampshire, SO31 9SA
Tel: 01489 575232
Email: dibles.park@btconnect.com
www.diblespark.co.uk
Pitches For ⚊ ⚊ ⚊ ⚊ **Total** 14
Open All Year
Access Good **Site** Level
Nearest Bus Stop (Miles) ½
Ideal for touring, walking and cycling. Excellent location for cross Channel ferries. Near Hamble Estuary and nature reserves.
Facilities ⚊⚊⚊⚊⚊⚊⚊⚊⚊⚊
Nearest Town Fareham/Southampton
Directions Leave the M27 at junc 9 and take the A27 for Fareham. At the next roundabout exit sp Park Gate A27. At the third roundabout take the exit onto Brook Lane. Continue along this road going across 3 roundabouts, at 4th roundabout (mini) take second exit into Dibles Road, Park entrance is 500 yards on the left.
⚊ Swanwick

FORDINGBRIDGE

Hill Cottage Farm Camping & Caravan Park, Sandleheath Road, Alderholt, Fordingbridge, Hampshire, SP6 3EG
Tel: 01425 650513
Email:
hillcottagefarmcaravansite@supanet.com
www.hillcottagefarmcampingandcaravanpark.com

Pitches For ⚊ ⚊ ⚊ ⚊ **Total** 90
Acreage 12 **Open** Mar **to** Oct
Access Good **Site** Level
Nearest Bus Stop (Miles) ½
Situated on the edge of the New Forest. Listed in Practical Caravans Top 100 Parks.
Facilities ⚊⚊⚊⚊⚊⚊⚊⚊⚊⚊⚊⚊⚊⚊⚊⚊⚊⚊⚊⚊⚊
Nearest Town Fordingbridge
Directions 2 miles from Fordingbridge on the B3078.
⚊ Salisbury

HAMBLE

Riverside Holidays, Satchell Lane, Hamble, Hampshire, SO31 4HR
Tel: 023 8045 3220
Email: enquiries@riversideholidays.co.uk
www.riversideholidays.co.uk
Pitches For ⚊ ⚊ ⚊ ⚊ **Total** 77
Acreage 2 **Open** March **to** October
Access Good **Site** Lev/Slight Slope
Nearest Bus Stop (Miles) 0.5
Overlooking the River Hamble with a marina below the park. In the very pretty village of Hamble. AA 4 Pennants, 3 Star Rose Award and David Bellamy Bronze Award for Conservation.
Facilities ⚊⚊⚊⚊⚊⚊⚊⚊⚊⚊⚊⚊⚊⚊⚊
Nearest Town Southampton
Directions Leave the M27 at junction 8, follow signs for Hamble Village on the B3397 for approx. 2 miles, then turn left into Satchell Lane. Riverside is on the left hand side of Satchell Lane above Mercury Marina.
⚊ Hamble

HAYLING ISLAND

Fleet Park, Yew Tree Road, Hayling Island, Hampshire, PO11 0QE
Tel: 02392 463684
www.haylingcampsites.co.uk
Pitches For ⚊ ⚊ ⚊ **Total** 150
Acreage 4 **Open** Mar **to** Oct
Access Good **Site** Level
Nearest Bus Stop (Miles) ¼
Level pitches surrounded by oak trees and by a tidal creek.
Facilities ⚊⚊⚊⚊⚊⚊⚊⚊⚊⚊
Nearest Town Hayling Island
Directions 4 miles south of Havent on A3023, site is on Yew Tree Road behind the pub.
⚊ Havant

HAYLING ISLAND

Oven Camping Site, Manor Road, Hayling Island, Hampshire, PO11 0QX
Tel: 02392 464695
Email: theovencampsite@talktalk.net
www.haylingcampsites.co.uk

Pitches For ▲ ⊕ ⊟ Total 330
Acreage 10 **Open** Mar **to** Dec Incl.
Access Good **Site** Level
Nearest Bus Stop (Miles) Outside
Heated swimming pool. Excellent touring area for Portsmouth, Chichester, New Forest etc. Safe, clean, Blue Flag beaches, excellent for water sports. Static caravan rental Excellent Rally site at discount prices.3 nights for the price in off peak times
Facilities ⬤ ✶ ⬚ ⬚ ⬚ ⊙ ⬚ ⬚ ⬚
⬚ ⬚ ⬚ ⬚ ✕ ⬚ ⬚ ⬚ ⬚ ⬚ ⬚ ⬚
Nearest Town Havant
Directions Exit M27 or the A37 at Havant. Take the A3023 from Havant, approx 3 miles after crossing bridge onto Hayling Island bear right at the roundabout. Site is on the left in 450yds.
⇌ Havant

LYNDHURST
Denny Wood Caravan & Camping Site, Beaulieu Road, Lyndhurst, Hampshire, SO43 7FZ
Tel: 02476 423008
Email:
enquiries@campingintheforest.co.uk
www.campingintheforest.co.uk
Pitches For ▲ ⊕ ⊟ Total 170
Open 10-Apr **to** 29-Sep
Access Good **Site** Level
Ideal for cyclists with Brockenhurst reachable without using any roads.
Facilities ⬚ ⬚ ⬚
Nearest Town Lyndhurst
Directions From Lyndhurst take the A35 (High Street), turn right onto the B3056 Beaulieu Road and stay on it for just over a mile before reaching Denny Wood.
⇌ Beaulieu

MILFORD-ON-SEA
Lytton Lawn Touring Park, Lymore Lane, Milford-on-Sea, Hampshire, SO41 0TX
Tel: 01590 648331
Email: holidays@shorefield.co.uk
www.shorefield.co.uk
Pitches For ⊕ ⊟ Total 136
Acreage 5 **Open** 06-Feb **to** 02-Jan
Access Good **Site** Level
Nearest Bus Stop (Miles) ¼
10 minutes walk to the beach. 10 minute drive from New Forest.
Facilities ⬤ ✶ ⬚ ⬚ ⬚ ⬚ ⊙ ⬚ ⬚ ⬚
⬚ ⬚ ⬚ ⬚ ⬚ ⬚ ⬚ ⬚
Nearest Town Lymington
Directions A337 from Lymington or New Milton then B3058 to Milford on Sea.
⇌ New Milton

NEW MILTON
Hoburne Bashley, Sway Road, New Milton, Hampshire, BH25 5QR
Tel: 01425 612340
Email: hoburnebashley@hoburne.com
www.hoburne.com
Pitches For ⊕ ⊟ Total 289
Open 05-Feb **to** 30-Oct
Access Good **Site** Lev/Slope
Nearest Bus Stop (Miles) 0.75
Within the boundaries of the New Forest, and within 2 miles of the beach. Perfect location for touring, 10 miles from Bournemouth. Own golf course and tennis. Many facilities.
Facilities ✶ ⬚ ⬚ ⬚ ⬚ ⬚ ⊙ ⬚ ⬚ ⬚ ⬚
⬚ ⬚ ⬚ ⬚ ✕ ⬚ ⬚ ⬚ ⬚ ⬚ ⬚ ⬚ ⬚
Nearest Town New Milton
Directions From the A35 Lyndhurst/Bournemouth road, take the B3055 signposted Sway. Over crossroads at 2¼ miles. Park is ½ a mile on the left.
⇌ New Milton

NEW MILTON
Setthorns Caravan & Camping Site, Wootton, New Milton, Hampshire, BH25 5WA
Tel: 02476 423008
Email:
enquiries@campingintheforest.co.uk
www.campingintheforest.co.uk
Pitches For ▲ ⊕ ⊟ Total 237
Open All Year
Access Good **Site** Level
Dismantled railwayline, fantastic trackways to explor. No showers and no WC.
Facilities ✶ ⬚ ⬚ ⬚ ⬚ ⬚ ✎
Nearest Town Sway
Directions From Brockenhurst take the B3055, after approx a mile turn right sp Burley. After 1 miles turn left then left again arriving in New Milton.
⇌ Brockenhurst

OWER
Green Pastures Park Ower, Romsey, Hampshire, SO51 6AJ
Tel: 023 8081 4444
Email: enquiries@greenpasturesfarm.com
www.greenpasturesfarm.com
Pitches For ▲ ⊕ ⊟ ⊟ Total 45
Acreage 5 **Open** 15-Mar **to** Oct
Access Good **Site** Level
A grassy site on family run farm, within easy reach of the New Forest. Pub with good food only a 20 minute walk. Paultons Park 1 mile. Convenient for ferries. Ample space for children to play in full view of units. Separate toilet/shower room for the disabled. Day kennelling available. Emergency telephone only.

Facilities ⬤ ✶ ⬚ ⬚ ⬚ ⬚ ⊙ ⬚ ⬚ ⬚
⬚ ⬚ ⬚ ⬚ ⬚ ⬚ ⬚ ⬚
Nearest Town Romsey
Directions Leave the M27 at junction 2 and follow signposts for Salisbury for ½ a mile. Then start to follow our own signs. Also signposted from the A36 and the A3090 at Ower.
⇌ Romsey

RINGWOOD
Oakdene Forest Park, St Leonards, Ringwood, Hampshire, BH24 2RZ
Tel: 01590 648331
Email: holidays@shorefield.co.uk
www.shorefield.co.uk
Pitches For ▲ Total 14
Acreage 55 **Open** 10-Feb **to** 02-Jan
Access Good **Site** Level
Nearest Bus Stop (Miles) ½
Bordering Avon Forest, surrounded by parkland and Forestry Commission land. 9 miles from Bournemouth beaches. Go Active activities.
Facilities ⬚ ⬚ ⊙ ⬚ ⬚
⬚ ⬚ ✕ ⬚ ⬚ ⬚ ⬚ ⬚ ⬚ ⬚ ⬚ ⬚ ⬚
Nearest Town Ringwood
Directions 3 miles west of Ringwood off the A31 just past St Leonards Hospital.
⇌ Bournemouth

RINGWOOD
The Red Shoot Camping Park, Linwood, Nr Ringwood, Hampshire, BH24 3QT
Tel: 01425 473789
Email: enquiries@redshoot-campingpark.com
www.redshoot-campingpark.com
Pitches For ▲ ⊕ ⊟ Total 130
Acreage 4 **Open** March **to** October
Access Good **Site** Lev/Slope
Situated in a beautiful part of the New Forest. Half hour drive to Bournemouth coast, Salisbury and Southampton. Excellent modern shower facilities. Good pub adjacent. Off peak tariff early season.
Facilities ⬤ ✶ ⬚ ⬚ ⬚ ⊙ ⬚ ⬚ ⬚
⬚ ⬚ ⬚ ⬚ ✕ ⬚ ⬚ ⬚ ⬚
Nearest Town Ringwood
Directions Fron Ringwood take A338, 2 miles north of Ringwood take right turn signed Moyles Court and Linwood. Follow signs to Linwood.
⇌ Brockenhurst

ROMSEY

Hill Farm Caravan Park, Branches Lane, Sherfield English, Romsey, Hampshire, SO51 6FH
Tel: 01794 340402
Email: joe@hillfarmpark.com
www.hillfarmpark.com
Pitches For Å ⚑ ⚑ ⚑ Total 0
Acreage 11 **Open** Mar to Oct
Access Good **Site** Level
Nearest Bus Stop (Miles) ¼
Close to Poultons Park, also central for Southampton, Winchester, Salisbury & coast.
Facilities ⚇ ⬩ 🖭 🛊 🔌 ⬩⊙⬩ 🔌 🖾 🛜
⬩ 🛒 Å ✱🛏⊞⬩ 🗠 ⬩ ☕
Nearest Town Romsey
🚲 Romsey

SOUTHSEA

Southsea Leisure Park, Melville Road, Southsea, Hampshire, PO4 9TB
Tel: 02392 735070
Email: info@southsealeisurepark.com
www.southsealeisurepark.com
Pitches For Å ⚑ ⚑ ⚑ Total 188
Acreage 12 **Open** All Year
Access Good **Site** Level
Nearest Bus Stop (Miles) ½
Direct beach access, ideal base to explore Portsmouth and Southsea.Ideal for continental ferries.
Facilities ⚇ ⬩ 🖭 🛊 🔌 ⊙⬩ 🗠 🖾 ☕
⬩ ✱🛒 🛜 ♠ Å ✱🛏⊞⬩ 🗠 ⬩ ☕
Nearest Town Southsea
Directions Follow seafront towards Eastney, as main road bends to the leftSouthsea leisure Park is first right.
🚲 Fratton

ST. LEONARDS

Shamba Holidays, 230 Ringwood Road, St Leonards, Ringwood, Hampshire, BH24 2SB
Tel: 01202 873302
Email: enquiries@shambaholidays.co.uk
www.shambaholidays.co.uk
Pitches For Å ⚑ ⚑ ⚑ Total 150
Acreage 7 **Open** March to October
Access Good **Site** Level
Nearest Bus Stop (Miles) 0.5
Close to Bournemouth and the New Forest. AA 4 Pennants, 4 Star Rose Award, David Bellamy Gold Award for Conservation and 5 Star Loo of the Year Award.
Facilities ⚇ ⬩ 🖭 🛊 ⊙⬩🗠 🛜 🔌 🖾✱ ☕ 🐕♠
🔌 🛒 🛏⊞⬩ 🗠 🛜
Nearest Town Ringwood
Directions Just off the A31 midway between Ringwood and Wimborne.
🚲 Bournemouth

WINCHESTER

Morn Hill Caravan Club Site, Morn Hill, Winchester, Hampshire, SO21 1HL
Tel: 01962 869877
www.caravanclub.co.uk
Pitches For Å ⚑ ⚑ Total 113
Acreage 9 **Open** Mar to Nov
Access Good **Site** Level
Nearest Bus Stop (Miles) ¼
Large site. Near Paultons Leisure Park, Marwell Zoo, Beaulieu, New Forest, Broadlands and Watercress Railway Line. Non members welcome. Booking essential.
Facilities ⚇ ⬩ 🖭 🛊 🔌 🖾 ☕
🛜 🛒 🔌 🐕✱🛏⊞⬩
Directions Leave the M3 onto A31. In 2½ miles at r/about continue on road sp Easton. Immediatly turn right at Neptune Homes, site entrance in 100 yards.
🚲 Winchester

HEREFORDSHIRE
BROMYARD

Boyce Caravan Park, Boyce Farm, Stanford Bishop, Bringsty, Worcestershire, WR6 5UB
Tel: 01886 884248
Email: enquiries@boyceholidaypark.co.uk
www.boyceholidaypark.co.uk
Pitches For Å ⚑ ⚑ Total 14
Open Mar to Oct
Access Good **Site** Level
Excellent area for walking and sight seeing. Close to the cities of Hereford and Worcester.
Facilities ⬩ 🖭 🛊 🔌 🗠⊙⬩ 🗠 🖾 ☕
🔌 🛒 Å 🛏⊞⬩ ⬩ 🗠
Nearest Town Bromyard
Directions From the A44 take the B4220 sp Malvern. On entering the village of Stanford Bishop turn sharp left then first right down a private drive.
🚲 Malvern

BROMYARD

Bromyard Downs Caravan Club Site, Brockhampton, Bringsty, Worcestershire, WR6 5TE
Tel: 01885 482607
www.caravanclub.co.uk
Pitches For ⚑ ⚑ Total 40
Acreage 4 **Open** Mar to Oct
Access Good **Site** Lev/Slope
Rural, woodland site situated in beautiful countryside. Ideal for walkers. Many historic houses, museums and steam railways nearby. Own sanitation required. Non members welcome. Booking essential.
Facilities ⬩ 🗠 🛜 🖾 🔌 🐕
Nearest Town Bromyard
Directions Site on the left of A44 (Worcester-Bromyard) 300 yards past Brockhampton NT entrance immed before sp Bromyard Down.

HAY-ON-WYE

Penlan Caravan & Campsite, Penlan, Brilley, Hay-on-Wye, Herefordshire, HR3 6JW
Tel: 01497 831485
Email: peter@penlan.org.uk
www.penlancampsite.co.uk
Pitches For ▲ ⊞ ⊟ **Total** 20
Acreage 2½ **Open** Easter **to** Oct
Site Level
Peaceful and relaxing site. Ideal for exploring Mid Wales and the black and white villages of Herefordshire. National Trust small holding. Advance booking essential.
Facilities ⨍ ⊞⊡⌐ ☉⨪⊠ ↯⊟ ⩫
Nearest Town Hay-on-Wye
Directions From Kington Church follow the Brilley to Whitney-on-Wye road for 4 miles. Look for National Trust signs on the left, turn sharp left into Apostles Lane, Penlan is first on the right.
⇌ Hereford

HEREFORD

Cuckoos Corner, Moreton-on-Lugg, Herefordshire, HR4 8AH
Tel: 01432 760234
Email: cuckooscorner@gmail.com
www.cuckoocorner.com
Pitches For ▲ ⊞ ⊟ ⊟≀ **Total** 20
Acreage 1½ **Open** All Year
Access Good **Site** Level
Nearest Bus Stop (Miles) Outside
ADULTS ONLY. Friendly site with pleasant views. 15 hard standings: 5' x 45' feet long. Free broadband. Good touring area. Shop and chip shop nearby. 3 miles north of Hereford. Very reasonable rates.
Facilities ⚿ ⨍ ⊞⊡⌐ ☉⨪⊠ ⊞ ⩫
⌇ ⊗ ⨇↯⊟▣⌇
Nearest Town Hereford
Directions 4 miles north of Hereford on the A49, 100 yards beyond signpost Village Centre and Marden. Or 10 miles south of Leominster opposite advance sign Village Centre and Marden.
⇌ Hereford

LEOMINSTER

Arrow Bank Holiday Park, Nun House Farm, Eardisland, Nr Leominster, Herefordshire, HR6 9BG
Tel: 01544 388312
Email: info@arrowbank.co.uk
www.arrowbank.co.uk
Pitches For ▲ ⊞ ⊟ ⊟≀ **Total** 36
Acreage 67 **Open** Mar **to** 07-Jan
Access Good **Site** Level
Nearest Bus Stop (Miles) ¼
ADULTS ONLY. Peaceful, landscaped park with very spacious and level pitches, set in a beautiful Black and White village. Ideal holiday base.
Facilities ⨍ ⊞⊡⌐ ☉⨪⊠ ⊞
⌇ ⊗↯⊟▣⌇ ⩫ ⧈
Nearest Town Leominster
Directions Take the B4360 out of Leominster then continie on the B4529, enter the village of Eardisland and we are signposted on the right hand side.
⇌ Leominster

LEOMINSTER

Nicholson Farm, Docklow, Leominster, Herefordshire, HR6 0SL
Tel: 01568 760346
Email: tjwbrooke@aol.com
www.nicholsonfarm.co.uk
Pitches For ▲ ⊞ ⊟ **Total** 18
Open Easter **to** Oct
Access Good **Site** Level
Fishing lake, Country Walks and Cycling direct from farm.
Facilities ⨍ ⊞⊡⌐ ☉⨪⊠ ▥↯⊟▣ ⩣ ⧈
Nearest Town Leominster
Directions Off the A44 between Leominster and Bromyard, 6 miles from each.
⇌ Leominster

LEOMINSTER

Pearl Lake Leisure Park, Shobdon, Leominster, Herefordshire, HR6 9NQ
Tel: 01568 708326
Email: info@pearllake.co.uk
www.pearllake.co.uk
Pitches For ▲ ⊞ ⊟ ⊟≀ **Total** 15
Acreage 80 **Open** Mar **to** Nov
Access Good **Site** Level
Outstanding park in a beautiful setting with a 15 acre fishing lake, 9 hole golf course, Crown bowls and woodland walks.
Facilities ⚿ ⨍ ⊞⊡⌐ ☉⨪⊠ ⊞
⌇ ⊗⨭♞⊠▥↯⊟▣⌇
Nearest Town Leominster
Directions Situated on the B4362 in the village of Shobdon.
⇌ Leominster

PETERCHURCH

Poston Mill Park, Peterchurch, Golden Valley, Herefordshire, HR2 0SF
Tel: 01981 550225
Email: info@poston-mill.co.uk
www.postonmill.co.uk
Pitches For ▲ ⊞ ⊟ **Total** 64
Acreage 35 **Open** All Year
Access Good **Site** Level
Nearest Bus Stop (Miles) Outside
Highly recommended, beautiful, well maintained park with electric, water and TV (cable) connections on fully serviced pitches. Set on the banks of the River Dore. Shop and Mill Restaurant alongside the Park.
Facilities ⚿ ⨍ ⊞⊡⊞⌐ ☉⨪⊠ ⊞
⌇ ⊗⨭✗⊠♞▥⊞▣⌇ ⩫ ⩣⧈
Nearest Town Hereford
Directions On the B4348, 11 miles from Hereford and 11 miles from Hay on Wye.
⇌ Hereford

ROSSONWYE

Lower Ruxton Farm, Kings Caple, Herefordshire, HR1 4TX
Tel: 01432 840223
Pitches For ▲ ⊟ **Total** 20
Acreage 8 **Open** Mid July **to** End Aug only
Site Level
Nearest Bus Stop (Miles) ½
Alongside a river.
Facilities ⨭ ⊞↯⊟
Nearest Town Ross-on-Wye
Directions A49 from Ross-on-Wye, 1 mile turn right follow signs for Hoarwithy (Kings Caple 4 miles) across river bridge ½ mile sign to Ruxton second farm on right.
⇌ Hereford

ROSS-ON-WYE

Broadmeadow Caravan Park, Broadmeadows, Ross-on-Wye, Herefordshire, HR9 7BW
Tel: 01989 768076
Email: broadm4811@aol.com
www.broadmeadow.info
Pitches For ▲ ⊞ ⊟ **Total** 150
Acreage 16 **Open** Easter/1st Apr **to** Sept
Access Good **Site** Level
Nearest Bus Stop (Miles) ¼
Lake walks. Fishing on site. Only 10 minutes to the centre of Ross-on-Wye. Ideal touring and walking in the Wye Valley. ETB 5 Star Graded.

Facilities ⚿ ⨍ ⊞⊡⌐ ☉⨪⊠ ⊞
⌇ ⊗⊠⊞↯⊟▣⌇ ⩫ ⧈ ⩣
Nearest Town Ross-on-Wye
Directions Adjacent to the A40 Ross relief road. Access from Pancake roundabout off relief road turning into Ross. Take the first turning right into Ashburton Estate Road, then turn right by Morrisons Supermarket.
⇌ Gloucester

SYMONDS YAT WEST

Doward Park Camp Site, Great Doward, Symonds Yat West, Nr Ross-on-Wye, Herefordshire, HR9 6BP
Tel: 01600 890438
Email: enquiries@dowardpark.co.uk
www.dowardpark.co.uk
Pitches For ▲ ⊟ **Total** 27
Acreage 4 **Open** Mar **to** Oct
Access Good **Site** Level
Very scenic and peaceful site with excellent, clean facilities. Close to the River Wye with woodland and river walks. Ideal base for touring the Wye Valley and the Forest of Dean.
Facilities ⨍ ⊞⊡⌐ ☉⊞↯⊟ ⩫
Nearest Town Monmouth
Directions On the A40 between Ross-on-Wye and Monmouth. Turn off at Symonds Yat West and follow signs for The Doward.
⇌ Hereford

SYMONDS YAT WEST

Sterretts Caravan Park, Symonds Yat (West), Nr RossonWye, Herefordshire, HR9 6BY
Tel: 01594 832888/833162
www.ukparks.co.uk/sterretts
Pitches For ▲ ⊞ ⊟ **Total** 8
Acreage 9 **Open** Feb **to** Nov
Access Good **Site** Level
Nearest Bus Stop (Miles) ½
Near a river. Ideal for walking, fishing, canoeing, rock climbing and touring the Forest of Dean. Pets welcome with tourers.Static holiday caravans for hire.
Facilities ⨍ ⊞⊡⌐ ☉⊞↯⊟ ⊞
⌇ ⊠↯⊟
Nearest Town Ross-on-Wye
Directions Take the A40 from Ross-on-Wye or Monmouth to Whitchurch, turn off and follow signs to Symonds Yat go over a small roundabout by the school, after 200 yards you will come to a large car park, drive through on the right road ignor the left hand road thats not us.
⇌ Hereford

HERTFORDSHIRE

HERTFORD

Hertford Camping & Caravanning Club Site, Mangrove Road (Not Ball Park), Hertford, Hertfordshire, SG13 8AJ
Tel: 01992 586696
Email: hertford.site@thefriendlyclub.co.uk
www.campingandcaravanningclub.co.uk/ hertford
Pitches For ▲ ⊞ ⊟ **Total** 250
Open All Year
Site Level
Set in acres of meadowland. 5 miles from Hatfield House and 20 miles from London. Non members welcome. You can also call us on 0845 130 7633. to book.
Facilities ⚿ ⨍ ⊞⊡⊞⌐ ☉⨪⊠ ⊞
⌇ ⊗⊠▥♞↯⊟▣ ⩫ ⩣⧈

Directions From the A10 follow the A414 Hertford signs to the next roundabout (Foxholes) and go straight across, after 200 yards turn left signposted Balls Park and Hertford University. Turn left at the T-Junction into Mangrove Road, go past Simon Balle School, University and Cricket Ground, site is 400 yards past the cricket club on the left.
⚲ North & East Hertford

HODDESDON

Lee Valley Caravan Park Dobbs Weir, Charlton Meadows, Essex Road, Hoddesdon, Herts, EN11 0AS
Tel: 08456 770609
Email:
dobbsweircampsite@leevalley.org.uk
www.visitleevalley.org.uk/wheretostay
Pitches For Å ⚏ 🚍 🚌 ⚐ **Total** 70
Open Mar **to** Nov
Access Good **Site** Level
Nearest Bus Stop (Miles) ¼
Lee Valley White Water Centre and other Lee Valley attractions.
Facilities ♿ ✦ 🖸 🖾 🚿 ⌂ ⊙ 🍴 🛢 🔲 🍽
♨ 🖸 🖾🏕🖃 ✦⚲
Nearest Town Hoddesdon
⚲ Broxbourne

WALTHAM CROSS

Theobalds Park Camping & Caravanning Club Site, Bulls Cross Ride, Waltham Cross, Hertfordshire, EN7 5HS
Tel: 01992 620604
Email:
theobalds.park@thefriendlyclub.co.uk
www.campingandcaravanningclub.co.uk/
theobaldspark
Pitches For Å ⚏ 🚍 **Total** 90
Acreage 14 **Open** 21-Mar **to** 04-Nov
Access Good **Site** Level
Leafy site just 13 miles from London. Plenty of wildlife to see on the site including birds, foxes, deer and rabbits. Lee Valley nearby which is ideal for boating, sailing and swimming. Non members welcome. You can also call us on 0845 130 7633. to book.
Facilities ✦ 🖸 🖾 🚿 ⌂ ⊙ 🍴 🛢 🔲 🍽
🏧 🖸 🖸 ⚓ 🖾🏕🖃 ⚐ ✦ 🎣
Nearest Town Waltham Cross
Directions Leave the M25 at junction 25, take the A10 towards London keeping to the right hand lane, turn right at the first set of traffic lights signposted Crews Hill. Turn right at the T-Junction (opposite Pied Bull), turn right behind the dog kennels, site is towards the top of the lane on the right.
⚲ Waltham Cross

ISLE OF MAN

UNION MILLS

Glenlough Campsite, Union Mills, Isle Of Man, IM4 4AT
Tel: 01624 822372/852057
Email: glenloughcampsite@manx.net
www.glenloughcampsite.com
Pitches For Å 🚍 **Total** 250
Acreage 10 **Open** Apr **to** Sept
Site Level
Nearest Bus Stop (Miles) Outside
Family run, sheltered site on the TT Course. Located in the scenic central valley.Ideally situated close to sea terminal. 3 Camping Pods available for the outdoor camping experience with a cosy and peaceful nights sleep! Everyone welcome.
Facilities ✦ 🖸 🖾 🚿 ⌂ ⊙ 🍴 🔲 🐕 🖃
Nearest Town Douglas
Directions 3 miles from Douglas on the A1 Douglas to Peel road.
⚲ Douglas

ISLE OF WIGHT

ATHERFIELD

Chine Farm Camping Site, Military Road, Atherfield Bay, Nr Chale, Ventnor, Isle Of Wight, PO38 2JH
Tel: 01983 740901
Email: jill@chine-farm.co.uk
www.chine-farm.co.uk
Pitches For Å ⚏ 🚍 🚌 ⚐ **Total** 80
Acreage 10 **Open** Easter **to** Sept
Access Good **Site** Level
Nearest Bus Stop (Miles) Outside
Footpath from the Site to the beach. Spacious pitches with wonderful views of the sea, coast and countryside.
Facilities ✦ 🖸 🖾 ⌂ ⊙ 🍴 🛢 🔲 🍽
♨ 🖸 🖾 ⚓🏕🖃 ✦⚲
Nearest Town Freshwater
Directions Situated on the A3055 coast road, halfway between Freshwater Bay and Ventnor.
⚲ Sandown

BRIGHSTONE BAY

Grange Farm Caravan & Camping Site, Military Road, Brighstone Bay, Isle Of Wight, PO30 4DA
Tel: 01983 740296
Email:
grangefarmholiday@googlemail.com
www.grangefarmholidays.com
Pitches For Å ⚏ 🚍 **Total** 60
Open Mar **to** 1st Nov
Access Good **Site** Level
Nearest Bus Stop (Miles) Outside
We have direct access to Brighstone Beach,in an area of outstanding beauty with great views.
Facilities ✦ 🖸 🖾 🚿 ⌂ ⊙ 🍴 🛢 🔲 🍽
♨ 🖸 🖸 ⚓ 🍴 🏕🖃🖃 🔲 ⚐
Nearest Town Freshwater
Directions From Freshwater Bay take the A3055 towards Ventnor we are approx 7 miles, on the right.
⚲ Shanklin

COWES

Waverley Park Holiday Centre, 51 Old Road, East Cowes, Isle Of Wight, PO32 6AW
Tel: 01983 293452
Email: sue@waverley-park.co.uk
www.waverley-park.co.uk
Pitches For Å ⚏ 🚍 🚌 ⚐ **Total** 45
Acreage 10½ **Open** All Year
Access Good **Site** Terraced
Nearest Bus Stop (Miles) ¼
Only holiday park with statics, tourers and camping within walking distance of Cowes and Osborne House. US RV's by arrangement.
Facilities ♿ ✦ 🖃 🖸 🖾 ⌂ ⊙ 🍴 🛢 🔲 🍽
♨ 🖸 🖸 ⚓ 🍴 🖾 🏕 🛶 🏕🖃🖃 ⚐
Nearest Town Cowes
Directions Signposted from Red Funnel Ferries, only 500 yards from the East Cowes Terminal.
⚲ Ryde

FRESHWATER

Compton Farm, Brook, Newport, Isle Of Wight, PO30 4HF
Tel: 01983 740215
www.comptonfarm.co.uk
Pitches For Å 🚍 **Total** 28
Acreage 17 **Open** May **to** Sept
Site Level
Nearest Bus Stop (Miles) ¼
A working farm near the beach and chalk downland. Wonderful walks locally. Booking essential. Sorry, No Touring Caravans.

Facilities 🖾 🖸 🍴 ⌂ ⊙ 🍴 🛢 🔲 🍽 ✦
Nearest Town Freshwater
Directions From Freshwater Bay take the A3055 (Military Road), after 1½ miles turn left at NT car park.

FRESHWATER

Heathfield Farm Camping, Heathfield Road, Freshwater, Isle Of Wight, PO40 9SH
Tel: 01983 407822
Email: web@heathfieldcamping.co.uk
www.heathfieldcamping.co.uk
Pitches For Å ⚏ 🚍 **Total** 60
Acreage 5 **Open** May **to** Sept **Site** Level
Nearest Bus Stop (Miles) Outside
Facilities ♿ ✦ 🖾 🖸 🍴 ⌂ ⊙ 🍴 🛢 🔲 🍽
🖸 ⚓ 🖾🏕🖃🖃 ⚐
Nearest Town Freshwater
Directions 2 miles from Yarmouth ferry port, head towards Freshwater
⚲ Shanklin

RYDE

Beaper Farm Camping & Caravan Park, Nr Ryde, Isle Of Wight, PO33 1QJ
Tel: 01983 615210/875184
Email: beaper@btinternet.com
www.beaperfarm.com
Pitches For Å ⚏ 🚍 **Total** 150
Acreage 13 **Open** May **to** Sept
Access Good **Site** Level
Nearest Bus Stop (Miles) ¼
Near to beaches, golf, water sports, fishing trips, horse riding, ice skating, ten pin bowling and nightclubs, plus Isle of Wight Steam Railway.
Facilities ♿ ✦ 🖾 🖸 🍴 ⌂ 🛢 🔲 🍽
🖸 🏕🖃🖃 ⚐
Nearest Town Ryde
Directions On the main A3055 Ryde to Sandown road, go past Tesco roundabout for ½ mile, Beaper Farm is second on the left.
⚲ Ryde

RYDE

Whitefield Forest Touring Park, Brading Road, Ryde, Isle Of Wight, PO33 1QL
Tel: 01983 617069
Email: pat&louise@whitefieldforest.co.uk
www.whitefieldforest.co.uk
Pitches For Å ⚏ 🚍 **Total** 90
Acreage 23 **Open** 28-Mar **to** 06-Oct
Access Good **Site** Level
Nearest Bus Stop (Miles) Outside
Set in the ancient woodland of Whitefield Forest. We provide ideal holidays for families, couples and individuals.
Facilities ♿ ✦ 🖾 🖸 🍴 ⌂ ⊙ 🍴 🛢 🔲 🍽
♨ 🖸 🖾🏕🖃🖃
Directions From Ryde take the A3055 to Brading, at Tescos roundabout go straight over and the Park is ½ a mile on the left.
⚲ Smallbrook

SANDOWN

Adgestone Camping & Caravanning Club Site, Lower Adgestone Road, Adgestone, Isle Of Wight, PO36 0HL
Tel: 01983 403432
Email: adgestone.site@thefriendlyclub.co.uk
www.campingandcaravanningclub.co.uk/
adgestone
Pitches For Å ⚏ 🚍 **Total** 270
Acreage 22 **Open** Apr **to** Sept
Access Difficult **Site** Level
Nearest Bus Stop (Miles) ¼
One of the best locations on the Isle of Wight, 1 mile from Sandown. Adjacent to the River Yar and nestled in the valley beneath Brading Downs, an area of natural beauty. Non members welcome. You can also call us on 0845 130 7633. to book.

Facilities ⚹ ⓘ 🔟 🚿 ⌂ ⊙ 🚻 🚮 🔲 🅿
🔊 🗑 🚿 🏪 🎣 ⚲ ⚡ 🔌 🔲 ✎ 🛜
Nearest Town Sandown
Directions Turn off the A3055 Sandown to Shanklin road at Manor House Pub in Lake. Go past the school and golf course on the left and turn right at the T-Junction, park is 200 yards on the right.
🚏 Sandown

SANDOWN
Old Barn Touring Park, Cheverton Farm, Newport Road, Sandown, Isle Of Wight, PO36 9PJ
Tel: 01983 866414
Email: oldbarn@weltinet.com
www.oldbarntouring.co.uk
Pitches For 𝘈 ⚑ ⛺ **Total** 60
Acreage 5 **Open** 01-May **to** 25-Sep
Access Good **Site** Level
Nearest Bus Stop (Miles) ¼
1½ miles from the seaside towns of Sandown and Shanklin. Grade II Listed Barn used as a TV and games room.
Facilities ⚹ ⓘ 🔟 🔲 🚿 ⌂ ⊙ 🚻 🚮 🔲 🅿
🔊 🗑 🚿 🔲 🅿 🔌 🔲 🛜
Nearest Town Sandown
Directions From Newport take the A3056, Park is on the right ½ mile after Apse Heath mini roundabout.
🚏 Lake

SANDOWN
Queen Bower Dairy Caravan Park, Alverstone Road, Queen Bower, Sandown, Isle Of Wight, PO36 0NZ
Tel: 01983 403840
Email: queenbowerdairy@btconnect.com
www.queenbowerdairy.co.uk
Pitches For 𝘈 ⚑ ⛺ **Total** 20
Acreage 2¼ **Open** May **to** Oct
Access Good **Site** Level
Nearest Bus Stop (Miles) ¼
Scenic views, ideal touring. Sell our own produced Dairy products (milk and cream). Public telephone ¼ mile.
Facilities ⚹ ⓘ 🔟 🔊 🚮 🔲
Nearest Town Sandown
Directions On the A3056 Newport to Sandown road, turn into Alverstone Road at Apse Heath crossroads. Park is 1 mile on the left.
🚏 Sandown

SANDOWN
Village Way Caravan & Camping Park, Newport Road, Apse Heath, Sandown, Isle Of Wight, PO36 9PJ
Tel: 01983 863279
Email: norma.smith@btconnect.com
www.villagewaypark.co.uk
Pitches For 𝘈 ⚑ ⛺ **Total** 14
Open All Year
Access Good **Site** Level
Nearest Bus Stop (Miles) ¼
Near the beach. Free carp fishing on site. Beautiful country walks to the woods and within walking distance of a garden centre and Morrisons. The Heights Leisure Centre is only a mile away.
Facilities ⓘ 🔟 🚿 ⌂ ⊙ 🚻 🚮 🔲
🔊 🗑 ✡ 🚮 ✎ 🚿
Nearest Town Sandown
Directions From Newport take the A22 to Blackwater then the A3056 to Apse Heath. We are on the main A3056.

SHANKLIN
Ninham Country Holidays, Shanklin, Isle Of Wight, PO37 7PL
Tel: 01983 864243
Email: office@ninham-holidays.co.uk
www.ninham-holidays.co.uk
Pitches For 𝘈 ⚑ ⛺ **Total** 98
Acreage 10 **Open** May **to** Sept
Access Very Good **Site** Level
Nearest Bus Stop (Miles) ¼
Country park setting close to Islands premier seaside resort. Outdoor heated swimming pool, on-site carp fishing. Great walking and cycling. Ferry travel arranged. On-line booking available.
Facilities ⚸ ⓘ 🔟 🚿 ⌂ ⊙ 🚻 🚮 🔲
🔊 🗑 🚿 🏪 ⚡ 🚮 🔌 🔲 ✎ 🚿 🛜
Nearest Town Shanklin
Directions Signposted off Newport/Sandown road (A3056). Site entrance is ¼ mile west of Morrisons on the left.
🚏 Shanklin

VENTNOR
Appuldurcombe Gardens Holiday Park, Wroxall, Ventnor, Isle Of Wight, PO38 3EP
Tel: 01983 852597
Email: info@appuldurcombegardens.co.uk
www.appuldurcombegardens.co.uk
Pitches For 𝘈 ⚑ ⛺ **Total** 130
Acreage 14 **Open** Mar **to** Nov
Access Good **Site** Lev/Slope
Nearest Bus Stop (Miles) ¼
Countryside location, ideal for walkers and cyclists
Facilities ⚹ ⓘ 🔟 🔟 🚿 ⌂ ⊙ 🚻 🚮 🔲
🔊 🗑 🚿 🏪 ⚡ 🔌 🚮 🔌 🔲 🛜
Nearest Town Ventnor
Directions From Newport take the A3020 and turn off towards Shanklin. Go through Godshill, turn right at Whiteley Bank roundabout towards Wroxall.
🚏 Shanklin

YARMOUTH
The Orchards Holiday Caravan & Camping Park, Newbridge, Yarmouth, Isle Of Wight, PO41 0TS
Tel: 01983 531331
Email: admin@orchards-holiday-park.co.uk
www.orchards-holiday-park.co.uk
Pitches For 𝘈 ⚑ ⛺ **Total** 175
Acreage 8 **Open** 28-Mar **to** 03-Nov
Access Good **Site** Lev/Slope
Nearest Bus Stop (Miles) Outside
Excellent multi award winning family park in a peaceful village setting amid downs and meadowland with glorious views. Luxury Facilities Centre has excellent touring facilities. Also take-away food, shop, pool table, table tennis, play areas and dog walk. Excellent walking and cycling. WiFi available. Booking essential. Special offers see web site.
Facilities ⚹ ⓘ 🔟 🚿 ⌂ ⊙ 🚻 🚮 🔲
🔊 🗑 🚿 🏪 🔲 ⚡ 🚮 ⚡ 🚮 🔌 🔲 🛜
Nearest Town Yarmouth
Directions 4 miles east of Yarmouth and 6 miles west of Newport on B3401. On main Road.
🚏 Lymington

KENT
ASHFORD
Broadhembury Caravan & Camping Park, Steeds Lane, Kingsnorth, Ashford, Kent, TN26 1NQ
Tel: 01233 620859
Email: holidaypark@broadhembury.co.uk
www.broadhembury.co.uk

Pitches For 𝘈 ⚑ ⛺ 🚐 **Total** 80
Acreage 8 **Open** All Year
Access Good **Site** Level
Nearest Bus Stop (Miles) ½
Open all year with centrally heated toilets and showers, en-suite facilities, wheelchair access, playgrounds, games room and every amenity for families. Also adults meadows, the ideal place for those who like things a little quieter! Picturesque villages, sandy beaches, Channel crossings, Canterbury, castles and gardens all within easy reach.
Facilities ⚹ ⓘ 🔟 🚿 ⌂ ⊙ 🚻 🚮 🔲
🔊 🗑 🗑 🚿 🏪 ⚡ 🚮 🔌 🔲 🔲 🚿 🛜
Nearest Town Ashford
Directions Leave the M20 at junction 10, take the A2070 following signs for Kingsnorth. Turn left at the second crossroads in the village.
🚏 Ashford

BIRCHINGTON
Quex Caravan Park, Park Road, Birchington, Kent, CT7 0BL
Tel: 01843 841273
Email: quex@keatfarm.co.uk
www.keatfarm.co.uk
Pitches For ⚑ ⛺ 🚐 **Total** 50
Acreage 3 **Open** 07-Mar **to** 07-Nov
Access Good **Site** Level
Ideal base for touring the areas around Thanet and Canterbury.
Facilities ⓘ 🔟 🚿 ⌂ ⊙ 🚻 🚮 🔲
🔊 🗑 🚿 🏪 🚮 🔌 🔲 🛜
Nearest Town Margate/Ramsgate
Directions Follow road signs to Margate. When in Birchington turn right at mini roundabout (sp Margate). Approximately 100yds after roundabout take the first turning on the right and then right again,left into park road, Park approx ¼ on right.
🚏 Birchington

BIRCHINGTON
St. Nicholas Camping Site, Court Road, St NicholasatWade, Birchington, Kent, CT7 0NH
Tel: 01843 847245
Pitches For 𝘈 ⚑ ⛺ **Total** 75
Acreage 3 **Open** Mar **to** Oct
Access Good **Site** Level
Nearest Bus Stop (Miles) ¼
On the edge of the village with two Pubs serving food and a Post Office.
Facilities ⚹ ⓘ 🔟 🚿 ⌂ ⊙ 🚻 🚮
🔊 🗑 🗑 🚮 🔲
Nearest Town Birchington
Directions Turn off the A28 9½ miles north east of Canterbury to St. Nicholas. Or take the A299 from Herne Bay and turn left signposted St. Nicholas-at-Wade, go over the bridge and into Court Road.
🚏 Birchington

BIRCHINGTON
Two Chimneys Holiday Park, Shottendane Road, Birchington, Kent, CT7 0HD
Tel: 01843 841068/843157
Email: info@twochimneys.co.uk
www.twochimneys.co.uk
Pitches For 𝘈 ⚑ ⛺ **Total** 200
Acreage 30 **Open** Mar **to** Oct
Access Good **Site** Level
Nearest Bus Stop (Miles) ¼
Country site near lovely beaches. Swimming pool with retractable roof, adventure play area and crazy golf on site. Sorry, No dogs. Holiday Caravans available for hire. Storage.
Facilities ⚹ ⓘ 🔟 🚿 ⌂ ⊙ 🚻 🚮 🔲
🔊 🗑 🗑 🚿 🏪 🔌 🔲 🚿 🛜
Nearest Town Margate

Directions 1½ miles from Birchington, turn right into park lane at Birchington Church, left fork "RAF Manston". First left onto B2048 site is ½ a mile on right.
⚐ Birchington

CANTERBURY

Canterbury Camping & Caravanning Club Site, Bekesbourne Lane, Canterbury, Kent, CT3 4AB
Tel: 01227 463216
Email: canterbury.site@thefriendlyclub.co.uk
www.campingandcaravanningclub.co.uk/canterbury
Pitches For ▲ ⚏ ⚍ **Total** 200
Acreage 20 **Open** All Year
Site Lev/Slope
Nearest Bus Stop (Miles) ¼
Close to Canterbury and within easy reach of the Channel ports. 2 miles from Canterbury Cathedral and Howletts Wildlife Park. Local produce sold in the site shop. Non members welcome. You can also call us on 0845 130 7633. to book.
Facilities ⚐ ⚐ ⚐ ⚐ ⚐ ⚐ ⚐ ⚐ ⚐ ⚐
⚐ ⚐ ⚐ ⚐ ⚐ ⚐ ⚐ ⚐
Directions From Canterbury follow the A257 towards Sandwich, turn right opposite the golf course.
⚐ Canterbury

CANTERBURY

Yew Tree Park, Stone Street, Petham, Canterbury, Kent, CT4 5PL
Tel: 01227 700306
Email: info@yewtreepark.com
www.yewtreepark.com
Pitches For ▲ ⚏ ⚍ **Total** 45
Acreage 2 **Open** Mar **to** Oct
Access Good **Site** Lev/Slope
Nearest Bus Stop (Miles) Outside
30 minutes drive from the coast. Ideal touring area.
Facilities ⚐ ⚐ ⚐ ⚐ ⚐ ⚐ ⚐ ⚐ ⚐ ⚐
⚐ ⚐ ⚐ ⚐ ⚐ ⚐
Nearest Town Canterbury
Directions 4 miles south of Canterbury on the B2068, turn right by the Chequers Public House, park entrance is on the left hand side.
⚐ Canterbury

DEAL

Clifford Park Caravans, Clifford Park, Thompson Close, Walmer, Deal, Kent, CT14 7PB
Tel: 01304 373373
Pitches For ▲ ⚏ ⚍ **Total** 15
Open Mar **to** Oct
Access Good **Site** Level
Nearest Bus Stop (Miles) Outside
Just 2 minutes from the village. Ideal for touring and close to ferry ports for the continent. Walmer, Deal and Dover Castles, sea fishing, beach.
Facilities ⚐ ⚐ ⚐ ⚐ ⚐ ⚐ ⚐ ⚐ ⚐ ⚐
Nearest Town Deal
Directions On the A249, 1½ miles from Deal and 6 miles from Dover.
⚐ Walmer

DOVER

Hawthorn Farm, Martin Mill, Dover, Kent, CT15 5LA
Tel: 01304 852658
Email: hawthorn@keatfarm.co.uk
www.keatfarm.co.uk
Pitches For ▲ ⚏ ⚍ **Total** 250
Acreage 27 **Open** Mar **to** Oct
Access Good **Site** Level

Beautiful Award Winning park in a quiet and peaceful location. Superb toilet and shower facilities.
Facilities ⚐ ⚐ ⚐ ⚐ ⚐ ⚐ ⚐ ⚐ ⚐ ⚐ ⚐
⚐ ⚐ ⚐ ⚐ ⚐ ⚐ ⚐ ⚐ ⚐
Nearest Town Dover
Directions Martin Mill is approx. 3 miles from Dover, signposted along the main A258 towards Deal.
⚐ Martin Mill

FOLKESTONE

Black Horse Farm Caravan Club Site, 385 Canterbury Road, Densole, Folkestone, Kent, CT18 7BG
Tel: 01303 892665
www.caravanclub.co.uk
Pitches For ▲ ⚏ ⚍ **Total** 121
Acreage 11 **Open** All Year
Access Good **Site** Level
Nearest Bus Stop (Miles) ¼
Situated in the heart of farming country. Limited hard standings available March to October only. Close to Canterbury, Dover Castle and the Channel Tunnel. Non members welcome. Booking essential.
Facilities ⚐ ⚐ ⚐ ⚐ ⚐ ⚐ ⚐ ⚐
⚐ ⚐ ⚐ ⚐ ⚐ ⚐ ⚐ ⚐
Nearest Town Folkestone
Directions Leave the M20 at junc 13 (at end) and continue onto the A20. Past the end of the tunnel turn off via slip road and roundabout onto the A260 sp Canterbury, go through Hawkinge into Densole. Site is on the left 200 yards past the Black Horse Inn.
⚐ Folkestone

FOLKESTONE

Folkestone Camping & Caravanning Club Site, The Warren, Folkestone, Kent, CT19 6NQ
Tel: 01303 255093
Email: folkestone.site@thefriendlyclub.co.uk
www.campingandcaravanningclub.co.uk/folkestone
Pitches For ▲ ⚍ **Total** 80
Open Apr **to** 03-Nov
Access Difficult **Site** Lev/Slope
Nearest Bus Stop (Miles) ½
Just a short walk to the beach. On a clear day you can see France. Fishing off the site on the sea front, 50 yards. Non members welcome. You can also call us on 0845 130 7633.to book.
Facilities ⚐ ⚐ ⚐ ⚐ ⚐ ⚐ ⚐ ⚐ ⚐ ⚐
⚐ ⚐ ⚐ ⚐ ⚐ ⚐
Directions From the M2 and Canterbury on the A260 take a left turn at the roundabout into Hill Road, Folkestone. Go straight over the crossroads onto Wear Bay Road, turn second left past Martello Tower, site is ½ mile on the right.
⚐ Folkestone

FOLKESTONE

Little Satmar Holiday Park, Winehouse Lane, Capel-le-Ferne, Nr Folkestone, Kent, CT18 7JF
Tel: 01303 251188
Email: satmar@keatfarm.co.uk
www.keatfarm.co.uk
Pitches For ▲ ⚏ ⚍ **Total** 60
Acreage 6 **Open** Mar **to** Oct
Access Good
Quiet, secluded park. Convenient for Channel ports and Tunnel.
Facilities ⚐ ⚐ ⚐ ⚐ ⚐ ⚐ ⚐ ⚐
⚐ ⚐ ⚐ ⚐ ⚐ ⚐ ⚐ ⚐ ⚐
Nearest Town Folkestone

Directions Travelling towards Folkestone on the A20 from Dover, exit left signposted Capel-le-Ferne onto the B2011. After 1 mile turn right into Winehouse Lane.
⚐ Folkestone

FOLKESTONE

Little Switzerland Caravan & Camping Park, Little Switzerland, Wear Bay Road, Folkestone, Kent, CT19 6PS
Tel: 01303 252168
Email: btony328@aol.com
www.caravancampingsites.co.uk
Pitches For ▲ ⚏ ⚍ ⚍ ⚍ **Total** 0
Open Mar **to** Oct
Access Good **Site** Level
Nearest Bus Stop (Miles) Outside
Facilities ⚐ ⚐ ⚐ ⚐ ⚐ ⚐ ⚐ ⚐ ⚐ ⚐ ⚐
⚐ ⚐ ⚐ ⚐ ⚐ ⚐ ⚐ ⚐
Nearest Town Folkestone
Directions From Dover follow Folkestone signs then Country Park signs.
⚐ Folkestone

HERNE BAY

Southview Camping, Southview, Maypole Lane, Hoath, Canterbury, Kent, CT3 4LL
Tel: 01227 860280
Email: southviewcamping@aol.com
www.southviewcamping.co.uk
Pitches For ▲ ⚏ ⚍ **Total** 45
Acreage 3 **Open** Apr **to** Sept
Access Good **Site** Level
Nearest Bus Stop (Miles) ¼
Peaceful country setting. Excellent local pub and restaurant. Central location for Canterbury and the beautiful beaches of Thanet.
Facilities ⚐ ⚐ ⚐ ⚐ ⚐ ⚐ ⚐ ⚐ ⚐ ⚐
⚐ ⚐
Nearest Town Canterbury
Directions Well signed from the A299 at Herne Bay or the A28 near Canterbury.
⚐ Herne Bay

LEYSDOWN-ON-SEA

Priory Hill Holiday Park, Wing Road, Leysdown-on-Sea, Isle of Sheppey, Kent, ME12 4QT
Tel: 01795 510267
Email: pat.lawrence@prioryhill.co.uk
www.prioryhill.co.uk
Pitches For ▲ ⚏ ⚍ **Total** 36
Acreage 1½ **Open** Mar **to** Oct
Access Good **Site** Level
Nearest Bus Stop (Miles) ¼
Seaside park with a clubhouse, indoor heated swimming pool and entertainment on site. Please see our Web Site for details.
Facilities ⚐ ⚐ ⚐ ⚐ ⚐ ⚐ ⚐ ⚐ ⚐ ⚐
Nearest Town Leysdown-on-Sea
Directions From the M2 or M20 onto the A249 then the B2231 to Leysdown, follow tourism signs to Priory Hill.
⚐ Sheerness

MAIDSTONE

Bearsted Caravan Club Site, Ashford Road, Hollingbourne, Maidstone, Kent, ME17 1XH
Tel: 01622 730018
www.caravanclub.co.uk
Pitches For ▲ ⚏ ⚍ **Total** 66
Acreage 6 **Open** Mar **to** Jan
Access Good **Site** Lev/Slope
Peaceful stop-off point (for ferries). Near to Leeds Castle. Non members welcome. Booking essential.
Facilities ⚐ ⚐ ⚐ ⚐ ⚐ ⚐ ⚐ ⚐ ⚐ ⚐
⚐ ⚐ ⚐ ⚐ ⚐
Nearest Town Maidstone

Directions Leave the M20 at junction 8, at the roundabout turn into road sp Bearsted and Maidstone, site is ½ mile on the left.
⚡ Maidstone

MAIDSTONE

Coldblow Camping, Coldblow Farm, Coldblow Lane, Thurnham, Kent, ME14 3LR
Tel: 01622 735038
Email: coldblow@btconnect.com
www.coldblow-camping.co.uk
Pitches For 𝗔 ⛺ 🚐 **Total** 10
Acreage 2 **Open** Apr to Nov
Access Poor **Site** Level
Stunning countryside location on top of Kent Downs in an area of outstanding natural beauty. Horse riding on site. Ideal for visiting Maidstone, Canterbury and central London. 40 minutes to ferries. Open all year subject to ground conditions.
Facilities 🛁 🚿 🍴 ⬛ 🚻 🅿 🔌 📦 ☎ 🛜
Nearest Town Maidstone
Directions From M26 at junc 7 North on A249 turn first right into Detling turn right Pilgrims Way then 2nd left.
⚡ Bearsted

MARDEN

Tanner Farm Touring Caravan & Camping Park, Goudhurst Road, Marden, Kent, TN12 9ND
Tel: 01622 832399
Email: enquiries@tannerfarmpark.co.uk
www.tannerfarmpark.co.uk
Pitches For 𝗔 ⛺ 🚐 **Total** 100
Acreage 15 **Open** All Year
Access Good **Site** Level
Nearest Bus Stop (Miles) Outside
Peaceful, secluded park surrounded by arable farmland, QIT 5 Star Graded Park and David Bellamy Gold Award. Booking essential.
Facilities 🛁 🚿 🍴 🚻 🔌 🅿 🧺 ⬛ ☎ 🛒 🏧 🎮 🏠 🎯 🔥 🎾 🍴 📦 🎣 🎾 🛜
Nearest Town Maidstone/Tunbridge Wells
Directions From the A262 or A229 onto the B2079. Midway between the village of Marden and Goudhurst.
⚡ Marden

RAMSGATE

Nethercourt Touring Park, Nethercourt Hill, Ramsgate, Kent, CT11 0RX
Tel: 01843 595485
Email: nethercourtcamp@aol.com
www.campsite-in-kent.co.uk
Pitches For 𝗔 ⛺ 🚐 **Total** 50
Acreage 2 **Open** All Year
Access Good **Site** Level
Nearest Bus Stop (Miles) Outside
1¼ miles from the beach and harbour. Sea fishing 1 mile. Indoor swimming pool nearby. 3 star site.
Facilities 🛁 🚿 🍴 🚻 🔌 🅿 🧺 ⬛ ☎ 🏧 🎮 🏠 🔥 🎯 🔥 📦 🔌 🎾 🛜
Directions Off Nethercourt Hill on the outskirts of the town.
⚡ Ramsgate

SEVENOAKS

East Hill Farm Park, East Hill Road, Nr Kemsing, Sevenoaks, Kent, TN15 6YD
Tel: 01959 522347
Pitches For 𝗔 **Total** 30
Acreage 6 **Open** Apr to Oct
Site Level
Facilities 🚻 🅿 ☎
Directions Off the A225. Please telephone for directions.
⚡ Otford

SEVENOAKS

Gate House Wood Touring Park, Ford Lane, Wrotham Heath, Sevenoaks, Kent, TN15 7SD
Tel: 01732 843062
Email: gatehousewood@btinternet.com
www.gatehousewoodtouringpark.com
Pitches For 𝗔 ⛺ 🚐 🚐⚡ **Total** 54
Acreage 7 **Open** Mar to Oct
Access Good **Site** Level
Nearest Bus Stop (Miles) ¼
Conveniently situated for Channel ports and sightseeing in South East London (45 minutes by train). Many country pubs, restaurants and take-away nearby.
Facilities 🛁 🚿 🍴 🚻 🔌 🅿 🧺 ⬛ ☎ 🏠 🎯 📦 🔌
Nearest Town Sevenoaks
Directions From North take M20, travelling West M20, Junc 2 turn off follow A20 southbound to Wrotham Heath, follow A20 heading to Maidstone at traffic lights straight over, 1st on left into Ford Lane site 100metres on left.
⚡ Borough Green

SEVENOAKS

Oldbury Hill Camping & Caravanning Club Site, Styants Bottom, Seal, Sevenoaks, Kent, TN15 0ET
Tel: 01732 762728
Email: oldbury.hillsite@thefriendlyclub.co.uk
www.campingandcaravanningclub.co.uk/oldburyhill
Pitches For 𝗔 ⛺ 🚐 **Total** 60
Acreage 6 **Open** 01-Apr to 03-Nov
Access Difficult **Site** Sloping
Nearest Bus Stop (Miles) ½
Set in a quiet countryside location, close to a number of National Trust properties. Non members welcome. You can also call us on 0845 130 7633. to book
Facilities 🛁 🚿 🍴 🚻 🔌 🅿 🧺 ⬛ ☎ 🏧 🎯 🔥 🔌 📦 🛜
Nearest Town Sevenoaks
Directions From Sevenoaks take the A25 towards Borough Green, turn left just after the Crown Point Inn, go down the lane to Styants Bottom, site is on the left.
⚡ Borough Green

SHEERNESS

Sheerness Holiday Park, Halfway Road, Minster-on-Sea, Sheerness, Kent, ME12 3AA
Tel: 01795 662638
Email: rodpluthero@gmail.com
www.sheernesshols.com
Pitches For 𝗔 ⛺ 🚐 **Total** 25
Open Apr to Sept
Access Good **Site** Level
Nearest Bus Stop (Miles) ¼
Indoor pool and a family entertainment venue. Watersports and sailing nearby.
Facilities 🛁 🚿 🍴 🚻 🔌 🅿 ☎ 🏧 🍴 ✖ 🏠 🎯 🔥 🔌 📦 🎾 🛜
Nearest Town Sheerness
Directions From the M2 and A2 follow signs to Sheerness. Site is ½ a mile from the town on the right.
⚡ Sheerness

TONBRIDGE

The Hop Farm Touring & Camping Park, Maidstone Road, Beltring, Nr Tonbridge, Paddock Wood, Kent, TN12 6PY
Tel: 01622 870838
Email: touring@thehopfarm.co.uk
www.thehopfarm.co.uk/touring
Pitches For 𝗔 ⛺ 🚐 **Total** 300
Acreage 400 **Open** Mar to Oct
Access Good **Site** Level
Nearest Bus Stop (Miles) Outside
Next door to the Hop Farm World of Activities Family Park. Ideal touring base for the heart of Kent. Book 3 nights and get a 4th night free and 10 tokens to use at the Hop Farm.
Facilities 🛁 🚿 🍴 🚻 🔌 🅿 🧺 ⬛ ☎ 🏧 🔥 📦 🔌 📦 🛜
Nearest Town Paddock Wood
Directions On the A228 near Paddock Wood. Leave the M20 at junction 4 or the M25 at junction 5 and follow brown tourism signs onto the A21 south.
⚡ Paddock Wood

WHITSTABLE

Primrose Cottage Caravan Park, Golden Hill, Whitstable, Kent, CT5 3AR
Tel: 01227 273694
Email: campbell_brian@btconnect.com
Pitches For 𝗔 ⛺ 🚐 **Total** 0
Acreage 1 **Open** Mar to Oct
Access Good **Site** Level
Nearest Bus Stop (Miles) ¼
Views of the sea and nearby Whitstable. Superstore nearby. 1 mile to the town centre, 15 minutes to Canterbury and within easy reach by road or rail of Herne Bay, Margate and Dover.
Facilities 🛁 🚿 🍴 🚻 🔌 🅿 ⬛ ☎ 🏧 🔥 🛒 🔌 📦
Nearest Town Whitstable
⚡ Whitstable

LANCASHIRE
BENTHAM

Riverside Caravan Park, High Bentham, Lancaster, Lancashire, LA2 7FJ
Tel: 015242 61272
Email: info@riversidecaravanpark.co.uk
www.riversidecaravanpark.co.uk
Pitches For ⛺ 🚐 **Total** 61
Open March to 02-Jan
Access Good **Site** Level
Nearest Bus Stop (Miles) ½
Alongside a river, just a short walk to the town for shops and pubs. Close to the famous Yorkshire Three Peaks for walking.
Facilities 🛁 🚿 🍴 🚻 🔌 🅿 🧺 ⬛ ☎ 🏧 🏠 🎯 🔥 🔌 📦 🎣 🎾 🛜
Nearest Town High Bentham
Directions Follow signs from the B6480 in the middle of High Bentham, turn south at the Black Bull Pub.
⚡ High Bentham

BLACKPOOL

Clifton Fields Caravan Park, Peel Road, Nr Blackpool, Lancashire, FY4 5JU
Tel: 01253 761676
www.cliftonfields.co.uk
Pitches For ⛺ 🚐 **Total** 46
Open Mar to Oct
Access Good **Site** Slightly Sloping
Nearest Bus Stop (Miles) ¼
Semi rural
Facilities 🚿 🍴 🚻 🔌 🅿 ⬛ ☎ 🔌 📦 🔌 📦
Nearest Town Blackpool
Directions Blackpool junction 4 on M55 turn left to Kirkham 400yds, straight on at the roundabout to traffic lights. Turn right and immediate left into Peel Road. 350yds second site on the right.
⚡ Blackpool

BLACKPOOL

Mossview Caravan Park, Bamber Lane, Blackpool, Lancashire, FY4 5LH
Tel: 01253 696640
Email: robsanlee1@gmail.com
Pitches For 𝗔 ⛺ 🚐 🚐⚡ **Total** 17

Acreage 1½ **Open** All year
Access Good **Site** Level
Nearest Bus Stop (Miles) ½
Pleasure beach, Tower.
Facilities ∮ ⊟ ⊞ �ቶ ⍾ ⊒ ☻ ⌦ ⦿ ⍾ ⌂ ☀ ⊹
Nearest Town Blackpool
Directions Exit junc. 2 M55 turn left then first right at next roundabout ¼ mile ahead on right.
⇌ Blackpool Southshore

CARNFORTH

Hollins Farm, Far Arnside, Off Cove Road, Silverdale, Carnforth, Lancashire, LA5 0SL
Tel: 01524 701508
Email: reception@holgates.co.uk
www.holgates.co.uk
Pitches For ▲ ⚑ ⊟ **Total** 0
Acreage 5 **Open** Mar to Oct
Access Good **Site** Lev/Slope
Nearest Bus Stop (Miles) ¼
Situated in an area of outstanding natural beauty, near the shore and a bird reserve. AA most improved campsite 2013 award winner.
Facilities ∮ ⊟ ⊞ ⊞ ቶ ⦿ ⌐ ⊒ ☻
⚲ ⍾ ⊓ ⚘ ⚒ ⌦ ⊟ ☀ ⚘
Nearest Town Arnside
Directions Leave the M6 at junction 35 into Carnforth, follow signs for Silverdale. Go over the level crossing and bear right, after ¾ miles bear left and after ¼ of a mile fork right into Cove Road.
⇌ Arnside/Silverdale

CARNFORTH

Old Hall Caravan Park, Capernwray, Carnforth, Lancashire, LA6 1AD
Tel: 01524 733276
Email: old@oldhallcaravanpark.co.uk
www.oldhallcaravanpark.co.uk
Pitches For ⚑ ⊟ **Total** 38
Open Mar to 10-Jan
Access Good **Site** Level
Quiet, peaceful, woodland retreat.
Facilities ⚬ ∮ ⊟ ⊞ ቶ ⦿ ⌐ ⊒ ☻ ⌦ ◨ ☻
⚲ ⦿ ☻ ⍾ ⌦ ⊟ ⊡ ☀ ⚘ ⚯
Nearest Town Carnforth
Directions Leave the M6 at junction 35, go to Over Kellet. Turn left in the village of Over Kellet and the park is 1½ miles on the right.
⇌ Carnforth

CARNFORTH

Red Bank Farm, The Shore, Bolton-le-Sands, Carnforth, Lancashire, LA5 8JR
Tel: 01524 823196
Email: mark@redbankfarm.co.uk
www.redbankfarm.co.uk
Pitches For ▲ ⊟ **Total** 60
Acreage 6 **Open** Easter to Oct
Site Lev/Slope
Nearest Bus Stop (Miles) 1
On beach, working farm, pets corner.
Facilities ∮ ⊞ ቶ ⦿ ⌐ ⊒ ⌦ ◨ ☻
⦿ ✗ ⌦ ⊟ ⊡
Nearest Town Morecambe
Directions From M6 Carnforth, south follow Morecambe
onto A5105 turn right on to Pasture Lane.
⇌ Lancaster/Morecambe

CARNFORTH

The Villa Holiday Park and Fishery
Borwick Lane, Carnforth, Lancashire, LA6 1UZ
Tel: 01524 889192
Email: enquiries@pureleisuregroup.com
www.pureleisuregroup.com
Pitches For ⚑ ⊟ **Total** 16
Access Good **Site** Level
Carnforth near Arnside and Silverdale area of outstanding natural beauty. 30 mins from Windermere and the Yorkshire Dales.
Facilities ∮ ⊟ ⊞ ቶ ⦿ ⌐ ☻
⦿ ⊟ ✗ ⚲ ⍾ ⊛ ⌦ ⊟ ⊡ ⚯
Nearest Town Carnforth
Directions Take Junc 35 on M6. Follow A6 signposted Milnthorpe for ¼ mile, at roundabout follow signs for Leisure Village.
⇌ Carnforth

CLITHEROE

Clitheroe Camping & Caravanning Club Site, Edisford Road, Clitheroe, Lancashire, BB7 3LA
Tel: 01200 425294
Email: clitheroe.site@thefriendlyclub.co.uk
www.campingandcaravanningclub.co.uk/clitheroe
Pitches For ▲ ⚑ ⊟ **Total** 80
Acreage 6 **Open** Mar to 10-Nov
Site Lev/Slope
Nearest Bus Stop (Miles) ½
In the Ribble Valley, on the banks of a river. Local ghost walks on a weekly basis. Near Clitheroe Castle. Near a swimming pool and a dog walk. Non members welcome. You can also call us on 0845 130 7633. to book.
Facilities ⚬ ∮ ⊟ ⊞ ቶ ⦿ ⌐ ⊒ ◨ ☻
⚲ ⦿ ⊛ ⌦ ⊟ ⊡ ☀ ⚯
Directions Nearest main road is the A59. From the west follow the A671 into Clitheroe. Look for the signpost indicating a left turn to Longridge/Sports Centre, turn into Greenacre Road approx 25 metres beyond the railway crossing. Continue until the T-Junction at Edisford Road, turn left and continue past the church on the right, look for the Sports Centre on the right and car park opposite.
⇌ Clitheroe

CLITHEROE

Rimington Caravan Park, Hardhouse Farm, Hardacre Lane, Rimington, Clitheroe, Lancashire, BB7 4EE
Tel: 01200 445355
Email:
rimingtoncaravanpark@btinternet.com
www.rimingtoncaravanpark.co.uk
Pitches For ⚑ ⊟ **Total** 4
Open Mid-Mar to Mid-Nov
Access Good **Site** Level
Nearest Bus Stop (Miles) 1
ADULTS ONLY PARK.
Facilities ⚬ ∮ ⊟ ⊞ ቶ ⦿ ⌐ ⊒ ◨ ☻
⚲ ⦿ ☻ ✗ ⦿ ⊟ ▲ ⚯
Nearest Town Clitheroe
Directions Follow A59 to Gisburn, turn right on A682 park on right after 1 mile.
⇌ Clitheroe

GARSTANG

Claylands Caravan Park, Weavers Lane, Cabus, Garstang, Nr Preston, Lancashire, PR3 1AJ
Tel: 01524 791242
www.wyreparks.co.uk
Pitches For ▲ ⚑ ⊟ **Total** 36
Acreage 10 **Open** Mar to Jan
Access Good **Site** Level
Nearest Bus Stop (Miles) Outside
On the doorstep to the Trough of Bowland. 20 miles from Blackpool and 40 minutes drive to the Lake District.
Facilities ⚬ ∮ ⊟ ⊞ ⊞ ቶ ⦿ ⌐ ◨ ☻
⚲ ⦿ ☻ ✗ ⚲ ⊓ ⌂ ⌦ ⊟ ⊡ ⚯
Nearest Town Garstang
Directions Leave the M6 at junction 33, 6 miles to Garstang. Drive past Quattro's and two garages on the left, then turn left into Weavers Lane.
⇌ Lancaster

GARSTANG

Fell View Park Sykes Farm, Scorton, Preston, Lancs, PR3 1DA
Tel: 01524 791283
Email: susan_atkingsin@btconnect.com
www.fellviewparkandfishing.co.uk
Pitches For ▲ ⚑ ⊟ **Total** 40
Acreage 4 **Open** Mar to Oct
Access Good **Site** Level
Nearest Bus Stop (Miles) 4
Lovely walks, 7 miles from Lancaster 5 miles from Garstang 20 miles from Blackpool.
Facilities ∮ ⊟ ⊞ ቶ ⦿ ⌐ ⊒ ◨ ⊡ ⚯
Nearest Town Garstang
Directions From J33 take 1st lt off the r/about on A6 south t immediately lt into Hampson Lane ar T Junc t rt.After ½ mile straight on at Xrds at Fleece Inn. Followroad for 1½ miles t rt at xrds sp Scorton,long lane. take 1st lane on lt sp Fell View Park and Ford site on rt.
⇌ Lancaster

GARSTANG

Six Arches Caravan Park, Scorton, Garstang, Nr Preston, Lancashire, PR3 1AL
Tel: 01524 791683
Email:
bookings@sixarchescaravanpark.co.uk
www.sixarchescaravanpark.co.uk
Pitches For ⚑ ⊟ **Total** 12
Open Mar to Oct
Access Good **Site** Level
Nearest Bus Stop (Miles) ¼
On the banks of the River Wyre.
Facilities ⚙ ∮ ⊟ ⊞ ቶ ⦿ ⌐ ⊒ ◨ ☻
⚲ ⦿ ☻ ⊓ ⊞ ⚘ ⚒ ⚘ ⊛ ⌦ ⊟ ⊡ ⚯ ⊹
Nearest Town Garstang
Directions Follow the main A6 to 2½ miles north of Garstang.
⇌ Lancaster

GARSTANG

Wyreside Farm Park, Allotment Lane, St Michaels-on-Wyre, Garstang, Lancashire, PR3 0TZ
Tel: 01995 679797
Email: penny.wyresidefarm@talktalk.net
www.wyresidefarmpark.co.uk

LANCASHIRE

Pitches For A ⚐ 🚐 **Total** 16
Acreage 7 **Open** Mar **to** Oct
Access Good **Site** Level
Nearest Bus Stop (Miles) Outside
On the banks of the River Wyre. Mowed field to play in. Central for Blackpool, the Lakes and the Trough of Bowland.
Facilities 🏠 ⚡ 🛁 ♿ 🍴 🔥 📷 🔒 🏪
Nearest Town Garstang
Directions From South, leave M6 at junc 32 and take A6 north to Garstang. In village of Billsborrow turn immediately left, after 4 miles at mini roundabout turn right, go past church, over bridge, past The Grapes Pub, right hand bend, bus stop on left, Allotment Lane is on the right hand side.
🚲 Preston

KIRKHAM
Whitmore Fisheries & Caravan Park, Bradshaw Lane, Greenhalgh, Blackpool, Lancashire, PR4 3HQ
Tel: 01253 836224
Pitches For ⚐ 🚐 **Total** 25
Acreage 40 **Open** Mar **to** Oct
Access Good **Site** Level
Nearest Bus Stop (Miles) 1
Whitmore Fisheries has 10 top class waters.
Facilities 🏠 ⚡ 🛁 📷 🔥 🔒 🏪
🏪 🍴 📷 ✉ 🔥
Nearest Town Kirkham
Directions Leave the M55 at junction 3 to Kirkham 50yds turn right Dowm Bradshaw Lane 1 mile.
🚲 Kirkham

LANCASTER
Cockerham Sands Country Park, Cockerham, Lancaster, Lancashire, LA2 0BB
Tel: 01524 751387
Email: bookings@cockerhamsands.co.uk
www.cockerhamsandsandcountrypark.co.uk
Pitches For **Total** 10
Open Mar **to** 10-Dec
Site Level
Nearest Bus Stop (Miles) 2
Unique coastal?countryside location adjacent to Lune estuary.
Facilities ⚡ 🛁 📷 ✉ 🔥 📷 🔒 🏪
🏪 🍴 📷 ♿ 🔥 🔒 🔥
Nearest Town Lancaster
Directions Situated off A588 Travelling from Garstang to Lancaster.
🚲 Lancaster

LANCASTER
New Parkside Farm Caravan Park, Denny Beck, Caton Road, Lancaster, Lancashire, LA2 9HH
Tel: 01524 770723
www.newparksidefarm.co.uk
Pitches For A ⚐ 🚐 **Total** 40
Acreage 4 **Open** Mar **to** Oct
Access Good **Site** Level
Nearest Bus Stop (Miles) ¼
A working farm with beautiful views of Lune Valley. On the edge of Forest of Bowland and close to historic Lancaster and Morecambe Bay. Central for lakes and dales.
Facilities 🍴 📷 ⚡ 🛁 📷 ✉ 🔥 📷 🔥
Nearest Town Lancaster
Directions Leave the M6 at junction 34 and take the A683 towards Kirkby Lonsdale. Park is situated 1 mile on the right.
🚲 Lancaster

LANCASTER
Wyreside Lakes Fishery, Sunnyside Farmhouse, Bay Horse, Lancaster, Lancashire, LA2 9DG
Tel: 01524 792093
Email: wyresidelakes@btconnect.com
www.wyresidelakes.co.uk
Pitches For ⚐ 🚐 **Total** 100
Acreage 120 **Open** All Year
Access Good **Site** Lev/Slope
Set in the beautiful Wyreside Valley with views of the Bowland Fells. 7 lakes to walk around and the beautiful Foxes Wood.
Facilities 🍴 📷 🛁 📷 ✉ 🔥 📷 🔒 🏪
🏪 🍴 🌲 ✕ ♿ 📷 ✉ 🔥 🔥 🔥
Nearest Town Garstang
Directions Leave the M6 at junction 33, turn left towards Garstang and follow brown tourism signs.
🚲 Lancaster

MORECAMBE
Glen Caravan Park, Westgate, Morecambe, Lancashire, LA3 3EL
Tel: 01524 423896
Pitches For ⚐ 🚐 **Total** 10
Acreage ½ **Open** Mar **to** Oct
Access Good **Site** Level
Nearest Bus Stop (Miles) ¼
15 minutes walk Morecambe Promenade.
Facilities 🍴 📷 🛁 📷 ✉ 🔥 📷 🔒 🏪
🏪 🔥 🔒 🔥
Nearest Town Morecambe
Directions In Morecambe itself close to promenade, Regent Road and Westgate.
🚲 Morecambe

MORECAMBE
Greendales Farm & Bowland View Holiday Park, Greendales Farm, Carr Lane, Middleton, Morecambe, Lancashire, LA3 3LH
Tel: 01524 852616
Email: greendalesfarm@tiscali.co.uk
www.greendalesfarmcaravanpark.co.uk
Pitches For ⚐ 🚐 **Total** 24
Acreage 2 **Open** Mar **to** 14-Jan
Access Good **Site** Level
Nearest Bus Stop (Miles) ¼
Close to the beach. Ideal for the Lake District, Blackpool and Morecambe.
Facilities 🍴 📷 🛁 📷 ✉ 🔥 📷 🔒 🏪
🏪 🔥 🔒 🔥 🔥
Nearest Town Morecambe
Directions Leave the M6 at junction 34 and follow signs to Middleton and Overton, turn left into Carr Lane, then turn left at the Greendales Farm sign.
🚲 Morecambe

MORECAMBE
Melbreak Caravan Park, Carr Lane, Middleton, Morecambe, Lancashire, LA3 3LH
Tel: 01524 852430
Pitches For A ⚐ 🚐 **Total** 40
Acreage 1½ **Open** Mar **to** Oct
Access Good **Site** Lev/Slope
Nearest Bus Stop (Miles) ½
Near the beach and some of the oldest churches in England. Lovely walking area.
Facilities 🍴 📷 🛁 📷 ✉ 🔥 📷 🔥
🏪 🔥 🔒 🔥
Nearest Town Morecambe
Directions Take the B5274 from Morecambe to the roundabout, go straight across until you get to Middleton, signposted from the junction.
🚲 Morecambe

MORECAMBE
Morecambe Lodge Caravan Park, Shore Lane, Bolton-le-Sands, Carnforth, Lancashire, LA5 8JP
Tel: 01524 824361
Email: andrew@morecambe-lodge.co.uk
www.morecambe-lodge.co.uk
Pitches For ⚐ 🚐 🚗 **Total** 25
Acreage 2 **Open** Mar **to** Oct
Access Good **Site** Level
Nearest Bus Stop (Miles) ½
Direct access to the beach. Excellent views over the bay across to the Lake Hills. Good for walking, fishing and cycling. US RVs welcome with 16 or 32 amp supply.
Facilities 🍴 📷 🛁 📷 ✉ 🔥 📷 🔒 🏪
🏪 🔥 🔒 🔥 🔥 🔥 🔥 🔥 🔥 🔥
Nearest Town Morecambe
Directions Take the A6 north from Lancaster to Bolton-le-Sands, turn left at the traffic lights onto the A5105. After 200yds turn right by the first house, travel down towards the beach and over the bridge, Park is on the left hand side.
🚲 Carnforth

MORECAMBE
Venture Caravan Park, Langridge Way, Westgate, Morecambe, Lancashire, LA4 4TQ
Tel: 01524 412986
Email: mark@venturecaravanpark.co.uk
www.venturecaravanpark.co.uk
Pitches For A ⚐ 🚐 **Total** 75
Acreage 17 **Open** All Year
Access Good **Site** Level
Beautifully landscaped Park offering a relaxing family holiday experience. Ideal for the Lake District and the Yorkshire Dales.
Facilities 🍴 📷 🛁 📷 ✉ 🔥 📷 🔒 🏪
🏪 🍴 ✕ ♿ 📷 ✉ 🔥 🔥 🔥 🔒 🔥 🔥
Nearest Town Morecambe
Directions Leave the M6 at junction 34 and take the A683 to Morecambe. At the roundabout go straight across onto the A589, at 3rd roundabout take 1st left onto Westgate (sp West Promenade, West End and Sandylands). Go over the bridge and straight across the traffic lights, after ¾ miles turn right after the Fire Station into Langridge Way, the Park is at the end of Langridge Way.
🚲 Morecambe

PREESALL
Maaruig Caravan Park, 69 Pilling Lane, Preesall, PoultonleFylde, Lancashire, FY6 0HB
Tel: 01253 810364
Pitches For ⚐ 🚐 **Total** 35
Acreage 15 **Open** Mar **to** 05-Jan
Access Good **Site** Level
Nearest Bus Stop (Miles) ¼
Near the beach, ideal walking. Central location for Blackpool, Preston, Lancaster and the Trough of Bowland. Less than 1 hours drive to the Lake District.
Facilities 🍴 📷 🛁 📷 ✉ 🔥 📷 🔒 🏪
🏪 🔥 🔒 🔥 🔥 🔥 🔥
Nearest Town Preesall
Directions Leave the M55 at junction 3 and take the A585 towards Fleetwood. At the third set of traffic lights turn right onto the A588. Follow Knott End (B5377) up to the T-Junction, turn left then the first right into Pilling Lane.
🚲 Poulton-le-Fylde

SOUTHPORT
Willowbank Holiday Home & Touring Park, Coastal Road, Ainsdale, Southport, Merseyside, PR8 3ST
Tel: 01704 571566
Email: info@willowbankcp.co.uk
www.willowbankcp.co.uk
Pitches For 🚐 🚗 **Total** 87
Acreage 10 **Open** Mid Feb **to** Jan
Access Good **Site** Level
Nearest Bus Stop (Miles) ¼
Ideal for woodland walks and all of Southports attractions. Close to the Trans-Penine Cycle Way. Motorhome service bay and dog walk area. Ideal touring. Bike hire on site.
Facilities 🚿 ♿ ✉ ⊞ 🌀 ♨ ⌂ ⊙ 🍴 💨 🔲 💇
⛱ 🏕 🔥 ⟐ ➡ 🔲 💻 📶
Nearest Town Southport
Directions From South M6-M57/M58 onto the A5036, then take the A5207 onto the A565 for Southport. After RAF Woodvale at traffic lights turn left, park is 150 metres on the left.
⚏ Ainsdale

THORNTON
Kneps Farm Holiday Park, River Road, Stanah, Thornton-Cleveleys, Blackpool, Lancashire, FY5 5LR
Tel: 01253 823632
Email: enquiries@knepsfarm.co.uk
www.www.knepsfarm.co.uk
Pitches For 🚐 🚗 **Total** 60
Acreage 3½ **Open** Mar **to** Mid Nov
Access Good **Site** Level
Nearest Bus Stop (Miles) Outside
Situated adjacent to the Stanah Amenity and Picnic Area, forming part of the River Wyre Estuary Country Park. A rural retreat close to Blackpool. Camping Pods for hire. We are proud to have been voted Regional Winner for North-West England and Overall Winner in the Practical Caravan Top 100 Sites 2011 Awards.
Facilities 🚿 ♿ ✉ 🔲 🌀 ⊞ ♨ ⌂ ⊙ 🍴 💨
🔲 💇 ⛱ 🔥 ➡ 🔲 💻 📶
Nearest Town Blackpool
Directions 5 mls, NNE of B/pool. From the M55 junc 3 take the A585 F/wood rd, to the River Wyre Hotel on lt, turn Rt at the r/about onto the B5412 sp Little Thornton. Turn Rt at the mini r/about after the school onto Stanah Road, go straight over the next r/about leading to River Road.
⚏ Poulton-le-Fylde

THORNTON
Stanah House Caravan Park, River Road, Thornton, Cleveleys, Lancashire, FY5 5LR
Tel: 01253 824000
Email: stanahhouse@talk21.com
Pitches For 🏕 🚐 🚗 **Total** 50

Acreage 6 **Open** Mar **to** Oct
Access Good **Site** Sloping
Nearest Bus Stop (Miles) ¼
Alongside the River Wyre and near Blackpool.
Facilities 🚿 ♿ 🔲 ⊞ ♨ ⌂ ⊙ 🍴 💨 🔲 💇
⛱ 🏕 🔥 🌀 ➡ 🔲 💇
Nearest Town Blackpool
Directions Follow signs for Stanah Ecology Centre.
⚏ Poulton-le-Fylde

LINCOLNSHIRE
BOSTON
Long Acres Touring Park, Station Road, Old Leake, Boston, Lincolnshire, PE22 9RF
Tel: 01205 871555
Email: enquiries@longacres-caravanpark.co.uk
www.longacres-caravanpark.co.uk
Pitches For 🏕 🚐 🚗 **Total** 40
Acreage 2 **Open** Mar **to** Oct
Access Good **Site** Level
Nearest Bus Stop (Miles) 3
ADULTS ONLY PARK with peace and tranquillity. Ideal starting point for exploring Lincolnshires many attractions.
Facilities 🚿 ♿ 🔲 ⊞ ♨ ⌂ ⊙ 🍴 💇
➡ 🔲 🔥 🌀 📶
Nearest Town Boston
Directions From the A16 take the B1184 (Station Road) at Sibsey. After approx 1 mile at the T-Junction turn left, then after approx 1½ miles turn right into Station Road.
⚏ Boston

BOSTON
Orchard Park, Frampton Lane, Hubberts Bridge, Boston, Lincolnshire, PE20 3QU
Tel: 01205 290328
Email: info@orchardpark.co.uk
www.orchardpark.co.uk
Pitches For 🏕 🚐 🚗 **Total** 87
Acreage 61 **Open** All Year
Access Good **Site** Level
ADULTS ONLY. ETB 3 Star Graded, AA 4 Pennants and David Bellamy Gold Award.
Facilities 🚿 ♿ 🔲 ⊞ ♨ ⌂ ⊙ 🍴 💨 💇
⛱ 🏕 🔥 ✖ 🍴 🌀 ➡ 🔲 💇 ➡ 📶 💻
Nearest Town Boston
Directions Take the A52 from Boston towards Grantham. After approx. 3½ miles turn right at Four Cross Roads Pub onto the B1192, Park is ¼ of a mile.
⚏ Hubberts Bridge

BOSTON
Pilgrims Way Caravan & Camping Park, Church Green Road, Fishtoft, Boston, Lincolnshire, PE21 0QY
Tel: 01205 366646
Email: pilgrimsway@caravanandcampingpark.com
www.pilgrimswaycaravanandcamping.com
Pitches For 🏕 🚐 🚗 🚗 **Total** 22
Acreage 2.5 **Open** All Year
Access Good **Site** Level
Nearest Bus Stop (Miles) Outside
Close to town & RSPB Reserves, easy drive to Skegness.
Facilities 🚿 ♿ 🔲 ⊞ ♨ ⌂ ⊙ 🍴 💨 🔲 💇
⛱ 🏕 🔥 🌀 ➡ 🔲 💇 📶
Nearest Town Boston/Skegness
Directions Take the A52 east from Boston, in 1 mile, after the junction with the A16 at The Ball Public House, turn right and follow international signs to the Park.
⚏ Boston

BOSTON
Walnut Lake Lodges & Camping, Main Road, Algarkirk, Boston, Lincolnshire, PE20 2LQ
Tel: 01205 460482
Email: mariawalnutlakes@yahoo.co.uk
Pitches For 🚐 🚗 🚗 **Total** 10
Acreage 4 **Open** Mar **to** Mid Sept
Access Good **Site** Level
Nearest Bus Stop (Miles) 1
ADULTS ONLY PARK with fishing on site. Award winning 1st place Caravan Club Site.
Facilities 🚿 ♿ 🔲 ⊞ ♨ ⌂ 🔲 ⊙ ➡ 🔲 📶 🌀 ➡ 🅿 ♿
Nearest Town Boston/Spalding
Directions From the A17/A16 roundabout heading towards Kings Lynn, site is 30 metres on the left.
⚏ Boston/Spalding

HORNCASTLE
Ashby Park, West Ashby, Nr Horncastle, Lincolnshire, LN9 5PP
Tel: 01507 527966
Email: ashbypark@btconnect.com
www.ukparks.co.uk/ashby
Pitches For 🏕 🚐 🚗 **Total** 130
Acreage 70 **Open** Mar **to** 06-Jan
Access Good **Site** Level
Nearest Bus Stop (Miles) 1
Lincoln Castle and Cathedral 20 miles, East coast beach 25 miles 7 fishing lakes on site, David Bellamy Gold award Park.
Facilities 🚿 ♿ 🔲 ⊞ ♨ ⌂ ⊙ 🍴 💨 🔲 💇
⛱ 🏕 🔥 🌀 ➡ 🔲 💇 📶
Nearest Town Horncastle
Directions 1½ miles north of Horncastle between the A153 and the A158.
⚏ Lincoln

HUTTOFT

Jolly Common Adult Only Caravan Park, Jolly Common, Sea Lane, Huttoft, Alford, Lincolnshire, LN13 9RW
Tel: 01507 490236
www.jollycommoncaravanpark.co.uk
Pitches For ⚌ ⚌ **Total** 0
Acreage 9 **Open** 15-Mar **to** 15-Oct
Access Good **Site** Level
Nearest Bus Stop (Miles) ½
ADULTS ONLY SITE set in peaceful countryside. 1 mile from a sandy beach.
Facilities ⚏ ⌂ ⚏⚏↺ ⚏ ⚏⚏⚏⚏⚏ ⚏/A
Nearest Town Sutton-on-Sea
Directions From Sutton-on-Sea head south on the A52 for 4 miles. In the village of Huttoft turn first left, after ¾ miles turn first right and the site is 200 yards on the left.
⚇ Skegness

INGOLDMELLS

Bridge End Touring Site, Boltons Lane, Ingoldmells, Skegness, Lincolnshire, PE25 1JJ
Tel: 01754 872456
Email: bridgeendsite@hotmail.co.uk
www.bridgeendsite.co.uk
Pitches For ⚌ ⚌ **Total** 40
Open Easter to Oct
Access Good **Site** Level
Nearest Bus Stop (Miles) ¼
Beach, fishing ,market.
Facilities ⚏ ⚏ ⌂ ⚏⚏↺ ⚏ ⚏ ⚏
Nearest Town Ingoldmells
Directions Situated 3 miles north of Skegness at the junction of the main Ingoldmells to Skegness road (A52) and Boltons Lane.
⚇ Skegness

INGOLDMELLS

Hardy's Touring Site, Sea Lane, Ingoldmells, Skegness, Lincolnshire, PE25 1PG
Tel: 01754 874071
Pitches For ⚌ ⚌ **Total** 112
Acreage 5 **Open** Easter to Oct
Access Good **Site** Level
Nearest Bus Stop (Miles) ¼
5 minutes walk from the beach. Next to Fantasy Island and 10 minutes from an animal farm.
Facilities ⚏ ⚏⌂↺ ⚏⚏⚏ ⚏ ⚏
⚏⚏ ⚏ ⚏✕⚏↺⚏⚏/
Nearest Town Skegness/Ingoldmells
Directions Take the A52 north from Skegness to Ingoldmells. At the Ship Inn in Ingoldmells turn right down Sea Lane, towards the sea. Site is ½ mile on the right.
⚇ Skegness

INGOLDMELLS

Valetta Farm Caravan Site, Mill Lane, Addlethorpe, Skegness, Lincolnshire, PE24 4TB
Tel: 01754 763758
Email: leeman22@btinternet.com
Pitches For ⚊ ⚌ ⚌ **Total** 55
Acreage 2 **Open** 25-Mar **to** 20-Oct
Access Good **Site** Level
Nearest Bus Stop (Miles) 1
Quite a pretty site in the country, 1 mile from the beach.
Facilities ✗ ⚏ ⌂⚏↺⚏⚏⚏⚏⚏⚏ ⚏
Nearest Town Skegness
Directions Turn left off the A158 (Horncastle to Skegness road) on Burgh-le-Marsh bypass at the signpost Ingoldmells and Addlethorpe. Follow signposts for Ingoldmells for 3 miles, turn right by disused mill into Mill Lane. Site is on the left in 150yds.
⚇ Skegness

LINCOLN

Oakhill Leisure, Swinderby Road, Norton Disney, Lincoln, Lincolnshire, LN6 9QG
Tel: 07582 42445
Email: ron@oakhillleisure.co.uk
www.oakhillleisure.co.uk
Pitches For ⚊ ⚌ ⚌ ⚌⚏ **Total** 60
Acreage 10 **Open** All Year
Access Good **Site** Level
Nearest Bus Stop (Miles) 1
Peaceful woodland site with open fields and a fishing lake.
Facilities ⚏ ⚏ ⌂⚏↺⚏⚏⚏ ⚏
⚏⚏⚏⚏⚏/⚏⚏
Nearest Town Lincoln
Directions A46 from A1 follow brown caravan signs.
⚇ Lincoln

LINCOLN

Shortferry Caravan Park, Ferry Road, Fiskerton, Lincoln, Lincolnshire, LN3 4HU
Tel: 01526 398021
Email: kay@shortferry.co.uk
www.shortferry.co.uk
Pitches For ⚌ ⚌ **Total** 75
Acreage 80 **Open** All Year
Access Good **Site** Level
Nearest Bus Stop (Miles) Outside
Situated by a river with 5 fishing ponds. Fishing tackle and bait shop. Entertainment most weekends. Bar meals and take-away in our public house. Seasonal outdoor heated swimming pool.
Facilities ⚏ ⚏ ⌂⚏⚏↺ ⚏⚏ ⚏ ⚏
⚏⚏⚏✕⚏⚏ ⚏⚏⚏↺⚏⚏⚏/⚏⚏ ⚏
Nearest Town Lincoln

Directions From the A46 Lincoln ring road take the A158 towards Skegness. After approx. 5 miles turn right at Shortferry sign, continue to follow signs for approx. 5 miles.
⚇ Lincoln

MABLETHORPE

Mablethorpe Camping & Caravanning Club Site, Highfield, 120 Church Lane, Mablethorpe, Lincolnshire, LN12 2NU
Tel: 01507 472374
Email:
mablethorpe.site@thefriendlyclub.co.uk
www.campingandcaravanningclub.co.uk/mablethorpe
Pitches For ⚊ ⚌ ⚌ **Total** 105
Acreage 11 **Open** 01-Apr **to** 03-Nov
Access Difficult **Site** Level
Nearest Bus Stop (Miles) 1
Just 1 mile from the sea and award winning beaches. Ideal for cyclists. Near the Lincolnshire Wolds. Swimming pool, play area, bicycle hire, horse racing and dog walk nearby. Non members welcome. You can also call us on 0845 130 7633. to book.
Facilities ⚏ ⚏ ⌂⚏↺⚏⚏⋅⚏ ⚏ ⚏ ⚏
⚏⚏⚏⚏⚏↺⚏⚏⚏⚏⚏⚏
Directions On the outskirts of Mablethorpe, on the A1104. Turn into Church Lane after the petrol station on the right, site is 800 yards along the lane on the right hand side.
⚇ Cleethorpes

MARKET DEEPING

The Deepings Caravan Park, Outgang Road, Towngate East, Market Deeping, Lincolnshire, PE6 8LQ
Tel: 01778 344335
Email: info@thedeepings.com
www.thedeepings.com
Pitches For ⚊ ⚌ ⚌ **Total** 60
Acreage 9 **Open** All Year
Access Good **Site** Level
Family run and owned park with a clubhouse and childrens play area. Fishing on site.
Facilities ⚏ ⚏ ⌂⚏↺⚏⚏ ⚏ ⚏ ⚏
⚏⚏⚏✕⚏⚏⚏↺⚏⚏⚏/⚏⚏ ⚏⚏
Nearest Town Market Deeping
Directions From Peterborough take the A15 to Market Deeping. At the roundabout take second exit, turn right at the Towngate Inn, Park is 2 miles on the left.
⚇ Peterborough

MARKET RASEN

Lincolnshire Lanes Caravan & Camping Site, Manor Farm, East Firsby, Market Rasen, Lincolnshire, LN8 2DB
Tel: 01673 878258
Email: robert@lincolnshire-lanes.com
www.lincolnshire-lanes.com

Pitches For 🏕 ⚡ 🚐 🚃 **Total** 21
Acreage 3 **Open** All Year
Access Good **Site** Level
Nearest Bus Stop (Miles) Outside
Small site shop. Disabled toilet. ETB 3 Star
Graded and Welcome Host.
Facilities ⚡ 🔲 🕮 ⚓ ⌂ ☉ 🍴 ⬛ 🔲 🍽
🌏 ☉ ⬛ 🚾 🔲 🔲
Nearest Town Market Rasen/Lincoln
Directions Take the A15 north from Lincoln,
2½ miles past RAF Scampton turn right and
follow brown tourism signs to the site
entrance.
🚏 Market Rasen/Lincoln

MARKET RASEN
Walesby Woodland Caravan Park,
Walesby Road, Market Rasen,
Lincolnshire, LN8 3UN
Tel: 01673 843285
Email: walesbywoodlands@hotmail.co.uk
www.walesbywoodlands.co.uk
Pitches For 🏕 ⚡ 🚐 🚃 **Total** 60
Acreage 5 **Open** All year
Access Good **Site** Lev/slope
Nearest Bus Stop (Miles) 1
Ideal sight seeing. Lincoln 16 miles. Set in
forestry land, many walks. Total peace yet
close to town. 20- 30 miles from
Cleethorpes,Mablethorpe and Skegness.
Facilities ⚓ ⚡ 🔲 🕮 ⚓ ⌂ ☉ 🍴 ⬛ 🔲 🍽
🌏 🌏 ☉ 🚾 🔲 🔲 ✦ 🍴 🍽
Nearest Town Market Rasen
Directions In Market Rasen, take the B1203
to Tealby. After ½ mile, turn left onto
unclassified road to Walesby. Park
entrance150 yds on left.
🚏 Market Rasen

MARKET RASEN
Wolds View touring Park 115 Brigg Road,
Caistor, Market Rasen, Lincs, LN7 6RX
Tel: 01479 851099
Email: phil@wvtp.co.uk
www.www.woldsviewtouringpark.co.uk
Pitches For 🏕 ⚡ 🚐 🚃 **Total** 60
Acreage 3 **Open** All Year
Access Good **Site** Level
Nearest Bus Stop (Miles) 1 Mile
Ideal for walks around the Lincolnshire
Wolds. CASSOA Gold storage site.
Facilities ⚓ ⚡ 🔲 🕮 ⚓ ⌂ ☉ 🍴 ⬛ 🔲 🍽
🌏 ☉ 🚾 🔲 🍴 🍽
Nearest Town Caistor
Directions 5 mins/1 mile from Caistor. Follow
Brigg Road.
🚏 Market Rasen

SCUNTHORPE
Brookside Caravan & Camping Park,
Stather Road, Burton-Upon-Stather,
Scunthorpe, Lincolnshire, DN15 9DH
Tel: 01724 721369
Email: brooksidecp@aol.com
www.brooksidecaravanpark.co.uk
Pitches For 🏕 ⚡ 🚐 **Total** 70
Acreage 10 **Open** 07-Mar to Early Nov
Access Good **Site** Level
Nearest Bus Stop (Miles) Outside
Our family run, superbly equipped park, set
in an area of outstanding beauty, is the ideal

location for visiting North Lincolnshire. 4½
miles from Scunthorpe town centre. Adults
only. All year ETB 5 Star Graded.
Facilities ⚓ ⚡ 🔲 🕮 ⚓ ⌂ ☉ 🍴 ⬛ 🔲 🍽
🔲 🚾 🔲 🍽
Nearest Town Scunthorpe
Directions B1430 from Scunthorpe town
centre to Burton-Upon-Stather (4 miles) turn
left in front of Sheffield Arms public house.
From the bottom of the hill travel 250 yards,
entrance to Brookside is on the right.
🚏 Scunthorpe

SKEGNESS
Homelands Caravan Park, Sea Road,
Anderby, Skegness, Lincolnshire, PE24
5YB
Tel: 01507 490511
Email: homelandspark@gmail.com
www.ukcampsite.co.uk
Pitches For 🏕 ⚡ 🚐 **Total** 10
Acreage 1 **Open** Mar to Nov
Access Good **Site** Level
Quiet, friendly site in the countryside. Within
walking distance of a sandy beach. 4 Berth
Static Van also available for hire.
Facilities ⚓ ⚡ 🔲 🕮 ⚓ ⌂ ☉ 🍴 ⬛ 🔲 🍽 🔲
Nearest Town Skegness/Mablethorpe
Directions Take the A52 Skegness to
Mablethorpe road, approx. ¾ miles past
Mumby (½ a mile past the B1449 junction)
turn right on a sharp bend signposted
Anderby, site is on the left in 1¼ miles.
🚏 Skegness

SKEGNESS
North Shore Holiday Centre, Elmhirst
Avenue, Roman Bank, Skegness,
Lincolnshire, PE25 1SL
Tel: 01754 763815
Email: reception@northshore-
skegness.co.uk
www.northshore-skegness.co.uk
Pitches For ⚡ 🚐 🚃 **Total** 133
Open 01-Mar to 30-Nov
Access Good **Site** Level
Nearest Bus Stop (Miles) Outside
Just a short walk to both the beach and
Skegness centre. Set well back from the
main road, ideal family holiday base. Pitch &
Putt and Miniature Golf on site. Camping
Pods and all weather touring pitches now
available. SORRY NO TENTS. Special long
vehicle pitches available for motor homes.
Facilities ⚓ ⚡ 🔲 🕮 ⚓ ⌂ ☉ 🍴 ⬛ 🔲 🍽
🌏 🌏 ☉ 🚾 🔲 🚾 🔲 🔲
Nearest Town Skegness
Directions A52 towards Mablethorpe,
500yds from the A158 junction.
🚏 Skegness

SKEGNESS
Pine Trees Leisure Park, Croft Bank,
Skegness, Lincolnshire, PE24 4RE
Tel: 01754 762949
Email: enquiries@pinetreesholidays.co.uk
www.pinetreesholidays.co.uk
Pitches For 🏕 ⚡ 🚐 🚃 **Total** 150
Acreage 8 **Open** Mar to Nov
Access Good **Site** Level
Nearest Bus Stop (Miles) Outside

Landscaped fishing lakes and a 180 acre
wetland conservation project with bird hides.
Facilities ⚓ ⚡ 🔲 🕮 ⚓ ⌂ ⬛ 🔲 🍽
🌏 ☉ ⬛ 🚾 🔲 🍴 🔲 🚾 🔲 🔲 🍴 🌿 🍴 🍴
Nearest Town Skegness
Directions Take the A52 from Skegness
(signposted Boston) for 1½ miles, turn right
at right hand turning lane.
🚏 Skegness

SKEGNESS
Richmond Holiday Centre, Richmond
Drive, Skegness, Lincolnshire, PE25 3TQ
Tel: 01754 762097
Email: sales@richmondholidays.com
www.richmondholidays.com
Pitches For ⚡ 🚐 **Total** 70
Open Mar to Nov **Access** Good **Site** Level
Nearest Bus Stop (Miles) Outside
A short walk to the bustling resort of
Skegness with funfairs, sandy beaches and
donkey rides. Just a short drive from the
Wolds or the wild open scenery of Gibraltar
Point Nature Reserve.
Facilities ⚓ ⚡ 🔲 🕮 ⚓ ⌂ ☉ 🍴 ⬛ 🔲 🍽
🌏 ☉ ⬛ 🚾 🔲 🔲 🍴 🍴 🚾 🔲 🔲 🍽
Nearest Town Skegness
Directions Follow signs to the coach park on
Richmond Drive, we are located approx. ½ a
mile past the coach park on the right hand side.
🚏 Skegness

SKEGNESS
Riverside Caravan Park, Wainfleet Bank,
Wainfleet, Skegness, Lincolnshire, PE24
4ND
Tel: 01754 880205
Pitches For 🏕 ⚡ 🚐 **Total** 30
Acreage 1¼ **Open** 15-Mar to Oct
Access Good **Site** Level
Nearest Bus Stop (Miles) Outside
Alongside a river. Golf 1 mile.
Facilities ⚡ 🔲 🕮 ⚓ ⌂ ☉ 🍴 ⬛ 🔲 🍽 ☉ 🌿
Nearest Town Skegness
Directions From the A52 Boston to
Skegness road, take the B1195 to Wainfleet
All Saints by-pass, Site is 1 mile from the by-
pass turn off.
🚏 Wainfleet

SKEGNESS
Ronam Cottage, Sea Road, Anderby,
Skegness, Lincolnshire, PE24 5YA
Tel: 01507 490750
Pitches For 🏕 ⚡ 🚐 **Total** 0
Acreage 1½ **Open** 15th March to 15th
November
Access Good **Site** Level
Near to Anderby Creek and beach.
Countryside walks. 2 hard standings
available. Rally Field available. Trailer tents
welcome. Camping & Caravanning Club site,
non members welcome.
Facilities ⚡ 🔲 🕮 ⚓ ⌂ 🍴 ⬛ 🍽
Nearest Town Skegness/Mablethorpe
Directions From Alford take the A1104 and
turn onto the A1111 to Bilsby. Turn right onto
the B1449 then left onto the A52, turn first right
to Anderby. After 1½ miles turn left on the
bend, site entrance is 50 yards on the right.
🚏 Skegness

Quiet park with beautiful views of open countryside.
Good facilities and a high standard of cleanliness.
28 Pitches available for tents, touring caravans
and motorhomes.
We Look Forward to Seeing You!
Ronam Cottage
01507 490750
Sea Road, Anderby, Nr Skegness PE24 5YA
OPEN 15th Mar 15th Nov

LINCOLNSHIRE

SKEGNESS

Skegness Water Leisure Park, Walls Lane, Ingoldmells, Skegness, Lincolnshire, PE25 1JF
Tel: 01754 899400
Email: enquiries@skegnesswaterleisurepark.co.uk
www.skegnesswaterleisurepark.co.uk
Pitches For Å ⌑ ⌑ **Total** 0
Acreage 133 **Open** Mar **to** Oct
Access Good **Site** Level
Nearest Bus Stop (Miles) ¼
A rural setting with on site fishing and a water ski centre. Close to Butlins (day visitors allowed) and Fantasy Island. Near to beaches.
Facilities ⌂ ✦ ⬚⬚⬚ ⍨ Γ ⊙ ⌐ ⬚ ⌑ ⬚
⬚ ⊙ ⬚ ✕ ☲ ⬚ ⬚ ⌂ ⬚ ⬚ ✂ ⚓ ⚲
Nearest Town Skegness
Directions From Skegness follow the A52 north (sp Mablethorpe) for 3 miles, turn left into Walls Lane at Cheers Pub, Park is ½ a mile on the left.
⇌ Skegness

SKEGNESS

Topyard Farm Caravan Site, Croft Bank, Croft, Skegness, Lincolnshire, PE24 4RL
Tel: 01754 880189
Email: topyardfarm@gmail.com
www.skegnesstouringinfo.com
Pitches For Å ⌑ ⌑ **Total** 40
Acreage 2 **Open** Mar **to** Nov
Access Good **Site** Level
Nearest Bus Stop (Miles) ¼
Beach, town.
Facilities ⌂ ✦ ⬚ ⬚⬚⬚ ⍨ Γ ⊙ ⌐ ⬚ ⬚
⬚ ⬚ ⬚ ⍟ ☲ ⬚ ⬚ ⬚ ⬚ ✂ ⚓
Nearest Town Skegness
Directions On the A52 Boston to Skegness road, 1½ mile from Skegness.
⇌ Skegness

SLEAFORD

Low Farm Touring & Camping Park, Spring Lane, Folkingham, Sleaford, Lincolnshire, NG34 0SJ
Tel: 01529 497322
Email: lowfarmpark@sky.com
www.lowfarmpark.co.uk
Pitches For Å ⌑ ⌑ **Total** 36
Acreage 2¼ **Open** Easter **to** Mid Oct
Access Good **Site** Lev/Slope
Nearest Bus Stop (Miles) ¼
Facilities ✦ ⬚⬚⬚ Γ ⊙ ⬚ ☂
⬚ ⊙ ⌐ ⬚ ⬚ ✂ ⚓
Nearest Town Sleaford
Directions 9 miles south of Sleaford on the A15. Go through village, turn right by the Village Hall.
⇌ Sleaford

SPALDING

Ashleigh Caravan Park, Ashleigh House, 45 Broadgate, Whaplode Drove, Spalding, Lincolnshire, PE12 0TN
Tel: 01406 330666
Email: ashleighcaravans@aol.com
Pitches For Å ⌑ ⌑ **Total** 12
Acreage ¾ **Open** Mar **to** Nov
Access Good **Site** Level
Nearest Bus Stop (Miles) Outside
Quiet Camping & Caravan Club Site with two fishing lakes stocked with nine species. Convenient for Fenland North Norfolk and South Lincs Attractions.
Facilities ✦ ⬚⬚⬚ Γ ⊙ ⬚ ☂ ⬚⌐⬚ ✂
Nearest Town Spalding

Directions From Spalding take the A16 towards Peterborough. 6 miles after A16/A1175 roundabout turn left onto the B1166, after approx 4 miles turn left into Broadgate. Site is ¾ miles on the right. From Peterborough take A16 to Spalding after 7 miles turn right onto B1166 then as above.
⇌ Spalding

SPALDING

Delph Bank Touring Caravan Park, Old Main Road, Fleet Hargate, Holbeach, Nr Spalding, Lincolnshire, PE12 8LL
Tel: 01406 422910
Email: enquiries@delphbank.co.uk
www.delphbank.co.uk
Pitches For ⌑ ⌑ **Total** 45
Acreage 3
Access Good **Site** Level
Nearest Bus Stop (Miles) ¼
ADULTS ONLY PARK. An attractive, quiet, tree lined site, convenient for touring the Fens and Lincolnshire/Norfolk coastal resorts. Pubs and eating places within walking distance. BH&HPA Member. ETB 5 Stars and David Bellamy Gold Award.
Facilities ✦ ⬚ ⬚⬚⬚ Γ ⊙ ⬚ ⬚ ☂
⬚ ⊙ ⬚ ⬚ ⬚ ⌐ ⬚ ✂ ⚓ ⚲ ⚲ ⬚
Nearest Town Holbeach
Directions From Kings Lynn take the A17, Turn left in the village of Fleet Hargate then right, site is on the left. From Spalding take the A151 to Holbeach, continue a further 3 miles to Fleet Hargate, turn right into the village and look for our sign on the right.
⇌ Spalding

SPALDING

Orchard View Caravan & Camping Park, 102 Broadgate, Sutton St Edmund, Nr Spalding, Lincolnshire, PE12 0LT
Tel: 01945 700482
Email: orchardview@hotmail.co.uk
www.orchardviewholidays.com
Pitches For Å ⌑ ⌑ **Total** 38
Acreage 6 **Open** Mid Mar **to** Nov
Access Good **Site** Level
Nearest Bus Stop (Miles) 1
Tranquil Fenland retreat in a unique landscape. Friendly family run park with all facilities and spacious plots. Ideal for touring or just relaxing. Numerous activities and places of interest nearby. You can also contact us on Mobile: 07891 223851.
Facilities ⌂ ✦ ⬚⬚⬚ Γ ⊙ ⌐ ⬚ ⬚ ☂
⬚ ⬚ ⊙ ⬚ ☲ ⬚ ⌐ ⬚ ⬚ ✂ ⚓ ⚲
Nearest Town Spalding
Directions From the A47 Peterborough to Wisbech road, turn left at the third roundabout (after McDonalds) sp Gedney Hill. After 2 miles turn right at the T-junction, turn third left into Broadgate and the Park is ½ a mile on the right.
⇌ March

SPILSBY

Meadowlands, Monksthorpe, Great Steeping, Spilsby, Lincolnshire, PE23 5PP
Tel: 01754 830794
www.meadowlandslodgepark.co.uk
Pitches For Å ⌑ ⌑ ⌑ **Total** 20
Acreage 5 **Open** All Year
Access Good **Site** Level
Nearest Bus Stop (Miles) ½
Quiet ADULTS ONLY site in a rural setting. Ideal for walking and cycling. Handy for Skegness and the beautiful Wolds. 3 miles from Spilsby.
Facilities ✦ ⬚ ⬚⬚⬚ Γ ⊙ ⬚ ⬚ ☂
⊙ ⌐ ⬚ ⬚ ✂ ⚓ ⚲
Nearest Town Skegness

Directions Take the A16 into Spilsby town then take the Wainfleet road, pass The Bell Inn and after approx. 1 mile turn left signposted Gunby and Heavy Horse Centre, Park is on the right after ¾ miles.
⇌ Wainfleet

SUTTON-ON-SEA

Cherry Tree Site, Huttoft Road, Sutton-on-Sea, Lincolnshire, LN12 2RU
Tel: 01507 441626
Email: info@cherrytreesite.co.uk
www.cherrytreesite.co.uk
Pitches For ⌑ ⌑ **Total** 60
Acreage 3 **Open** Mar **to** Oct
Access Good **Site** Level
Nearest Bus Stop (Miles) Outside
ADULTS ONLY SITE. Beach, golf course and Lincolnshire Wolds. ETB 5 Star Graded.
Facilities ⌂ ✦ ⬚ Γ ⬚⬚⬚ ⬚ Γ ⊙ ⬚ ⬚ ☂
⬚ ⊙ ⬚ ⌐ ⬚ ⬚ ✂ ⚲
Nearest Town Sutton-on-Sea
Directions Take the A52 south from Sutton-on-Sea, 1½ miles on the left hand side. Entrance via a lay-by. Tourist Board signs on road.
⇌ Skegness

SUTTON-ON-SEA

Kirkstead Holiday Park, North Road, Trusthorpe, Sutton-on-Sea, Lincolnshire, LN12 2QD
Tel: 01507 441483
Email: mark@kirkstead.co.uk
www.kirkstead.co.uk
Pitches For Å ⌑ ⌑ **Total** 60
Acreage 6 **Open** Mar **to** 01-Dec
Access Good **Site** Level
Nearest Bus Stop (Miles) ¼
10 minute walk to the beach. Clubhouse, new shower block. Familys welcome.
Facilities ⌂ ✦ ⬚ Γ ⬚⬚⬚ Γ ⊙ ⌐ ⬚ ⬚ ☂
⬚ ⬚ ⊙ ⬚ ✕ ☲ ⬚ ⬚ ⌐ ⬚ ⬚ ✂ ⚓ ⚲
Nearest Town Sutton-on-Sea
Directions Take the A52 coast road from Sutton to Mablethorpe, turn off left at Trusthorpe. Signposted from the A52.
⇌ Skegness

TATTERSHALL

Orchard Holiday Park Witham Bank, Chapel Hill, Tattershal, Lincs., LN4 4PZ
Tel: 01524 889192
Email: enquiries@pureleisuregroup.com
www.pureleisuregroup.com
Pitches For Å ⌑ ⌑ **Total** 39
Acreage 3 **Open** All Year
Access Good **Site** Level
Riverside setting with views of Lincolnshire countryside.
Facilities ✦ ⬚ ⬚⬚⬚ Γ ⊙ ⬚ ⬚ ☂
⬚ ⊙ ⬚ ☲ ⬚ ⬚⌐ ⬚ ✂
Nearest Town Tattershall
Directions From Sleaford take A153 to Tattershall and then turn right on Twenty Foot Bank.
⇌ Heckington

TATTERSHALL

Willow Holt Caravan & Camping Park, Lodge Road, Tattershall, Lincolnshire, LN4 4JS
Tel: 01526 343111
Email: enquiries@willowholt.co.uk
www.willowholt.co.uk
Pitches For Å ⌑ ⌑ ⌑ **Total** 90
Acreage 25 **Open** 15-Mar **to** Oct
Access Good **Site** Level
Nearest Bus Stop (Miles) 1
Peaceful site, all level pitches, abundant wildlife. Ten acres of fishing lakes on site, free to site occupants.

Facilities � ♿ ⚿ ⛽ ⚑ ⚑ ⊙⌐ ⚑ ▣ ☎
⚺ ⏻ ⚑ ⚑ ⚑ ✂ ☀☀ ⚒
Nearest Town Woodhall Spa
Directions Take the A153 Sleaford/
Skegness road, in Tattershall turn at the
market place onto country road signposted
Woodhall Spa. In 1½ miles site is on the left.
Good wide entrance.
⇌ Metheringham

WOODHALL SPA
Glen Lodge Touring Park, Glen Lodge,
Edlington Moor, Woodhall Spa,
Lincolnshire, LN10 6UL
Tel: 01526 353523
www.glenlodgetouringpark.com
Pitches For ⚑ ⚑ ⚑ **Total** 35
Acreage 3 **Open** Mar **to** Nov
Access Good **Site** Level
Nearest Bus Stop (Miles) 1
Ideal for the woods, the Battle of Britain
Memorial Flight, Tattershall Castle and
Horncastle (with its antiques).
Facilities ⚑ ♿ ⚿ ⛽ ⚑ ⚑ ⊙⌐ ⚑ ☎
⚑ ⚑⚑ ⚑
Nearest Town Woodhall Spa
Directions From the mini roundabout in the
village turn northeast towards Bardney, after
1 mile turn left, turn right after the bend and
the site is 300 yards on the left.
⇌ Metheringham

WOODHALL SPA
**Woodhall Spa Camping & Caravanning
Club Site,** Wellsyke Lane, Kirkby-on-Bain,
Woodhall Spa, Lincolnshire, LN10 6YU
Tel: 01526 352911
Email:
woodhall.spasite@thefriendlyclub.co.uk
**www.campingandcaravanningclub.co.uk/
woodhallspa**
Pitches For ▲ ⚑ ⚑ **Total** 90
Acreage 6½ **Open** Apr **to** 03-Nov
Access Good **Site** Level
Nearest Bus Stop (Miles) 1
A nature lovers dream with many varieties
of birds seen on site. Dish washing facilities.
Non members welcome. You can also call
us on 0845 130 7633,to book.
Facilities ⚑ ♿ ⚿ ⛽ ⚑ ⚑ ⊙⌐ ⚑ ☎
⚑ ⚑ ⚑⚑ ⚑ ⚑
Nearest Town Horncastle
Directions From Sleaford or Horncastle take
the A153 to Haltham. At the garage turn left
towards Kirkby-on-Bain. At the Ebrington
Arms turn right, site is 1 mile.
⇌ Metheringham

LONDON
ABBEY WOOD
Abbey Wood Caravan Club Site,
Federation Road, Abbey Wood, London,
SE2 0LS
Tel: 020 8311 7708
www.caravanclub.co.uk
Pitches For ▲ ⚑ ⚑ **Total** 210
Acreage 9 **Open** All Year
Access Good **Site** Lev/Slope
Nearest Bus Stop (Miles) ½
Spacious site screened by mature trees.
Within walking distance of railway link to
central London for its attractions. Near the
London Eye, Thames Barrier and Splash
World at Woolwich. Non members welcome.
Booking essential.
Facilities ♿ ⚿ ⛽ ⚑ ⊙ ▣ ☎
⚺ ⏻ ⚑ ⚑ ⚑⚑ ⚑ ⚑

Directions From central London on A2 turn
off at A221 junc into Danson Rd, follow signs
for Bexleyheath to Crook Log (A207 junc).
At lights turn right and immediately left into
Brampton Rd. After 1½ miles at lights turn
left into Bostal Rd (A206), at lights turn right
into Basildon Rd (B213). In 300yds turn right
into McLeod Rd, at roundabout turn right into
Knee Hill, turn second right into Federation
Rd, site is 50yds on the left.
⇌ Abbey Wood

CHINGFORD
Lee Valley Campsite, Sewardstone Road,
Chingford, London, E4 7RA
Tel: 020 8529 5689
Email:
sewardstonecampsite@leevalleypark.org.uk
www.visitleevalley.org.uk
Pitches For ▲ ⚑ ⚑ ⚑ **Total** 200
Acreage 14 **Open** Mar **to** Jan
Access Good **Site** Lev/Slope
Nearest Bus Stop (Miles) Outside
Very close to London and historical Waltham
Abbey.
Facilities ⚑ ♿ ⚿ ⛽ ⚑ ⊙⌐ ⚑ ▣ ☎
⚺ ⏻ ⚑ ⚑ ⚑⚑ ⚑
Nearest Town Chingford
Directions From Chingford take the A379.
⇌ Chingford

CRYSTAL PALACE
Crystal Palace Caravan Club Site,
Crystal Palace Parade, London, SE19 1UF
Tel: 020 8778 7155
www.caravanclub.co.uk
Pitches For ▲ ⚑ ⚑ **Total** 126
Acreage 6 **Open** All year
Access Good **Site** Level
Nearest Bus Stop (Miles) ¼
On the edge of a pleasant park. Ideal for the
sights of central London which is easily
accessible by public transport (Travelcards
sold on site April to November). Non
members welcome. Booking essential.
Facilities ⚑ ♿ ⚿ ⛽ ⚑ ⊙⌐ ⚑ ▣ ☎
⚺ ⏻ ⚑ ⚑⚑ ⚑ ⚑ ⚑
Nearest Town London
Directions Site entrance is off the A212 at
the junction of Crystal Palace Parade and
Westwood Hill.
⇌ Crystal Palace

EDMONTON
Lee Valley Camping & Caravan Park,
Meridian Way, Edmonton, London, N9 0AS
Tel: 020 8803 6900
Email:
edmontoncampsit@leevalleypark.org.uk
www.visitleevalley.org.uk
Pitches For ▲ ⚑ ⚑ ⚑ **Total** 0
Nearest Bus Stop (Miles) Outside
Direct buses, trains and tubes to London and
the West End. Golf course and athletics
centre on site, plus a cinema.
Facilities ⚑ ♿ ⚿ ⛽ ⚑ ⊙⌐ ⚑ ▣ ☎
⚺ ⏻ ⚑ ⚑ ⚑⚑ ⚑ ⚑ ⚑
Nearest Town London
Directions Exit the M25 at junction 25 and
follow signs to the city on the A10. Follow
signs to Freezywater A1055. Continue for 6
miles and follow signs to Lee Valley Leisure
Complex.
⇌ Edmonton Green

MANCHESTER
LITTLEBOROUGH
Hollingworth Lake Caravan Park, Round
House Farm, Rakewood, Littleborough,
Manchester, OL15 0AS
Tel: 01706 378661
Pitches For ▲ ⚑ ⚑ **Total** 45
Acreage 3 **Open** All Year
Access Good **Site** Level
Nearest Bus Stop (Miles) 1
Near a large lake that covers 120 acres.
Cafe/Restaurant nearby.
Facilities ⚑ ♿ ⚿ ⛽ ⚑ ⊙⌐ ⚑ ▣
⚺ ⏻ ⚑ ⚑ ▣
Nearest Town Rochdale
Directions Leave the M62 at junction 21,
Milnrow B6255. Follow Hollingworth Lake
Country Park signs to The Fishermans Inn/
The Wine Press. Take Rakewood Road, then
the second on the right.
⇌ Littleborough

NORFOLK
BURGH ST. PETER
Waveney River Centre, Staithe Road,
Burgh St Peter, Norfolk, NR34 0BT
Tel: 01502 677343
Email: info@waveneyrivercentre.co.uk
www.waveneyrivercentre.co.uk
Pitches For ▲ ⚑ ⚑ **Total** 48
Open All Year
Access Poor **Site** Level
Nearest Bus Stop (Miles) ¾
Alongside the River Waveney. Heated
showers and toilet blocks.
Facilities ⚑ ♿ ⚑ ⚿ ⛽ ⚑ ⊙⌐ ⚑ ▣ ☎
⚺ ⏻ ⚑ ✕ ⚑ ⚑ ⚑ ⚑⚑ ⚑ ✂ ⚑
Nearest Town Beccles
Directions From the A143 at Haddiscoe, turn
into Wiggs Road following brown tourism
signs. After 2 miles turn left into Burgh Road
and the site is 2½ miles.
⇌ Haddiscoe

CAISTER-ON-SEA
Grasmere Caravan Park, Bultitudes Loke,
Yarmouth Road, Caister-on-Sea, Great
Yarmouth, Norfolk, NR30 5DH
Tel: 01493 720382
www.grasmerewentworth.co.uk
Pitches For ⚑ ⚑ **Total** 46
Acreage 2 **Open** Apr **to** Mid Oct
Access Good **Site** Level
Nearest Bus Stop (Miles) ¼
½ a mile from the beach, 3 miles to centre of
Great Yarmouth. Advance bookings taken for
touring site pitches. Each pitch with its own
electric, water tap and foul water drain. Some
hard standings.
Facilities ⚑ ♿ ⚑ ⛽ ⚑ ⚿ ⚑ ⊙⌐ ⚑ ▣ ☎
⚺ ⏻ ⚑ ⚑ ▣ ▣
Nearest Town Great Yarmouth
Directions Enter Caister from roundabout
near Yarmouth Stadium at Yarmouth end of
bypass. After ½ mile turn sharp left just before
the bus stop.
⇌ Great Yarmouth

CLIPPESBY
Clippesby Hall, Clippesby, Norfolk, NR29
3BL
Tel: 01493 367800
Email: holidays@clippesby.com
Pitches For ▲ ⚑ ⚑ **Total** 110
Acreage 34 **Open** All Year
Access Good **Site** Level
Nearest Bus Stop (Miles) Outside
Set in the heart of the Norfolk Broads National
Park. Near to nature reserves and tourist
attractions.

79

Facilities ⬡ ⌇ 🗖 🗔 📠 ⌐ ⊙ ⏚ 📰 🗔 🛢 🛎 🗖 ⊛ ✕ 🗓 🗚 🚲 ⟲ ✿ 🗗 📺 ⚡ 🌱 📶
Nearest Town Great Yarmouth
Directions From the A47 Norwich bypass follow tourism signs to the The Broads. At Acle take the A1064, after 2½ miles turn left onto the B1152, after ½ a mile turn left at the Clippesby Village sign, after 400 yards turn right.
🚉 Acle

CROMER
Forest Park Caravan Site Ltd.,
Northrepps Road, Cromer, Norfolk, NR27 0JR
Tel: 01263 513290
Email: info@forestpark.co.uk
www.forestpark.co.uk
Pitches For ⋀ ⬜ 🚐 **Total** 355
Acreage 90 **Open** 15-Mar **to** 15-Jan
Access Good **Site** Sloping
Overlooking Cromer Golf Course and surrounded by forest with many woodland walks.
Facilities ⬡ ⌇ 🗔 📠 ⌐ ⊙ ⏚ 📰 🗔 🛢
🛎 🗓 🗚 🗓 🚲 🗗 🗖 ⚡ 📶
Directions Go through the town centre until you reach traffic lights, turn left into Overstrand Road. Follow until you reach a right hand fork featuring a horse trough, turn right and Forest Park is on the left.
🚉 Cromer

CROMER
Manor Farm Caravan & Camping Site,
Manor Farm, East Runton, Cromer, Norfolk, NR27 9PR
Tel: 01263 512858
Email:
manorfarmcampingsite@btconnect.com
www.manorfarmcaravansite.co.uk

Pitches For ⋀ ⬜ 🚐 **Total** 230
Acreage 16 **Open** Easter **to** Oct
Access Good **Site** Lev/Slope
Panoramic sea and woodland views. Spacious, quiet, family run farm site. Ideal for families. Separate field for dog owners.
Facilities ⬡ ⬡ ⌇ 🗔 📠 ⌐ ⊙ ⏚ 📰 🗔
🛢 ⛃ 🚲 🗗
Nearest Town Cromer
Directions Signposted Manor Farm from the A148 and the A149. The A149 is the preferable route if towing.
🚉 Cromer

CROMER
Woodhill Park, Cromer Road, East Runton, Cromer, Norfolk, NR27 9PX
Tel: 01263 512242
Email: info@woodhill-park.com
www.woodhill-park.com
Pitches For ⋀ ⬜ 🚐 🚐⟨ **Total** 251
Acreage 32 **Open** Mar **to** Oct
Access Good **Site** Lev/Slope
Nearest Bus Stop (Miles) Outside
Peace and tranquillity with views of the sea and surrounding countryside. A choice of pitch styles and excellent amenity buildings.
Facilities ⬡ ⌇ 🗖 🗔 📠 ⌐ ⊙ ⏚ 📰 🗔 🛢
🛎 🗓 🗓 🛢 ✿ 🗗 📺 ⚡ 🌱 📶
Nearest Town Cromer
Directions Set between East and West Runton on the seaside of the A149 Cromer to Sheringham road.
🚉 West Runton

DISS
The Willows Camping & Caravan Park,
Diss Road, Scole, Diss, Norfolk, IP21 4DH
Tel: 01379 740271
Pitches For ⋀ ⬜ 🚐 **Total** 32
Acreage 8 **Open** Easter **to** Sept

Access Good **Site** Level
Nearest Bus Stop (Miles) ¼
Alongside the River Waveney.
Facilities ⌇ 🗔 📠 ⌐ ⊙ ⏚ 🚐 🛢
🛎 ⬡ 🗚 🗚 🚲 ⌐ ⚡ 🌱
Nearest Town Diss
Directions 1½ miles east of Diss on the A1066.
🚉 Diss

DISS
Waveney Valley Holiday Park, Airstation Farm, Airstation Lane, Rushall, Diss, Norfolk, IP21 4QF
Tel: 01379 741690/741228
Email: waveneyvalleyhp@aol.com
www.caravanparksnorfolk.co.uk
Pitches For ⋀ ⬜ 🚐 🚐⟨ **Total** 45
Acreage 4 **Open** Apr **to** Oct
Access Good **Site** Level
Nearest Bus Stop (Miles) ¼
Family run site in a rural position. Horse riding for all ages and abilities on site. Good fishing locally.
Facilities ⌇ 🗔 📠 ⌐ ⊙ ⏚ 📰 🗔 🛢
🛎 ⬡ ✕ 🗓 🗚 🚲 🗗 📺
Nearest Town Harleston
Directions From Diss take the A140, at Dickleburgh in Rushall turn at telephone box towards Pulham, turn into Airstation Lane and site is on the right.
🚉 Diss

DOCKING
The Garden Caravan Site, Barmer Hall Farm, Syderstone, Kings Lynn, Norfolk, PE31 8SR
Tel: 01485 578220/178
Email: nigel@mason96.fsnet.co.uk
www.gardencaravansite.co.uk
Pitches For ⋀ ⬜ 🚐 **Total** 30

Open Mar **to** Nov
Access Good **Site** Lev/Slope
A lovely secluded and sheltered site in a walled garden. Close to the famous North Norfolk coast.
Facilities ☖ ✚ 🅷 🖧 🏕 ☋ ⌁ 🍴 ➡ 🍷 ⌦ 🅿 🎇
Nearest Town Fakenham
Directions From Fakenham or Kings Lynn take the A148, then take the B1454 towards Hunstanton, 4 miles on the right hand side.

DOWNHAM MARKET

Grange Farm Touring Park, Whittington Hill, Whittington, Kings Lynn, Norfolk, PE33 9TF
Tel: 01366 500075
Email: relax@grangefarmtouringpark.co.uk
www.grangefarmtouringpark.co.uk
Pitches For ⛺ 🚐 **Total** 25
Open Feb **to** Dec
Access Good **Site** Level
Nearest Bus Stop (Miles) Outside
Alongside a river for fishing and boating. Only suitable for adults. Within 1 hours drive of Hunstanton, Sheringham and Cromer.
Facilities ☖ ✚ 🅾 🏕 ☋ ➡ 🍷 ⌫ ✚ 🐾 ⟋ A
Nearest Town Downham Market
Directions Just off the A134.
🚃 Downham Market

FAKENHAM

Crossways Caravan & Camping Park, Crossways, Holt Road, Little Snoring, Norfolk, NR21 0AX
Tel: 01328 878335
Email: joyholland@crosswayscaravanpark.co.uk
Pitches For ⛺ ⛺ 🚐 **Total** 26
Acreage 2½ **Open** All Year
Access Good **Site** Level

Nearest Bus Stop (Miles) ½
Central location in North Norfolk. Easy access.
Facilities ☖ ✚ 🅷 🆎 🏕 ☋ ⌁ ➡ 🍷 ⌦ 🅿
🆊 🅵 ☋ ✚ 🅿 🎇
Nearest Town Fakenham
Directions On the A148, 3 miles past Fakenham towards Cromer
🚃 Kings Lynn

FAKENHAM

Greenwoods Campsite, Old Fakenham Road, Tattersett, Kings Lynn, Norfolk, PE31 8RS
Tel: 07917 842371
Email: info@greenwoodscampsite.co.uk
www.greenwoodscampsite.co.uk
Pitches For ⛺ 🚐 🚐 **Total** 25
Open Mar **to** Oct
Access Good **Site** Sloping
Nearest Bus Stop (Miles) ¼
Beaches 12 miles from the campsite.
Facilities ✚ 🅷 🆎 🏕 ☋ ➡ 🍷 🆊 🅾 ✚ 🅿 🎇
Nearest Town Fakenham
Directions From Fakenham take the A148 west for 4 miles, turn left at the Coxford sign, turn left again onto Old Fakenham Road and the site entrance is on the right.
🚃 Kings Lynn

FAKENHAM

The Old Brick Kilns, Little Barney Lane, Barney, Fakenham, Norfolk, NR21 0NL
Tel: 01328 878305
Email: enquires@old-brick-kilns.co.uk
www.old-brick-kilns.co.uk
Pitches For ⛺ ⛺ 🚐 **Total** 65
Acreage 13 **Open** 12-Mar **to** 04-Jan
Access Good **Site** Level
Nearest Bus Stop (Miles) 1

Beaches within 20 minutes drive. Near to Sandringham, Blicking Hall, Pensthorpe Nature Reserve, Thursford, Walsingham and Norwich. Strictly no arrivals til after 1.30pm due to narrow access lane. NB: Money Off Vouchers will NOT be accepted on Bank Holidays.
Facilities ☖ ✚ 🅵 🅷 🆎 🏕 ☋ ⌁ ➡ 🍷 ⌦ 🅿
🆊 🅾 ☋ ✖ 🛎 ✚ 🅼 ✚ 🅿 ⌫ ⟋ 🎇 🎇 🍷
Nearest Town Fakenham
Directions From the A148 Fakenham to Cromer road, take the B1354 to Melton Constable. After 300 yards turn right to Barney, then turn first left down Little Barney Lane, Park is at the end in ¾ miles.
🚃 Kings Lynn

GREAT HOCKHAM

Thetford Forest Camping & Caravanning Club Site, Puddledock Farm, Great Hockham, Thetford, Norfolk, IP24 1PA
Tel: 01953 498455
Email: thetford@thefriendlyclub.co.uk
www.campingandcaravanningclub.co.uk/thetfordforest
Pitches For ⛺ ⛺ 🚐 🚐 🍴 **Total** 150
Acreage 12 **Open** All Year
Access Good **Site** Level
Nearest Bus Stop (Miles) ½
Very quiet site backing onto the forest, with a network of paths and picnic areas which provide an abundance of birds and wildlife. Camping Pods available for hire. Dog exercise area. Non members welcome. You can also call us on 0845 130 7633 to book.
Facilities ☖ ✚ 🅷 🆎 🏕 ☋ ⌁ ➡ 🍷 ⌦ 🅿
🆊 🅾 ☋ ✚ 🅴 ✚ 🅿 ⌫ ⟋ 🎇 🎇 🍷 ⌒
Nearest Town Watton
Directions Midway between Thetford and Watton on the A1075. Turn left at 83 post Forestry Commission picnic site, no roadside sign.
🚃 Thetford

GREAT YARMOUTH

Bureside Holiday Park, Boundary Farm, Oby, Great Yarmouth, Norfolk, NR29 3BW
Tel: 01493 369233
www.www.bureside.com
Pitches For A ⊕ ⊞ **Total** 170
Acreage 10 **Open** End May Bank Hol **to** Mid Sept
Access Good **Site** Level
Miles of country and riverside walks in open and unspoilt Norfolk Broadland. An abundance of wildlife. Launching slipway.
Facilities ⬚ ⬚ ⬚ ⬚ ⬚ ⬚ ⬚ ⬚ ⬚ ⬚ ⬚ ⬚
Nearest Town Great Yarmouth
Directions From Norwich take the A47 to Acle, then take the A1064. Go over the river bridge and in approx 1 mile turn first left onto the B1152, then follow signs to Oby.
⇥ Acle

GREAT YARMOUTH

Burgh Castle Marina, Butt Lane, Burgh Castle, Norfolk, NR31 9PZ
Tel: 01493 780331
Email: info@burghcastlemarina.co.uk
www.burghcastlemarina.co.uk
Pitches For A ⊕ ⊞ **Total** 45
Acreage 19 **Open** Mar **to** Oct
Access Good **Site** Level
Nearest Bus Stop (Miles) Outside
Spectacular Broads views, Fishermans Inn 2 mins walk,good food.
Facilities ⬚ ⬚ ⬚ ⬚ ⬚ ⬚ ⬚ ⬚
⬚ ⬚ ⬚ ⬚ ⬚ ⬚
Nearest Town Great Yarmouth
Directions A12 bypass from Gt Yarmouth A143 to Beccles, then follow signs to Belton and Burgh Castle.
⇥ Great Yarmouth

GREAT YARMOUTH

Drewery Caravan Park, California Road, California, Great Yarmouth, Norfolk, NR29 3QW
Tel: 01493 730845
Email: drewerycp@btinternet.com
www.drewerycaravanpark.co.uk
Pitches For A ⊕ ⊞ **Total** 135
Acreage 4 **Open** Easter **to** Oct
Access Good **Site** Level
Nearest Bus Stop (Miles) ¼
Near the beach. Ideal for Norfolk Broads and Great Yarmouth.
Facilities ⬚ ⬚ ⬚ ⬚ ⬚ ⬚ ⬚ ⬚ ⬚ ⬚
⬚ ⬚ ⬚ ⬚ ⬚
Nearest Town Great Yarmouth
Directions Take the A149 from Great Yarmouth, at the Greyhound Stadium roundabout turn left, at next roundabout take the second exit onto the B1159. Go to roundabout and take the second exit, after ¼ mile turn right into California Road and follow to the end. Site is opposite California Tavern. 6 miles from Great Yarmouth.
⇥ Great Yarmouth

GREAT YARMOUTH

Great Yarmouth Racecourse Caravan Club Site, Jellicoe Road, Great Yarmouth, Norfolk, NR30 4AU
Tel: 01493 855223
www.caravanclub.co.uk
Pitches For ⊕ ⊞ **Total** 111
Acreage 5¼ **Open** Mar **to** Nov
Access Good **Site** Level
Nearest Bus Stop (Miles) Outside
300yds from the lively seafront. Adjacent to a racecourse and golf course. Near the Norfolk Broads and Pleasurewood Hills. Dogs on leads at all times. Non members welcome. Booking essential.

Facilities ⬚ ⬚ ⬚ ⬚ ⬚ ⬚ ⬚
⬚ ⬚ ⬚ ⬚ ⬚ ⬚ ⬚
Nearest Town Great Yarmouth
Directions From north on the A149, at the traffic lights on the south outskirts of Caister turn left into Jellicoe Road. After ¼ mile turn left into the Racecourse entrance (BEWARE of blind turning), go across the racetrack to the site.
⇥ Great Yarmouth

GREAT YARMOUTH

Pampas Lodge Holiday Park, The Street (A143), Haddiscoe, Norfolk, NR14 6AA
Tel: 01502 677265
Email: colinshirley@btinternet.com
Pitches For ⊕ ⊞ **Total** 54
Acreage 4 **Open** Apr **to** Oct
Access Good **Site** Level
Nearest Bus Stop (Miles) Outside
Near rivers and sae.
Facilities ⬚ ⬚ ⬚ ⬚ ⬚ ⬚ ⬚ ⬚
⬚ ⬚ ⬚ ⬚ ⬚ ⬚
Nearest Town Great Yarmouth
Directions On the A143 between Beccles and Great Yarmouth.
⇥ Haddiscoe

GREAT YARMOUTH

Rose Farm Touring & Camping Park, Stepshort, Belton, Great Yarmouth, Norfolk, NR31 9JS
Tel: 01493 780896
Email: myhra@rosefarmtouringpark.co.uk
www.rosefarmtouringpark.co.uk
Pitches For A ⊕ ⊞ **Total** 120
Acreage 10 **Open** All Year
Access Good **Site** Level
Nearest Bus Stop (Miles) ¼

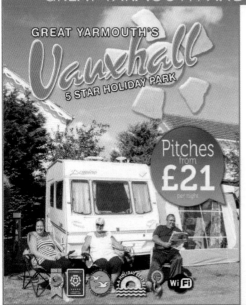

NORFOLK

A clean site in peaceful surroundings. Special offers.
Facilities ⟨icons⟩
⟨icons⟩
Nearest Town Gorleston
Directions From Great Yarmouth on the bypass take the A143 to Beccles, through Bradwell up to the small dual carriageway. Turn right into new road signposted Belton and Burgh Castle. Down New Road first right at Stepshort, site is first on right.
⇌ Great Yarmouth

GREAT YARMOUTH
The Grange Touring Park, Yarmouth Road, Ormesby St Margaret, Great Yarmouth, Norfolk, NR29 3QG
Tel: 01493 730306
Email: info@grangetouring.co.uk
www.grangetouring.co.uk
Pitches For ⟨icons⟩ **Total** 70
Acreage 3½ **Open** Easter **to** Sept
Access Good **Site** Level
Nearest Bus Stop (Miles) ¼
Rural, sheltered site, very convenient for Great Yarmouth and the Norfolk Broads.
Facilities ⟨icons⟩
⟨icons⟩
Nearest Town Great Yarmouth
Directions 2 miles north of Great Yarmouth, by the roundabout on the B1159 at the north end of Caister bypass.
⇌ Great Yarmouth

GREAT YARMOUTH
Vauxhall Holiday Park, Acle New Road, Great Yarmouth, Norfolk, NR30 1TB
Tel: 01493 857231
Email: info@vauxhallholidays.co.uk
www.vauxhallholidaypark.co.uk
Pitches For ⟨icons⟩ **Total** 213
Acreage 48 **Open** Easter then Mid May **to** Sept
Access Good **Site** Level
Nearest Bus Stop (Miles) Outside
Ideal centre for attractions of Great Yarmouth and for exploring the famous Norfolk Broads. 13 Super Pitches available.
Facilities ⟨icons⟩
⟨icons⟩
Nearest Town Great Yarmouth
Directions Situated on the A47.
⇌ Great Yarmouth

GREAT YARMOUTH
Willowcroft Camping & Caravan Park, Staithe Road, Repps-with-Bastwick, Norfolk Broads, Norfolk, NR29 5JU
Tel: 01692 670380
Email: willowcroftsite@btinternet.com
www.willowcroft.net

Pitches For ⟨icons⟩ **Total** 32
Acreage 2 **Open** Mar **to** Oct
Access Good **Site** Level
Nearest Bus Stop (Miles) ½
Beautiful, tranquil site, just a two minute walk to a river for fishing. Safe footpath along the river which leads to Potter Heigham. Excellent new ladies toilets for 2009.
Facilities ⟨icons⟩
Nearest Town Wroxham
Directions From Great Yarmouth take the A149 to Stalham, in Repps turn left into Church Road, then turn right into Staithe Road. Or from Acle take the B1152 to Caister, then take the A149 and follow as above.
⇌ Acle

HARLESTON
Little Lakeland Caravan Park, Wortwell, Harleston, Norfolk, IP20 0EL
Tel: 01986 788646
Email: info@littlelakeland.co.uk
www.littlelakeland.co.uk
Pitches For ⟨icons⟩ **Total** 40
Acreage 4 **Open** Mar **to** Oct
Access Good **Site** Level
Nearest Bus Stop (Miles) ¼
Half acre fishing lake, site library.
Facilities ⟨icons⟩
⟨icons⟩
Nearest Town Harleston
Directions Turn off A143 (Diss to Lowestoft) at roundabout signposted Wortwell. In village turn right about 300 yards after Bell P.H. at bottom of lane turn right into site.
⇌ Diss

HEMSBY
Long Beach Caravan Park, Hemsby, Great Yarmouth, Norfolk, NR29 4JD
Tel: 01493 730023
Email: info@long-beach.co.uk
www.long-beach.co.uk
Pitches For ⟨icons⟩ **Total** 100
Acreage 5 **Open** Mid Mar **to** Oct
Access Good **Site** Level
Nearest Bus Stop (Miles) ¼
Park adjoins its own private sandy beach and dunes. Sea fishing on site.
Facilities ⟨icons⟩
⟨icons⟩
Nearest Town Great Yarmouth
Directions 5 miles north of Great Yarmouth, turn east from the B1159 at Hemsby.
⇌ Great Yarmouth

HOLT
Kelling Heath Holiday Park, Weybourne, Holt, Norfolk, NR25 7HW
Tel: 01263 588181
Email: info@kellingheath.co.uk
www.kellingheath.co.uk

Pitches For ⟨icons⟩ **Total** 300
Acreage 250 **Open** Mid Feb **to** Dec
Access Good **Site** Level
A 250 acre estate of woodland and heather, with magnificent views of the Weybourne coastline. Rose Award.
Facilities ⟨icons⟩
⟨icons⟩
Nearest Town Sheringham
Directions Turn north at site sign at Bodham on the A148 or turn south off the A149 at Weybourne Church.
⇌ Sheringham

HORSEY
Waxham Sands Holiday Park, Warren Farm, Horsey, Norfolk, NR29 4EJ
Tel: 01692 598325
www.waxhamsandsholidaypark.co.uk
Pitches For ⟨icons⟩ **Total** 200
Acreage 22 **Open** 20-May **to** Sept
Access Good **Site** Level
Adjacent to the beach, ideal for sea fishing.
Facilities ⟨icons⟩
⟨icons⟩
Nearest Town Great Yarmouth
Directions Situated on the B1159 main coast road, 12 miles north of Great Yarmouth.
⇌ Great Yarmouth

KINGS LYNN
Kings Lynn Caravan & Camping Park, Parkside House, New Road, North Runcton, Kings Lynn, Norfolk, PE33 0RA
Tel: 01553 840004
Email: klcc@btconnect.com
www.kl-cc.co.uk
Pitches For ⟨icons⟩ **Total** 150
Acreage 9 **Open** All Year
Access Good **Site** Level
Nearest Bus Stop (Miles) Outside
Situated in a beautiful parkland setting with mature trees. Well situated for Kings Lynn, inland market towns, the North Norfolk coast, watersports and good pubs. Tescos nearby. Rallies welcome.
Facilities ⟨icons⟩
⟨icons⟩
Directions 1½ miles from the A17, A47, A10 and A149 main Kings Lynn Hardwick roundabout. Take the A47 towards Swaffham and take the first right at North Runcton.
⇌ Kings Lynn

KINGS LYNN
Pentney Park, Main Road, Pentney, Kings Lynn, Norfolk, PE32 1HU
Tel: 01760 337479
Email: holidays@pentney-park.co.uk
www.pentney-park.co.uk
Pitches For ⟨icons⟩ **Total** 170
Acreage 16 **Open** 11 months

Relax and enjoy the best of North Norfolk

Award-winning Kelling Heath offers a beautiful, natural environment with pitches set amongst rare open heathland with a backdrop of native woodland and pine. Connect with nature... come to Kelling.

Activities
- Woodland walks & nature trails
- Guided walks & events
- Cycle Routes on & off park
- Trim trail, orienteering, petanque and adventure play

Relax
- Health & Fitness Club with indoor pool
- Free outdoor leisure pool
- The Forge: bars, restaurants, take-away
- Village Store
- The Folly open air jazz, folk

We also offer lodges and luxurious holiday homes.

Bookings or brochure 01263 588181
or online www.kellingheath.co.uk
Kelling Heath, Weybourne, Holt,
Norfolk NR25 7HW

KELLING HEATH
THE NATURAL ESCAPE

Access Good **Site** Level
Nearest Bus Stop (Miles) 1
Near the River Nar Valley Walk, linking to Peddars Way Walk. Ideal base for visiting beautiful Norfolk. Washing up facilities.
Facilities ⬛ ⬛ ⬛ ⬛ ⬛ ⬛ ⬛ ⬛ ⬛ ⬛ ⬛ ⬛ ⬛ ⬛ ⬛ ⬛ ⬛ ⬛ ⬛
Nearest Town Kings Lynn
Directions Situated on the A47 9 miles east of Kings Lynn and 7 miles west of Swaffham. Turn onto the B1153 to Gayton, entrance is 200 yards.
⚞ Kings Lynn

METHWOLD

Warren House Caravan Park, Warren House, Brandon Road, Methwold, Thetford, Norfolk, IP26 4RL
Tel: 01366 728238
Email: janescarrott@btinternet.com
Pitches For ⬛ ⬛ ⬛ **Total** 40
Acreage 4 **Open** Mar **to** Oct
Access Good **Site** Level
Situated in Thetford Forest and close to Lakenheath Fen RSPB site and NNT Weeting Heath. Good central location for touring East Anglia. Good cycling area.
Facilities ⬛ ⬛ ⬛ ⬛ ⬛ ⬛ ⬛
Nearest Town Thetford
Directions 5 miles from Brandon on the B1112.
⚞ Thetford

MUNDESLEY

Sandy Gulls Cliff Top Touring Park, Cromer Road, Mundesley, Norfolk, NR11 8DF
Tel: 01263 720513
Email: info@sandygulls.co.uk
www.sandygulls.co.uk
Pitches For ⬛ ⬛ ⬛ **Total** 40
Acreage 2½ **Open** Easter **to** Nov
Access Good **Site** Level
Nearest Bus Stop (Miles) Outside
ADULTS ONLY TOURING PARK on a cliff top location, overlooking the beach. Near to the Broads National Park. TV Hook-ups. ETB 4 Star Graded Park.
Facilities ⬛ ⬛ ⬛ ⬛ ⬛ ⬛ ⬛ ⬛ ⬛ ⬛ ⬛ ⬛ ⬛ ⬛ ⬛
Nearest Town Cromer
Directions South along the coast road for 4 miles.
⚞ Cromer

NORTH WALSHAM

Two Mills Touring Park, Yarmouth Road, North Walsham, Norfolk, NR28 9NA
Tel: 01692 405829
Email: enquiries@twomills.co.uk
www.twomills.co.uk
Pitches For ⬛ ⬛ ⬛ **Total** 81
Acreage 8 **Open** Mar **to** 03-Jan
Access Good **Site** Level
Nearest Bus Stop (Miles) Outside
ADULTS ONLY. Ideally situated for visiting North Norfolks many attractions.
Facilities ⬛ ⬛ ⬛ ⬛ ⬛ ⬛ ⬛ ⬛ ⬛ ⬛ ⬛ ⬛ ⬛ ⬛ ⬛ ⬛ ⬛
Nearest Town North Walsham
Directions Follow Hospital signs passing the Police Station on route. 1 mile on the left from the town centre.
⚞ North Walsham

NORWICH

Norwich Camping & Caravanning Club Site, Martineau Lane, Norwich, Norfolk, NR1 2HX
Tel: 01603 620060
Email: norwich.site@thefriendlyclub.co.uk
www.campingandcaravanningclub.co.uk/norwich

Pitches For ⬛ ⬛ ⬛ **Total** 50
Acreage 2½ **Open** Apr **to** 03-Nov
Access Good **Site** Level
Nearest Bus Stop (Miles) ¼
A rural location close to the city of Norwich. Near to the Norfolk Broads. Non members welcome. You can also call us on 0845 130 7633 to book.
Facilities ⬛ ⬛ ⬛ ⬛ ⬛ ⬛ ⬛ ⬛ ⬛ ⬛ ⬛ ⬛
Nearest Town Norwich
Directions From the A47 join the A146 towards Norwich city centre. At the traffic lights turn left, then left again at the Cock Public House. Site is 150 yards on the right.
⚞ Thorpe

POTTER HEIGHAM

Causeway Cottage Caravan Park, Bridge Road, Potter Heigham, Nr Great Yarmouth, Norfolk, NR29 5JB
Tel: 01692 670238
Email: sue324@btinternet.com
www.causewaycottage.webs.com
Pitches For ⬛ ⬛ ⬛ **Total** 0
Access Good **Site** Level
Nearest Bus Stop (Miles) ¼
Static caravans for hire. Restaurant nearby.
Facilities ⬛ ⬛ ⬛ ⬛ ⬛ ⬛ ⬛ ⬛
Nearest Town Great Yarmouth
Directions Potter Heigham is between Great Yarmouth and Norwich. Turn off the A149 at Potter Heigham, we are 250yds from the river and old bridge.
⚞ Acle

REEDHAM

Reedham Ferry Complex Ltd., Ferry Road, Reedham, Norwich, Norfolk, NR13 3HA
Tel: 01493 700999
Email: reedhamferry@aol.com
www.reedhamferry.co.uk
Pitches For ⬛ ⬛ ⬛ **Total** 30
Acreage 4 **Open** Mar **to** Oct
Access Good **Site** Level
Nearest Bus Stop (Miles) ¼
Tranquil site alongside a river. Ideal touring.
Facilities ⬛ ⬛ ⬛ ⬛ ⬛ ⬛ ⬛ ⬛ ⬛ ⬛ ⬛ ⬛
Nearest Town Norwich/Great Yarmouth
Directions From Acle follow signs for Reedham Ferry.
⚞ Reedham

SANDRINGHAM

Sandringham Camping & Caravanning Club Site, The Sandringham Estate, Double Lodges, Sandringham, Norfolk, PE35 6EA
Tel: 01485 542555
Email: sandringham.site@thefriendlyclub.co.uk
www.campingandcaravanning.club.co.uk/sandringham
Pitches For ⬛ ⬛ ⬛ **Total** 275
Acreage 28 **Open** 13-Feb **to** 17-Nov
Access Good **Site** Lev/Slope
Nearest Bus Stop (Miles) 1
In the grounds of the Royal Estate. Motorhome stop-off. Ice pack and freezing facilities. Non members welcome. You can also call us on 0845 130 7633 to book.
Facilities ⬛ ⬛ ⬛ ⬛ ⬛ ⬛ ⬛ ⬛ ⬛ ⬛
Nearest Town Kings Lynn
Directions From the A148 Kings Lynn to Cromer road, turn left onto the B1440 sp West Newton. Follow signs indicating tents and caravans to reach the site.
⚞ Kings Lynn

SANDRINGHAM

The Sandringham Estate Caravan Club Site, Glucksburg Woods, Sandringham, Norfolk, PE35 6EZ
Tel: 01553 631614
www.caravanclub.co.uk
Pitches For ⬛ ⬛ ⬛ **Total** 136
Acreage 13 **Open** All Year
Access Good **Site** Lev/Slope
Nearest Bus Stop (Miles) ¼
Set in the heart of the Royal estate, with Sandringham House, museum and grounds on the doorstep. Then theres the Country Park with nature trails, train ride, Visitor Centre, tea room, gift shop and flower stall. Non members welcome. Booking essential.
Facilities ⬛ ⬛ ⬛ ⬛ ⬛ ⬛ ⬛ ⬛ ⬛ ⬛ ⬛ ⬛ ⬛ ⬛
Nearest Town Sandringham
Directions From north on the A149, at the end of Dersingham bypass turn left onto the B1439 at signpost for West Newton, site is within ½ a mile on the left at rustic signpost SECC.

SCRATBY

Green Farm Caravan Park, 100 Beach Road, Scratby, Great Yarmouth, Norfolk, NR29 3NW
Tel: 01493 730440
Email: contact@greenfarmcaravanpark.com
www.greenfarmcaravanpark.com
Pitches For ⬛ ⬛ ⬛ **Total** 25
Open 26-Mar **to** Oct
Access Good **Site** Level
Nearest Bus Stop (Miles) Outside
Near the beach.
Facilities ⬛ ⬛ ⬛ ⬛ ⬛ ⬛ ⬛ ⬛ ⬛ ⬛ ⬛ ⬛ ⬛ ⬛ ⬛ ⬛
Nearest Town Great Yarmouth
Directions 5 miles north of Great Yarmouth along the coast road between Caister and Hemsby.
⚞ Great Yarmouth

SCRATBY

Scratby Hall Caravan Park, Thoroughfare Lane, Scratby, Great Yarmouth, Norfolk, NR29 3SR
Tel: 01493 730283
Email: scratbyhall@aol.com
www.scratbyhall.co.uk
Pitches For ⬛ ⬛ ⬛ **Total** 85
Acreage 5 **Open** Easter **to** Sept
Access Good **Site** Level
Nearest Bus Stop (Miles) ½
Set in countryside and off the main road. Ideal for visiting the Norfolk Broads and only ½ a mile from the coast.
Facilities ⬛ ⬛ ⬛ ⬛ ⬛ ⬛ ⬛ ⬛ ⬛ ⬛ ⬛ ⬛ ⬛ ⬛ ⬛ ⬛
Nearest Town Great Yarmouth
Directions Approx. 5 miles north of Great Yarmouth. Take the A149 then the B1159, signposted.
⚞ Great Yarmouth

SHERINGHAM

Beeston Regis Caravan Park, Cromer Road, West Runton, Nr Sheringham, Norfolk, NR27 9QZ
Tel: 01263 823614
Email: info@beestonregis.co.uk
www.beestonregis.co.uk
Pitches For ⬛ ⬛ ⬛ **Total** 45
Acreage 60 **Open** 24-Mar **to** Oct
Access Good **Site** Level
Nearest Bus Stop (Miles) Outside
Cliff top setting with stunning views and direct access to the beach via steps. Within walking distance of Sheringham and Cromer. Woodland walks in an area of natural beauty.

Facilities [symbols]
Nearest Town Sheringham
Directions On the A149 coast road between Sheringham and Cromer, at Beeston Regis opposite the school.
West Runton

SNETTISHAM

Diglea Caravan & Camping Park, 32 Beach Road, Snettisham, Kings Lynn, Norfolk, PE31 7RA
Tel: 01485 541367
Email: diglea@hotmail.co.uk
Pitches For A ⊞ ⊟ ⊟ **Total** 0
Acreage 10 **Open** Apr to Sept
Access Good **Site** Level
Nearest Bus Stop (Miles) 1
Friendly, family run Park in a rural setting.
Facilities [symbols]
Nearest Town Hunstanton
Directions Take the A149 from Kings Lynn towards Hunstanton to Snettisham. After approx 10½ miles turn left signposted Snettisham Beach, Park is on the left after 1½ miles.
Kings Lynn

STANHOE

The Rickels Caravan & Camping Park, Bircham Road, Stanhoe, Kings Lynn, Norfolk, PE31 8PU
Tel: 01485 518671
Pitches For A ⊞ ⊟ **Total** 30
Acreage 2¼ **Open** All year
Access Good **Site** Lev/Slope
ADULTS ONLY PARK. Close to local beaches, stately homes, Sandringham and market towns. Dogs £1 per night, short dog walk.
Facilities [symbols]
Nearest Town Hunstanton
Directions From Kings Lynn take the A148 to Hillington, turn left onto the B1153 to Great Bircham. Fork right onto the B1155 to the crossroads, straight over. Park is 100yds on the left.
Kings Lynn

SWAFFHAM

Breckland Meadows Touring Park, Lynn Road, Swaffham, Norfolk, PE37 7PT
Tel: 01760 721246
Email: info@brecklandmeadows.co.uk
www.brecklandmeadows.co.uk
Pitches For A ⊞ ⊟ ⊟ **Total** 45
Acreage 3 **Open** All Year
Access Good **Site** Level
Nearest Bus Stop (Miles) ½
ADULTS ONLY. Small, friendly and very clean park. Within walking distance of the town centre for shops, pubs, restaurants, etc.. Dog walk adjacent to the park. Central for touring Norfolk. Ideal for walking and cycling.
Facilities [symbols]
Nearest Town Swaffham/Hunstanton
Directions Take the A47 from Kings Lynn to Swaffham, approx 15 miles. Take the first exit off the dual carriageway, site is ¾ miles before Swaffham town centre.
Kings Lynn

THETFORD

Lowe Caravan Park, Ashdale, 134 Hills Road, Saham Hills (Nr Watton), Thetford, Norfolk, IP25 7EZ
Tel: 01953 881051
www.lowecaravanpark.co.uk
Pitches For A ⊞ ⊟ **Total** 20

Acreage 2 **Open** All Year
Access Good **Site** Lev/Slope
Quiet, relaxing site in the countryside. Only closed for Christmas and New Year.
Facilities [symbols]
Nearest Town Watton
Directions Take the A11 from Thetford then take the road to Watton. Go through the high street and take second turn into Saham Road (past the golf club). Take the second turning right, turn right at the T-Junction and the Park is the first drive on the right.
Thetford

THETFORD

The Dower House Touring Park, Thetford Forest, East Harling, Norwich, Norfolk, NR16 2SE
Tel: 01953 717314
Email: info@dowerhouse.co.uk
www.dowerhouse.co.uk
Pitches For A ⊞ ⊟ **Total** 140
Acreage 20 **Open** 18-Mar to 02-Oct
Access Good **Site** Level
Set in Thetford Forest, the site is spacious and peaceful. Although we have a bar, we have no amusement arcade or gaming machines.
Facilities [symbols]
Nearest Town Thetford
Directions From Thetford take A1066 East for 5 miles, fork left at camping sign onto unclassified road, site on left after 2 miles, signposted.
Harling Road

WELLSNEXTTHESEA

Stiffkey Campsite, The Greenway, Vale Farm, Stiffkey, WellsNexttheSea, Norfolk, NR23 1QP
Tel: 01328 830235
Pitches For A ⊞ **Total** 80
Acreage 6 **Open** Easter to Mid Oct
Site Lev/Slope
Nearest Bus Stop (Miles) Outside
Adjoining marsh saltings and the beach. Near to steam and miniature railway. Good shop and pub in the village. Local Coast-Hopper bus.
Facilities [symbols]
Nearest Town Wells Next The Sea
Directions Take the A149 east towards Cromer, Stiffkey is the next village 3½ miles from Wells.
Kings Lynn/Cromer

WYMONDHAM

Rose Cottage Caravan Site Rose Cottage, Wicklewood, Wymondham, Norfolk, NR18 9PX
Tel: 01953 602158
Email:
info@thegreenselfstoragecompany.com
Pitches For ⊞ ⊟ **Total** 5
Acreage 2 **Open** All year
Access Good **Site** Level
Nearest Bus Stop (Miles) ¾
A quite secluded site
Facilities [symbols]
Nearest Town Wymondham
Wymondham

PLEASE REMEMBER TO MENTION CADE'S WHEN BOOKING

ALWAYS CHECK DIRECTLY WITH THE PARK, THAT ANY FACILITIES YOU PARTICULARLY REQUIRE WILL BE AVAIALABLE AT THE TIME OF YOUR VISIT

PITCH FEE DISCOUNT VOUCHERS TO THE VALUE OF £40, CAN BE FOUND ON PAGE 185

AN INDEX TO PARKS WITH FISHING ON SITE, PARKS OPEN ALL YEAR and PARKS FOR ADULTS ONLY CAN BE FOUND ON PAGE 163

NORTHAMPTONSHIRE

CORBY

Stamford Caravan Club Site, Fineshade, Corby, Northamptonshire, NN17 3BB
Tel: 01780 444617
www.caravanclub.co.uk
Pitches For 🚐 🚙 **Total** 85
Acreage 5½ **Open** Mar **to** Nov
Access Good **Site** Level
Tranquil, meadowland site surrounded by woodland. Ideal for walking, cycling and bird watching. Within easy reach of the Fens and Rutland Water. Own sanitation required. Non members welcome. Booking essential.
Facilities 🗑 🚿 ⌂ 🛈 🚽🏪🔌🕶 📶
Nearest Town Corby
Directions From north on the A43, 2¼ miles past the roundabout on the A47 junction turn left signposted Fineshade. After crossing the railway bridge turn left in front of Forestry Commission Station into site.
🚆 Corby

KETTERING

Kestrel Caravans, Windy Ridge, Warkton Lane, Kettering, Northamptonshire, NN16 9XG
Tel: 01536 514301
Pitches For 🏕 🚐 🚙 **Total** 20
Acreage 2 **Open** All Year
Access Good **Site** Level
Very quiet park.
Facilities 🛉 ⌂ 🛈 ⌐ ⌂ 🕶 🅿 🟥🔌
Nearest Town Kettering
Directions Leave the A14 at junction 10 and go into Kettering, go past the petrol station and turn next right into Warkton Lane, Park is ½ a mile on the right.
🚆 Kettering

NORTHAMPTON

Billing Aquadrome, Crow Lane, Great Billing, Northampton, Northamptonshire, NN3 9DA
Tel: 01524 889192
Email: enquiries@aquadrome.co.uk
www.billingaquadrome.com
Pitches For 🏕 🚐 🚙 **Total** 2107
Acreage 235 **Open** 6th Feb **to** 6th Jan
Access Good **Site** Level
Set in 235 acres of countryside within the stunning Nene Valley whose numerous rivers and lakes run throughout.
Facilities ⌂ 🛉 ⌐ 🛈 ⌐ 🕶 🟥🔌 🅿 🟥
🟇 🕙 🛈 🚽🏪✗ 🍴 🍺 🔫🟥 🚽🏪🔌🅿 🕶 📶
Nearest Town Northampton
Directions Located 5 mins off the A45 in Northamptonshire.
🚆 Northampton

NORTHUMBERLAND

ALNWICK

Railway Inn Caravan Park, Acklington, Morpeth, Northumberland, NE65 9BP
Tel: 01670 760320
Email: info@railway-inn.co.uk
www.railway-inn.co.uk
Pitches For 🚐 🚙 **Total** 22
Acreage 1½ **Open** All Year
Access Good **Site** Level
Only 3 miles from the beach and near to castles.
Facilities 🛉 ⌐ 🔌 🕶 🟥
✗ 🟥🔌🅿 🟥
Nearest Town Amble

Directions From the A1 take the B6345 sp Felton and Amble, after approx 3 miles the Railway Inn is over the bridge on the right.
🚆 Acklington

ALNWICK

River Breamish Caravan Club Site, Powburn, Alnwick, Northumberland, NE66 4HY
Tel: 01665 578320
www.caravanclub.co.uk
Pitches For 🏕 🚐 🚙 **Total** 79
Acreage 10 **Open** 22-Mar **to** 04-Nov
Access Good **Site** Sloping
Nearest Bus Stop (Miles) ½
Near national cycle network nunber 68 and The Northumberland National Park. Historic Area.
Facilities 🛉 🛉 ⌂ 🛈 ⌐ 🅿 🟫 🌀 ⌂ 🟥🕶📶
Nearest Town Alnwick
Directions From the A1 take the A697 for Wooler. After going through Powburn, immediately after Hedgeley Service Station, turn left signposted Branton, site is ½ mile on the right.
🚆 Alnwick

BAMBURGH

Waren Caravan & Camping Park, Waren Mill, Bamburgh, Northumberland, NE70 7EE
Tel: 01668 214366
Email: waren@meadowhead.co.uk
www.meadowhead.co.uk
Pitches For 🏕 🚐 🚙 **Total** 180
Open 08-Mar **to** Oct
Access Good **Site** Lev/Slope
Nearest Bus Stop (Miles) ½
Close to Bamburgh Castle, Holy Island and Alnwick Castle & Gardens.
Facilities 🛉 🛉 ⌂ 🛈 ⌐ 🕶 🟥🔌 🅿 🟥
🟇 🕙 🛈 🚽✗ 🍴 🟥 🔫 🟥 🚽🏪🔌🅿 🕶 📶
Nearest Town Bamburgh
Directions From the A1 take the B1342 towards Bamburgh to Waren Mill. By Budle Bay turn right and follow signs for Waren Caravan Park.
🚆 Berwick-upon-Tweed

BEADNELL BAY

Beadnell Bay Camping & Caravanning Club Site, Beadnell, Chathill, Northumberland, NE67 5BX
Tel: 01665 720586
Email: beadnell.site@thefriedlyclub.co.uk
www.campingandcaravanningclub.co.uk/beadnell bay
Pitches For 🏕 🚐 🚙 **Total** 150
Acreage 14 **Open** Apr **to** 10-Nov
Site Lev/Slope
Nearest Bus Stop (Miles) Outside
2 miles of sandy beach just over the road. 6 miles from Bamburgh Castle. Laundry drying room. Non members welcome. You can also call us on 0845 130 7633, to book.
Facilities 🛉 🛉 ⌂ 🛈 ⌐ 🅿 🕶 🟥🔌 🅿 🟥
🕙 🛈 🚽🏪🔌🅿 🕶 📶
Directions From south leave the A1 and follow the B1430 signposted Seahouses. At Beadnell ignore signs for Beadnell Village, site is on the left after the village, just beyond the left hand bend. From north leave the A1 and follow the B1342 via Bamburgh and Seahouses, site is on the right just before Beadnell Village.

BELLINGHAM

Bellingham Camping & Caravanning Club Site, Tweed House, Brown Rigg, Bellingham, Hexham, Northumberland, NE48 2JY
Tel: 01434 220175
Email:
bellingham.site@thefriendlyclub.co.uk
www.campingandcaravanningclub.co.uk
Pitches For 🏕 🚐 🚙 **Total** 90
Acreage 5 **Open** Mar **to** 05-Nov
Access Good **Site** Level
Nearest Bus Stop (Miles) ½
Set in Northumberland National Park. Pennine Way passes the site. Near to Kielder Water, Kielder Castle and Hadrians Wall. Ideal for Newcastle and Gateshead shopping. Non members welcome. You can also call us on 0845 130 7633 to book. Camping pod available for hire.
Facilities 🛉 🛉 ⌂ 🛈 ⌐ 🅿 🕶 🟥🔌🅿 🟥
🟇 🕙 🛈 🚽🏪🔌🅿 🕶 📶
Nearest Town Kielder
Directions Take the A69, after Hexham in ½ mile turn right signposted Acomb, Chollerford and Bellingham. At Chollerford turn left onto the B6318, go over the river and turn second left onto the B6320 signposted Wark and Bellingham.
🚆 Hexham

BELLINGHAM

Stonehaugh Campsite, Stonehaugh Shields, Hexham, Northumberland, NE48 3BU
Tel: 01434 230798
Email:
enquiries@stonehaughcampsite.com
www.stonehaughcampsite.com
Pitches For 🏕 🚐 🚙 **Total** 50
Acreage 3½ **Open** Apr **to** Sept
Access Good **Site** Level
Rural site set within Northumberland National Park. Situated between Kielder Water and Hadrians Wall, and close to the Penine Way and cycle routes.
Facilities 🛈 ⌐ 🕶 🟥🔌🅿 ☀
Nearest Town Hexham
Directions From Hexham take the A6079 to Chollerford, go over the bridge and staright over at the roundabout. Then follow the B6320 for Wark and Bellingham, after 5 miles turn left to Stonehaugh.
🚆 Hexham

BERWICKUPONTWEED

Berwick Seaview Caravan Club Site, Billendean Road, Spittal, BerwickuponTweed, Northumberland, TD15 1QU
Tel: 01289 305198
www.caravanclub.co.uk
Pitches For 🏕 🚐 🚙 **Total** 93
Acreage 6 **Open** Mar **to** Nov
Access Good **Site** Lev/Slope
Nearest Bus Stop (Miles) Outside
Overlooking a river estuary with views of Holy Island. Just a short walk into Berwick. Near a safe sandy beach. Close to Swan Leisure Pool, Lindisfarne Priory and Paxton House. Non members welcome. Booking essential.
Facilities 🛉 🛉 ⌂ 🛈 ⌐ 🅿 🕶 🟥
🟇 🕙 🛈 🚽🏪🔌🅿 🕶 📶
Nearest Town Berwick-on-Tweed
Directions From the A1 take the A1167 signposted Spittal, at the roundabout turn right into Billendean Terrace, site is ½ mile on the right.
🚆 Berwick-upon-Tweed

BERWICKUPONTWEED

Ord House Country Park, East Ord, BerwickuponTweed, Northumberland, TD15 2NS
Tel: 01289 305288
Email: enquiries@ordhouse.co.uk
www.ordhouse.co.uk
Pitches For ▲ ⛺ 🚐 🚲 **Total** 75
Acreage 42 **Open** All Year
Access Good **Site** Lev/Slope
Nearest Bus Stop (Miles) Outside
Idealfor exploring north Northumberladn and the Scottish Borders.
Facilities (icons)
Nearest Town BerwickuponTweed
Directions Take the A1 Berwick bypass and turn off at roundabout for East Ord.
🚉 BerwickuponTweed

HALTWHISTLE

Haltwhistle Camping & Caravanning Club Site, Burnfoot Park Village, Haltwhistle, Northumberland, NE49 0JP
Tel: 01434 320106
Email: enquiries@thefriendlyclub.co.uk
www.campingandcaravanningclub.co.uk/haltwhistle
Pitches For ▲ ⛺ 🚐 **Total** 50
Acreage 3½ **Open** Apr to 10-Nov
Site Level
Nearest Bus Stop (Miles) ¾
On the banks of the River South Tyne for fishing. Close to the Pennine Way. BTB 4 Star Graded and AA 3 Pennants. Non members welcome. You can also call us on 0845 130 7633.
Facilities (icons)
Directions Follow signs from the A69 by-pass, DO NOT go into Haltwhistle.
🚉 Haltwhistle

HALTWHISTLE

Seldom Seen Caravan Park, Haltwhistle, Northumberland, NE49 0NE
Tel: 01434 320571
www.seldomseencaravanpark.co.uk
Pitches For ⛺ 🚐 **Total** 20
Open Mar to Jan
Access Good **Site** Level
Nearest Bus Stop (Miles) ¼
Central touring area, ideal for the Roman wall. David Bellamy Gold Award for Conservation.
Facilities (icons)
Nearest Town Haltwhistle
Directions Off the A69 east of Haltwhistle, signposted.
🚉 Haltwhistle

HEXHAM

Hexham Racecourse Caravan Site, High Yarridge, Hexham, Northumberland, NE46 2JP
Tel: 01434 606847
Email: hexrace.caravan@btconnect.com
Pitches For ▲ ⛺ 🚐 **Total** 50
Open May to Sept
Access Good **Site** Sloping
Nearest Bus Stop (Miles) 2
Set in beautiful open countryside.
Facilities (icons)
Nearest Town Hexham
Directions From the A69 follow signs for Hexham. Follow the main street to the traffic lights and bear left onto the B6305 signposted Allendale. After 3 miles turn left at the T-Junction, site is 1½ miles.
🚉 Hexham

ROTHBURY

Clennell Hall Riverside Holiday Park, Alwinton, Rothbury, Northumberland, NE65 7BG
Tel: 01669 650341
Email: enquiries@clennellhall.co.uk
www.clennellhall.co.uk
Pitches For ▲ ⛺ 🚐 **Total** 50
Open Mar to Oct **Access** Good **Site** Level
Nearest Bus Stop (Miles) ½
Lovely quiet park on the fringe of Northumberland National Park. Perfect for relaxing. A walkers and cyclists paradise. By Alnwick Castle featuring Alnwick Garden & Treehouse and Cragside Hall. Within driving distance of the spectacular Northumbrian coastline, Kielder Water & Forest Park and Hadrians Wall.
Facilities (icons)
Nearest Town Rothbury
Directions From the A1 north of Newcastle take the A697 Coldstream road. After 8 miles take the B6344, after 5 miles take the B6341 Rothbury road. Travel through Rothbury and Thropton and turn off to Sharperton and Harbottle. Site is after the bridge on the right, just before Alwinton Village.
🚉 Morpeth

ROTHBURY

Nunnykirk Caravan Club Site, Nunnykirk, Morpeth, Northumberland, NE61 4PZ
Tel: 01669 620762
www.caravanclub.co.uk
Pitches For ⛺ 🚐 **Total** 84
Acreage 14 **Open** Mar to Sept
Access Good **Site** Level
Attractive and peaceful site, a wildlife and bird watchers paradise. Simonside Hills nearby, perfect for hill walkers. Close to Hadrians Wall and Wallington Hall & Gardens. Own sanitation required. Non members welcome. Booking essential.
Facilities (icons)
Nearest Town Morpeth
Directions From A1 take A696 sp Jedburgh, after approx. 19¼ miles turn right at Knowesgate Hotel sp Scots Gap. After 2¼ miles turn left onto B6342, after 6 miles cross the bridge at foot of the hill and turn right into a private road, site is ¼ mile on the right.
🚉 Morpeth

SEAHOUSES

Seafield Caravan Park, Seafield Road, Seahouses, Northumberland, NE68 7SP
Tel: 01665 720628
Email: info@seafieldpark.co.uk
www.seafieldpark.co.uk
Pitches For ⛺ 🚐 **Total** 18
Open 09-Feb to 09-Jan
Access Good **Site** Level
Nearest Bus Stop (Miles) ¼
In the centre of Seahouses, near the harbour and just a short walk to the beach.
Facilities (icons)
Nearest Town Alnwick
Directions Travelling south leave the A1 at Alnwick and take the B1340 to Seahouses. Travelling north leave the A1 at Belford and take the B1342 through Bamburgh to Seahouses.
🚉 Alnmouth

WOOLER

Highburn House Caravan & Camping Park, Wooler, Northumberland, NE71 6EE
Tel: 01668 281344
Email: relax@highburn-house.co.uk
www.highburn-house.co.uk
Pitches For ▲ ⛺ 🚐 **Total** 100
Acreage 12 **Open** Apr to Dec
Access Good **Site** Level
Nearest Bus Stop (Miles) ¼
Stream runs through middle of site, beautiful view over hills and valley.
Facilities (icons)
Nearest Town Wooler
Directions Off A1 take A697 to Wooler town centre, at the top of Main Street take left turn, 400 metres on left is our site.
🚉 Berwick

NOTTINGHAMSHIRE

MANSFIELD

Tall Trees Park, Old Mill Lane, Forest Town, Mansfield, Nottinghamshire, NG19 0JP
Tel: 01623 626503
Email: info@talltreestouringpark.co.uk
www.talltreestouringpark.co.uk
Pitches For ▲ ⛺ 🚐 🚲 **Total** 37
Acreage 3 **Open** All Year
Access Good **Site** Sloping
Nearest Bus Stop (Miles) Outside
Peaceful rural Park surrounded by open farmland. Within walking distance of amenities. Close to Clumber Park.
Facilities (icons)
Nearest Town Mansfield
Directions From the A60 at Worksop turn at Fourways onto Old Mill Lane, the Park is on the left hand side.
🚉 Mansfield

NEWARK

Milestone Caravan Park, Great North Road, Cromwell, Newark, Nottinghamshire, NG23 6JE
Tel: 01636 821244
Email: enquiries@milestonepark.co.uk
www.milestonepark.co.uk
Pitches For ⛺ 🚐 🚲 **Total** 100
Acreage 22 **Open** All Year
Access Good **Site** Level
Nearest Bus Stop (Miles) Outside
River Trent walks, level cycling, lock walk.
Facilities (icons)
Nearest Town Newark
Directions From Newark 5 miles on A1 north, HGV garage, come off A1 ai signs to Cromwell behind garage we are on the left.
🚉 Newark

NEWARK

Robin Hood Retreat, Middle Plantation, Belle Eau Park, Bilsthorpe, Nottinghamshire, NG22 8TY
Tel: 01623 871457
Email: robinhoodretreat@live.co.uk
www.robinhoodretreat
Pitches For ▲ ⛺ 🚐 **Total** 30
Acreage 6¼ **Open** All Year
Access Good **Site** Level
Nearest Bus Stop (Miles) 1
Near to Rufford Park, Sherwood Forest, Newark and Nottingham.
Facilities (icons)
Nearest Town Mansfield/Newark
Directions From the A617/A614 follow signs for Belle Eau Park Industrial Estate, go through the industrial estate following signs for Robin Hood Retreat.
🚉 Mansfield/Newark

NOTTINGHAM

Manor Farm Caravan Site, Manor Farm, Church Lane, Thrumpton, Nottinghamshire, NG11 0AX
Tel: 0115 983 0341
Pitches For ⬜ 🚐 **Total** 12
Acreage 3 **Open** All Year
Access Good **Site** Level
Nearest Bus Stop (Miles) Outside
Facilities ƒ 🔟 🅿 ⊙ ➔ 🍴 ➡ 🔧
Nearest Town Nottingham
Directions From the M1 junction 24, take the A453 Nottingham South, after 3 miles turn left to Thrumpton Village.
⌖ Nottingham

NOTTINGHAM

Riverdale Park, Gunthorpe Bridge, Gunthorpe, Nottinghamshire, NG14 7RP
Tel: 01159 665173
Email: jane@rongrundy.co.uk
Pitches For 🚐 🚐 **Total** 5
Open Mar to 06-Jan
Access Good **Site** Level
Nearest Bus Stop (Miles) ¼
Near the River Trent.
Facilities 🔟 🅿 ⌇
Nearest Town Nottingham
Directions Take the A612 east from Nottingham, go through Burton Joyce to Lowdham, then take the A6097 to the village of Gunthorpe.
⌖ RadcliffeonTrent/Nottingham

NOTTINGHAM

Thorntons Holt Camping Park, Stragglethorpe, Radcliffe-on-Trent, Nottinghamshire, NG12 2JZ
Tel: 0115 933 2125
Email: camping@thorntons-holt.co.uk
www.thorntons-holt.co.uk
Pitches For ⬜ 🚐 🚐 **Total** 155
Acreage 15 **Open** All Year
Access Good **Site** Level
Nearest Bus Stop (Miles) Outside
Only 3 miles from Nottingham. Ideal base for touring Sherwood Forest and the Vale of Belvoir. Pub and restaurant nearby.
Facilities ƒ 🔟 🅿 ⊙ ➔ ➡ 🔧
🏪 🗑 ⊙ 🛢 🍴 ⚑ ⊙ ➔ ➡ ⌇ 🔧
Nearest Town Nottingham
Directions 3 miles east of Nottingham turn south of A52 towards Cropwell Bishop. Park is ¼ mile on left.
⌖ Radcliffe-on-Trent

OLLERTON

Shannon Caravan & Camping Park, The Shannon, Wellow Road, Ollerton, Nottinghamshire, NG22 9AP
Tel: 01623 869002
Email: Buxts@aol.com
www.caravansitefinder.co.uk
Pitches For ⬜ 🚐 🚐 **Total** 37
Acreage 4 **Open** All Year
Access Good **Site** Level
Within 10 minutes of Sherwood Forest and the Robin Hood Centre. Close to Rufford Park, Clumber Park and much more.
Facilities 🔟 ƒ 🔟 🅿 ⊙ ➔ ➡ ⚑
Directions On the A616 between Ollerton and Newark.
⌖ Newark/Retford

TUXFORD

Greenacres Caravan & Touring Park, Lincoln Road, Tuxford, Newark, Nottinghamshire, NG22 0JN
Tel: 01777 870264
Email: stay@greenacres-tuxford.co.uk
www.greenacres-tuxford.co.uk

Pitches For ⬜ 🚐 🚐 **Total** 67
Acreage 4½ **Open** Mid Mar to Oct
Access Good **Site** Level
Nearest Bus Stop (Miles) Outside
Ideal for night halt or for touring Robin Hood country. Static caravans for sale and hire. Secure Storage during Winter.
Facilities ƒ 🔟 ⊙ ➔ ➡ 🔧
🏪 🗑 🛢 🍴 🅿 🛢 ➡ ⌇ 🔧
Nearest Town Retford
Directions From A1 (north or south) follow signs. Park is on the left 250yds after Fountain Public House.
⌖ Retford

TUXFORD

Marnham Meadows Holiday Park, Hollowgate Lane, High Marnham, Newark, Nottinghamshire, NG23 6SG
Tel: 01636 822775
Pitches For ⬜ 🚐 🚐 **Total** 35
Open Apr to Oct **Access** Good **Site** Level
Near the River Trent, the National Cycle Path to Lincoln and Sundown Adventure Park. Brownlow Arms Pub just a few minutes walk. Ralley Field.
Facilities ƒ 🔟 ➔ 🍴 ➡ 🔧 ⌇
Nearest Town Newark/Lincoln
Directions From Newark take the A1 north to Tuxford, or from Lincoln take the A57 to Dunham.
⌖ Newark/Lincoln

TUXFORD

Orchard Park Touring Caravan & Camping, Orchard Park, Marnham Road, Tuxford, Newark, Nottinghamshire, NG22 0PY
Tel: 01777 870228
Email: info@orchardcaravanpark.co.uk
www.orchardcaravanpark.co.uk
Pitches For ⬜ 🚐 🚐 **Total** 60
Acreage 7 **Open** Mar to Nov
Access Good **Site** Level
Nearest Bus Stop (Miles) ½
A quiet, sheltered park, spaciously set in an old fruit orchard. Central for Sherwood Forest, Clumber Park, Lincoln and Nottingham.
Facilities 🔟 ƒ 🔟 🅿 ⊙ ➔ ➡ 🔧
🏪 🏪 🗑 🛢 🍴 🅿 ➡ ⌇ ⚑ ⌇
Nearest Town Newark
Directions Turn off the A1 dual carriageway at Tuxford, when you reach the T-Junction in the village turn right signposted Darlton. In ¼ mile turn right signposted Marnham, site is ½ a mile on the right.
⌖ Retford

WORKSOP

Clumber Park Caravan Club Site, Lime Tree Avenue, Clumber Park, Worksop, Nottinghamshire, S80 3AE
Tel: 01909 484758
www.caravanclub.co.uk
Pitches For ⬜ 🚐 🚐 **Total** 178
Acreage 20 **Open** All Year
Access Good **Site** Level
Situated in 4000 acres of parkland (once part of Sherwood Forest), ideal for walking and cycling. Visitor Centre 10 minutes away. Close to Creswell Crags Cave Tours. Non members welcome. Booking essential.
Facilities ƒ 🔟 🅿 ⊙ ➡ 🔧
🏪 🗑 🛢 🍴 🅿 ⊙ ⌇
Nearest Town Worksop
Directions From the A1, at the roundabout junction of the A57 and the A614 turn onto the A614 signposted Nottingham. After ½ a mile turn right into Clumber Park through a stone arch, after 1 mile turn right, site is 50 yards on the left.
⌖ Worksop

WORKSOP

Riverside Caravan Park, Central Avenue, Worksop, Nottinghamshire, S80 1ER
Tel: 01909 474118
www.riversideworksop.co.uk
Pitches For ⬜ 🚐 🚐 **Total** 60
Acreage 6 **Open** All Year
Site Level
Nearest Bus Stop (Miles) ¼
Just a 5 minute walk from the town centre, where Market days are wednesday, friday and saturday. Ideal for canal walks and cycling. Showers take £1 coins.
Facilities ƒ 🔟 🅿 🅿 ⊙ ➔ 🅿 ➡ ⌇
Nearest Town Worksop
Directions From the A57 roundabout turn into Newcastle Avenue, turn first left into Stubbing Lane. Turn next right into Central Avenue, go past the cricket ground and into the Park.
⌖ Worksop

OXFORDSHIRE
BANBURY

Barnstones Caravan & Camping Site, Barnstones, Main Street, Great Bourton, Nr Banbury, Oxfordshire, OX17 1QU
Tel: 01295 750289
Pitches For ⬜ 🚐 🚐 🚐 **Total** 49
Acreage 3 **Open** All Year
Access Good **Site** Level
Very beautiful countryside. Ideal for the Cotswolds, Oxford, Stratford-upon-Avon and Warwick.
Facilities 🔟 ƒ 🅿 🔟 🅿 🅿 ⊙ ➔ ➡ 🔧
🏪 🗑 🛢 🍴 ⚑ 🅿 ➡ ⌇
Nearest Town Banbury
Directions Leave the M40 at junction 11 and follow signs to Southam and Banbury over two roundabouts, at the third roundabout turn onto the A423. After 2 miles turn right signposted Great Bourton, the Site entrance is 120yds on the right.
⌖ Banbury

BLETCHINGDON

Diamond Caravan & Camping Park, Islip Road, Bletchingdon, Oxford, Oxfordshire, OX5 3DR
Tel: 01869 350909
Email: warden@diamondpark.co.uk
www.diamondpark.co.uk
Pitches For ⬜ 🚐 🚐 **Total** 37
Open All Year
Access Good **Site** Level
Nearest Bus Stop (Miles) ½
Small family run site. Ideal for Oxford, the Cotswolds and the Chilterns.
Facilities ƒ 🔟 🅿 ⊙ ➔ ➡ 🔧
🏪 ⊙ 🍴 🛢 ⚑ 🅿 ➡ ⌇
Nearest Town Kidlington
Directions From Kidlington take the A34 and leave at the junction sp Bletchingdon, Park is 1 mile on the left hand side.
⌖ Islip

NEVER TAKE A BARBECUE IN TO A TENT OR AWNING EVEN WHEN YOU HAVE FINISHED COOKING.

BLETCHINGDON
Greenhill Leisure Park, Greenhill Farm, Station Road, Bletchingdon, Oxfordshire, OX5 3BQ
Tel: 01869 351600
Email: info@greenhill-leisure-park.co.uk
www.greenhill-leisure-park.co.uk
Pitches For Å ⊞ ⇔ ⇔ ⧉ **Total** 92
Acreage 7 **Open** All Year
Access Good **Site** Lev/Slope
Quiet and spacious farm site. Pets Corner, farm animals and riverside walks. Two new fishing lakes have been created. Rally field available. 3 miles from Blenheim Palace. Ideal for touring the Cotswolds.
Facilities ⅙ ∤ 🛒 🕮 🅿 ⊙ ♨ 🔔 🖭 🌰
Ⓢ 🕿 🖳 🏕 🛒 🖳 🎨 🖭 🖬 ✕ ⚲ 🌦 🌲 🛜
Nearest Town Woodstock
Directions 3 miles east of Woodstock and 8 miles north of Oxford on the B4027. 2½ miles from the A34 and 7 miles south of the M40 junction 9.
⚞ Islip

BURFORD
Burford Caravan Club Site, Bradwell Grove, Burford, Oxfordshire, OX18 4JJ
Tel: 01993 823080
www.caravanclub.co.uk
Pitches For ⊞ ⇔ ⇔ **Total** 120
Acreage 10 **Open** Mar **to** Nov
Access Good **Site** Level
Attractive and spacious site. Area for volleyball, netball and football (goal posts). Opposite Cotswold Wildlife Park. Non members welcome. Booking essential.
Facilities ⅙ ∤ 🕮 🛒 🅿 🕮 🌰
Ⓢ 🕿 🖳 🏕 🛒 🖳 🎨 🖭 🖬 ⚲ 🛜
Directions Leave Oxford on A40, after approx. 23 miles at large roundabout in Burford turn left onto A361 and follow signs for Cotswold Wildlife Park. After 2 miles at crossroads turn right, DO NOT turn right into New Bradwell Village, site is 70 yards on the right opposite entrance to Wildlife Park.

BURFORD
Wysdom Touring Park, Burford School, Burford, Oxfordshire, OX18 4JG
Tel: 01993 823207
Pitches For ⊞ ⇔ ⇔ **Total** 25
Open All year **Access** Good **Site** Level
Nearest Bus Stop (Miles) ¼
Ideally situated to visit the Cotswolds.
Facilities ∤ 🕮 🛒 🅿 ⊙ ♨ 🛒 🅰
Nearest Town Burford
Directions From the A40 towards Cheltenham Burford take the A361 towards Lechlade we are 2nd turning on right.
⚞ Kingham

CHIPPING NORTON
Chipping Norton Camping & Caravanning Club Site, Chipping Norton Road, Chadlington, Chipping Norton, Oxfordshire, OX7 3PE
Tel: 01608 641993
Email: enquiries@thefriendlyclub.co.uk
www.campingandcaravanningclub.co.uk/chippingnorton
Pitches For Å ⊞ ⇔ **Total** 105
Open Apr **to** 03-Nov **Site** Lev/Slope
Nearest Bus Stop (Miles) Outside
Perfect for exploring the Cotswolds. 11 miles from Blenheim Palace. BTB 4 Star Graded and AA 3 Pennants. Non members welcome. You can also call us on 0845 130 7633.
Facilities ⅙ ∤ 🛒 🅿 🅿 ⊙ ♨ 🛒 🅰 🌰
🖭 ⓪ 🛒 🕮 🖭 🖭 🛜
Directions Take the A44 or the A361 to Chipping Norton. Pick up the A361 Burford road, turn left at the crossroads and the site is 150 yards. From Burford stay on the A361 and turn right at the sign for Chadlington.

OXFORD
Camping & Caravanning Club Site, 426 Abingdon Road, Oxford, Oxfordshire, OX1 4XG
Tel: 01865 244088
Email: enquiries@thefriendlyclub.co.uk
www.campingandcaravanningclub.co.uk/oxford
Pitches For Å ⊞ ⇔ **Total** 85
Acreage 5 **Open** All Year
Access Good **Site** Level
Nearest Bus Stop (Miles) Outside
In one of Britains most popular tourist destinations, this university city has a lot more to offer with more than 650 listed buildings. AA 3 Pennants. Non members welcome. You can also call us on 0845 130 7633.
Facilities ∤ 🛒 🅿 ⊙ ♨ 🛒 🖭 🌰
🖭 ⓪ 🛒 🕮 🖭 🛜
Nearest Town Oxford
Directions From the M40 take the A34 at the A423, turn left immediately after junction into Abingdon Road, site is on the left behind Touchwood Sports.
⚞ Oxford

WALLINGFORD
Bridge Villa Camping & Caravan Park, The Street, Crowmarsh Gifford, Wallingford, Oxfordshire, OX10 8HB
Tel: 01491 836860
Email: bridge.villa@btconnect.com
www.bridgevilla.co.uk
Pitches For Å ⊞ ⇔ ⇔ ⧉ **Total** 99
Acreage 4 **Open** Feb **to** Dec
Access Good **Site** Level
Nearest Bus Stop (Miles) ¼

Within 300 metres of the River Thames. Easy walk in Wallingford. Ideal for visiting Henley-on-Thames, Oxford and Windsor. Close to The Ridgeway and The Chilterns.
Facilities ⅙ ∤ 🛒 🅿 ⊙ ♨ 🖭 🌰
Ⓢ 🕿 ⓪ 🛒 ✕ ⚲ 🛒 🖭 🖭 ✐ 🌦 ⚲
Directions From Wallingford travel along the High Street towards the River Thames, cross wallingford Bridge. Our site entrance is approx 100metres on the right.
⚞ Cholsey

WITNEY
Hardwick Parks, Downs Road, Standlake, Nr Witney, Oxfordshire, OX29 7PZ
Tel: 01865 300501
Email: info@hardwickparks.co.uk
www.hardwickparks.co.uk
Pitches For Å ⊞ ⇔ ⇔ ⧉ **Total** 214
Acreage 40 **Open** Apr **to** Oct
Access Good **Site** Level
Nearest Bus Stop (Miles) Outside
On the edge of the Cotswolds. Two lakes on the park. Holiday homes for hire.
Facilities ⅙ ∤ 🛒 🅿 ⊙ ⊙ 🌰
Ⓢ 🕿 ⓪ 🛒 🖁 ✕ 🖁 🕮 🖭 🖭 ✐ 🛜
Nearest Town Witney
Directions A415 Witney to Abingdon road. signposted 4 miles out of Witney on the main road.
⚞ Oxford

WITNEY
Lincoln Farm Park, High Street, Standlake, Nr Witney, Oxfordshire, OX29 7RH
Tel: 01865 300239
Email: info@lincolnfarmpark.co.uk
www.lincolnfarmpark.co.uk
Pitches For Å ⊞ ⇔ **Total** 90
Acreage 8 **Open** Feb **to** Mid Nov
Access Good **Site** Level
Nearest Bus Stop (Miles) Outside
Leisure centre with two indoor swimming pools, saunas, spa and fitness centre. Two village pubs each serving food nearby.
Facilities ⅙ ∤ 🛒 🕮 🛒 🅿 ⊙ ♨ 🛒 🖭 🌰
Ⓢ 🕿 ⓪ 🛒 🖁 🛒 🕮 🖭 🛜
Nearest Town Witney
Directions On the A415 5 miles from Witney and 9 miles from Abingdon.
⚞ Oxford

SHROPSHIRE
BISHOPS CASTLE
Daisy Bank Caravan Park, Snead, Montgomery, Powys, SY15 6EB
Tel: 01588 620471
Email: enquiries@daisybank.co.uk
www.daisybank.co.uk

Pitches For ⋀ ⊕ ⊕ Total 55
Acreage 8 **Open** All Year
Access Good **Site** Lev/Slope
Nearest Bus Stop (Miles) 4
Facilities ⨍ 🖪 🕀 🚿 ♿ ⌂ ⊙ 🚻
㎡ ⌾ ⊙ 🔌 🗑 🅿 🔄 ⚡ 🛜
Nearest Town Bishops Castle
Directions A489 between Lydham and
Churchstoke.
🚂 Craven Arms

BISHOPS CASTLE

The Green Caravan Park, Wentnor,
Bishops Castle, Shropshire, SY9 5EF
Tel: 01588 650605
Email: lin@greencaravanpark.co.uk
www.greencaravanpark.co.uk
Pitches For ⋀ ⊕ ⊕ **Total** 140
Open Easter **to** Oct
Access Good **Site** Level
Picturesque, riverside site in an area of
outstanding natural beauty. Superb walking
in the countryside. Excellent birdlife. Central
for touring. David Bellamy Gold Award for
Conservation 2000-2010. Pub 2 mins walk
from site entrance.
Facilities ⨍ 🖪 🕀 🚿 ♿ ⊙ 🚻
㎡ ⌾ ⌂ 🔌 🗑 🅿 🔄 ⚡ 🔧
Nearest Town Bishops Castle
Directions Follow brown tourism signs from
the A488 and the A489.
🚂 Craven Arms

BRIDGNORTH

Millstone Cottage Touring Site Millstone
Cottage, Severnside, Highley, Bridgnorth,
Shropshire, WV16 6NU
Tel: 01746 862604
Email: jill_perkins@hotmail.co.uk
www.shropshirefishingholidays.co.uk
Pitches For ___ **Total** 4
Acreage 1 **Open** All Year
Access Good **Site** Level
On the banks of the River Severn. Five
minutes walk from Highley Severn Valley
Railway Station and five minutes walk from
The Ship Inn.
Facilities ⨍ 🖪 🕀 🚿 ♿ ⊙ 🚻 🔌 🅿 🔧
Nearest Town Bridgnorth
Directions From Bewdley, take the B4194
to Highley. Take road signposted to Severn
Valley Railway Station.
From Bridgnorth,
take B4555 to Highley, turn left in to Station
Road.
🚂 Highley SVR

BRIDGNORTH

The Riverside Caravan Park,
Kidderminster Road, Bridgnorth,
Shropshire, WV15 6BY
Tel: 01746 762393
www.theriversidecaravanpark.co.uk
Pitches For ⊕ ⊕ **Total** 8
Open Mar **to** Jan
Access Good **Site** Level
Nearest Bus Stop (Miles) Outside
On the banks of the River Severn. Just a 10
minute walk to Bridgnorth. Watch the Severn
Valley Railway steam by.
Facilities ⨍ 🖪 🕀 ⌾ ⊙ 🚻 ♿ ⌂ 🔧
Nearest Town Bridgnorth
Directions From Bridgnorth on the A442
road to Kidderminster, take the first turning
on the right (150 metres).
🚂 Telford

BRIDGNORTH

Woodend Farm, Woodend Lane, Highley,
Shropshire, WV16 6HY
Tel: 01746 861571
Email: charlesdavies07@btinternet.com

Pitches For ⋀ ⊕ ⊕ Total 0
Open All Year
Access Good **Site** Lev/Slope
Nearest Bus Stop (Miles) ½
Access to the River Severn and Severn
Valley Railway. Village has a new Leisure
Centre, large outdoor pool, with gardens and
a new 18 hole golf course at nearbyAstbury
Hall. Ideal base for Ludlow, Much Wenlock,
Shrewsbury, Ironbridge, Bewdley and safari
park. You can also contact us on Mobile:
07976 247473.
Facilities ⨍ 🖪 🕀 🚿 ♿ ⌂ 🚻 ⊙ 🔧
Nearest Town Bridgnorth
Directions From Bridgnorth take the B4555
to Highley. In Highley turn left opposite the
leisure centre, follow the lane down hill
bearing to the left until in the farm yard.
🚂 Highley

CRAVEN ARMS

Kevindale, Broome, Craven Arms,
Shropshire, SY7 0NT
Tel: 01588 660199
Email: keith@kevindale.co.uk
www.kevindale.co.uk
Pitches For ⋀ ⊕ ⊕ **Total** 12
Acreage 2 **Open** Apr **to** Oct
Access Good **Site** Level
Nearest Bus Stop (Miles) Outside
Scenic views, near village inn with good food.
Close to Mid Wales Border, ideal walking.
Two acre field, rallys welcome.
Facilities ⨍ 🖪 🕀 🚿 ⌂ ⊙ 🚻 🔌 🅿
Nearest Town Craven Arms
Directions From Craven Arms which is situated
on the A49 Hereford to Shewsbury road, take
the B4368 Clun/Bishops Castle road, in 2 miles
take the B4367 Knighton road and after 1¼
miles turn right into Broome Village.
🚂 Broome

ELLESMERE

Fernwood Caravan Park, Lyneal, Nr
Ellesmere, Shropshire, SY12 0QF
Tel: 01948 710221
Email: enquiries@fernwoodpark.co.uk
www.fernwoodpark.co.uk
Pitches For ⊕ ⊕ **Total** 60
Acreage 7 **Open** Mar **to** Nov
Access Good **Site** Lev/Slope
Nearest Bus Stop (Miles) 1
40 acres of woodland open to caravanners.
Lake with wildfowl and coarse fishing.
Facilities ♿ ⨍ 🖪 🕀 🚿 ⌂ ⊙ 🚻 ⌂ 🔌 ⊙ 🚻
㎡ ⌾ ⊙ 🔌 🗑 🅿 🔄 🔧
Directions A495 from Ellesmere signposted
Whitchurch. In Welshampton, right turn on
B5063 signed Wem. Over canal bridge right
sign Lyneal.
🚂 Wem

LUDLOW

Westbrook Park, Lynch Lane, Little
Hereford, Ludlow, Shropshire, SY8 4AU
Tel: 01584 711280
Email: info@westbrookpark.co.uk
www.westbrookpark.co.uk
Pitches For ⋀ ⊕ ⊕ **Total** 63
Acreage 10 **Open** Mar **to** Nov
Access Good **Site** Level
Nearest Bus Stop (Miles) ¼
Half a mile of river fishing. Close to the
famous town of Ludlow and within a short
distance of Tenbury Wells.
Facilities ♿ ⨍ 🖪 🕀 🚿 ⌂ ⊙ 🚻 ⊙ 🔌 ⊙ 🚻
⌂ 🔌 🗑 🅿 🔄 🔧 🛜
Nearest Town Ludlow
Directions A456. Tenbury road, turn into
Lynch Lane.
🚂 Ludlow

MARKET DRAYTON

Wharf Caravan Park, Goldstone, Market
Drayton, Shropshire, TF9 2LP
Tel: 01630 661226
Email: info@wharfcaravanpark.co.uk
www.wharfcaravanpark.co.uk
Pitches For ⊕ ⊕ **Total** 50
Acreage 5 **Open** All Year
Access Good **Site** Level
Alongside Shropshire Union Canal with a pub
on the doorstep. Picturesque, peaceful
countryside. Ideal for fishing, walking and
cycling. Central location for Shrewsbury, The
Potteries and Iron Bridge.
Facilities ⨍ 🖪 🕀 🚿 ⌂ ⊙ 🚻
🛠 🔌 ㎡ 🅿 🔄 🔧 🛜
Directions From the A41 take the A529, go
through Hinstock Village for approx 2 miles
and turn right for Cheswardine. Follow the
lane and signs for approx 1 mile, Park is over
the canal bridge on the right.
🚂 Wem

MINSTERLEY

The Old School Caravan Park, Shelve,
Minsterley, Shrewsbury, Shropshire, SY5 0JQ
Tel: 01588 650410
www.oldschoolcaravanpark.co.uk
Pitches For ⋀ ⊕ ⊕ **Total** 22
Acreage 1½ **Open** Mar **to** Jan
Site Slight Slope
Nearest Bus Stop (Miles) Outside
In an area of outstanding natural beauty,
good walks and fishing. Close to Stiperstones
and Long Mynd. Reduced rates available
from 4th continous nights stay. Excluding
Bank Holidays. Interested please ring.
Facilities ⨍ 🖪 🕀 🚿 ⌂ ⊙ 🚻
㎡ ⌾ 🔌 🗑 🅿 🔄 🔧 🔧
Nearest Town Shrewsbury
Directions On the A5 in Shrewsbury turn
onto the A488 to Bishops Castle. After 16
miles go through the village of Hope and the
site is on the left 50 metres after the bus stop
and phone box.
🚂 Shrewsbury

MUCH WENLOCK

Much Wenlock Caravan Club Site,
Stretton Road, Much Wenlock, Shropshire,
TF13 6DQ
Tel: 01746 785234
www.caravanclub.co.uk
Pitches For ⊕ ⊕ **Total** 70
Acreage 10 **Open** Apr **to** Oct
Access Good **Site** Level
Interesting site with abundant wildlife, set on
the slopes of Wenlock Edge. A walkers
paradise. Close to Ironbridge Gorge,
museum and bridge. Near Severn Valley
Railway and Blists Hill Open Air Museum.
Own sanitation required. Non members
welcome. Booking essential.
Facilities ⨍ 🖪 ㎡ ⌾ 🔌 🗑 🅿 🔄
Nearest Town Much Wenlock
Directions M54 at junc 6 take A5223 sp l/
bridge, watch for change of signs from l/
bridge to Much Wenlock. At Jiggers r/about t
rt on A4169, after 1¾ miles t lt sp Much
Wenlock. At T-junc opposite Gaskell Arms t
rt on A458, after ¼ mile t lt on B4371, site 3
miles on the lt.
🚂 Much Wenlock

OSWESTRY

**Oswestry, Cranberry Moss Camping &
Caravanning Club Site,** Cranberry Moss,
Kinnerley, Oswestry, Shropshire, SY10 8DY
Tel: 01743 741118
Email: enquiries@thefriendlclub.co.uk
www.campingandcaravanningclub.co.uk/
oswestry

SHROPSHIRE

Pitches For 🏕 🚐 🚍 **Total** 65
Open All Year
Access Good **Site** Level
Nearest Bus Stop (Miles) Outside
Close to the old Oswestry Hill Fort, Park Hall, Whittington Castle, Shrewsbury Abbey, Attingham Park, Wroxeter Roman City, Offas Dyke and Pistyll Falls. Local produce sold in the site shop. Non members welcome. You can also call us on 0845 130 7633.
Facilities
Nearest Town Oswestry
Directions Turn off the A5 at the roundabout at the north end of the dual carriageway signed B4396 Knockin.
≠ Shrewsbury

SHREWSBURY

Beaconsfield Farm Holiday Park,
Battlefield, Shrewsbury, Shropshire, SY4 4AA
Tel: 01939 210370
Email: mail@beaconsfield-farm.co.uk
www.beaconsfield-farm.co.uk
Pitches For 🚐 🚍 **Total** 60
Acreage 15 **Open** All Year
Access Good **Site** Level
Exclusively for ADULTS over 21 years. 5 Star, well landscaped, level park with coarse fishing. A La Carte restaurant on the park. 1½ miles to Park & Ride. Ideal base for Shrewsbury and the Welsh border. Holiday homes for sale and hire.
Facilities
Nearest Town Shrewsbury
Directions 1½ miles north of Shrewsbury on the A49.
≠ Shrewsbury

SHREWSBURY

Cartref Caravan & Camping Site, Cartref, Fords Heath, Nr Shrewsbury, Shropshire, SY5 9GD
Tel: 01743 821688
Email: alanpat@edwardscartref.wanadoo.co.uk
www.cartrefcaravansite.co.uk
Pitches For 🏕 🚐 🚍 **Total** 47
Acreage 2½ **Open** Easter **to** Oct
Access Good **Site** Level
Peaceful countryside. Ideal for touring or an overnight stop. Adult Only section of 11 pitches.
Facilities
Nearest Town Shrewsbury
Directions From Shrewsbury bypass A5 trunk road take the A458 Welshpool West. 2 miles to Ford Village, turn south at Ford, follow camp signs. Signposted from the A5 bypass on the Montgomery junction B4386.
≠ Shrewsbury

SHREWSBURY

Middle Darnford Farm, Ratlinghope, Pontesbury, Shrewsbury, Shropshire, SY5 0SR
Tel: 01694 751320
Pitches For 🏕 🚐 🚍 **Total** 0
Acreage 2 **Open** 15-Mar **to** Dec
Access Good **Site** Level
Excellent views.
Facilities
Nearest Town Church Stretton
Directions From the A49 turn at Leebotwood and follow the road through Woolstaston over Long Myn Hill and the Farm is on the left hand side.
≠ Church Stretton

SHREWSBURY

Severn House, Montford Bridge, Shrewsbury, Shropshire, SY4 1ED
Tel: 01743 850229
Email: booking@severnhousecampsite.co.uk
www.severnhousecampsite.co.uk
Pitches For 🏕 🚐 🚍 **Total** 25
Acreage 2½ **Open** Apr **to** Oct
Access Good **Site** Level
Nearest Bus Stop (Miles) ¼
Riverside site with 300 metres of river for fishing. Dog walk, local shop, buses, pub and meals nearby. Regular bus service.
Facilities
Nearest Town Shrewsbury
Directions 4 miles north west of Shrewsbury on the A5 towards Oswestry and North Wales. At signposts for the site turn onto the B4380 and Montford Bridge is ½ mile.
≠ Shrewsbury

TELFORD

Pool View Caravan Park, Buildwas, Telford, Shropshire, TF8 7BS
Tel: 07722 206181
Email: tomles28@live.co.uk
Pitches For 🏕 🚐 🚍 **Total** 50
Open Mar **to** Oct
Access Good **Site** Level
Nearest Bus Stop (Miles) 1
Panoramic views of fields and countryside. Short walk from the Buildwas Nature Trail, museum and Ironbridge Bridge itself. Caravan storage available.
Facilities
Nearest Town Ironbridge
Directions From Ironbridge follow the main road through the village (with the main car park on your left), go over the roundabout to the Tjunction and turn left. Go over the Buildwas Bridge (approx 150 yards) to the private road on your left. Follow the road straight up to the Park and follow signs to the Wardens Home at No.3.
≠ Telford/Wellington

TELFORD

Severn Gorge Park, Bridgnorth Road, Telford, Shropshire, TF7 4JB
Tel: 01952 684789
Email: info@severngorgepark.co.uk
Pitches For 🚐 🚍 **Total** 12
Open All Year
Access Good **Site** Level
Nearest Bus Stop (Miles) Outside
ADULTS ONLY PARK ideal for Ironbridge, Severn Gorge Cosford Air Museum Bridgenorth.
Facilities
Nearest Town Telford
≠ Telford

WEM

Lower Lacon Caravan Park, Wem, Shropshire, SY4 5RP
Tel: 01939 232376
Email: info@llcp.co.uk
www.llcp.co.uk
Pitches For 🏕 🚐 🚍 **Total** 270
Acreage 48 **Open** All Year
Access Good **Site** Level
Nearest Bus Stop (Miles) Outside
Facilities
Nearest Town Wem
Directions 1 mile from Wem on the B5065. From the A49 then the B5065, 3 miles.
≠ Wem

WHITCHURCH

Green Lane Farm Caravan & Camp Site, Green Lane Farm, Prees, Whitchurch, Shropshire, SY13 2AH
Tel: 01948 840460
Email: greenlanefarm@tiscali.co.uk
www.greenlanecaravanpark.co.uk
Pitches For 🏕 🚐 🚍 **Total** 36
Acreage 2½ **Open** Mar **to** Oct
Access Good **Site** Level
Nearest Bus Stop (Miles) ¼
Central for all local attractions, Hawkstone, Shrewsbury, Chester, Llangollen, Nantwich, etc..
Facilities
Nearest Town Whitchurch
Directions 350 yards off the the main A41 between Whitchurch and Newport.
≠ Whitchurch

WHITCHURCH

Roden View Caravan & Camping, Roden View, Dobsons Bridge, Whixall, Whitchurch, Shropshire, SY13 2QL
Tel: 01948 710320
Email: jean@roden-view.co.uk
www.roden-view.co.uk
Pitches For 🏕 🚐 🚍 **Total** 14
Acreage 4½ **Open** All Year
Access Good **Site** Level
Near to the Shropshire Union Canal and Whixall Moss. 5 miles from Ellesmere, Shropshires Lake District. Large fishing pool.
Facilities
Nearest Town Wem
Directions From Shrewsbury Wem Church turn left after second garage, then turn right for Whixall, at the next T-Junction turn left then immediately right, 2½ miles to the next T-Junction turn right. ½ mile the house is on the right before Dobsons Bridge.
≠ Wem

SOMERSET
BATH

Bath Chew Valley Caravan Park, Ham Lane, Bishop Sutton, Somerset, BS39 5TZ
Tel: 01275 332127
Email: enquiries@bathchewvalley.co.uk
www.bathchewvalley.co.uk
Pitches For 🚐 🚍 **Total** 45
Acreage 4 **Open** All Year
Access Good **Site** Level
Nearest Bus Stop (Miles) ¼
ADULTS ONLY PARK. A site for peace and tranquility, set in an area of outstanding natural beauty. Luxury bathroom and toilets. ETB 5 Star Graded, the only 5 Star Park in North East Somerset. Practical Caravan Top 100 Overall Winner 2009, 2012 & 2013.
Facilities
Nearest Town Bath
Directions Approaching Bath on A37 or A38 Bristol to Wells or Bristol to Taunton roads, take A368 which links both to Bishop Sutton, turn opposite the Red Lion Pub.
≠ Bath

BATH

Bury View Farm, Corston Fields, Nr. Bath, Somerset, BA2 9HD
Tel: 01225 873672
Email: salbowd@btinternet.com
www.buryviewfarm.co.uk
Pitches For 🏕 🚐 🚍 **Total** 18
Acreage 2 **Open** All Year
Access Good **Site** Level

Nearest Bus Stop (Miles) ¼
Quiet site, close to the city of Bath and Bristol. Within easy reach of Cheddar, Wells and Longleat. Open all year subject to weather.
Facilities ♿ ⓕ ☏ 🏪 ♒ ⌂ 🚻 🔥 ⌷ 🅿
Nearest Town Keynsham/Bath
Directions From Bath take the A4 Bristol road, at Newton-St-Loe roundabout take second left onto the A39 for Wells and Weston-super-Mare, Park is 1 mile.
⚏ Keynsham/Bath

BREAN SANDS
Channel View Touring Park, Warren Road, Brean, BurnhamonSea, Somerset, TA8 2RR
Tel: 01278 751055
www.breanfarm.co.uk
Pitches For ⚑ ☗ ☗ **Total** 50
Acreage 3 **Open** Apr to Oct
Access Good **Site** Gentle Slope
Nearest Bus Stop (Miles) ½
Quiet and friendly site, overlooking the beach.
Facilities ♿ ⓕ ☏ 🏪 ♒ ⌂ 🔥 🛎 🏪 ⌷ 🎣🔥
Nearest Town Brean Sands
Directions Leave the M5 at junction 22 and follow signs to Brean. Site is ¼ mile past the Brean Down Inn on the left hand side.
⚏ Highbridge

BREAN SANDS
Holiday Resort Unity at Unity Farm, Coast Road, Brean Sands, Somerset, TA8 2RB
Tel: 01278 751235
Email: admin@hru.co.uk
www.hru.co.uk
Pitches For ⚑ ☗ ☗ ⌷≋ **Total** 400
Acreage 200 **Open** Feb to Nov
Access Good **Site** Level
Nearest Bus Stop (Miles) Outside
200yds from 7 mile beach, own leisure centre with 30 fun fair attractions, pool complex with 3 giant water slides, 18 hole golf course, lake for fishing, horse riding and 10 Pin Bowling. Family entertainment - Easter to November.
Facilities ♿ ⓕ 🖻 ☏ 🏪 ♒ ⌂ 🚻 🔥 ⌷ 🅿 🔥
🔥🛎🖻 🖻 ⌷ 🎣 ≋ 📶
Directions Leave M5 at junction 22. Follow signs for Berrow and Brean Leisure Park, site on right 4½ miles from the M5.
⚏ Burnham

BREAN SANDS
Warren Farm Holiday Centre, Brean Sands, Burnham-on-Sea, Somerset, TA8 2RP
Tel: 01278 751227
Email: enquiries@warren-farm.co.uk
www.warren-farm.co.uk
Pitches For ⚑ ☗ ☗ **Total** 500
Acreage 100 **Open** Apr to Oct
Access Good **Site** Level
Nearest Bus Stop (Miles) ¼
Flat, grassed and hardstanding pitches family park with excellent facilities, indoor play area and family entertainment at the Beachcomber Inn. 100 metres from 5 miles of sandy beach. Dogs are welcome free in designated areas. AA Holiday Centre.
Facilities ♿ ⓕ 🏪 ♒ ⌂ 🚻 🔥 ⌷ 🅿 🔥
🔥🛎 🖻 ☏ 🖻 ✕ ⌷ 🖻 🔥 🛎 🔥🛎🖻 ⌷ ≋
🔥 📶
Nearest Town Burnham-on-Sea
Directions Leave M5 at junction 22, follow signs to Burnham-on-Sea, Berrow and Brean on the B3140. Site is 1¼ miles past the leisure centre.
⚏ Weston-super-Mare

BRIDGWATER
Currypool Mill, Cannington, Bridgwater, Somerset, TA5 2NH
Tel: 01278 671135
Email: info@currypoolmill.co.uk
www.currypoolmill.co.uk
Pitches For ⚑ ☗ ☗ **Total** 42
Open Easter to Mid Nov
Access Good **Site** Level
Quiet location near the Quantock Hills and Somerset coast. Set amongst streams and waterfalls. Dog walking fields, putting and croquet. Disabled toilet and shower.
Facilities ♿ ⓕ 🏪 ♒ ⌂ 🚻 🔥 ⌷ 🅿 🔥
🔥 🖻 🔥 🔥🛎🖻 🖻 ⌷ ≋ 🔥
Nearest Town Bridgwater
Directions From Bridgwater take the A39 Minehead road, after approx. 5 miles take a left hand turning signposted Spaxton and Aisholt. Currypool is approx. ½ a mile on the left.
⚏ Bridgwater

BRIDGWATER
Hawkridge Farm, Lawyers Hill, Hawkridge, Spaxton, Bridgwater, Somerset, TA5 1AL
Tel: 01278 671341
Email: ling680@btinternet.com
Pitches For ☗ **Total** 5
Acreage 1½ **Open** All year
Access Good **Site** Lev/Slope
Nearest Bus Stop (Miles) ¼
Tranquil site in an area of outstanding natural beauty, with panoramic views over the Bristol Channel and Hawkridge Reservoir. Close to the Quantock Hills. Trout fishing at the reservoir. Lovely walks.
Facilities ⓕ 🔥 🖻 🔥🖻 ▢
Nearest Town Bridgwater
Directions Leave M5 at junc 23 and take A38 towards Bridgwater. Continue straight until you pass Morrisons and B&Q, at the next traffic lights turn left into West Street (sp Durleigh and Spaxton). Go through the village, continue up the hill and fork right sp Nether Stowey. Site entrance is on the right just past Hawkridge Reservoir.
⚏ Bridgwater/Taunton

BRIDGWATER
Mill Farm Caravan & Camping Park, Fiddington, Bridgwater, Somerset, TA5 1JQ
Tel: 01278 732286
www.millfarm.biz
Pitches For ⚑ ☗ ☗ **Total** 0
Open Mar to 01-Dec
Access Good **Site** Level
Lovely family park situated between the Quantock hills and the north Somerset coastline.
Facilities ♿ ⓕ ☏ 🏪 ♒ ⌂ 🚻 🔥 ⌷ 🅿 🔥
🔥 🖻 🔥 ☏ 🖻 ✕ ⌷ 🔥 ↘ 🔥 🔥🛎🖻 🖻 ⌷ ≋ 🔥 📶
Nearest Town Bridgwater
Directions Follow the A39 towards Minehead for 6 miles. At Keenthorne turn right for Fiddington, Mill Farm is 1 milefrom main road.
⚏ Bridgwater

BRUTON
Batcombe Vale Caravan & Camping Park, Batcombe, Shepton Mallet, Somerset, BA4 6BW
Tel: 01749 831207
Email: gary.butler1@virgin.net
www.batcombevale.co.uk
Pitches For ⚑ ☗ ☗ **Total** 32
Acreage 7 **Open** Apr to Sept
Access Good **Site** Level
Own secluded valley of lakes and wild gardens. Fishing and boating on site. Near

Longleat, Stourhead and Glastonbury. All shops are 2 miles away.
Facilities ⓕ ☏ 🏪 ♒ ⌂ 🚻 🔥 ⌷ 🅿 🔥
🔥 🖻 🔥🖻 🔥
Nearest Town Bruton
Directions Access must be via Bruton or Evercreech from where it is well signed.
⚏ Bruton

BURNHAM-ON-SEA
Westbrook Farm, Harp Road, Brent Knoll, Somerset, TA9 4HQ
Tel: 01278 760386
www.westbrookfarm.co.uk
Pitches For ⚑ ☗ ☗ **Total** 45
Acreage 2 **Open** Mar to Oct
Access Good **Site** Level
Nearest Bus Stop (Miles) ½
Quiet friendly park, ideal location for sightseeing in Somerset. Easy access from M5.
Facilities ♿ ⓕ ☏ 🏪 ♒ ⌂ 🚻 🔥 🔥
🔥🛎🖻 🖻 ⌷ ≋ 🔥
Nearest Town Burnham-on-Sea
Directions Leave the M5 at junction 22 and take the A38 towards Bristol, after ½ mile turn right at Fox and Goose Pub, site is ½ a mile on the left.
⚏ Highbridge

BURNHAM-ON-SEA
Diamond Farm Caravan & Touring Park, Diamond Farm, Weston Road, Brean, Nr Burnham-on-Sea, Somerset, TA8 2RL
Tel: 01278 751263
Email:
trevor@diamondfarm42.freeserve.co.uk
www.diamondfarm.co.uk
Pitches For ⚑ ☗ ☗ **Total** 100
Acreage 6 **Open** Apr to 15-Oct
Access Good **Site** Level
Nearest Bus Stop (Miles) Outside
A quiet, family site alongside River Axe and only 800yds from the beach. All modern facilities.
Facilities ♿ 🔥 ⓕ ☏ 🏪 ♒ ⌂ 🚻 🔥 ⌷ 🅿 🔥
🔥 🖻 🔥 ✕ ♒ 🔥🛎🖻 🔥 ≋ 🔥
Nearest Town Burnham-on-Sea
Directions M5 junction 22, follow signs to Brean, ½ mile past leisure park turn right to Lympsham/Weston-super-Mare. Diamond Farm is 800yds on the left hand side.
⚏ Weston-super-Mare

CHARD
Alpine Grove Woodland Park, Forton, Chard, Somerset, TA20 4HD
Tel: 01460 63479
Email: stay@alpinegrovetouringpark.com
www.alpinegrovetouringpark.com
Pitches For ⚑ ☗ ☗ **Total** 40
Acreage 8 **Open** Apr to Sept
Access Good **Site** Level
Nearest Bus Stop (Miles) ¼
Ideal for woodland walks and fossil hunting. 20 minutes from the World Heritage coastline. New self catering log cabins available for hire all year round. ETC 4 Star Graded, and Gold David Bellamy Award.
Facilities ♿ ⓕ ☏ 🏪 ♒ ⌂ 🚻 🔥 ⌷ 🅿 🔥
🔥 🖻 🔥 🖻 🔥🛎🖻 🖻 🔥 📶
Nearest Town Chard
Directions From Chard take the A30 signposted Cricket St Thomas, turn right onto the B3167 and follow brown tourism signs.
⚏ Crewkerne

CHARD
Barleymows Farm Shop & Restaurant, Snowdon Hill Farm, Chard, Somerset, TA20 3PS
Tel: 01460 62130
Email: barleymows@btconnect.com

www.barleymowsfarmshop.co.uk
Pitches For ⚫ ⚫ ⚫ ⚫ **Total** 5
Acreage 5 **Open** All Year
Access Good **Site** Level
Nearest Bus Stop (Miles) 1
Maize maze & activity field open July to Sept Fully comprehensive farm shop and resturant.
Facilities ⚫ ⚫ ⚫ ⚫ ⚫ ⚫ ⚫ ⚫
Nearest Town Chard/Lyme Regis
Directions Take the A30 west from Chard, Park is ¾ miles on the right hand side.
✚ Axminster

CHARD

South Somerset Holiday Park, A30 Exeter Road, Howley, Nr Chard, Somerset, TA20 3EA
Tel: 01460 66036
Email: sshpltd@btconnect.com
www.southsomersetholidaypark.co.uk
Pitches For ⚫ ⚫ **Total** 110
Acreage 7 **Open** All Year
Access Good **Site** Gentle Slope
30 minutes drive from the south coast, many other attractions within 40 minutes ie Fleet air Arm Museum.
Facilities ⚫ ⚫ ⚫ ⚫ ⚫ ⚫ ⚫ ⚫ ⚫ ⚫
⚫ ⚫ ⚫ ⚫ ⚫ ⚫
Nearest Town Chard
Directions 3 miles west of Chard on the A30. Towards Honiton.

CHEDDAR

Cheddar Bridge Touring Park, Draycott Road, Cheddar, Somerset, BS27 3RJ
Tel: 01934 743048
Email: enquiries@cheddarbridge.co.uk
www.cheddarbridge.co.uk
Pitches For ⚫ ⚫ ⚫ **Total** 40
Acreage 4 **Open** Mar **to** 10-Nov
Access Good **Site** Level
Nearest Bus Stop (Miles) ¼
Alongside River Yeo. Gypsy wagon.
Facilities ⚫ ⚫ ⚫ ⚫ ⚫ ⚫ ⚫ ⚫ ⚫ ⚫
⚫ ⚫ ⚫ ⚫ ⚫ ⚫ ⚫ ⚫
Nearest Town Cheddar
Directions On the A371, 100 yards south of Cheddar Village orange signs.
✚ Weston-Super-Mare

CHEDDAR

Netherdale Caravan & Camping Site, Bridgwater Road, Sidcot, Winscombe, Somerset, BS25 1NH
Tel: 01934 843007/843481
Email: camping@netherdale.net
www.netherdale.net
Pitches For ⚫ ⚫ ⚫ **Total** 25
Acreage 3½ **Open** Mar **to** Oct
Access Good **Site** Lev/Slope

Excellent walking area, footpath from site to valley and Mendip Hills. Good views. Cafe/restaurant adjoining site. Many historical places and beaches within easy reach. Pets welcome on a lead. Only individual motorcycles accepted, not groups. 3 miles from a dry ski slope and a well equipped sports centre.
Facilities ⚫ ⚫ ⚫ ⚫ ⚫ ⚫ ⚫
⚫ ⚫ ⚫ ⚫ ⚫ ⚫
Nearest Town Cheddar
Directions Midway between Bristol and Bridgwater on A38. From Weston-super-Mare follow A371 to join A38 at Sidcot Corner, site is ¼ mile south. From Wells and Cheddar follow A371 westwards to join A38, a mile south of site.
✚ Weston-super-Mare

CHEDDAR

Rodney Stoke Inn, Rodney Stoke, Nr Cheddar, Somerset, BS27 3XB
Tel: 01749 870209
Email: annetteneil@aol.com
www.rodneystokeinn.co.uk
Pitches For ⚫ ⚫ ⚫ **Total** 31
Acreage 2 **Open** Mar **to** Oct
Access Good **Site** Level
Nearest Bus Stop (Miles) ¼
ADULTS ONLY SITE in a central location for the Cheddar Gorge and Caves, the City of Wells and Wookey Hole Caves.
Facilities ⚫ ⚫ ⚫ ⚫ ⚫ ⚫ ⚫ ⚫ ⚫
Nearest Town Cheddar
Directions Take the A371 from Cheddar towards Wells for 3 miles.
✚ Weston-Super-Mare

CHEDDAR

Splott Farm, Blackford, Nr Wedmore, Somerset, BS28 4PD
Tel: 01278 641522
Pitches For ⚫ ⚫ **Total** 37
Acreage 4 **Open** Mar **to** Oct
Access Good **Site** Sloping
Nearest Bus Stop (Miles) 1
Very peaceful site with views of the Mendip Hills (and Quantocks), very rural area. Ideal touring, Weston-super-Mare, Wells, Cheddar, Burnham-on-Sea, Wookey.
Facilities ⚫ ⚫ ⚫ ⚫ ⚫ ⚫ ⚫ ⚫ ⚫
⚫ ⚫ ⚫ ⚫ ⚫
Nearest Town Burnham-on-Sea/Cheddar
Directions Leave M5 at junction 22, take 1st left and follow signs for Mark approx 4 miles.
✚ Highbridge

CONGRESBURY

Oak Farm Touring Park, Weston Road, Congresbury, Somerset, BS49 5EB
Tel: 01934 833246
Pitches For ⚫ ⚫ **Total** 40

Acreage 2 **Open** Apr **to** 01-Oct
Access Good **Site** Level
Nearest Bus Stop (Miles) Outside
Near river on bus route, cycling close by on closed railway line.
Facilities ⚫ ⚫ ⚫ ⚫ ⚫ ⚫ ⚫ ⚫ ⚫ ⚫
Nearest Town Weston-super-Mare
Directions 4 miles from junc. 21 on M5, on the A370 midway between Bristol and Weston Super Mare.
✚ Yatton

CROWCOMBE

Quantock Orchard Caravan Park, Flaxpool, Crowcombe, Taunton, Somerset, TA4 4AW
Tel: 01984 618618
Email: member@flaxpool.freeserve.co.uk
www.quantock-orchard.co.uk
Pitches For ⚫ ⚫ ⚫ **Total** 77
Acreage 7½ **Open** All Year
Access Good **Site** Level
Nearest Bus Stop (Miles) ¼
Award winning campsite surrounded by stunning panoramic views of the Quantock Hills, and situated next to the West Somerset Railway. Luxury holiday homes available for hire.
Facilities ⚫ ⚫ ⚫ ⚫ ⚫ ⚫ ⚫ ⚫ ⚫ ⚫
⚫ ⚫ ⚫ ⚫ ⚫ ⚫ ⚫ ⚫ ⚫ ⚫ ⚫ ⚫
Nearest Town Taunton/Minehead
Directions Midway between Taunton and Minehead on the A358. Approx. 1 mile from south of Crowcombe Village.
✚ Taunton

EXFORD

Westermill Farm, Exford, Exmoor, Somerset, TA24 7NJ
Tel: 01643 831238
Email: cad@westermill.com
www.westermill.com
Pitches For ⚫ ⚫ **Total** 60
Acreage 6 **Open** All Year
Access Poor **Site** Level
Nearest Bus Stop (Miles) 2½
Beautiful, secluded site in a hidden valley beside a river for fishing, bathing and paddling. Fascinating 500 acre farm with Waymarked walks. Centre of Exmoor National Park. Free hot showers. Camp fire areas. Charming cottages nestling by trees for hire. David Bellamy Gold Award for Conservation.
Facilities ⚫ ⚫ ⚫ ⚫ ⚫ ⚫ ⚫
⚫ ⚫ ⚫ ⚫ ⚫ ⚫
Nearest Town Minehead
Directions Leave Exford on the Porlock road. After ½ a mile fork left, continue for 2 miles along the valley until Westermill is seen on a tree and fork left.
✚ Taunton

FROME

Seven Acres Touring Caravan & Camping Park, West Woodlands, Frome, Somerset, BA11 5EQ
Tel: 01373 464222
Pitches For Å ⬜ 🚐 **Total** 32
Acreage 7 **Open** Mar **to** Oct
Access Good **Site** Level
As seen on national television. Acres of level, landscaped grounds with a stream meandering through. On the outskirts of the Longleat Estate and within easy reach of Stourhead, Cheddar Caves and Stonehenge.
Facilities ✝ 🅗 🆎 ⌂ ⊙ 🐕 � 🛢 ⊞ ▣
Nearest Town Frome
Directions From the Frome by-pass take the B3092 towards Maiden Bradley and Mere. Seven Acres is situated approx. 1 mile from the by-pass.
⚶ Frome

GLASTONBURY

Greenacres Camping, Barrow Lane, North Wootton, Glastonbury, Somerset, BA4 4HL
Tel: 01749 890497
Email: stay@greenacres-camping.co.uk
www.greenacres-camping.co.uk
Pitches For Å 🚐 **Total** 40
Acreage 4½ **Open** Apr **to** Sept
Site Level
Nearest Bus Stop (Miles) 2
Quiet site in stunning Somerset countryside, with views of Glastonbury Tor and the Mendip Hills. Ideal for families. Huge pitches! Cycle hire on site. Facebook pagewww.facebook.com/camping in Somerset.
Facilities ✝ 🆎 ⌂ ⊙ 🛢 ⅏
⅊ ♒ ⅋ ⊙ ⅍ ✳ ⊞ ⊟ ⏣ ⋐ ☂
Nearest Town Glastonbury

Directions Leave the M5 at junction 23 and take the A39 to Glastonbury. Follow signs from Brownes Garden Centre. Or follow signs from the A361 at Steanbow for 2 miles.
⚶ Castle Cary

GLASTONBURY

The Old Oaks Touring Park, Wick Farm, Wick, Glastonbury, Somerset, BA6 8JS
Tel: 01458 831437
Email: info@theoldoaks.co.uk
www.theoldoaks.co.uk
Pitches For Å ⬜ 🚐 🚐 ⅊ **Total** 100
Acreage 10 **Open** Feb **to** 16-Nov
Access Good **Site** Level/Sloping
Nearest Bus Stop (Miles) 1½
ADULT ONLY Park in a stunning location with beautiful views. Blissfully tranquil. Ideal for walking, cycling or just relaxing. ¾ miles from Glastonbury Tor. Camping Cabins/Pods for Glamping.
Facilities ⅄ ✝ ⊟ 🆎 ⌂ ⊙ ⅃ 🛢 ▣ ☎
⅊ ⅊ ⊟ ♒ ⊞ ⊟ ⅂ 🅐 ⋐ ☂
Nearest Town Glastonbury
Directions From Glastonbury take the A361 towards Shepton Mallet. In 2 miles turn left at signpost for Wick, Park is on the left in 1 mile.
⚶ Castle Cary

HIGHBRIDGE

Greenacre Place Touring Caravan Park, Bristol Road, Edithmead, Highbridge, Somerset, TA9 4HA
Tel: 01278 785227
Email: info@greenacreplace.com
www.greenacreplace.com
Pitches For ⬜ 🚐 **Total** 10
Acreage 1 **Open** Mar **to** Nov
Access Good **Site** Level
Nearest Bus Stop (Miles) ½

ADULTS ONLY. Small, peaceful caravan park with easy access. Short drive to sandy beaches. Ideally placed for touring Somerset.
Facilities ⅄ 🅗 🆎 ⌂ ⊙ ☎ ⅊ 🛢 ♒ ⊞ ⊟ 🅐 ☂
Nearest Town Burnham-on-Sea
Directions Just off the M5 junction 22.
⚶ Highbridge

ILMINSTER

Thornleigh Caravan Park, Hanning Road, Horton, Ilminster, Somerset, TA19 9QH
Tel: 01460 53450
Email: thornleighsite@btinternet.com
www.thornleighcaravansite.co.uk
Pitches For Å ⬜ 🚐 **Total** 20
Acreage 1¼ **Open** Mar **to** Oct
Access Good **Site** Level
Nearest Bus Stop (Miles) ¼
Flat site in a village location, ideal for touring Somerset and Devon. Heated shower block. ½ hour drive to the south coast. 6 miles to Cricket St Thomas Gardens. National Trust properties nearby. Village Inn with restaurant, Post Office, stores and public telephone nearby. Ideal rally site with village hall close by.Booking essential.
Facilities ⅄ ✝ 🅗 🆎 ⌂ ⊙ ⅃ ☎ ⅊ ⊞ ⊟ ☂
Nearest Town Ilminster
Directions A303 West Ilminster, take the A358 signposted Chard. ¼ mile turn right signposted Horton and Broadway. Site on the left opposite the church, ¾ mile.
⚶ Taunton/Crewkerne

LANGPORT

Bowdens Crest Caravan & Camping Park, Bowdens, Langport, Somerset, TA10 0DD
Tel: 01458 250553
Email: bowcrest@btconnect.com
www.bowdenscrest.co.uk

Pitches For ▲ ⌂ ⛟ Total 30
Acreage 16 Open All Year
Access Good Site Level
Nearest Bus Stop (Miles) 2
Countryside
Facilities ⚅ ⌗ 🚻🎮🏧🅿 ⊙ 🍴 ⬛ 🔌 🖳 ☎
🐕 ⊙ ✗ ♀ ⛟ 🦺 🏸 🔌 🔲 ⚡ 🛜
Nearest Town Langport
Directions Off the A372 Langport to
Bridgwater road.
⚌ Bridgwater

LANGPORT

Thorney Lakes Caravan Site, Thorney
Lakes, Muchelney, Langport, Somerset,
TA10 0DW
Tel: 01458 250811
Email: info@thorneylakes.co.uk
www.thorneylakes.co.uk
Pitches For ▲ ⌂ ⛟ ⛟ ⌞ Total 36
Acreage 7 Open Mar to Nov
Access Good Site Level
Site is an orchard on Somerset Moors. Ideal
for walking and cycling.
Facilities ⌗ 🚻🏧🅿 ⊙ 🍴 ✴🍴🖳 ✈ ⚘
Nearest Town Langport
Directions Turn off the A303 dual
carriageway signposted Martock, Ash and
Kingsbury Episcopi. Follow signs to
Kingsbury Episcopi, at the T-Junction in the
village turn right, site is 1 mile on the right.
⚌ Yeovil/Taunton

MARTOCK

Southfork Caravan Park, Parrett Works,
Martock, Somerset, TA12 6AE
Tel: 01935 825661
Email: southforkcaravans@btconnect.com
www.southforkcaravans.co.uk
Pitches For ▲ ⌂ ⛟ Total 27
Acreage 2 Open All Year
Access Good Site Level
Set in open countryside near River Parrett.
Numerous places of interest nearby for all
age groups. Ideal base for touring. 3 holiday
homes for hire. Caravan storage available.
Facilities ⌗ 🚻🏧🅿 ⊙ 🍴 ⬛ 🔲 ☎
🐕 ⊙ 🏧 🦺 🔌 🔲
Nearest Town Martock/Yeovil
Directions Situated 2 miles north west of
A303 (between Ilchester and Ilminster). From
A303 east of Ilminster, at roundabout take
first exit sp South Petherton and follow
camping signs. From A303 west of Ilchester,
after Cartgate roundabout (junction with
A3088 to Yeovil) take exit sp Martock and
follow camping signs.
⚌ Yeovil

MINEHEAD

Hoburne Blue Anchor, Blue Anchor Bay,
Nr Minehead, Somerset, TA24 6JT
Tel: 01643 821360
Email: blueanchor@hoburne.com
www.hoburne.com
Pitches For ⌂ ⛟ Total 103
Acreage 29 Open 26-Feb to 30-Oct
Access Good Site Level
Nearest Bus Stop (Miles) Outside
On the seafront and bordered by Exmoor,
this is a peaceful touring and static Park in a
prefect location.
Facilities ⌗ 🚻🎮🏧🅿 ⊙ 🍴 ⬛ 🔌 🔲 ☎
🐕 ⊙ ✗ ♀ ⛟ 🏸 🔌 🔲 🦺 🛜
Nearest Town Minehead
Directions Leave the M5 at junction 25 and
take the A358 signposted Minehead. After
approx 12 miles, at Carhampton, turn left
onto the B3191 signposted Blue Anchor. Park
is 1½ miles on the right.
⚌ Minehead

MINEHEAD

Minehead & Exmoor Caravan &
Camping Park, Porlock Road, Minehead,
Somerset, TA24 8SW
Tel: 01643 703074
www.minheadandexmoorcamping.co.uk
Pitches For ▲ ⌂ ⛟ Total 50
Acreage 3½
Access Good Site Level
Nearest Bus Stop (Miles) Outside
Situated on the edge of Exmoor National
Park.
Facilities ⚅ ⌗ 🚻🎮🏧🅿 ⊙ 🍴 ⬛ 🔲 ☎
🏵 🐕 ⊙ 🏧 🔌 🔲 🦺 ⚘ 🔍
Directions 1 mile west of Minehead town
centre on the A39, Park is on the right.
⚌ Taunton

MINEHEAD

Minehead Camping & Caravanning Club
Site, Hill Road, North Hill, Minehead,
Somerset, TA24 5LB
Tel: 01643 704138
Email: enquiries@thefriendlyclub.co.uk
www.campingandcaravanningclub.co.uk/
minehead
Pitches For ⌂ ⛟ Total 60
Acreage 3¾ Open 27-Apr to Sept
Access Poor Site Sloping
In Exmoor National Park with fine views of
the town of Minehead. Sloping site, chocks
required. BTB 4 Star Graded and AA 3
Pennants. Non members welcome. You can
also call us on 0845 130 7633.
Facilities ⌗ 🚻🎮🏧🅿 ⊙ 🍴 ⬛ 🔲 ☎
🏵 🐕 ⊙ 🏧 🔌 🔲 🛜

Nearest Town Minehead
Directions From the A39 head towards the
town centre, in the main street turn opposite
W.H.Smith into Blenheim Road, after 50
yards turn left again. Go up the hill and left
around a hairpin bend, turn right at the
cottages. Go past the church on the right and
continue round two bends, site is on the right.
⚌ Minehead

MINEHEAD

St. Audries Bay Holiday Club, West
Quantoxhead, Minehead, Somerset, TA4
4DY
Tel: 01984 632515
Email: info@staudriesbay.co.uk
www.staudriesbay.co.uk
Pitches For ▲ ⌂ ⛟ Total 20
Acreage 12 Open Easter to Oct
Access Good Site Level
Nearest Bus Stop (Miles) ½
Since 1933 we have provided relaxing
holidays at our family owned, award winning
Park. Situated in a beautiful coastal position
with splendid sea views and beach access.
Facilities ⚅ ⌗ 🚻🎮🏧🅿 ⊙ 🍴 ⬛ 🔲 ☎
🐕 ⊙ ✗ ♀ ⛟ 🏵 🏸 🔌 🔲 🛜
Nearest Town Minehead
Directions 15 miles from the M5 junction 23,
off the A39. 15 miles from Taunton, follow
the A358 to Williton then the A39.
⚌ Taunton

PORLOCK

Porlock Caravan Park, Highbank,
Porlock, Nr Minehead, Somerset, TA24
8ND
Tel: 01643 862269
Email: info@porlockcaravanpark.co.uk
www.porlockcaravanpark.co.uk
Pitches For ▲ ⌂ ⛟ Total 40
Acreage 3½ Open Mid Mar to Oct
Access Good Site Level
Nearest Bus Stop (Miles) ¼
Scenic views, Ideal touring and walking.
Facilities ⚅ ⌗ 🚻🎮🏧🅿 ⊙ 🍴 ⬛ 🔲 ☎
🐕 ⊙ 🏧 🔌 🔲 🛜
Nearest Town Minehead
Directions A39 from Minehead to Lynton,
take the B3225 in Porlock to Porlock Weir.
Site signposted.
⚌ Taunton

SPARKFORD

Long Hazel Park, High Street, Sparkford,
Nr Yeovil, Somerset, BA22 7JH
Tel: 01963 440002
Email: longhazelpark@hotmail.com
www.longhazelpark.co.uk

Pitches For ▲ ⊟ ⊟ ⊟ Total 50
Acreage 3½ **Open** All Year
Access Good **Site** Level
Nearest Bus Stop (Miles) Outside
ADULTS ONLY. Full disabled shower unit. Near to an inn and restaurant. Ideal for touring or an overnight halt. Haynes International Motor Museum and Fleet Air Arm Museum nearby. Two pine lodges for hire with wheelchair access and 12 pine lodges for sale. Please note, dogs are not permitted in the pine lodges.
Facilities ♿ �ʄ ⬚ ⬚ ⋔ ⌐ ⊙ ⌐ ⌐ ⬚ ☎
⌗ ⊙ ⬚ ⋔ ⬚ ▲ ⩗ ≈
Directions From Wincanton take the A303 to the end of Sparkford by-pass. At the services turn left into Sparkford Village, site is approx. 400 yards on the left.
⇥ Yeovil/Sherborne/Castle Cary

TAUNTON

Ashe Farm Caravan & Camp Site, Ashe Farm, Thornfalcon, Taunton, Somerset, TA3 5NW
Tel: 01823 443764
Email: info@ashefarm.co.uk
www.ashefarm.co.uk
Pitches For ▲ ⊟ ⊟ Total 30
Acreage 7 **Open** Apr to Oct
Access Good **Site** Level
Nearest Bus Stop (Miles) ¼
Ideal touring centre, easy reach of Quantock and Blackdown Hills.
Facilities ♿ ʄ ⬚ ⋔ ⌐ ⊙ ⌐ ⬚ ☎
⌗ ⬚ ⩗ ≈
Nearest Town Taunton
Directions 4 miles southeast Taunton on A358, turn right at the Nags Head towards West Hatch, site is ¼ mile on the right.
⇥ Taunton

TAUNTON

Cornish Farm Touring Park, Cornish Farm, Shoreditch, Taunton, Somerset, TA3 7BS
Tel: 01823 327746
Email: info@cornishfarm.com
www.cornishfarm.com
Pitches For ▲ ⊟ ⊟ Total 50
Acreage 3½ **Open** All Year
Access Good **Site** Level
Nearest Bus Stop (Miles) ½
Excellent facilities. Ideal touring park. Good for the racecourse and Somerset County Cricket Ground. AA 4 Pennants.
Facilities ♿ ʄ ⬚ ⋔ ⌐ ⊙ ⌐ ☎
⌗ ⊙ ⬚ ⬚ ≈
Nearest Town Taunton
Directions Leave the M5 at junction 25, at first traffic lights turn left, turn third left into Ilminster Road. At the roundabout turn right, next roundabout turn left, at the T-Junction follow brown tourism signs to the site. Total of 3 miles from the M5.
⇥ Taunton

TAUNTON

Holly Bush Park, Culmhead, Taunton, Somerset, TA3 7EA
Tel: 01823 421515
Email: info@hollybushpark.com
www.hollybushpark.com
Pitches For ▲ ⊟ ⊟ Total 30
Acreage 2 **Open** All Year
Site Level
Nearest Bus Stop (Miles) ¼
In an Area of Outstanding Natural Beauty.
Facilities ʄ ⬚ ⬚ ⌐ ⊙ ⌐ ⬚ ☎
⌗ ⊙ ⬚ ⬚ ⬚ ≈
Nearest Town Taunton
Directions Take B3170 from Taunton, past racecourse, left at xroads at top of hill.
⇥ Taunton

TAUNTON

Waterrow Touring Park, Waterrow, Wiveliscombe, Taunton, Somerset, TA4 2AZ
Tel: 01984 623464
Email: info@waterrowpark.co.uk
www.waterrowpark.co.uk
Pitches For ▲ ⊟ ⊟ Total 45
Acreage 8 **Open** All Year
Access Good **Site** Landscaped
Nearest Bus Stop (Miles) Outside
EXCLUSIVELY FOR ADULTS. In a peaceful, attractive location in the Tone Valley with a woodland river walk. Excellent heated facilities. Elizabethan cottage (sleeps 3) for hire. Good pub nearby. Watercolour painting holidays. Ideal touring base.
Facilities ♿ ʄ ⬚ ⬚ ⬚ ⌐ ⊙ ⌐ ⬚ ☎
⌗ ⬚ ⋔ ⬚ ⬚ ⩗ ⬚ ≈
Nearest Town Taunton
Directions Leave the M5 at junc 25 and take the A358 sp Minehead. Then take the B3227 sp Wiveliscombe, 3 miles after Wiveliscombe you will pass the Rock Pub, the park is on the left within 300 yards. Do not follow Sat Nav
⇥ Taunton/Tiverton

WELLINGTON

Cadeside Caravan Club Site, Nynehead Road, Wellington, Somerset, TA21 9HN
Tel: 01823 663103
www.caravanclub.co.uk
Pitches For ⊟ ⊟ Total 16
Acreage 4¾ **Open** All Year
Access Good **Site** Level
Nearest Bus Stop (Miles) Outside
Rural site with countryside views. Surrounded by Quantock Hills, Brendon Hills and Blackdown Hills. Non members welcome. Booking essential. Own sanitation required
Facilities ʄ ⬚ ⌗ ⊙ ⬚ ⋔ ⬚ ≈
Nearest Town Wellington
Directions Leave the M5 at junction 26 and take the A38 signposted Wellington, at roundabout turn onto the B3187 signposted Wellington. After ½ mile turn right signposted Nynehead, site is 80 yards on the right.

WELLINGTON

Gamlins Farm Caravan Park, Gamlins Farmhouse, Greenham, Wellington, Somerset, TA21 0LZ
Tel: 01823 672859
Email:
gamlinsfarmcaravanpark@hotmail.co.uk
www.gamlinsfarmcaravanpark.co.uk
Pitches For ▲ ⊟ ⊟ Total 30
Acreage 4 **Open** Mar to Oct
Access Good **Site** Level
Nearest Bus Stop (Miles) Outside
Scenic valley setting with a Free coarse fishing lake. 45 minutes from the coast. Ideal for touring, Exmoor, Quantocks and The Blackdowns. Static caravans available for hire. You can also telephone us on mobile: 07967 683738 or 07814 742462.
Facilities ʄ ⬚ ⬚ ⌐ ⊙ ⌐ ⬚ ⬚ ☎
⌗ ⋔ ⬚ ⬚ ⩗ ≈ ⬚ ≈
Nearest Town Wellington
Directions Take the M5 to junction 26 Wellington, then take the A38 towards Tiverton and Exeter. On the dual carriageway turn right to Greenham, go over two sets of crossroads, round a bend and the site is on the right. Follow brown tourism signs from J26 for 6 miles to the site.
⇥ Taunton/Tiverton

WELLINGTON

Greenacres Touring Park, Haywards Lane, Chelston, Wellington, Somerset, TA21 9PH
Tel: 01823 652844
Email:
enquiries@greenacreswellington.co.uk
www.greenacreswellington.co.uk
Pitches For ⊟ ⊟ Total 30
Acreage 2½ **Open** Apr to Sept
Access Good **Site** Level
Nearest Bus Stop (Miles) ¼
Nr Pub, bus stop, Camping & caravan Leisure shop, fishing, Garden Nurseries. Information room with book exchange.
Facilities ♿ ⬚ ʄ ⬚ ⬚ ⬚ ⌐ ⊙ ⬚ ⋔ ⬚ A
Nearest Town Wellington
Directions Approx 1 mile to Wellington.
⇥ Taunton

WELLS

Cheddar & Mendip Heights Camping & Caravanning Club Site, Mendip Heights, Townsend, Priddy, Wells, Somerset, BA5 3BP
Tel: 01749 870241
Email: enquires@thefriendlyclub.co.uk
www.campingandcaravanningclub.co.uk/cheddar
Pitches For ▲ ⊟ ⊟ Total 90
Acreage 4½ **Open** 13-Mar to 10-Nov
Access Good **Site** Lev/Slope
Situated in a designated area of outstanding natural beauty, in the heart of the Mendip Hills. Holiday caravan available for hire. Non members welcome. You can also call us on 0845 130 7633.
Facilities ♿ ʄ ⬚ ⬚ ⋔ ⌐ ⊙ ⌐ ⬚ ⬚ ☎
⌗ ⌗ ⊙ ⬚ ⋔ ⬚ ⬚ ≈
Directions From Wells take the A39 north east for 3½ miles, then take the B3135 towards Cheddar for 4½ miles. Signposted ¼ mile north west of Priddy.

WELLS

Homestead Park, Wookey Hole, Wells, Somerset, BA5 1BW
Tel: 01749 673022
Email: homesteadpark@onetel.com
www.homesteadpark.co.uk
Pitches For ▲ Total 30
Acreage 2 **Open** Easter to Oct
Access Good **Site** Level
Nearest Bus Stop (Miles) Outside
ADULTS ONLY - Sorry no children. TENTS ONLY. Sheltered site on the banks of the River Axe. Ideal for Wookey Hole Caves, National Trust sites, Mendip Hills, walking and climbing. Leisure centre nearby.
Facilities ⬚ ⬚ ⌐ ⊙ ⌐ ⬚ ⬚ ☎
Directions Leave Wells by A371 towards Cheddar, turn right for Wookey Hole. Site 1¼ miles on the left in the village.
⇥ Bristol/Bath

WESTON-SUPER-MARE

Country View Holiday Park, 29 Sand Road, Sand Bay, Weston-super-Mare, Somerset, BS22 9UJ
Tel: 01934 627595
Email: info@cvhp.co.uk
www.cvhp.co.uk
Pitches For ▲ ⊟ ⊟ Total 185
Acreage 10 **Open** Mar to Jan
Access Good **Site** Level
Nearest Bus Stop (Miles) ¼
200 yards from Sand Bay beach. Heated swimming pool and bar on site. Excellent toilet/shower facilities.
Facilities ♿ ʄ ⬚ ⬚ ⌐ ⊙ ⌐ ⬚ ⬚ ☎
⌗ ⬚ ⬚ ⬚ ⬚ ⬚ ⋔ ⬚ ⬚ ⩗ ⬚ ≈
Nearest Town Weston-super-Mare

Directions Leave the M5 at junction 21, follow signs to Sand Bay along The Queensway into Lower Norton Lane, turn right into Sand Road.
🚆 Weston-super-Mare

WESTON-SUPER-MARE
Dulhorn Farm Holiday Park, Weston Road, Lympsham, Weston-super-Mare, Somerset, BS24 0JQ
Tel: 01934 750298
Email: dfhp@btconnect.com
www.dulhornfarmholidaypark.co.uk
Pitches For 🏕 ⛺ 🚐 **Total** 87
Acreage 3 **Open** Mar **to** Oct
Access Good **Site** Level
Nearest Bus Stop (Miles) ¼
Quiet family site situated on a working farm in the countryside. Some facilities for the disabled. Ideal touring. Only 5 miles from Weston-super-Mare.
Facilities 🚿 ⯑ 🛁 ⯑ ⯑ ⯑ ⯑ ⯑ ⯑ ⯑ ⯑ ⯑ ⯑ ⯑
Nearest Town Weston-super-Mare
Directions On the A370, 5 miles from Weston-super-Mare and 4 miles from Burnham-on-Sea.
🚆 Weston-super-Mare

WESTON-SUPER-MARE
Sand Farm, Sand Farm Lane, Sand Bay, Weston-super-Mare, Somerset, BS22 9UF
Tel: 01934 620995
Email: christine.bates@tiscali.co.uk
www.kewstoke.com/stay.htm
Pitches For 🏕 ⛺ 🚐 **Total** 11
Acreage 1¼ **Open** Easter **to** Oct
Access Good **Site** Level
Quiet, farm site, 100 yards from the beach. Ideal for touring and walking. Regular (open top) bus service to W-S-M, 2½ miles from the town centre. Static caravans available for hire. Ralleys welcome. Bring Your Horse On Holiday, stables available. You can also contact us on Mobile: 07949 969722. We are motorbike and pet friendly.
Facilities 🚿 ⯑ ⯑ ⯑ ⯑ ⯑ ⯑ ⯑
Nearest Town Weston-super-Mare
Directions Leave M5 at junc 21 and head towards W-S-M, then take the slip road for Sand Bay. Follow all signs to Sand Bay until the beach is in front of you, turn right into Beach Road then next right into Sand Farm Lane.
🚆 Weston-super-Mare

WESTON-SUPER-MARE
West End Farm Caravan Park, Laneys Drove, Locking, Weston-super-Mare, Somerset, BS24 8RH
Tel: 01934 822529
Email: robin@westendfarm.org
www.westendcaravan.com
Pitches For 🏕 ⛺ 🚐 **Total** 75
Acreage 10 **Open** All Year
Access Good **Site** Level
Nearest Bus Stop (Miles) ½
Just 2½ miles from the beach. Ideal for touring and the Mendips.
Facilities 🚿 ⯑ ⯑ ⯑ ⯑ ⯑ ⯑ ⯑ ⯑ ⯑
⯑ ⯑ ⯑ ⯑
Nearest Town Weston-super-Mare

Directions Leave the M5 at junction 21 and follow signs for the Helicopter Museum. Turn right after the Helicopter Museum into Laney's Drove.
🚆 Weston-super-Mare

WILLITON
Home Farm Holiday Centre, St Audries Bay, Williton, Somerset, TA4 4DP
Tel: 01984 632487
www.homefarmholidaycentre.co.uk
Pitches For 🏕 ⛺ 🚐 **Total** 40
Open All Year **Access** Good **Site** Lev/slope
Nearest Bus Stop (Miles) 1½
Private beach, Secluded Park.
Facilities ⯑ ⯑ ⯑ ⯑ ⯑ ⯑ ⯑ ⯑ ⯑ ⯑ ⯑
⯑ ⯑ ⯑ ⯑ ⯑ ⯑ ⯑ ⯑ ⯑ ⯑ ⯑ ⯑
Nearest Town Watchet
Directions 17 miles from Bridgwater on A39 to West Quantoxhead B3191 for ½ mile to drive entrance.
🚆 Taunton

WINCANTON
Wincanton Racecourse Caravan Club Site, Wincanton, Somerset, BA9 8BJ
Tel: 01963 34276
www.caravanclub.co.uk
Pitches For 🏕 ⛺ 🚐 **Total** 57
Acreage 5 **Open** Mar **to** Oct
Access Good **Site** Level
Nearest Bus Stop (Miles) ½
Attractive site with beautiful views of Bruton Forest and the Downs. Close to Stourhead House and Haynes Motor Museum, Glastonbury Abbey. 9 hole Pay & Play golf adjacent, discounts available. Non members welcome. Booking essential.
Facilities ⯑ ⯑ ⯑ ⯑ ⯑ ⯑ ⯑ ⯑ ⯑ ⯑ ⯑
Directions From east on the A303 take the B3081 signposted Wincanton Racecourse, follow signs for the racecourse through Charlton Musgrove. At junction turn left signposted racecourse, site is 1½ miles on the right.
🚆 Wincanton

WINSFORD
Halse Farm Caravan & Tent Park, Halse Farm, Winsford, Exmoor, Somerset, TA24 7JL
Tel: 01643 851259
Email: cad@halsefarm.co.uk
www.halsefarm.co.uk
Pitches For 🏕 ⛺ 🚐 **Total** 44
Acreage 3 **Open** Mid Mar **to** Oct
Access Good **Site** Lev/Slope
Nearest Bus Stop (Miles) 1
In Exmoor National Park, on a working farm with beautiful views. Ideal for those who enjoy peaceful countryside. Quality heated toilet block and FREE showers. David Bellamy Gold Award for Conservation and ETC 4 Star Graded.
Facilities ⯑ ⯑ ⯑ ⯑ ⯑ ⯑ ⯑ ⯑ ⯑ ⯑ ⯑
⯑ ⯑ ⯑ ⯑ ⯑ ⯑ ⯑ ⯑
Nearest Town Dulverton
Directions Signposted from the A396 Tiverton to Minehead road. In Winsford take small road in front of Royal Oak Inn. 1 mile up hill and over cattle grid, our entrance is immediately on the left.
🚆 Taunton

STAFFORDSHIRE
ALTON
Alton, The Star Camping & Caravanning Club Site, Star Road, Cotton, Stoke-on-Trent, Staffordshire, ST10 3DW
Tel: 01538 702219
Email: enquiries@thefriendlyclub.co.uk
www.campingandcaravanningclub.co.uk
Pitches For 🏕 ⛺ 🚐 **Total** 195
Open Mar **to** 10-Nov
Access Good **Site** Sloping
Nearest Bus Stop (Miles) ¼
Situated in the centre of beautiful countryside within 9 miles of Leek, Uttoxeter and Ashbourne. Close to Alton Towers. Within easy reach of the Peak District and Dovedale. Non members welcome. You can also call us on 0845 130 7633.
Facilities 🚿 ⯑ ⯑ ⯑ ⯑ ⯑ ⯑ ⯑ ⯑ ⯑ ⯑
⯑ ⯑ ⯑ ⯑ ⯑
Nearest Town Cheadle
Directions From the A52 take the B5417, 1¼ miles from Alton Towers.
🚆 Blyth Bridge

CHEADLE
Hales Hall Caravan & Camping Park, Oakamoor Road, Cheadle, Staffordshire, ST10 4QR
Tel: 01538 753305
Email: enquiries@haleshallcaravanandcampingpark.com
www.haleshallcaravanandcampingpark.com
Pitches For 🏕 ⛺ 🚐 ⯑ **Total** 50
Acreage 6 **Open** Mar **to** Oct
Access Good **Site** Sloping
Nearest Bus Stop (Miles) Outside
Only 5 miles from Alton Towers.
Facilities ⯑ ⯑ ⯑ ⯑ ⯑ ⯑ ⯑ ⯑ ⯑ ⯑ ⯑
⯑ ⯑ ⯑ ⯑ ⯑ ⯑ ⯑ ⯑ ⯑ ⯑ ⯑ ⯑ ⯑ ⯑
Nearest Town Cheadle
Directions 1 mile from Cheadle on the B5417 en-route to Alton Towers.
🚆 Stoke-on-Trent

LEEK
Blackshaw Moor Caravan Club Site, Leek, Staffordshire, ST13 8TW
Tel: 01538 300203
www.caravanclub.co.uk
Pitches For ⛺ 🚐 **Total** 89
Acreage 8½ **Open** Mar **to** Jan
Access Good **Site** Level

Nearest Bus Stop (Miles) ¼
Situated on the edge of the Peak District with lovely views and walks. Just a short walk from Tittesworth Reservoir & Nature Reserve. Only 9 miles from Alton Towers. Non members welcome. Booking essential.
Facilities 🚿 ♿ 🅿 🛒 🍴 🎮 🍺
♨ 🎣 🔥 🍼 📞 🛝 📶
Nearest Town Leek
Directions From Leek take the A53, site is on the right ¼ mile past the Three Horseshoes Inn.
🚏 Leek

LEEK

Glencote Caravan Park, Station Road, Nr Leek, Staffordshire, ST13 7EE
Tel: 01538 360745
Email: canistay@glencote.co.uk
www.glencote.co.uk
Pitches For ⛺ 🚐 🚙 **Total** 70
Acreage 6 **Open** Feb to Dec
Access Good **Site** Level
Nearest Bus Stop (Miles) Outside
Situated in the heart of the Churnet Valley. Close to the Heritage Railway and canalside pubs. Ideal base for the Peak District and Potteries. ETC 5 Star Graded, David Bellamy Gold Award and Top 100 Sites Regional Winner.
Facilities 🚿 ♿ 🅿 🛒 🍴 ⊙ 🍺 🔥 📞 🎣 🎮 ❄ 🛝 🍼 📞 ♿ ✆ 📶
Nearest Town Leek
Directions 3½ miles south of Leek off the A520 Stone to Leek road.
🚏 Stoke-on-Trent

LEEK

Leek Camping & Caravanning Club Site, Blackshaw Grange, Blackshaw Moor, Leek, Staffordshire, ST13 8TL
Tel: 01538 300285
Email: enquiries@thefriendlyclub.co.uk
www.campingandcaravanningclub.co.uk/leek
Pitches For ⛺ 🚐 🚙 **Total** 70
Acreage 6 **Open** All Year
Site Lev/Slope
Nearest Bus Stop (Miles) ¼
On the edge of the Peak District. Ideal for visiting Alton Towers. BTB 4 Star Graded and AA 3 Pennants. Non members welcome. You can also call us on 0845 130 7633.
Facilities 🚿 ♿ 🅿 🛒 🍴 ⊙ 🍺 🔥 📞 🎣 🛝 📞 📶
Directions Just 2 miles from Leek on the A53 Leek to Buxton road. The site is located 200 yards past the sign for Blackshaw Moor on the left hand side.
🚏 Buxton

LICHFIELD

Cathedral Grange Touring Caravan Park, Grange Lane, Lichfield, Staffordshire, WS13 8HX
Tel: 07980 685093
Pitches For ⛺ 🚐 🚙 🚙 **Total** 0
Open All Year
Access Good **Site** Level
Nearest Bus Stop (Miles) ¼
Near to Lichfield Cathedral. Just a short drive to Drayton Manor Park, Darwin House, a snowdome and an Odeon. You can also call us on Mobile: 07966 403938.
Facilities ♿ 🅿 🛒 🍴 🍺 🔥 🎮 🍼
Nearest Town Lichfield
Directions From Lichfield take the A51 towards Rugeley, at the traffic lights turn right onto Eastern Avenue, then turn first left into Grange Lane.
🚏 Lichfield

LONGNOR

Longnor Wood Holiday Park, Newtown, Longnor, Near Buxton, Derbyshire, SK17 0NG
Tel: 01298 83648
Email: info@longnorwood.co.uk
www.longnorwood.co.uk
Pitches For ⛺ 🚐 🚙 🚙 **Total** 47
Acreage 10½ **Open** Mar to 10-Jan
Access Good **Site** Level
Nearest Bus Stop (Miles) 1¼
ADULTS ONLY PARK surrounded by woods and set in rolling countryside.
Facilities 🚿 ♿ 🅿 🛒 🍴 ⊙ 🍺 🔥 📞 🎣 🎮 ❄ 🛝 🍼 ✆ 📶
Nearest Town Buxton
Directions From the village of Longnor, follow brown tourism caravan signs along the Leek road.
🚏 Buxton

STOKE-ON-TRENT

Cross Inn Caravan & Campsite, Cross Inn, Hoftens Cross, Cauldon Low, Stoke-on-Trent, Staffordshire, ST10 3EX
Tel: 01538 308338
Email: thecrossinncouldonlow@live.co.uk
www.thecrossinncouldonlow.co.uk
Pitches For ⛺ 🚐 🚙 🚙 **Total** 50
Acreage 3 **Open** All year
Access Good **Site** Sloping
Nearest Bus Stop (Miles) Outside
Close to Alton Towers, the Peak District National Park and Blackbrook Zoo.
Facilities 🚿 ♿ 🅿 🛒 🍴 ⊙ 🍺 🔥 📞 🎣 🍴 ♨ 🍼 📞 🛝 ❄ ✆ 📶
Nearest Town Cheadle
Directions On the A52 Leek to Ashbourne road.
🚏 Stoke on Trent

UTTOXETER

Uttoxeter Racecourse Caravan Club Site, Wood Lane, Uttoxeter, Staffordshire, ST14 8BD
Tel: 01889 564172
www.caravanclub.co.uk
Pitches For ⛺ 🚐 🚙 **Total** 76
Acreage 3 **Open** Mar to Nov
Access Good **Site** Level
Surrounded by the Weaver Hills. Free admission to racecourse, bar, betting area, picnic area and play area. Golf course adjacent. Close to Alton Towers, Lichfield Cathedral and Sudbury Hall. Non members welcome. Booking essential.
Facilities 🚿 ♿ 🅿 🔥 📞 🍼 🎮
♨ 🎣 🔥 🍺 🍼 📞 🛝 🍴
Nearest Town Uttoxeter
Directions From the A50 take the A518 sp Racecourse, site is 1½ miles on the left. Turn into third gate at Caravan Club sign.
🚏 Uttoxeter

SUFFOLK

BUNGAY

Outney Meadow Caravan Park, Bungay, Suffolk, NR35 1HG
Tel: 01986 892338
Email: info@outneymeadow.co.uk
www.outneymeadow.co.uk
Pitches For ⛺ 🚐 🚙 🚙 **Total** 65
Acreage 6 **Open** Mar to Oct
Access Good **Site** Level
Nearest Bus Stop (Miles) ¼
Beside the golf course and River Waveney for fishing and canoeing.
Facilities ♿ 🅿 🍴 🔥 📞 ⊙ 🍺 ♨ 📞 🎣 🍼 📞 🛝 🍴 🎮 🍼 ✆ ❄ 📶
Nearest Town Bungay
Directions Signposted from the roundabout junction of the A143 and A144 ¼ mile north of Bungay.
🚏 Diss/Beccles

BURY ST EDMUNDS

The Dell Touring Park, Beyton Road, Thurston, Bury St Edmunds, Suffolk, IP31 3RB
Tel: 01359 270121
Email: thedellcaravanpark@btinternet.com
www.thedellcaravanpark.co.uk
Pitches For ⛺ 🚐 🚙 **Total** 60
Open All Year
Access Good **Site** Level
Nearest Bus Stop (Miles) Outside
Ideal for touring East Anglia. 1 hour from Cambridge, Norwich and coast. Free Wi-Fi. New hard standing pitches. Excellent toilet blocks.
Facilities 🚿 ♿ 🅿 🔥 📞 ⊙ 🍼 🎮 🍼
🍼 📞 🛝 🍺 ✆ 📶
Nearest Town Bury St Edmunds
Directions Take A14 eastbound 6 miles from Bury follow Thurston signs.
🚏 Thurston

EYE

Honeypot Caravan & Camping Park, Wortham, Eye, Suffolk, IP22 1PW
Tel: 01379 783312
Email: honeypotcamping@talk21.com
www.honeypotcamping.co.uk
Pitches For ⛺ 🚐 🚙 **Total** 35
Acreage 7 **Open** Mid April to Mid Sept
Access Good **Site** Level
Nearest Bus Stop (Miles) Outside
Highly recommended site with plenty of peace and quiet. Fishing on site. South facing farmland setting with some lakeside pitches. Free hot water Celebrating 40 years of the same family ownership.
Facilities ♿ 🅿 🍴 🔥 📞 ⊙ 🍼 🍺 🍼
🍼 🍴 🛝 🍺 ✆ 🎣
Nearest Town Eye
Directions Four miles south west of Diss, on the south side of the A143.
🚏 Diss

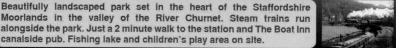

SUFFOLK

FELIXSTOWE

Peewit Caravan Park, Walton Avenue, Felixstowe, Suffolk, IP11 2HB
Tel: 01394 284511
Email: peewitpark@aol.com
www.peewitcaravanpark.co.uk
Pitches For 🏕 ⛺ 🚐 **Total** 40
Acreage 3 **Open** Easter/1 April **to** Oct
Access Good **Site** Level
Nearest Bus Stop (Miles) ½
Quiet and secluded setting, 900 metres from the seafront. Central for North Essex and coastal Suffolk.
Facilities 🚽 ♿ 🔥 🅿 ⊙ ⊿ 🔌 🍴
♿ 🎯 🏪 🛢 📶 🚲 📞 🛒
Nearest Town Felixstowe
Directions Take the A14 to Felixstowe Docks, at Gate No.1 turn towards the town centre, site is 100 metres on the left.
🚆 Felixstowe

IPSWICH

Low House Touring Caravan Centre, Low House, Bucklesham Road, Foxhall, Ipswich, Suffolk, IP10 0AU
Tel: 01473 659437
Email: low.house@btinternet.com
www.tourbritain.ukcampsites.com
Pitches For 🏕 ⛺ 🚐 **Total** 30
Acreage 3½ **Open** All Year
Access Good **Site** Level
Camp in a beautiful garden packed with ornamental trees and plants, arches and bower doves, rabbits. Wildlife all around. Ornamental Tree Walk and Pets Corner. New friendly wardens. Heated toilet and shower block.
Facilities ♿ 🔥 🅿 ⊙ ⊿ 🔌 🍴
♿ 🎯 🏪 🛢 🚲 📞 🛒
Nearest Town Ipswich
Directions Turn off A14 Ipswich Ring Road (South) via slip road onto A1156 (sp East Ipswich). In 1 mile turn right (signposted), in ½ mile turn right sp Low House, site is on the left in ¼ mile.
🚆 Ipswich

IPSWICH

Orwell Meadows Leisure Park, Priory Lane, Ipswich, Suffolk, IP10 0JS
Tel: 01473 726666
Email: reception@orwellmeadows.co.uk
www.orwellmeadows.co.uk
Pitches For 🏕 ⛺ 🚐 🚗 **Total** 80
Open Mar **to** 14-Jan
Access Good **Site** Level
A quiet, family run park, ideally situated for touring beautiful Suffolk. Adjacent to the Orwell Country Park. Forest and river walks.
Facilities 🚽 ♿ 🔥 🅿 ⊙ ⊿ 🔌 🍴
♿ 🎯 🏪 🛢 🍷 🛢 🚲 🛢 🕿 📶
Nearest Town Ipswich
Directions From the A14 heading towards Felixstowe take first exit after Orwell Bridge, at the roundabout turn left and first left again, then follow signs.
🚆 Ipswich

KESSINGLAND

Kessingland Camping & Caravanning Club Site, Whites Lane, Kessingland, Nr Lowestoft, Suffolk, NR33 7TF
Tel: 01502 742040
Email: enquiries@thefriendlyclub.co.uk
www.campingandcaravanningclub.co.uk/kessingland
Pitches For 🏕 ⛺ 🚐 **Total** 90
Acreage 5 **Open** Apr **to** 03-Nov
Access Good **Site** Level
Nearest Bus Stop (Miles) ½

Next to Suffolk Wildlife Park. Set in a quiet seaside resort, close to Great Yarmouth. 5 miles from Pleasurewood Hills. BTB 4 Star Graded, AA 4 Pennants and Loo of the Year Award. Non members welcome. You can also call us on 0845 130 7633.
Facilities 🚽 🔥 🅿 ⊙ ⊿ 🔌 🍴
♿ ⊙ 🛢 🚲 🕿
Nearest Town Lowestoft
Directions From Lowestoft on the A12, leave at roundabout in Kessingland following Wildlife Park signs. Turn right through park entrance.
🚆 Lowestoft

LEISTON

Beach View holiday Park, Sizewell Common, Leiston, Suffolk, IP16 4TU
Tel: 01728 830724
Email:
enquiries@beachviewholidaypark.co.uk
www.beachviewholidaypark.co.uk
Pitches For 🏕 ⛺ 🚐 **Total** 60
Acreage 17 **Open** 15-Mar **to** Nov
Access Good **Site** Level
On the beach. Sea fishing from a private beach. Ideal for bird watching, shore fishing, walking and cycling.
Facilities 🔥 🅿 ⊙ ⊿ 🔌 🍴
♿ 🎯 🏪 🍷 🛢 🚲 🕿 📶
Nearest Town Leiston
Directions From Leiston take the turning to Sizewell Beach (2 miles), turn right sp Sizewell Hall, before the entrance gates to the Hall turn left to Cliff House.
🚆 Saxmundham

LOWESTOFT

Beach Farm Residential & Holiday Park Ltd., Arbor Lane, Pakefield, Lowestoft, Suffolk, NR33 7BD
Tel: 01502 572794
Email: beachfarmpark@aol.com
www.beachfarmpark.co.uk
Pitches For ⛺ 🚐 **Total** 2
Acreage ¼ **Open** Mar **to** 02-Jan
Access Good **Site** Level
Nearest Bus Stop (Miles) ¼
Beach 500 yards, Africa alive 2 miles.
Facilities 🔥 🅿 ⊙ ⊿ 🔌 🍴
♿ 🎯 🏪 🍷 🛢 🚲 🕿 📶
Nearest Town Lowestoft
Directions Follow A12 Ipswich to main roundabout (water Tower) 2 miles Pakefield.
🚆 Lowestoft

LOWESTOFT

Heathland Beach Holiday Park Ltd., London Road, Kessingland, Lowestoft, Suffolk, NR33 7PJ
Tel: 01502 740337
Email: heathlandbeach@btinternet.com
www.heathlandbeach.co.uk
Pitches For 🏕 ⛺ 🚐 **Total** 63
Acreage 5 **Open** Apr **to** Oct
Access Good **Site** Level
Nearest Bus Stop (Miles) Outside
Privately owned park surrounded by countryside. Beach access.
Facilities 🔥 🅿 ⊙ ⊿ 🔌 🍴
♿ 🎯 🏪 🍷 🛢 🚲 🛢 🕿 🛒
Nearest Town Lowestoft
Directions 3 miles south of Lowestoft off the old A12, take the B1437.
🚆 Lowestoft

NAYLAND

Rushbanks Farm, Bures Road, Wiston/Nayland, Colchester, Essex, CO6 4NA
Tel: 01206 262350
Pitches For 🏕 ⛺ 🚐 **Total** 0

Acreage 3 **Open** Apr **to** Oct
Access Good **Site** Level
Nearest Bus Stop (Miles) 1
On the north banks of the River Stour. Please book in advance. You can also telephone us on Mobile: 07860 325053.
Facilities 🚐 🅿 🔥 🍴 ⊿
Nearest Town Colchester
Directions A134 from Colchester turn left at Nayland towards Bures
🚆 Colchester

SAXMUNDHAM

Carlton Park Camping & Caravan Site, North Entrance, Saxmundham, Suffolk, IP17 1AT
Tel: 07716 884322
Email: info@carltonpark.info
www.carltonpark.info
Pitches For 🏕 ⛺ 🚐 **Total** 75
Acreage 7½ **Open** Apr **to** Oct
Access Good **Site** Sloping
Nearest Bus Stop (Miles) ¼
Situated in rolling countryside, close to the Suffolk heritage coast.
Facilities 🚽 🔥 🅿 ⊙ ⊿ 🔌 🍴
♿ 🛢 🍷 🛢 🚲
Nearest Town Saxmundham
Directions From the A12 Ipswich to Lowestoft road, take the B1121, go through the town and the site is on the left.
🚆 Saxmundham

SAXMUNDHAM

Mill Hill Farm Camping & Carvan Park. Westleton Road, Darsham, Saxmundham, Suffolk, IP17 3BS
Tel: 01728 668555
Email: millhillfarmcamping@live.co.uk
www.suffolkcamping.webs.com
Pitches For 🏕 ⛺ 🚐 **Total** 70
Acreage 12 **Open** Apr **to** Oct
Access Good **Site** Sloping
Nearest Bus Stop (Miles) 1
Quiet, friendly, family owned site.
Facilities 🔥 🅿 ⊙ ⊿ 🔌 🍴
♿ 🛢 🚲 🛢 🕿 🛒
Nearest Town Southwold
Directions From A12 Yoxford take Westleton road signposted Westleton Crown We are 1½ miles on left.
🚆 Darsham

SAXMUNDHAM

Whitearch Touring Park, Main Road, Benhall, Saxmundham, Suffolk, IP17 1NA
Tel: 01728 604646
www.caravancampingsites.co.uk
Pitches For 🏕 ⛺ 🚐 **Total** 50
Acreage 14½ **Open** Apr **to** Oct
Access Good **Site** Level
Nearest Bus Stop (Miles) ¼
Fishing and tennis on site. No cycling on site. Near the Suffolk coast, Snape Maltings Concert Hall, Minsmere Bird Reserve, American Theme Park and castles.
Facilities 🚽 🔥 🅿 ⊙ ⊿ 🔌 🍴
♿ 🛢 🚲 🛢 🕿 🛒
Nearest Town Saxmundham
Directions Just off the main A12 junction with the B1121 at the Ipswich end of Saxmundham by-pass.
🚆 Saxmundham

SHOTLEY

Shotley Caravan Park, Gate Farm Road, Shotley, Suffolk, IP9 1QH
Tel: 01473 787421
www.shotleycaravanpark.com
Pitches For ⛺ 🚐 **Total** 0
Acreage 7 **Open** Mar **to** Oct

Access Good **Site** Lev/Slope
Nearest Bus Stop (Miles) Outside
Enjoy peace and tranquillity in this area of outstanding natural beauty, with panoramic views over the River Orwell. Large pond with ducks. Free eggs from our chickens for all caravanners. Ideal site for the over 50s. Tourers/rallies welcome. Close to a marina, restaurants, pubs, fish & chips, church, doctors and garage. Easy access from the A12/A14.
Facilities ⫪ 🖪 🖾 ⬚ 🅙⤒🄳🄰⤱ ⚲
Nearest Town Ipswich/Felixstowe
Directions From Orwell Bridge take exit A137 and follow the B1456 once in Shotley (10 miles from Ipswich). Go past the Rose Pub on the right and after 1 mile turn left into Gate Farm Road and go through the green gates.
⌗ Ipswich

SUDBURY

Willowmere Caravan Park, Bures Road, Little Cornard, Sudbury, Suffolk, CO10 0NN
Tel: 01787 375559/310422
Email: awillowmere@aol.com
Pitches For 🅐 ⊞ 🚌 **Total** 40
Acreage 2 **Open** Easter **to** 01-Oct
Access Good **Site** Level
Nearest Bus Stop (Miles) Outside
Quiet country park near a river.
Facilities ⬧ ⫪ 🖾⬚🄵 ⬚🖃 ⊞ 🄾 ⊞⤒⤳
Nearest Town Sudbury
Directions Leave Sudbury on the B1508 to Bures and Colchester, 1 mile from Sudbury.
⌗ Sudbury

THEBERTON

Cakes & Ale, Abbey Lane, Theberton, Suffolk, IP16 4TE
Tel: 01728 831655
Email: reception@cakesandalepark.co.uk
www.cakesandale.co.uk
Pitches For 🅐 ⊞ 🚌 ⌤ **Total** 170
Open Apr **to** Oct
Access Good **Site** Level
Nearest Bus Stop (Miles) 1
Central to Suffolk Heritage coast.
Facilities ⬧ ⫪ 🖪 🖾 🖾⬚🄵 ⬚🖃 🄾 ⬚ 📷 ⊞ 🄾
🅢🅛 🄾 ⬚ ⚲ 🅙 ⊞ 🄿🄳 ⤱ ⤒ 📶
Nearest Town Aldeburgh
⌗ Saxmundham

WOODBRIDGE

Moat Barn Touring Caravan Park, Dallinghoo Road, Bredfield, Woodbridge, Suffolk, IP13 6BD
Tel: 01473 737520
www.moatbarn.co.uk
Pitches For 🅐 ⊞ 🚌 **Total** 34
Acreage 2 **Open** Mar **to** Mid Jan
Access Good **Site** Level
Nearest Bus Stop (Miles) Outside
Quiet, family run park in a rural location. No facilities for children. No large campers vans accepted. Ideal for touring and exploring the Heritage Coast.
Facilities ⫪ 🖾⬚🄵 ⬚🖃 ⊞ 🅙 🄳🄰⤱ ⤒ 📶
Nearest Town Woodbridge
Directions Off the A12 (north) turn left into Bredfield village, Turn right at Bredfield Pump site 1 mile.
⌗ Woodbridge

WOODBRIDGE

Moon and Sixpence, Newbourne Road, Waldringfield, Woodbridge, Suffolk, IP12 4PP
Tel: 01473 736650
Email: info@moonandsixpence.eu

www.moonandsixpence.eu
Pitches For 🅐 ⊞ 🚌 **Total** 75
Acreage 5 **Open** Apr **to** Oct
Access Good **Site** Level
Nearest Bus Stop (Miles) 1½
Picturesque location. Sheltered, terraced site. Own private lake and sandy beach. Compact 9 hole golf course, 3 hard tennis courts and volley ball/basket ball courts. Extensive trails walking and cycling.
Facilities ⫪ 🖪 🖾⬚🄵🄿 ⬚🖃 🄾 ⬚ ⊞
🅢🅛 🄾 ⚲ 🄹 ⬚🖃 🄰🄼 ⤱⤒🄿🄳 ⊞ 📶
Nearest Town Woodbridge
Directions Turn off A12, Ipswich Eastern By-Pass, onto unclassified road signposted Waldringfield, Newbourn. Follow caravan direction signs.
⌗ Woodbridge

WOODBRIDGE

Run Cottage Touring Park, Alderton Road, Hollesley, Woodbridge, Suffolk, IP12 3RQ
Tel: 01394 411309
Email: contact@run-cottage.co.uk
www.run-cottage.co.uk
Pitches For 🅐 ⊞ 🚌 **Total** 45
Acreage 4½ **Open** All Year
Access Good **Site** Level
Nearest Bus Stop (Miles) ¼
Quiet, peaceful and secluded site set in 3½ acres of parkland. On Suffolks Heritage Coast, ideal for walking, cycling and bird watching.
Facilities ⬧ ⫪ 🄷 🖾⬚🄵🄿 ⬚🖃 ⊞ 🅙⤒🄳
Nearest Town Woodbridge
Directions Turn off the A12 at Melton onto the A1152, at next roundabout turn right onto the B1083. Turn next left to Hollesley then turn right into The Street at Hollesley, go through the village and over the small bridge, site is 100 yards on the left.
⌗ Woodbridge

SURREY

CHERTSEY

Chertsey Camping & Caravanning Club Site, Bridge Road, Chertsey, Surrey, KT16 8JX
Tel: 01932 562405
Email: enquiries@thefriendlyclub.co.uk
www.campingandcaravanningclub.co.uk/chertsey
Pitches For 🅐 ⊞ 🚌 **Total** 200
Acreage 12 **Open** All Year
Site Level
Nearest Bus Stop (Miles) 1
On the banks of the River Thames, fishing on site. Table tennis on site. 4 miles from Thorpe Park. Close to London. BTB 4 Star Graded and AA 4 Pennants. Non members welcome. You can also call us on 0845 130 7633.
Facilities ⬧ ⫪ 🖪 🄷 🖾⬚🄵🄿 ⬚🖃 ⬚ 📷 ⊞ 🄾
⬚ 🄾 🅃 🄴 ⤒🄿🄳 🄵⤱ 📶
Directions Leave the M25 at junction 11 and follow the A317 to Chertsey. At the roundabout take the first exit to the traffic lights and go straight across to the next set of traffic lights, turn right and after 400 yards turn left into the site.
⌗ Chertsey

LALEHAM

Laleham Camping Club, Laleham Park, Thameside, Laleham, Middlesex, TW18 1SS
Tel: 01932 564149
Email: lalehamcampingclub@gmail.com
www.lalehamcampingclub.co.uk
Pitches For 🅐 ⊞ 🚌 **Total** 0
Open Apr **to** 01-Oct
Access Good **Site** Level
Nearest Bus Stop (Miles) ½
Alongside the River Thames.
Facilities ⬧ ⫪ 🖪 🖾⬚🄵 ⬚🖃 🄾 ⬚ 📷 ⊞
🅢🅛 🅙 ⚲⤒🄳 📶
Nearest Town Staines
⌗ Staines

REDHILL

Alderstead Heath Caravan Club Site, Dean Lane, Redhill, Merstham, Surrey, RH1 3AH
Tel: 01737 644629
www.caravanclub.co.uk
Pitches For 🅐 ⊞ 🚌 **Total** 150
Acreage 30 **Open** All Year
Access Good **Site** Level
Nearest Bus Stop (Miles) ½
Quiet, level pitched site which drops into rolling wooded countryside, and has wonderful views of the North Downs. Close to Wisley Gardens, NT Chartwell, Thorpe Park and Chessington World of Adventure. Non members welcome. Booking essential.
Facilities ⬧ ⫪ 🄷 🖾⬚🄵 ⬚🖃 🄾 ⬚
🅢🅛 🅙 ⚲ 🄾 ⊞⤒ 📶
Nearest Town Redhill
Directions Leave M25 at junc 8 take A217 signposted Reigate, after 300yds fork left signposted Merstham. At T-junc turn left onto A23, after ½ mile turn right into Shepherds Hill signposted Caterham, after 1 mile turn left into Dean Lane site in ½ mile
⌗ Redhill

SUSSEX (EAST)

BATTLE
Battle Normanhurst Court Caravan Club Site, Stevens Crouch, Battle, East Sussex, TN33 9LR
Tel: 01424 773808
www.caravanclub.co.uk
Pitches For ⊞ ⊟ **Total** 144
Acreage 18 **Open** Mar to Nov
Access Good **Site** Lev/Slope
Set in a former garden with splendid trees and shrubs, and lovely views of the Downs. Close to Battle Abbey, Hastings, Rye and Sussex vineyards. Non members welcome. Booking essential.
Facilities
Nearest Town Battle
Directions From the A269 in Ninfield take the B2204 signposted Battle. Just past Catsfield keep left, after 1¼ miles turn left onto the A271 signposted Eastbourne, site is ½ mile on the left.
⇌ Battle

BATTLE
Brakes Coppice Park, Forewood Lane, Crowhurst, East Sussex, TN33 9AB
Tel: 01424 830322
Email: brakesco@btinternet.com
www.brakescoppicepark.co.uk
Pitches For ⋏ ⊞ ⊟ **Total** 30
Acreage 3¼ **Open** Mar to Oct
Access Good **Site** Sloping
Nearest Bus Stop (Miles) 1
Secluded, 11 acre woodland park with level pitches. TV aerial point to serviced pitches.
Facilities
Directions Turn right off the A2100 (Battle to Hastings road) 2 miles from Battle. Follow signs to Crowhurst, 1¼ miles turn left into site.
⇌ Crowhurst

BATTLE
Meadow View Park Whydown Farm, Crazy Lane, Sedlescombe, East Sussex, TN33 0QT
Tel: 01424 870147
www.crazylane.co.uk
Pitches For ⋏ ⊞ ⊟ **Total** 36
Acreage 3 **Open** Mar to Oct
Access Good **Site** Level
Nearest Bus Stop (Miles) Outside
15 minutes to the beach. Ideal for the countryside and Hastings. NEW shower and toilet block.
Facilities
Nearest Town Battle/Hastings
Directions Travelling south on A21, turn left into Crazy Lane, 100 yds past junction A21/B2244, opposite Black Brooks Garden Centre.
⇌ Battle

PLEASE REMEMBER TO MENTION CADE'S WHEN BOOKING

BATTLE
Senlac Wood, Catsfield Road, Catsfield, Nr Battle, East Sussex, TN33 9LN
Tel: 01424 773969
Email: senlacwood@xlninternet.co.uk
www.senlacwood.co.uk
Pitches For ⋏ ⊞ ⊟ **Total** 50
Acreage 10 **Open** Mar to Oct
Access Good **Site** Level
Nearest Bus Stop (Miles) Outside
In a woodland setting with walks and fishing nearby. Ideal for touring this historic 1066 country. Approx. 7 miles from the beach.
Facilities
Nearest Town Battle
Directions From Battle take the A271 North Trade Road, after about 2½ miles turn left onto the B2204. Site is on the left in ½ a mile.
⇌ Battle

BEXHILL-ON-SEA
Cobbs Hill Farm Caravan & Camping Park, Watermill Lane, Bexhill-on-Sea, East Sussex, TN39 5JA
Tel: 01424 213460
Email: cobbshillfarmuk@hotmail.com
www.cobbshillfarm.co.uk
Pitches For ⋏ ⊞ ⊟ ⊟≶ **Total** 55
Acreage 17½ **Open** Apr to Oct
Access Good **Site** Level
Situated on a small farm in quiet countryside with a network of footpaths leading from the Park. Spacious play area and an animal viewing area. Two static caravans for hire.
Facilities
Nearest Town Bexhill-on-Sea
Directions Signposted off the A269. Turn into Watermill Lane and the Site is 1 mile on the left.
⇌ Bexhill-on-Sea

BEXHILL-ON-SEA
Kloofs Caravan Park, Sandhurst Lane, Bexhill-on-Sea, East Sussex, TN39 4RG
Tel: 01424 842839
Email: camping@kloofs.com
www.kloofs.com
Pitches For ⋏ ⊞ ⊟ **Total** 62
Acreage 22 **Open** All Year
Access Good **Site** Level
Nearest Bus Stop (Miles) ½
Quiet, tranquil, rural park only 2 miles from the beach. USRV's upto 40'.
Facilities
Nearest Town Bexhill-on-Sea
Directions From the A259 at the Bexhill/Little Common roundabout turn into Peartree Lane, go up the hill to the crossroads and turn left into Whydown Road, Sandhurst Lane is 300 metres on the left.
⇌ Cooden Beach

BRIGHTON
Brighton Caravan Club Site, East Brighton Park, Brighton, East Sussex, BN2 5TS
Tel: 01273 626546
www.caravanclub.co.uk
Pitches For ⋏ ⊞ ⊟ **Total** 269
Acreage 17 **Open** All Year
Access Good **Site** Level
Nearest Bus Stop (Miles) ½

Situated in the South Downs, adjacent to recreation grounds. Only 2 miles from Brighton with its beach, pier, Royal Pavilion, sea life centre, boutiques and seafront attractions. Non members welcome. Booking essential.
Facilities
Nearest Town Brighton
Directions From A27 take B2123 signed Falmer, at lights by Downs Hotel t rt into Warren Rd. At next lights t lt into Wilson Avenue, cross the racecourse and after 1¼ miles t lt at foot of hill (last turn before the lights) into East Brighton Park, site is ½ mile on lt.
⇌ Brighton

CROWBOROUGH
Crowborough Camping & Caravanning Club Site, Goldsmith Recreation Ground, Crowborough, East Sussex, TN6 2TN
Tel: 01892 664827
Email: enquiries@thefriendlyclub.co.uk
www.campingandcaravanningclub.co.uk/crowborough
Pitches For ⋏ ⊞ ⊟ **Total** 90
Acreage 13 **Open** Apr to 10-Nov
Site Lev/Slope
Nearest Bus Stop (Miles) Outside
On the edge of Ashdown Forest. Adjacent to a sports centre. Kitchen available at extra charge. BTB 4 Star Graded and AA 3 Pennants. Non members welcome. You can also call us on 0845 130 7633.
Facilities
Directions Take the A26 turn off into the entrance to Goldsmiths Ground signposted leisure centre, at the top of the road turn right into site lane.
⇌ Jarvis Brook

EASTBOURNE
Fairfields Farm Caravan & Camping Park, Eastbourne Road, Westham, Pevensey, East Sussex, BN24 5NG
Tel: 01323 763165
Email: enquiries@fairfieldsfarm.com
www.fairfieldsfarm.com
Pitches For ⋏ ⊞ ⊟ **Total** 60
Acreage 3 **Open** Apr to Oct
Access Good **Site** Level
Nearest Bus Stop (Miles) ¼
2 miles from the beach and 3 miles from Eastbourne town centre.
Facilities
Nearest Town Eastbourne
Directions On the B2191 in the village of Westham. 3 miles east of Eastbourne.
⇌ Pevensey & Westham

HASTINGS
Hastings Touring Park, c/o Shearbarn Holiday Park, Barley Lane, Hastings, Sussex (East), TN35 5DX
Tel: 01424 423583
Email: info@hastingstouring.co.uk
www.hastingstouringpark.co.uk
Pitches For ⋏ ⊞ ⊟ **Total** 431
Acreage 7 **Open** Mar to 15-Jan
Access Poor **Site** Level
Nearest Bus Stop (Miles) ¼
Above Hastings old town and adjacent to Hastings Country Park.
Facilities
Nearest Town Hastings
Directions Head East along the sea front, up Harold Road and follow signs to Shearbarn Holiday Park.
⇌ Hastings

HORAM

Woodland View Touring Park, Horebeech Lane, Horam, Heathfield, East Sussex, TN21 0HR
Tel: 01435 813597
Pitches For Å ⊞ ⊟ **Total** 25
Acreage 2 **Open** All year
Access Good **Site** Sloping
Nearest Bus Stop (Miles) ¼
Next to the Cuckoo Trail.
Facilities ƒ ⊞♠ſ⊙⊿◩☐❤️łℓ⊙A❤️
Nearest Town Eastbourne/Polegate
Directions ¼ of a mile off the A267.
⚌ Eastbourne/Polegate

LEWES

Blackberry Wood Caravan Park, Streat Lane, Streat, Ditchling, Sussex (East), BN6 8RS
Tel: 01273 890035
Email: stay@blackberrywood.com
www.blackberrywood.com
Pitches For Å **Total** 40
Acreage 30 **Open** All Year
Access Good **Site** Level
In South Downs National Park nr to Lewes and Brighton.
Facilities ⊞♠ſ⊿łℓ ◩❤️♠❄️
Nearest Town Lewes
Directions 2 miles east of Ditchling.
⚌ Plumpton

PEVENSEY

Normans Bay Camping & Caravanning Club Site, Normans Bay, Pevensey, East Sussex, BN24 6PR
Tel: 01323 761190
Email: normans.baysite@thefriendlyclub.co.uk
www.campingandcaravanningclub.co.uk/normansbay
Pitches For Å ⊞ ⊟ **Total** 200
Acreage 13 **Open** Apr to 03-Nov
Access Good **Site** Level
Nearest Bus Stop (Miles) ½
Site has its own beach and is close to where the Normans landed. BTB 4 Star Graded and AA 3 Pennants. Non members welcome. You can also call us on 0845 130 7633.
Facilities ƒ ⊞ ⊞♠ſ⊙⊿❤️◩❤️
łℓ ℓ⊙⊛♠◩❤️☐❄️❤️
Nearest Town Pevensey
Directions From the A259 in Pevensey Bay Village take the first turn left (coast road) signed Beachlands only. After 1¼ miles site is on the left hand side.
⚌ Normans Bay

ROBERTSBRIDGE

Park Farm Camp Site, Bodiam, Robertsbridge, East Sussex, TN32 5XA
Tel: 01580 831982
Email: info@parkfarmcamping.co.uk
www.parkfarmcamping.co.uk
Pitches For Å ⊞ ⊟ ⊟⧸ **Total** 180
Acreage 18 **Open** Apr to Oct
Access Good **Site** Level
Nearest Bus Stop (Miles) 1
Alongside the River Rother in a beautiful area. Within walking distance of the pub and Bodiam Castle. Camp fires allowed. 10 miles to beach
Facilities ƒ ⊞ ⊞♠ſ⊙⊿❤️
łℓ ℓ⊙ ❤️❄️❄️
Nearest Town Hawkhurst
Directions 3 miles south of Hawkhurst on the B2244. 3 miles north of Sedlescombe.
⚌ Robertsbridge

UCKFIELD

Heaven Farm, Furners Green, Uckfield, East Sussex, TN22 3RG
Tel: 01825 790226
Email: heavenfarmleisure@btinternet.com
www.heavenfarm.co.uk
Pitches For Å ⊞ ⊟ ⊟⧸ **Total** 30
Acreage 4 **Open** All Year
Access Good **Site** Lev/Slope
Nearest Bus Stop (Miles) 1
Farm museum, The Stable Reataurant & Tea Rooms, nature trail. Ideal for National Trust gardens, Bluebell Railway and Brighton. Booking is essential. Granery Flowers and gift shop.
Facilities ⊙ ƒ ⊞♠ſ⊙⊿❤️łℓ ✕❤️◩⧸
Nearest Town Uckfield
Directions On the A275 between East Grinstead (A22) and Haywards Heath (A272).
⚌ Haywards Heath

UCKFIELD

Honeys Green Caravan Park, Easons Green, Halland, Uckfield, East Sussex, TN22 5GJ
Tel: 01732 860205
Email: honeysgreenpark@tiscali.co.uk
Pitches For Å ⊞ ⊟ **Total** 22
Acreage 17 **Open** All year
Access Good **Site** Level
Nearest Bus Stop (Miles) ¼
Small, peaceful, rural park in a pretty wooded location with our own course fishing lake. Lovely walks nearby.
Facilities ƒ ⊞ ⊞♠ſ⊙⊿❤️
łℓ ⊙ ◩❤️◩⧸❄️
Nearest Town Uckfield
Directions On the A22, 3 miles south of Uckfield at the Halland roundabout take the B2192 signposted Blackboys/Heathfield, Park is a few hundred yards on the left.
⚌ Uckfield

WINCHELSEA

Rye Bay Caravan Park, Pett Level Road, Winchelsea Beach, East Sussex, TN36 4NE
Tel: 01797 226340
Pitches For ⊞ ⊟ **Total** 40
Open Whitsun to Mid Sept
Access Good **Site** Fairly Level
Nearest Bus Stop (Miles) Outside
Near the beach.
Facilities ⊞ ſ⊙⊿❤️
łℓ ⊙ ◩❤️◩❤️
Nearest Town Hastings
Directions 3 miles west of Rye and 7 miles east of Hastings.
⚌ Rye

SUSSEX (WEST)

ARUNDEL

Maynards Caravan & Camping Park, Crossbush, Arundel, West Sussex, BN18 9PQ
Tel: 01903 882075
Pitches For Å ⊞ ⊟ **Total** 70
Acreage 3 **Open** All Year
Access Good **Site** Level
Nearest Bus Stop (Miles) Outside
3 miles from a sandy beach. Near Arundel Castle and Wild Fowl Reserve.
Facilities ƒ ⊞♠ſ⊙⊿❤️łℓ ⊙ ◩❤️◩
Nearest Town Arundel
Directions Just off the main A27, turn into the Beefeater Restaurant car park.
⚌ Arundel

ARUNDEL

Ship & Anchor Marina, Heywood & Bryett Ltd, Ford, Arundel, West Sussex, BN18 0BJ
Tel: 01243 551262
Email: enquiries@shipandanchormarina.co.uk
Pitches For Å ⊞ ⊟ **Total** 160
Acreage 12 **Open** Mar to Oct
Access Good **Site** Level
Beside the River Arun with a public house on site. 3 miles to beaches. Advance booking is advisable for hook-ups and groups.
Facilities ♿ ƒ ⊞♠ſ⊙⊿❤️
łℓ ⊙⊛✕◩❤️◩❤️❄️
Nearest Town Arundel/Littlehampton
Directions From the A27 at Arundel, follow road signposted to Ford for 2 miles. Site is on the left after level-crossing at Ford.
⚌ Ford

BILLINGHURST

Limeburners (Camping) Ltd., Lordings Road, Newbridge, Billinghurst, West Sussex, RH14 9JA
Tel: 01403 782311
Email: chippy.sawyer@virgin.net
Pitches For Å ⊞ ⊟ ⊟⧸ **Total** 40
Open Apr to Oct
Access Good **Site** Level
Nearest Bus Stop (Miles) 1½
Attached to a public house.
Facilities ƒ ⊞♠ſ⊙⊿❤️
⊛✕◩❤️◩❤️
Nearest Town Billinghurst
Directions 1½ miles west of Billinghurst on the A272, turn left onto the B2133, Park is 500 yards on the right.
⚌ Billinghurst

BOGNOR REGIS

Rowan Park Caravan Club Site, Rowan Way, Bognor Regis, West Sussex, PO22 9RP
Tel: 01243 828515
www.caravanclub.co.uk
Pitches For Å ⊞ ⊟ **Total** 96
Acreage 8 **Open** Mar to Nov
Access Good **Site** Level
Nearest Bus Stop (Miles) ½
2 miles from the beach, South Coast World and a leisure centre. Close to Weald & Downland Open Air Museum, D-Day Museum & Battle of Britain Aviation and Amberley Chalk Pits Museum. Non members welcome. Booking essential.
Facilities ♿ ƒ ⊞♠ſ⊙⊿❤️ ◩❤️
łℓ ⊙⊛◩❤️◩❄️
Nearest Town Bognor Regis
Directions From north on the A29, ½ mile past Shripney Village at the roundabout turn right into Rowan Way, site is 100 yards on the right, opposite Halfords.
⚌ Bognor Regis

CHICHESTER

Bell Caravan Park, Bell Lane, Birdham, Nr Chichester, West Sussex, PO20 7HY
Tel: 01243 512264
Pitches For ⊞ ⊟ **Total** 15
Acreage ¼ **Open** Mar to Oct
Access Good **Site** Level
Nearest Bus Stop (Miles) ¼
Facilities ƒ ⊞♠ſ⊙⊛◩❤️◩
Nearest Town Chichester
Directions From Chichester take the A286 towards Wittering for approx. 4 miles. At Birdham turn left into Bell Lane, site is 500yds on the left.
⚌ Chichester

CHICHESTER
Chichester Camping & Caravanning Club Site, Main Road, Southbourne, Hampshire, PO10 8JH
Tel: 01243 373202
Email: enquiries@thefriendlyclub.co.uk
www.campingandcaravanningclub.co.uk/chichester
Pitches For ▲ ⌂ ⌂ **Total** 58
Acreage 3 **Open** 06-Feb **to** 16-Nov
Access Good **Site** Level
Nearest Bus Stop (Miles) outside
500 yards through a footpath to the beach. Ideal touring, well placed for visiting the Sussex Downs and south coast resorts. Close to the City of Portsmouth. BTB 3 Star Graded and AA 3 Pennants. Non members welcome. You can also call us on 0845 130 7633.
Facilities ⌂ ⌂ ⌂ ⌂ ⌂ ⌂ ⌂ ⌂ ⌂
⌂ ⌂ ⌂ ⌂ ⌂ ⌂ ⌂
Nearest Town Chichester
Directions On the A259 from Chichester, site is on the right past Inlands Road.
⇥ Southbourne

CHICHESTER
Ellscott Park, Sidlesham Lane, Birdham, Chichester, West Sussex, PO20 7QL
Tel: 01243 512003
Email: camping@ellscottpark.co.uk
www.ellscottpark.co.uk
Pitches For ▲ ⌂ ⌂ **Total** 50
Acreage 3 **Open** April **to** Mid Oct
Access Good **Site** Level
Nearest Bus Stop (Miles) ¼
The famous West Wittering beach. 1½ miles from Chichester Harbour for yachting and boating. Ideal site for walking, cycling and sight-seeing.
Facilities ⌂ ⌂ ⌂ ⌂ ⌂ ⌂ ⌂
⌂ ⌂ ⌂ ⌂ ⌂ ⌂ ⌂
Nearest Town Chichester
Directions From the A27 Chichester by-pass turn south onto the A286 towards Witterings. Travel for approx. 4 miles then turn left towards Butterfly Farm, site is 500 metres on the right.
⇥ Chichester

CHICHESTER
Red House Farm, Earnley, Chichester, West Sussex, PO20 7JG
Tel: 01243 512959
Email: bookings@rhfcamping.co.uk
www.rhfcamping.co.uk
Pitches For ▲ ⌂ ⌂ **Total** 50
Acreage 4½ **Open** Easter **to** Oct
Access Good **Site** Level
Nearest Bus Stop (Miles) ¼
Flat and open site on a working farm in a country area. 1 mile from the village and beach. No all male or female groups permitted.
Facilities ⌂ ⌂ ⌂ ⌂ ⌂ ⌂ ⌂ ⌂ ⌂ ⌂
Nearest Town Bracklesham Bay
Directions From Chichester take the A286 south to Witterings, after 5 miles turn left onto the B2198 opposite the garage to Bracklesham Bay. After 1 mile on sharp right hand bend turn left to Earnley, site is 200 yards on the left.
⇥ Chichester

CHICHESTER
Stubcroft Farm Campsite, Stubcroft Lane, East Wittering, Chichester, West Sussex, PO20 8PJ
Tel: 01243 671469
Email: mail@stubcroft.com
www.stubcroft.com
Pitches For ▲ ⌂ ⌂ ⌂ **Total** 50

Acreage 5 **Open** All Year
Access Good **Site** Level
Nearest Bus Stop (Miles) ¼
Secluded site on a working sheep farm. Within walking distance of the South Coasts best beaches and Chichester Harbour. Many attractions within a 15-20 minute drive.
Facilities ⌂ ⌂ ⌂ ⌂ ⌂ ⌂
⌂ ⌂ ⌂ ⌂ ⌂ ⌂
Nearest Town Chichester/The Witterings
Directions From the A27 Chichester by-pass, take the A286 south for The Witterings. After 3-4 miles at the mini roundabout by the Total Garage fork left onto the B2198. ½ a mile past the Bell Pub turn right into Tile Barn Lane, after the S bend go 200 yards over 2 speed humps and turn first left, site is ½ a mile on the right hand side.
⇥ Chichester

GRAFFHAM
Graffham Camping & Caravanning Club Site, Great Bury, Graffham, Petworth, West Sussex, GU28 0QF
Tel: 01798 867476
Email: graffham.site@thefriendlyclub.co.uk
www.campingandcaravanningclub.co.uk/graffham
Pitches For ▲ ⌂ ⌂ **Total** 90
Open Apr **to** 03-Nov
Site Sloping
Set in 20 acres of woodland with many walks. Gas BBQs only. BTB 4 Star Graded and AA 3 Pennants. Non members welcome. You can also call us on 0845 130 7633.
Facilities ⌂ ⌂ ⌂ ⌂ ⌂ ⌂ ⌂ ⌂ ⌂ ⌂
⌂ ⌂ ⌂ ⌂ ⌂ ⌂ ⌂ ⌂
Directions From Petworth take the A285, pass Badgers Pub on the left and the BP Garage on the right, take the next right turn signposted Selham Graffham (with brown camping sign), follow signs to site. From Chichester take the A285 through Duncton and turn left signposted Selham Graffham (with brown camping sign).
⇥ Chichester

HENFIELD
Farmhouse Caravan & Camping Site, Tottington Drive, Small Dole, Henfield, West Sussex, BN5 9XZ
Tel: 01273 493157
Pitches For ▲ ⌂ ⌂ **Total** 70
Acreage 4 **Open** Mar **to** Nov
Access Good **Site** Level
Nearest Bus Stop (Miles) ¼
Small farm site within the South Downs National Park. Beach 5 miles, Brighton and Worthing 10 miles. Sorry no vans or pickups.
Facilities ⌂ ⌂ ⌂ ⌂ ⌂ ⌂ ⌂ ⌂ ⌂
Nearest Town Brighton
Directions Turn first left off A2037 (Henfield/Upperbeeding). After Small Dole sign into Tottington Drive, farm at end.
⇥ Shoreham

HORSHAM
Honeybridge Park, Honeybridge Lane, Dial Post, Nr Horsham, West Sussex, RH13 8NX
Tel: 01403 710923
Email: enquiries@honeybridgepark.co.uk
www.honeybridgepark.co.uk
Pitches For ▲ ⌂ ⌂ **Total** 200
Acreage 15 **Open** All Year
Access Good **Site** Level
Nearest Bus Stop (Miles) ¼

Delightfully situated within an Area of Outstanding Natural Beauty. A rural retreat with a relaxed atmosphere providing spacious touring and camping pitches, heated amenity blocks, licensed shop and play area. Ideal touring base, convenient for the coast, London and theme parks. Luxury lodges and static caravans for sale.
Facilities ⌂ ⌂ ⌂ ⌂ ⌂ ⌂ ⌂ ⌂ ⌂ ⌂ ⌂
⌂ ⌂ ⌂ ⌂ ⌂ ⌂ ⌂ ⌂ ⌂ ⌂ ⌂ ⌂
Nearest Town Worthing
Directions 10 miles south of Horsham on the A24, turn at Old Barn Nurseries.
⇥ Horsham

HORSHAM
Sumners Ponds Fishery & Campsite, Chapel Road, Barns Green, Horsham, West Sussex, RH13 0PR
Tel: 01403 732539
Email: bookings@sumnersponds.co.uk
www.sumnersponds.co.uk
Pitches For ▲ ⌂ ⌂ **Total** 86
Acreage 40 **Open** All Year
Access Good **Site** Level
Nearest Bus Stop (Miles) ¼
Extensive fishing on four lakes. Woodland paths and pasture. Lakeside cafe, village pub and shop within a 5 minute walk.
Facilities ⌂ ⌂ ⌂ ⌂ ⌂ ⌂ ⌂ ⌂ ⌂
⌂ ⌂ ⌂ ⌂ ⌂ ⌂ ⌂ ⌂ ⌂
Nearest Town Horsham
Directions Take the A264 from Horsham towards Billingshurst and Bognor. Pass the Toyota garage on the right and turn left on the humpback bridge. Follow road to Barns Green and pass the pub and shop then look for signs on the right.
⇥ Horsham

LITTLEHAMPTON
Daisyfields Touring Park, Cornfield Close, Worthing Road, Littlehampton, West Sussex, BN17 6LD
Tel: 01903 714240
Email: daisyfields@bt.connect.com
www.camping-caravaning.co.uk
Pitches For ▲ ⌂ ⌂ **Total** 80
Acreage 6½ **Open** All Year
Access Good **Site** Level
Nearest Bus Stop (Miles) ¼
1½ miles to a sandy beach. 1 mile to the River Arun. Open all year dependant on the weather. Pets welcome with camper vans and caravans only. No commercial vehicles.
Facilities ⌂ ⌂ ⌂ ⌂ ⌂ ⌂ ⌂ ⌂ ⌂ ⌂ ⌂
Directions The site is situated on the A259 Worthing to Bognor Regis, between two Body Shop roundabouts. 3 miles from Arundel.
⇥ Littlehampton

LITTLEHAMPTON
Littlehampton Caravan Club Site, Mill Lane, Wick, Littlehampton, West Sussex, BN17 7PH
Tel: 01903 716176
www.caravanclub.co.uk
Pitches For ⌂ ⌂ **Total** 116
Acreage 6½ **Open** Mar **to** Jan
Access Good **Site** Lev/Slope
Nearest Bus Stop (Miles) ¼
Beach/coast,fishing,golf and water sports all within 5 miles. Arundel Castle,Chichester Cathedral, South Downs National Park.
Facilities ⌂ ⌂ ⌂ ⌂ ⌂ ⌂ ⌂ ⌂ ⌂
⌂ ⌂ ⌂ ⌂ ⌂ ⌂ ⌂
Nearest Town Littlehampton
Directions From the A27 take the A284 signposted Littlehampton. Site entrance is on the left of Mill Lane just past the village of Lyminster.
⇥ Littlehampton

SELSEY

Warner Farm Touring Park, Warner Lane, Selsey, West Sussex, PO20 9EL
Tel: 01243 604499
Email: touring@bunnleisure.co.uk
www.warnerfarm.co.uk
Pitches For Å ⊕ ♠ **Total** 250
Acreage 12½ **Open Mar to** 04-Jan
Access Good **Site** Level
Nearest Bus Stop (Miles) ¼
Full use of 3 clubhouses located on our caravan parks
Facilities ⌂ ⌁ ⊡ ⊞⌖⌔ ⊙⌐ ⚊ ▣ ⛟
⚄ ⍾ ⚅ ⚇ ✕ ⍜ ⍀ ⚐ ⤳ ⚒ ✦⤼⊡⊟ ⚡
⬚

Nearest Town Selsey
Directions A27 west join B2145 signs Selsey. At Selsey go 2 miniroundabouts turn left into School Lane, right into Paddock Lane finally left into Warner Lane.
⇌ Chichester

SLINDON

Slindon Camping & Caravanning Club Site, Slindon Park, Nr Arundel, West Sussex, BN18 0RG
Tel: 01243 814387
Email: slindon.site@thefriendlyclub.co.uk
www.campingandcaravanningclub.co.uk/slindon
Pitches For Å ⊕ ♠ **Total** 40
Acreage 2 **Open** Apr **to** 05-Oct
Access Good **Site** Lev/Slope
Nearest Bus Stop (Miles) ½
Within the National Trust property of Slindon Park. 6 miles from Goodwood Racecourse. BTB 2 Star Graded and AA 1 Pennant. Non members welcome. You can also call us on 0845 130 7633.
Facilities ⌁ ⛟ ⚄ ⊙ ⚅⤼▣⊟ ⚡
Nearest Town Chichester
Directions From the A27 Chichester to Fontwell turn, turn left into Brittons Lane (second turn left after the B2233 on the right), then take the second turn right to Slindon. Site is on this road.
⇌ Barnham

WEST WITTERING

Nunnington Farm Camping Site,
Nunnington Farm, West Wittering, West Sussex, PO20 8LZ
Tel: 01243 514013 No Booking
Email: enquiries@nunningtonfarm.com
www.camping-in-sussex.com
Pitches For Å ⊕ ♠ **Total** 125
Acreage 4½ **Open** Easter **to** Mid Oct
Access Good **Site** Level
Nearest Bus Stop (Miles) Outside
Near the beach.
Facilities ⌂ ⌁ ⊞⌖⌔ ⊙⌐ ⚊ ▣ ⛟

⚄ ⚇ ⊙ ⍾ ♠⤼⊡
Nearest Town Chichester
Directions 7 miles south of Chichester on the A286 B2179. 200yds before village on left, look for signs.
⇌ Chichester

WEST WITTERING

Wicks Farm Camping Park, Redlands Lane, West Wittering, Chichester, West Sussex, PO20 8QE
Tel: 01243 513116
www.wicksfarm.co.uk
Pitches For Å ⊕ ♠¦ **Total** 40
Acreage 2¼ **Open** Apr **to** Nov
Access Good **Site** Level
Nearest Bus Stop (Miles) ¼
Facilities ⌁ ⊡ ⊞⌖⌔ ⊙⌐ ⚊ ▣ ⛟
⚄ ⍾ ⊙ ⚇ ⍾⤼⊡ ⚐
Nearest Town West Wittering/Chichester
Directions From Chichester take the A286 for Birdham, then take the B2179 for West Wittering.
⇌ Chichester

WORTHING

Northbrook Farm Caravan Club Site,
Titnore Way, Worthing, West Sussex, BN13 3RT
Tel: 01903 502962
www.caravanclub.co.uk
Pitches For ⊕ ♠ **Total** 79
Acreage 12½ **Open** Mar **to** Nov
Access Good **Site** Level
Nearest Bus Stop (Miles) ½
Set in open countryside yet only 2 miles from the coast. West Worthing Tennis Club adjacent for tennis, squash, restaurant and bar. Near to Arundel Castle. NB: Own sanitation required. Non members welcome. Booking essential.
Facilities ⌁ ⊞⌖⚊
⚄ ⍾ ⊙ ⍾⤼⊡⊟ ⚐
Nearest Town Worthing
Directions From north on A24, in Findon at r/about junc with A280 t rt sp Chichester. After 4 miles at r/about take 2nd exit to r/about on far side of bridge over A27 t lt (first exit sp Ferring). After ¾ mile at brown sign t lt into Titnore Way, site is 120 yds on lt.
⇌ Worthing

WARWICKSHIRE

LEAMINGTON SPA

Lairhillock Touring Park Sandy Lane, Marton, Rugby, Warwicks, CV23 9TP
Tel: 01926 632119
Email: lairhillockpark@aol.com
www.lairhillocktouringpark.co.uk
Pitches For Å ⊕ ♠ ♠¦ **Total** 38

Acreage 2½ **Open** All year
Access Good **Site** Level
Nearest Bus Stop (Miles) ½
Close to Warwick Castle, Stratford on Avon snd Coventry Cathedral
Facilities ⌖ ⌁ ⊡ ⊞⌖⌔ ⊙⌐ ⚊ ▣ ⛟
⤼⊡ ⊟ ⚅A
Nearest Town Leamington Spa
Directions B4453 to Princethorpe turn right onto A423 through Marton follow brown tourist signs to site.
⇌ Leamington Spa

LONG COMPTON

Long Compton Camping, Mill Farm, Barton Road, Long Compton, ShipstononStour, Warwickshire, CV36 5NZ
Tel: 01608 684663
Pitches For Å ⊕ ♠ **Total** 11
Acreage 3 **Open** Apr **to** Oct
Access Good **Site** Level
Nearest Bus Stop (Miles) ½
On the fringe of the Cotswolds.
Facilities ⊞⌖⊙⌐ ⚄⚅
Nearest Town Moreton-in-Marsh
Directions Turn off A3400 in Long Compton for Barton-on-the-Heath. Site on right in ½ a mile.
⇌ Moreton-in-Marsh

RUGBY

Lodge Farm, Bilton Lane, Long Lawford, Rugby, Warwickshire, CV23 9DU
Tel: 01788 560193
Email: lodgefarm.com
www.lodgefarm.com
Pitches For Å ⊕ ♠ **Total** 15
Acreage 3 **Open** Easter **to** Oct
Access Good **Site** Level
Very quiet get away site.
Facilities ⌁ ⊞⌖⌔ ⊙⌐ ⊙ ⚅ ⊙⤼⊟ ⤳
⬚
Nearest Town Rugby
Directions Take the A428 from Rugby towards Coventry. 2½ miles to Long Lawford turn left by Sheaf & Sickle pub, site is 400 yards on the left.
⇌ Rugby

STRATFORD-UPON-AVON

Island Meadow Caravan Park, Aston Cantlow, Warwickshire, B95 6JP
Tel: 01789 488273
Email:
holiday@islandmeadowcaravanpark.co.uk
www.islandmeadowcaravanpark.co.uk
Pitches For Å ⊕ ♠ **Total** 34
Acreage 3 **Open** Mar **to** Oct
Access Good **Site** Level
Nearest Bus Stop (Miles) ¼

Small, quiet island, adjacent to a picturesque village. Cafe/Restaurant and childrens play area nearby. Ideal centre for Shakespeare Country.
Facilities ⚫ ✦ 🖽 ⛁ ⌒ ⊙ ⟍ ⬛ ▣ ☎
⛟ 🛇 ⬛ ✿⤆⬛ ▣ ✔
Nearest Town Stratford-upon-Avon
Directions From the A46 or the A3400 follow signs for Aston Cantlow Village. Park is ½ mile west of the village in Mill Lane.
⛺ Wilmcote

STUDLEY

Outhill Caravan Park, Outhill, Studley, Warwickshire, B80 7DY
Tel: 01527 852160
Pitches For 🚐 🚍 **Total** 15
Acreage 11 **Open** Apr **to** Oct
Access Good **Site** Level
Peace and quiet. No electricity and no hot water. Advance booking is essential. No tents.
Facilities ⛁⤆☀
Nearest Town Henley-in-Arden
Directions From A435 (Birmingham to Evesham road) turn towards Henley-in-Arden on A4189. Take third turning to the right (approx 1¼ miles), check in at Outhill Farm (first on left).

WARWICK

Warwick Racecourse Caravan Club Site, Hampton Street, Warwick, Warwickshire, CV34 6HN
Tel: 01926 495448
www.caravanclub.co.uk
Pitches For 🚐 🚍 **Total** 55
Acreage 3¼ **Open** Mar **to** Jan
Access Good **Site** Level
Nearest Bus Stop (Miles) ¼
Grass and tarmac site in the racecourse enclosure. Very short walk to the centre of Warwick and its castle. Only 8 miles from Stratford-upon-Avon. Non members welcome. Booking essential.
Facilities ⚫ ✦ 🖽 ⛁ ⌒ ▣ ☎
⛟ ⛟ 🛇 ⤆⬛ ▣
Nearest Town Warwick
Directions Leave the M40 at junction 15 and take the A429 sp Warwick. After 1 mile at brown camping sign turn left into Shakespeares Avenue, at T-junction turn right onto the B4095, site is ½ mile on the left.
⛺ Warwick

WOLVEY

Wolvey Caravan & Camping Park, Villa Farm, Wolvey, Nr Hinckley, Leicestershire, LE10 3HF
Tel: 01455 220493/220630
www.wolveycaravanpark.itgo.com
Pitches For ⛺ 🚐 🚍 🚊 **Total** 110
Acreage 7 **Open** All Year
Access Good **Site** Level
Nearest Bus Stop (Miles) Outside

A quiet site, ideally situated to explore the many places of interest in the Midlands. Licensed Shop.
Facilities ⚫ ✦ 🖽 ⛁ ⌒ ⊙ ⟍ ⬛ ▣ ☎
⛟ 🛇 ⬛ ⤆⬛ ▣ ✔ ✦
Nearest Town Hinckley
Directions Leave the M6 at junction 2 and take the B4065, follow signs for Wolvey and camping signs. Or leave the M69 at junction 1 and take the B4065, follow signs for Wolvey and camping signs.
⛺ Hinckley

WEST MIDLANDS

HALESOWEN

Clent Hills Camping & Caravanning Club Site, Fieldhouse Lane, Romsley, Halesowen, West Midlands, B62 0NH
Tel: 01562 710015
Email: clent.site@thefriendlyclub.co.uk
www.campingandcaravanning.co.uk/clenthills
Pitches For ⛺ 🚐 🚍 **Total** 95
Acreage 7½ **Open** Apr **to** 03-Nov
Access Good **Site** Sloping
Nearest Bus Stop (Miles) ½
In the heart of the West Midlands. Ideal for walkers and cyclists. BTB 4 Star Graded and AA 3 Pennants. Non members welcome. You can also call us on 0845 130 7633.
Facilities ⚫ ✦ 🖽 ⛁ ⌒ ⊙ ⟍ ⬛ ▣ ☎
⛟ 🛇 ⬛ ⤆⬛ ▣ ☏ 🛜
Nearest Town Halesowen
Directions Travelling northwest on the M5, leave at junction 3 onto the A456. Then take the B4551 to Romsley, turn right at Sun Hotel, take the 5th left turn then the next left and the site is 330 yards on the left hand side.
⛺ Old Hill

MERIDEN

Somers Wood Caravan Park, Somers Road, Meriden, North Warwickshire, CV7 7PL
Tel: 01676 522978
Email: enquiries@somerswood.co.uk
www.somerswood.co.uk
Pitches For 🚐 🚍 🚊 🚊 **Total** 48
Acreage 4 **Open** All Year
Access Good **Site** Level
Nearest Bus Stop (Miles) ½
ADULTS ONLY SITE. Adjacent to a golf course with clubhouse. Approx. 3 miles from the N.E.C. Birmingham. Fishing adjacent.
Facilities ⚫ ✦ 🖽 ⛁ ⌒ ⊙ ⟍ ▣ ☎
⛟ 🛇 ⬛ ✿⤆⬛ ▣ ⬛A☏ 🛜
Nearest Town Solihull
Directions Leave the M42 at junction 6, take the A45 to Coventry. Immediately on the left pick up signs for the A452 Leamington. Down to roundabout and turn right onto the A452 signed Leamington/Warwick, at the next roundabout turn left into Hampton Lane. Site is ½ mile on the left hand side.
⛺ Hampton-in-Arden

SUTTON COLDFIELD

Kingsbury Water Park Camping & Caravanning Club Site, Bodymoor Heath Lane, Sutton Coldfield, West Midlands, B76 0DY
Tel: 01827 874101
Email:
kingsbury.site@thefriendlyclub.co.uk
www.campingandcaravanning.co.uk/kingsburywaterpark
Pitches For ⛺ 🚐 🚍 **Total** 150
Open All Year
Site Level
Nearest Bus Stop (Miles) 1
Surrounding the site are the 600 acres of Kingsbury Water Park. BTB 5 Star Graded, AA 4 Pennants and Loo of the Year Award. Non members welcome. You can also call us on 0845 130 7633.
Facilities ⚫ ✦ 🖽 ⛁ ⌒ ⊙ ⟍ ⬛ ▣ ☎
⛟ 🛇 ⬛ ⤆⬛ ▣ ☏
Directions Leave the M42 at junction 9 and take the B4097 towards Kingsbury. At the roundabout turn left and continue past the main entrance to the water park, go over the motorway and turn next right, follow lane for ½ mile to the site.
⛺ Tamworth

SUTTON COLDFIELD

Marston Caravan & Camping Park, Kingsbury Road, Marston, Near Sutton Coldfield, West Midlands, B76 0DP
Tel: 01675 470902
www.marstoncaravanandcamping.co.uk
Pitches For ⛺ 🚐 🚍 **Total** 125
Acreage 10 **Open** All Year
Access Good **Site** Level
Nearest Bus Stop (Miles) Outside
Facilities ⚫ ✦ 🖽 ⛁ ⌒ ⊙ ⟍ ⬛ ▣ ☎
⛟ ⛟ 🛇 ⬛ ⤆⬛
Nearest Town Sutton Coldfield
Directions 2 miles approx
⛺ Sutton Coldfield

WILTSHIRE

CALNE

Blackland Lakes, Blackland Leisure Ltd, Stockley Lane, Calne, Wiltshire, SN11 0NQ
Tel: 01249 810943
Email: enquiries@blacklandlakes.co.uk
www.blacklandlakes.co.uk
Pitches For ⛺ 🚐 🚍 **Total** 180
Acreage 15 **Open** All Year
Access Good **Site** Level
Nearest Bus Stop (Miles) Outside
A natural, interesting, scenic and secure site with three lakes for super coarse fishing. 1 mile perimeter trail for dogs, walking and cycling. Winter bookings must be prepaid.
Facilities ⚫ ✦ 🖽 ⛁ ⌒ ⊙ ⟍ ⬛ ▣ ☎
⛟ 🛇 ⬛ ⤆⬛ ▣ ✔ ☀ ☏
Nearest Town Calne
Directions Signposted from the A4 east of Calne.
⛺ Chippenham

CHIPPENHAM

Piccadilly Caravan Park, Folly Lane West, Lacock, Chippenham, Wiltshire, SN15 2LP
Tel: 01249 730260
Email: piccadillylacock@aol.com
Pitches For ▲ ⊞ ⊞ **Total** 43
Acreage 2½ **Open** Apr to Oct
Access Good **Site** Level
Nearest Bus Stop (Miles) ¼
Close to the National Trust village of Lacock, Piccadilly is a small, family run, beautifully maintained Park.
Facilities ⨍ ⊞ ⊞ ⌐ ⌐ ⊙ ⌐ ◢ ⌾ ☎
⊞ ⊙ ⊗ ⋀ ✿ ⊬ ⊟ ⌘
Nearest Town Chippenham
Directions Turn right off the A350 Chippenham to Melksham road, 5 miles south of Chippenham, close to Lacock. Signposted to Gastard (with caravan symbol).
⇌ Chippenham

CHIPPENHAM

Plough Lane Caravan Site, Kington Langley, Chippenham, Wiltshire, SN15 5PS
Tel: 01249 750146
Email: enquiries@ploughlane.co.uk
www.ploughlane.co.uk
Pitches For ⊞ ⊞ **Total** 50
Acreage 4 **Open** Easter to Oct
Access Good **Site** Level
Nearest Bus Stop (Miles) Outside
ADULTS ONLY SITE. Pre booking only.
Facilities ᎣᎣ ⨍ ⊟ ⊞ ⊞ ⌐ ⌐ ⊙ ⌐ ◢ ⌾ ☎
⊞ ⊗ ⊬ ⊟ ⋀ ⌘
Nearest Town Chippenham
Directions Well signposted from the A350 north of Chippenham.
⇌ Chippenham

DEVIZES

Devizes Camping & Caravanning Club Site, Spout Lane, Nr Seend, Melksham, Wiltshire, SN12 6RN
Tel: 01380 828839
Email: devizes.site@thefriendlyclub.co.uk
www.campingandcaravanningclub.co.uk/devizes
Pitches For ▲ ⊞ ⊞ **Total** 90
Open All Year
Site Level
Nearest Bus Stop (Miles) ¼
Bordering the Kennett & Avon Canal. Non members welcome. You can also call us on 0845 130 7633.
Facilities ᎣᎣ ⨍ ⊞ ⊞ ⌐ ⌐ ⊙ ⌐ ◢ ⌾ ☎
⊙ ⊗ ⋀ ✿ ⊬ ⊟ ⌘ ⌘
Directions Take the A365 from Melksham, turn right down the lane beside Three Magpies Public House, site is on the right.
⇌ Melksham

DEVIZES

The Bell Camping, Touring & Motorcaravan Site, Andover Road, Lydeway, Devizes, Wiltshire, SN10 3PS
Tel: 01380 840230
www.thebellcampsite.org.uk
Pitches For ▲ ⊞ ⊞ ⊞ ⋜ **Total** 26
Acreage 5 **Open** Apr to Oct
Access Good **Site** Level
Nearest Bus Stop (Miles) Outside
Ideal for Stonehenge, Avebury, Bath, Longleat Safari Park, National Trusts Lacock and Bowood.
Also mobile phone 07763 344388
Facilities ⨍ ⊞ ⌐ ⌐ ⊙ ⌐ ◢ ⌾ ⊞ ⋊ ⊟ ⊟
Nearest Town Devizes
Directions 5 miles east of Devizes on the A342 Andover road.
⇌ Pewsey

MARLBOROUGH

Hillview Park, Hillview Park House, Sunnyhill Lane, Oare, Marlborough, Wiltshire, SN8 4JG
Tel: 01672 563151
Pitches For ▲ ⊞ **Total** 10
Open Apr to Sept
Access Good **Site** Level
Nearest Bus Stop (Miles) Outside
½ a mile from Kennet & Avon Canal. Cycleway nearby. No hard standings, caravans and motor vans over 20 feet cannot be accommodated. Sorry, no children over the age of 5.
Facilities ⨍ ⊞ ⌐ ⌐ ⊙ ⌐ ◢ ☎ ⊬ ⊟
Nearest Town Marlborough
Directions 5 miles south of Marlborough on the A345 junction.
⇌ Pewsey

MARLBOROUGH

Postern Hill Caravan & Camping Site, Postern Hill, Marlborough, Wiltshire, SN8 4ND
Tel: 01672 515195
www.campingintheforest.co.uk
Pitches For ▲ ⊞ ⊞ ⊞ ⋜ **Total** 170
Open All Year
Access Good **Site** Level
Nearest Bus Stop (Miles) Outside
Facilities ⨍ ⊞ ⌐ ⊙ ⌐ ◢ ⊙ ⊗ ⊬ ⊟ ⌘ ⋙
⚲
Nearest Town Marlborough
Directions On A345
⇌ Bedwyn

NETHERHAMPTON

Coombe Caravan Park, Coombe Nurseries, Race Plain, Netherhampton, Salisbury, Wiltshire, SP2 8PN
Tel: 01722 328451
Email: enquiries@coombecaravanpark.co.uk
www.coombecaravanpark.co.uk
Pitches For ▲ ⊞ ⊞ **Total** 60
Acreage 3 **Open** All year
Access Good **Site** Level
Adjacent to racecourse (flat racing), ideal touring, lovely views. Dish washing area and 4 static caravans.
Facilities ⨍ ⊞ ⊞ ⌐ ⌐ ⊙ ⌐ ◢ ⌾ ☎
⊞ ⋀ ⊬ ⊟
Nearest Town Salisbury
Directions Take A36-A30 Salisbury - Wilton road, turn off at traffic lights onto A3094 Netherhampton - Stratford Tony road, cross on bend following Stratford Tony road, 2nd left behind racecourse, site on right, signposted.
⇌ Salisbury

ORCHESTON

Stonehenge Touring Park, Orcheston, Nr Shrewton, Wiltshire, SP3 4SH
Tel: 01980 620304
Email: stay@stonehengetouringpark.com
www.stonehengetouringpark.com
Pitches For ▲ ⊞ ⊞ **Total** 30
Acreage 2 **Open** All Year
Access Good **Site** Level
Nearest Bus Stop (Miles) ¼
5 miles from Stonehenge and Salisbury Plain. Within easy reach Bath and the New Forest. ETB 3 Star Graded and AA 3 Pennants.
Facilities ⨍ ⊞ ⌐ ⌐ ⊙ ⌐ ◢ ⌾ ☎
⊞ ⊙ ⊗ ⋀ ⊬ ⊟ ⌘ ⌘
Nearest Town Salisbury
Directions On the A360, 11 miles from both Salisbury and Devizes.
⇌ Salisbury

SALISBURY

Green Hill Farm Caravan & Camping Park, Greenhill Farm, New Road, Landford, Salisbury, Wiltshire, SP5 2AZ
Tel: 01794 324117
Email: info@greenhillholidays.co.uk
www.greenhillholidays.co.uk
Pitches For ▲ ⊞ ⊞ ⊞ ⋜ **Total** 160
Acreage 15 **Open** All Year
Access Good **Site** Level
Nearest Bus Stop (Miles) Outside
On the edge of the New Forest, you can walk into the forest directly from the Park. Brand new toilet facilities opened in 2012
Facilities ⨍ ⊞ ⊞ ⌐ ⌐ ⊙ ⌐ ◢ ⌾ ☎
⊞ ⊙ ⊗ ⋀ ✿ ⊬ ⊟ ⌘ ⋙
Nearest Town Romsey/Salisbury
Directions Leave the M27 at junction 2 and take the A36 towards Salisbury. In Plaitford look out for the BP garage, turn next left into New Road.
⇌ Romsey

SALISBURY

Salisbury Camping & Caravanning Club Site, Hudsons Field, Castle Road, Salisbury, Wiltshire, SP1 3SA
Tel: 01722 320713
Email: Salisbury.site@thefriendlyclub.co.uk
www.campingandcaravanningclub.co.uk/salisbury
Pitches For ▲ ⊞ ⊞ **Total** 150
Acreage 4½ **Open** Apr to 03-Nov
Access Good **Site** Lev/Slope
Nearest Bus Stop (Miles) ¼
1½ miles from Salisbury, plenty to do in the area. BTB 4 Star Graded and AA 4 Pennants. Non members welcome. You can also call us on 0845 130 7633.
Facilities ᎣᎣ ⨍ ⊞ ⊞ ⌐ ⌐ ⊙ ⌐ ◢ ⌾ ☎
⊞ ⊙ ⊗ ✿ ⊬ ⊟ ⌘ ⌘
Nearest Town Salisbury
Directions 1½ miles from Salisbury and 7 miles from Amesbury on the A345. Hudsons Field is a large open field next to Old Sarum.
⇌ Salisbury

SALISBURY

Summerlands Caravan Park, Rockbourne Road, Coombe Bissett, Salisbury, Wiltshire, SP5 4LP
Tel: 01722 718259
Email: enquiries@summerlandscaravanpark.co.uk
www.summerlandscaravanpark.co.uk
Pitches For ▲ ⊞ ⊞ **Total** 26
Open Apr to Oct
Access Good **Site** Level
Nearest Bus Stop (Miles) 1
Off the beaten track in an area of outstanding natural beauty. Rally field available.
Facilities ᎣᎣ ⨍ ⊞ ⌐ ⌐ ⊙ ⌐ ◢ ☎ ⊞ ⊬ ⊟
Nearest Town Salisbury
Directions A354 from Salisbury to Blandford (6 miles) fork left to Rockbourne,300m left onto Byway ¾ to site. (Byway a little bumpy)
⇌ Salisbury

TROWBRIDGE

Stowford Manor Farm, Stowford, Wingfield, Trowbridge, Wiltshire, BA14 9LH
Tel: 01225 752253
Email: stowford1@supanet.com
www.stowfordmanorfarm.co.uk
Pitches For ▲ ⊞ ⊞ **Total** 20
Acreage 1½ **Open** Easter to Oct
Access Good **Site** Level
Alongside a river for fishing and swimming. Next to a Medieval farm.
Facilities ⨍ ⊞ ⌐ ⌐ ⊙ ⌐ ◢ ☎ ⊬ ⊟ ⫽
Nearest Town Trowbridge

Directions From Trowbridge take the A366 west towards Radstock for 3 miles, farm is on the left hand side.
🚶 Trowbridge

WARMINSTER
Longleat Caravan Club Site, Warminster, Wiltshire, BA12 7NL
Tel: 01985 844663
www.caravanclub.co.uk
Pitches For 🚐 🚙 **Total** 165
Acreage 14 **Open** Mar to Nov
Access Good **Site** Level
The Caravan Clubs most beautiful parkland site, set in the heart of the Longleat Estate. Miles of woodland walks. Just a short walk from Longleat House & Safari Park with its maze and childrens adventure castle. Non members welcome. Booking essential.
Facilities ♿ ♒ 🅿 📶 ☕ 🍴 ⊙ 🛒 💷 🔌 🌊
🕎 🅾 🏪 📫 🔌 🍴 🛢 🛜
Nearest Town Warminster
Directions From the A36 Warminster bypass take the A362 sp Frome. At roundabout turn left into Longleat Estate entrance and follow Longleat House route through the toll booths for 2 miles, then Caravan Club pennant signs for 1 mile.

WESTBURY
Brokerswood Country Park,
Brokerswood, Nr Westbury, Wiltshire, BA13 4EH
Tel: 01373 822238
Email:
info@brokerswoodcountrypark.co.uk
www.brokerswoodcountrypark.co.uk
Pitches For 🏕 🚐 🚙 **Total** 65
Acreage 5 **Open** Apr to Oct
Access Good **Site** Level
Site adjoins an 80 acre area of forest open to the public. Woodland walks, narrow gauge railway, adventure playground and fishing lake.
Facilities ♿ ♒ 🅿 📶 🅿 📶 ⊙ 🛒 💷 🔌 🌊
🕎 🅾 🍴 ✗ 📶 🏪 📫 🔌 🌊
Nearest Town Westbury/Trowbridge
Directions At Yarnbrook on the A350, turn onto the A363 and follow road. At The Rising Sun Pub turn left, then turn left off the right hand bend before Southwick and continue for 2½ miles.
🚶 Westbury

WORCESTERSHIRE
BEWDLEY
Bank Farm Holiday Parks Ltd., Bank Farm, Arley, Bewdley, Worcestershire, DY12 3ND
Tel: 01299 401277
Email: bankfarm@tinyworld.co.uk
www.bankfarmholidaypark.co.uk
Pitches For 🚐 🚙 **Total** 5
Open All Year
Access Good **Site** Level
Alongside a river in the Wyre Forest with river and valley views. 9 hole pitch n putt on site. Near the River Severn and the Severn Valley Railway Station at Arley. Additional seasonal pitches available on our sister site.
Facilities ♒ 🅿 📶 🅿 ⊙ 🔌 💷 🛜
🕎 🅾 🏪 📫 🔌 🔌
Nearest Town Bewdley
Directions Just off the B4194 3½ miles outside Bewdley, near Kidderminster.
🚶 Kidderminster

EVESHAM
Evesham Vale Caravan Park, Yessell Farm, Boston Lane, Charlton, Nr Evesham, Worcestershire, WR11 2RD
Tel: 01386 860377
Pitches For 🏕 🚐 🚙 **Total** 40
Acreage 20 **Open** Apr to Oct
Access Good **Site** Level
Nearest Bus Stop (Miles) Outside
On the Blossom Trail route, near a river for fishing. Central for the Cotswolds, Stratford and Worcester.
Facilities ♒ 🅿 📶 🅿 🔌 ⊙ 🔌 💷
🕎 🅾 🏪 📫 🔌 🌊
Nearest Town Evesham
Directions From Evesham take the A44, after approx 1½ miles turn right for Charlton. Park is on the left hand side after approx. ¾ miles.
🚶 Evesham

EVESHAM
Ranch Caravan Park, Station Road, Honeybourne, Nr Evesham, Worcestershire, WR11 7PR
Tel: 01386 830744
Email: enquiries@ranch.co.uk
www.ranch.co.uk
Pitches For 🚐 🚙 **Total** 120
Acreage 48 **Open** Mar to Nov
Access Good **Site** Level
Nearest Bus Stop (Miles) ¼
Situated in meadow land in Vale of Evesham on north edge of Cotswolds. Meals available in licensed club.
Facilities ♿ ♒ 🅿 🅿 📶 🅿 ⊙ 🔌 💷 🔌 🖥
🕎 🅾 🏪 🍴 ✗ 📶 🏪 📫 🔌 🌊
Nearest Town Evesham
Directions From Evesham take B4035 to Badsey and Bretforton. Turn left to Honeybourne. At village crossroads take Bidford direction, site on left in 400 yards.
🚶 Honeybourne

GREAT MALVERN
Blackmore Camping & Caravanning Club Site, Blackmore Camp Site, No 2 Hanley Swan, Worcestershire, WR8 0EE
Tel: 01684 310280
Email:
blackmore.site@thefriendlyclub.co.uk
www.campingandcaravanningclub.co.uk/blackmore
Pitches For 🏕 🚐 🚙 **Total** 180
Acreage 17 **Open** All Year
Access Good **Site** Level
Close to the River Severn. Situated in the Malvern Hills, ideal walking country. Close to the market towns of Ledbury, Tewkesbury and Evesham. BTB 5 Star Graded and AA 4 Pennants. Non members welcome. You can also call us on 0845 130 7633.
Facilities ♒ 🅿 🅿 📶 🅿 ⊙ 🔌 💷 🖥 ☕
🕎 🅾 🏪 📶 🔌 📫 🔌 🌊 🌊 🛜
Nearest Town Great Malvern
Directions Take the A38 to Upton-on-Severn, turn north over the river bridge, turn second left then first left signposted Hanley Swan. Site is on the right after 1 mile.
🚶 Malvern

KIDDERMINSTER
Wolverley Camping & Caravanning Club Site, Brown Westhead Park, Wolverley, Nr Kidderminster, Worcestershire, DY10 3PX
Tel: 01562 850909
Email:
wolverley.site@thefriendlyclub.co.uk
www.campingandcaravanningclub.co.uk/wolverley
Pitches For 🏕 🚐 🚙 **Total** 105
Acreage 12 **Open** 14-Mar to 03-Nov

Access Good **Site** Lev/Slope
Nearest Bus Stop (Miles) ¼
A quiet and secluded site with pretty walks along the canal, and some excellent pubs. BTB 3 Star Graded and AA 3 Pennants. Non members welcome. You can also call us on 0845 130 7633.
Facilities ♒ 🅿 🅿 📶 🅿 ⊙ 🔌 💷 🖥 ☕
🕎 🅾 🏪 📶 🏪 📫 🔌 🌊 🛜
Nearest Town Kidderminster
Directions From Kidderminster take the A449 to Wolverhampton, turn left at the traffic lights onto the B4189 signposted Wolverley. Look for brown camping sign and turn right, the site entrance is on the left.
🚶 Kidderminster

MALVERN
Kingsgreen Caravan Park, Berrow, Nr Malvern, Worcestershire, WR13 6AQ
Tel: 01531 650272
Pitches For 🏕 🚐 🚙 **Total** 45
Acreage 3 **Open** Mar to Oct
Access Good **Site** Level
Beautiful walks on the Malvern Hills and Malvern with its famous Elgar Route. Historic Black and White timber towns, Tewkesbury and Upton-on-Severn. BH & HPA Member.
Facilities 🕎 🅾 🅿 🔌 📫 🔌 🌊 🔌
Nearest Town Ledbury/Malvern
Directions From Ledbury take the A417 towards Gloucester. Go over the M50 then take the first turning left to Malvern, we are 1 mile on the right. OR M50 Southbound junction 2, turn left onto the A417, in 1 mile turn left to the Malverns.
🚶 Ledbury/Malvern

SHRAWLEY
Brant Farm Caravan Park, Shrawley, Worcestershire, WR6 6TD
Tel: 01905 621008
Pitches For 🏕 🚐 🚙 **Total** 12
Acreage 1 **Open** Apr to Oct
Access Good **Site** Level
Nearest Bus Stop (Miles) ¼
Quiet walks in scenic woodland. Pub within a 5 minute walk serving real ale and good food.
Facilities ♒ 🅿 🅿 🔌 🔌 💷 🅾 🛢 🌊
Nearest Town Stourport-on-Severn
Directions Take the A449 from Worcester to Holt Heath, then take the B4196 signposted Shrawley. Continue to the Rose & Crown Pub and the Park is 100 yards further on on the left hand side.
🚶 Kidderminster/Worcester

STOURPORT-ON-SEVERN
Lickhill Manor Caravan Park, Lickhill Manor, Stourport-on-Severn, Worcestershire, DY13 8RL
Tel: 01299 871041/877820
Email: excellent@lickhillmanor.co.uk
www.lickhillmanor.co.uk
Pitches For 🏕 🚐 🚙 **Total** 120
Acreage 9 **Open** All Year
Access Good **Site** Level
Nearest Bus Stop (Miles) ¼
Alongside river (fishing rights held). Walks through the unspoilt Wyre Forest. West Midlands Safari Park and Severn Valley Railway nearby.
Facilities ♒ 🅿 🅿 📶 🅿 ⊙ 🔌 💷 🖥 ☕
🕎 🅾 📶 🏪 📫 🔌 🔌 🌊 🛜
Nearest Town Stourport-on-Severn
Directions From Stourport take the B4195 to Bewdley, at traffic lights on the crossroads follow caravan signs, after ½ mile turn right at the sign.
🚶 Kidderminster

STOURPORT-ON-SEVERN

Lincomb Lock Caravan Park, Lincomb Lock, Titton, Stourport-on-Severn, Worcestershire, DY13 9QR
Tel: 01299 823836
Email: lincomb@hillandale.co.uk
www.hillandale.co.uk
Pitches For ▲ ⚏ ⛟ ⚏⛟ **Total** 14
Acreage 1 **Open** Mar **to** 06-Jan
Access Good **Site** Level
Nearest Bus Stop (Miles) ½
ADULTS ONLY. Alongside River Severn. Many local attractions including West Midlands Safari Park, Severn Valley Railway, Riverside Amusements, the ancient Wyre Forest and local museums.
Facilities ⫽ ⌂ ⬭ ⚲ �℮ ☉ ⬱ ⚑
⛽⤚⬚⬛ ✎ A
Nearest Town Stourport-on-Severn
Directions 1 mile from Stourport on the A4025 turn right at park signs. Or from the A449 join the A4025 at Crossway Green, after 1 mile turn left at park signs.
⇻ Kidderminster

WORCESTER

Ketch Caravan Park, Bath Road, Worcester, Worcestershire, WR5 3HW
Tel: 01905 820430
Pitches For ▲ ⚏ ⛟ **Total** 32
Acreage 6½ **Open** Apr **to** Oct
Access Good **Site** Level
Nearest Bus Stop (Miles) ¼
On the River Severn.
Facilities ⫽ ⬭⚲⌔☉⬱⚑ ⛽⬛✖⤚✎
Nearest Town Worcester
Directions Leave the M5 at junction 7 and follow signs for Malvern until you come to the A38. Turn for Worcester and park entrance is approx. 100 yards on the left.
⇻ Worcester

WYTHALL

Chapel Lane Caravan Club Site, Chapel Lane, Wythall, Birmingham, B47 6JX
Tel: 01564 826483
www.caravanclub.co.uk
Pitches For ⚏ ⛟ **Total** 120
Acreage 14 **Open** All Year
Access Good **Site** Level
Nearest Bus Stop (Miles) Outside
Rural and open site set in the shadow of an old chapel. The Transport Museum is adjacent, and a short walk takes you to Becketts Farm Shop which has a restaurant. Only 9 miles from the NEC and close to many museums. Non members welcome. Booking essential.
Facilities ⬲ ⫽ ⌂ ⬭ ⚲ ⌔ ☉ ⚑
⛽ ⛽ ⬚ ⬱⤚⬛⬱ ⚑
Nearest Town Birmingham

Directions M1 leave at junc 23A and take A42/M42, exit at junc 3 and take A435. At r/about turn left into Middle Lane, after 150 yards turn left into Chapel Lane, after 300 yards turn right by the church then immediately turn right again into site.
⇻ Birmingham NEC

YORKSHIRE (EAST)

BRANDES BURTON

Fosse Hill Caravan Park, Catwick Lane, Brandes Burton, Driffield, East Yorkshire, YO25 8SB
Tel: 01964 542608
Email: janet@fossehill.co.uk
www.fossehill.co.uk
Pitches For ▲ ⚏ ⛟ **Total** 110
Open Mar **to** Oct
Access Good **Site** Level
Nearest Bus Stop (Miles) 1
Family run site set in countryside. Just 1 mile from the village of Brandesburton, and only 3 miles from the seaside town of Hornsea. Excellent base for visiting the North Yorks Moors, York, Beverley, Hull and the famous Deep.
Facilities ⬲ ⫽ ⌂ ⬭ ⚲ ⌔ ⬛ ☉ ⚑
⛽ ⬚ ⬛✖ ⚑ ⬛ ⚑⬱⤚⬛⬛ ⚑⬱ ⚑
Nearest Town Hornsea
Directions ½ a mile east of the A165 Hull to Bridlington road.
⇻ Beverley

BRIDLINGTON

Old Mill Caravan Park, Bempton, Bridlington, Yorkshire (East), YO16 6XE
Tel: 01262 673565
Pitches For ⚏ ⛟ **Total** 55
Acreage 2 **Open** Apr **to** Oct
Access Good **Site** Level
Nearest Bus Stop (Miles) ½
Bempton Bird Sanctuary, Flamborough Head cliffs, Danes Dyke.
Facilities ⫽ ⬭⌔☉⬱ ⬚ ⬱⚑ A⚑
Nearest Town Bridlington
Directions From Bridlington take the B1255 to Flamborough turn for Bempton 1 mile on the right.
⇻ Bempton

BRIDLINGTON

Poplars Touring Park, 45 Jewison Lane, Sewerby, Bridlington, East Yorkshire, YO15 1DX
Tel: 01262 677251
www.thepoplars.co.uk
Pitches For ▲ ⚏ ⛟ **Total** 30
Acreage 1½ **Open** 05-Mar **to** Oct
Access Good **Site** Level
Nearest Bus Stop (Miles) ½

Small quiet site in a good touring location. ¾ miles to the beach. Pub with food adjacent.
Facilities ⫽ ⌂ ⬭ ⚲ ⚑ ☉⬱ ⚑
Nearest Town Bridlington
Directions From Bridlington take the B1255 towards Flamborough for 1½ miles. Jewison Lane is a left turn off the Z bend after Marton Hall.
⇻ Bridlington

BRIDLINGTON

Thornwick & Sea Farm Holiday Centre, North Marine Road, Flamborough, Bridlington, Yorkshire (East), YO15 1AU
Tel: 01262 850369
Email: enquiries@thornwickbay.co.uk
www.thornwickbay.co.uk
Pitches For ▲ ⚏ ⛟ **Total** 180
Acreage 15 **Open** Mar **to** Oct
Access Good **Site** Level
Nearest Bus Stop (Miles) Outside
Set on Flamborough Headland Heritage Coast. Ideal for families with varied entertainment. All pitches individualy paddocked.
Facilities ⬲ ⫽ ⬚ ⬭⚲⌔☉ ⬛ ⬚ ⚑
⛽ ⬚ ⬛ ⬱✖ ⚑⬛⚑⬱⚑⚑⬛⬛⚑ ✎ ⚑⚑
⚑
Directions From Bridlington follow B1255 east to Flamborough village and onward yo North Landing.
⇻ Bridlington

HULL

SandleMere Holiday Village Main Street, Tunstall, East Yorkshire, HU12 0JF
Tel: 01964 670403
Email: info@sandlemere.co.uk
www.sandlemere.co.uk
Pitches For ▲ ⚏ ⛟ **Total** 100
Acreage 140 **Open** Mar **to** Nov
Access Good **Site** Level
Nearest Bus Stop (Miles) Outside
Near the beach and all facilities.
Facilities ⬲ ⫽ ⬚ ⬭⚲⌔☉ ⬛ ⬚ ⚑
⛽ ⬚ ✖ ⚑⬛ ⬚ ⚑⬱⤚⬛⬛ ✎ ⚑⚑ ⚑
Nearest Town Withernsea
Directions From Hull take the A1033 to Hedon, turn left at the roundabout to Preston and follow signs for Burton Pidsea and Roos.
⇻ Hull

POCKLINGTON

South Lea Caravan Park, The Balk, Pocklington, East Yorkshire, YO42 2NX
Tel: 01759 303467
Email: info@south-lea.co.uk
www.south-lea.co.uk
Pitches For ▲ ⚏ ⛟ **Total** 72
Acreage 15 **Open** Mar **to** Oct
Access Good **Site** Level
Nearest Bus Stop (Miles) Outside

Spacious 4 Star site, ideally situated for York (12 miles) and the coast (25 miles). Gold David Bellamy Award for Conservation. You can also contact us on Mobile: 07989 616095.
Facilities ∮ 🖽 🕮 ♒ ♪ ☉ 📶
💵 🅿 🛢 🔥 ⚙ 🔥 📞 🍴 🚻 ☼
Nearest Town Pocklington
Directions From the A64 take the A1079 York to Hull road. At the Yorkway Motel turn onto the B1247 signposted Pocklington, the Park is 400 yards on the left.
🚲 York

SKIPSEA

Mill Farm Country Park, Mill Lane, Skipsea, East Yorkshire, YO25 8SS
Tel: 01262 468211
Pitches For ⚠ 🚐 🚏 **Total** 56
Acreage 6 **Open** 14-Mar **to** 28-Sep
Access Good **Site** Level
Nearest Bus Stop (Miles) Outside
Farm walk, beach nearby. RSPB site at Bempton. Good centre for many places of local interest. Nearby there is a village shop and Post Office, a pub and a heated swimming pool.
Facilities ∮ 🖽 🕮 ♒ ♪ ☉ 📶
💵 🔥 🍴 🅿 🛢 ☼
Nearest Town Hornsea
Directions The A165 Hull to Bridlington Road, at Beeford take B1249 to Skipsea. At crossroads turn right, then first left up Cross Street which leads on to Mill Lane, site is on the right.
🚲 Bridlington

STAMFORD BRIDGE

Weir Caravan Park, Stamford Bridge, East Yorkshire, YO41 1AN
Tel: 01759 371377
Email: enquiries@yorkshireholidayparks.co.uk
www.yorkshireholidayparks.co.uk
Pitches For ⚠ 🚐 🚏 **Total** 20
Acreage 7 **Open** Mar **to** Oct
Access Good **Site** Level
Nearest Bus Stop (Miles) ¼
On the edge of a river. 5 minute walk from the village and shops, pubs, etc..
Facilities 🛁 ∮ 🖽 🕮 ♒ ☉ 🍴 🛢 📶
💵 ☉ 🔥 🍴 🅿 ☼ ✿
Nearest Town York
Directions From the A166 Bridlington road, turn left before the bridge.
🚲 York

WILBERFOSS

Fangfoss Park, Fangfoss, York, East Yorkshire, YO41 5QB
Tel: 01759 380491
Email: info@fangfosspark.co.uk
www.fangfosspark.co.uk
Pitches For ⚠ 🚐 🚏 🚐∫ **Total** 75
Acreage 5 **Open** Mar **to** Nov
Access Good **Site** Level
Nearest Bus Stop (Miles) ½
Ideal for York, North Yorkshire Moors and Castle Howard. 40 minutes from the coast.
Facilities ∮ 🖽 🕮 ♒ ♪ ☉ 🍴 🛢 📶
💵 💵 ☉ 🔥 🍴 🅿 ☼ ✿
Nearest Town York
Directions From the A64 take the A1079 towards Hull. After 5 miles turn left into Wilberfoss Village, turn next left and the site is 2 miles.
🚲 York

112

WITHERNSEA

Willows Holiday Park, Hollym Road, Withernsea, East Yorkshire, HU19 2PN
Tel: 01964 612233
Email: info@highfield-caravans.co.uk
www.willowsholidaypark.co.uk
Pitches For 🚐 🚏 **Total** 28
Acreage 9 **Open** 04-Mar **to** Oct
Access Good **Site** Level
Nearest Bus Stop (Miles) Outside
Only a 10 minute walk to the beach and a 15 minute walk to the town.
Facilities ∮ 🖽 🕮 ♒ ♪ ☉ 🍴 🛢 📶
💵 💵 ☉ ♀ 🔥 🍴 🅿 ☼ ✿
Nearest Town Withernsea
Directions Take the M62 to Hull then take the A1033 to Withernsea. Willows is the first site on the left on entering Withernsea.
🚲 Hull

YORKSHIRE (NORTH)

BARDEN

Howgill Lodge, Barden, Skipton, North Yorkshire, BD23 6DJ
Tel: 01756 720655
Email: fiona@howgilllodge.co.uk
www.howgilllodge.co.uk
Pitches For ⚠ 🚐 🚏 **Total** 50
Acreage 7 **Open** Apr **to** Oct
Access Good (Narrow) **Site** sloping
Nearest Bus Stop (Miles) ¼
Facilities ∮ 🖽 🕮 ♒ ♪ ☉ 🍴 🛢 📶
💵 ☉ 🔥 🍴 🅿
Nearest Town Skipton
Directions A59 to Bolton Abbey. B6160 signed Burnsall. Turn off for Appletreewick.
🚲 Ilkley

BEDALE

Pembroke Caravan Park, 19 Low Street, Leeming Bar, Northallerton, Yorkshire (North), DL7 9BW
Tel: 01677 422652
Pitches For 🚐 🚏 **Total** 25
Acreage 2 **Open** Mar **to** Dec
Access Good **Site** Level
Nearest Bus Stop (Miles) ¼
Between the Yorkshire Dales and North Yorks Moors. Excellent A1 stopover.
Facilities ∮ 🖽 🕮 ♒ ♪ ☉ 🍴 🛢 📶
💵 ☉ 🔥 🅿 ☼
Nearest Town Bedale
Directions ½ mile off junc 51 (A1M).
🚲 Northallerton

BENTHAM

Riverside Caravan Park, High Bentham, Lancaster, Lancashire, LA2 7FJ
Tel: 015242 61272
Email: info@riversidecaravanpark.co.uk
www.riversidecaravanpark.co.uk
Pitches For 🚐 🚏 🚐∫ **Total** 61
Acreage 6 **Open** Mar **to** 02-Jan
Access Good **Site** Level
Nearest Bus Stop (Miles) ½
Riverside site, great for families. Flat footpaths for easy walking. We sell milk, eggs, tea and coffee. Local shops and pub just a 5 minute walk.
Facilities 🛁 ∮ 🍴 🖽 🕮 ♒ ♪ ☉ 🍴 🛢 📶
💵 💵 ☉ 🛢 🔥 🍴 🅿 ☼ ✿ 🔥 🌐
Nearest Town High Bentham
Directions Follow caravan signs off the B6480 at The Black Bull Hotel in High Bentham.
🚲 High Bentham

BOLTON ABBEY

Bolton Abbey Estate Caravan Club Site, Bolton Abbey, Skipton, North Yorkshire, BD23 6AN
Tel: 01756 710433
www.caravanclub.co.uk
Pitches For 🚐 🚏 **Total** 57
Acreage 4 **Open** Mar **to** Jan
Access Good **Site** Level
Nearest Bus Stop (Miles) Outside
Situated in the Bolton Abbey estate, this pretty site is surrounded by woodland and the Yorkshire Dales. Many miles of walks around the site. Close to Bolton Priory and Skipton castle. Non members welcome. Booking essential.
Facilities 🛁 ∮ 🖽 🕮 ♒ ♪ ☉ 🍴
💵 ☉ 🛢 🔥 🅿 🌐
Nearest Town Skipton
Directions From the A59 Gisburn to Harrogate road, at Bolton Bridge roundabout take the B6160 sp Bolton Abbey. After 2¾ miles turn right into Strid car park, go through the double gates ahead into the site.
🚲 Skipton

BOROUGHBRIDGE

Blue Bell Caravan Park, Kirby Hill, Boroughbridge, North Yorkshire, YO51 9DS
Tel: 07946 549529
Email: townend450@btinternet.com
Pitches For 🚐 🚏 **Total** 24
Acreage 2 **Open** Mar **to** Dec
Nearest Bus Stop (Miles) Outside
Well drained and dry site.
Facilities ∮ 🕮 ♒ ☉ 🍴 🛢 💵 💵 ♀ 🍴 🅿 ☼
Nearest Town Ripon
Directions On the B6265 in Kirby Hill, at the rear of the Blue Bell Pub.
🚲 Harrogate

BOROUGHBRIDGE

Boroughbridge Camping & Caravanning Club Site, Bar Lane, Roecliffe, Boroughbridge, North Yorkshire, YO51 9LS
Tel: 01423 322683
Email: boroughbridge.site@thefriendlyclub.co.uk
www.campingandcaravanningclub.co.uk/boroughbridge
Pitches For ⚠ 🚐 🚏 **Total** 85
Acreage 5 **Open** All Year
Site Level
Nearest Bus Stop (Miles) Outside
On the banks of the River Ure for fishing, boat launching facility. Table tennis and pool table on site. Close to the Yorkshire Dales. Lodges available for hire. BTB 5 Star Graded and AA 4 Pennants. Non members welcome. You can also call us on 0845 130 7633.
Facilities 🛁 ∮ 🖽 🕮 ♒ ♪ ☉ 🍴 🛢 📶
💵 💵 ☉ 🛢 🔥 🍴 🅿 ☼ ✿
Directions From junction 48 of the A1M north and southbound slip roads, follow signs for Bar Lane Industrial Estate and Roecliffe Village. Site entrance is ¼ mile from the roundabout.
🚲 Harrogate

ELVINGTON

Elvington Lake Caravan Park, Lake Cottage, Wheldrake Lane, Elvington, York, North Yorkshire, YO41 4AZ
Tel: 01904 607504
Email: stanbritton@apl.com
www.elvingtonfisheries.com
Pitches For ⚠ 🚐 🚏 **Total** 13
Acreage 3 **Open** All Year
Access Good **Site** Level
Nearest Bus Stop (Miles) Outside

Award winning park. The only working windmill water pump. York maze, Elvington Airfield.

Facilities ✦ ⬆️ ⌐ 🍽 ⛟ ➕ ✕ ☀
Nearest Town York
Directions From York take the A1079 Hull road, immediately straight over first roundabout then turn right onto the B1228, follow signs to Wheldrake.
⭎ York

FILEY

Centenary Way Camping & Caravan Park, Muston Grange, Filey, North Yorkshire, YO14 0HU
Tel: 01723 516415
Pitches For ⛺ ⬛ 🚐 **Total** 75
Acreage 3½ **Open** Mar **to** Oct
Access Good **Site** Level
Nearest Bus Stop (Miles) ¼
Just a ten minute walk to the beach and Filey town. Handy for Scarborough and Bridlington. 45 minutes to the North Yorkshire Moors, York and Whitby. The fariy Garden, tea, coffee, cakes etc.
Facilities ✦ ⬆️ ⬆️ ⌐ ⊙ 🍽 ☀
♨️ 🏧 🛒 🛢 🅿️ ⬛
Directions Take the A165 from Bridlington, at the roundabout turn right onto the A1039, after 200 yards turn right into Centenary Way, follow lane to the very end.
⭎ Filey

FILEY

Orchard Farm Holiday Village,
Stonegate, Hunmanby, Filey, North Yorkshire, YO14 0PU
Tel: 01723 891582
Email:
info@orchardfarmholidayvillage.co.uk
www.orchardfarmholidayvillage.co.uk
Pitches For ⛺ ⬛ 🚐 **Total** 85
Acreage 14 **Open** Mar **to** Oct
Access Good **Site** Level
Nearest Bus Stop (Miles) ¼
1 mile from the beach. Ideal base for all North Yorkshire attractions.
Facilities ✦ ⬆️ ⬆️ ⌐ ⊙ 🍽 ☀ 🛢 🅿️ 🛒
♨️ 🏧 🛒 🍴 ⛽ 🔥 🏧 ➕ 🅿️ ✕
Nearest Town Filey
Directions From Filey take the A165 towards Bridlington, Hunmanby is 2 miles on the right.
⭎ Hunmanby

GRASSINGTON

Hawkswick Cote Park, Arncliffe, Skipton, North Yorkshire, BD23 5PX
Tel: 01756 770226
Email: hawkswickcote@northdales.co.uk
www.northdales.co.uk
Pitches For ⛺ ⬛ 🚐 **Total** 30
Open Mar **to** Nov
Access Good **Site** Level
Nearest Bus Stop (Miles) 2½
We are in the heart of Yorkshire Dales, with quintesential villages all around with pubs and eating houses.
Facilities ♿ ✦ 🛢 ⬆️ ⬆️ ⌐ ⊙ 🍴 🛢 🅿️ 🛒
♨️ 🏧 🛒 🔥 ➕ 🅿️ ⛽ ✕ ☀
Nearest Town Grassington
Directions Take the B6160 towards Kettlewell. After Kilnsey Cray take a left toward Amcliffe. Park 1¼ mileson left.
⭎ Skipton

GRASSINGTON

Threaplands Camping & Caravan Park,
Threaplands House, Cracoe, Nr Skipton, North Yorkshire, BD23 6LD
Tel: 01756 730248
Pitches For ⛺ ⬛ 🚐 **Total** 30

Acreage 8 **Open** Mar **to** Oct
Access Good **Site** Level
Nearest Bus Stop (Miles) ¼
Scenic views. Bakery on site selling fresh bread, cakes and milk etc.. Ideal for touring and walking.
Facilities ♿ ✦ 🛢 ⬆️ ⌐ ⊙ 🍽 🍴 🛢 ➕ 🅿️ ☀
Nearest Town Skipton
Directions 6 miles from Skipton on the B6265 to Cracoe. ¼ mile past Cracoe keep going straight on, site is ¼ mile on the left.
⭎ Skipton

GUISBOROUGH

Margrove Park Holidays, Margrove Park, Boosbeck, SaltburnbytheSea, Yorkshire (North), TS12 3BZ
Tel: 01287 653616
Email: margrovepark@btconnect.com
www.margroveparkholidays.co.uk
Pitches For ⬛ 🚐 **Total** 10
Open Apr **to** Oct
Access Good **Site** Level
Nearest Bus Stop (Miles) Outside
5 miles from Saltburn beach. Good walking, ½ mile from Cleveland Way.
Facilities ♿ ✦ ⬆️ ⬆️ ⌐ ⊙ ☀
🍴 🏧 ➕ 🅿️ ☀ 🛒
Nearest Town Guisborough
Directions Follow the A171 towards Whitby, after approx. 2 miles follow signs for Boosbeck.
⭎ Saltburn

HARROGATE

Bilton Park, Village Farm, Bilton Lane, Harrogate, North Yorkshire, HG1 4DH
Tel: 01423 565070
Email: welcome@biltonpark.co.uk
www.biltonpark.co.uk
Pitches For ⛺ ⬛ 🚐 🚃 **Total** 25
Acreage 8½ **Open** Apr **to** Oct
Access Good **Site** Level
Nearest Bus Stop (Miles) ½
Conversation area, cycle ways
Facilities ✦ ⬆️ ⬆️ ⌐ ⊙ 🛢 🅿️ 🛒
♨️ 🏧 ➕ 🅿️ ⬛
Nearest Town Harrogate
Directions From the A59 in Harrogate, turn at Skipton Pub into Bilton Lane, Park is 1½ miles down the road.
⭎ Harrogate

HARROGATE

High Moor Farm Caravan Park, Skipton Road, Harrogate, North Yorkshire, HG3 2LT
Tel: 01423 563637
Email: highmoorfarmpark@btconnect.com
www.highmoorfarmpark.co.uk
Pitches For ⬛ 🚐 **Total** 300
Open Apr/Easter **to** Oct
Access Good **Site** Level
Facilities ✦ ⬆️ ⬆️ ⌐ ⊙ 🛢 🅿️ 🛒
♨️ 🏧 🛒 ✕ ⛽ 🔥 🏧 ➕ 🅿️ 🛢 🅿️ ✕ ☀
Nearest Town Harrogate
Directions On the A59 4 miles from Harrogate on the left hand side.
⭎ Harrogate

HARROGATE

Ripley Caravan Park, Ripley, Harrogate, North Yorkshire, HG3 3AU
Tel: 01423 770050
Email: ripleycaravanpark@talk21.com
www.ripleycaravanpark.com
Pitches For ⛺ ⬛ 🚐 🚃 **Total** 100
Acreage 25 **Open** Easter **to** Oct
Access Good **Site** Level
Nearest Bus Stop (Miles) ¼

Quiet family site, ideal for touring the Dales, Harrogate and York. David Bellamy Gold Award, AA 5 Pennants and ETB 5 Star Graded.
Facilities ♿ ✦ 🛢 ⬆️ ⬆️ ⌐ ⊙ 🛢 🅿️ 🛒
♨️ 🏧 🛒 🛢 🍴 🔥 ➕ 🅿️ ⬛ ✕ ☀ 📶
Nearest Town Harrogate
Directions From Harrogate take A61 towards Ripon, after 3 miles at Ripley roundabout take the B6165 Knaresborough road, site is 300 yards on the left.
⭎ Harrogate

HARROGATE

Rudding Holiday Park, Follifoot, Harrogate, North Yorkshire, HG3 1JH
Tel: 01423 870439
Email: holidaypark@ruddingpark.com
www.ruddingholidaypark.co.uk
Pitches For ⛺ ⬛ 🚐 **Total** 0
Open Mar **to** Jan
Access Good **Site** Level
Nearest Bus Stop (Miles) Outside
Ideal location for exploring the Moors, Dales and cities. Only 3 miles from the Spa town of Harrogate. Golf on site.
Facilities ♿ ✦ 🛢 ⬆️ ⬆️ ⌐ ⊙ 🛢 🅿️ 🛒
♨️ 🏧 🛒 🍴 ⛽ 🔥 🏧 ➕ 🅿️ ⬛ ✕ 📶
Nearest Town Harrogate
Directions From the A1 take the A59 to the A658 and turn south signposted Bradford. Continue for 4½ miles then turn right and follow signs.
⭎ Harrogate

HARROGATE

The Yorkshire Hussar Inn Holiday Caravan Park, Markington, Harrogate, North Yorkshire, HG3 3NR
Tel: 01765 677327
Email: enquiry@yorkshire-hussar-inn.co.uk
www.yorkshire-hussar-inn.co.uk
Pitches For ⛺ ⬛ 🚐 **Total** 20
Acreage 5 **Open** Apr **to** Oct
Access Good **Site** Level
Ideal touring centre for the Dales. LUXURY HOLIDAY CARAVANS FOR HIRE. Situated at the rear of an Inn in a garden setting in the village. Fountains Abbey 1¼ miles.
Facilities ✦ 🛢 ⬆️ ⬆️ ⌐ ⊙ 🛢 🅿️ 🛒
♨️ 🏧 🛒 🛢 🔥 ➕ 🅿️ ✕ 📶
Nearest Town Harrogate/Ripon
Directions 1 mile west of A61 (Harrogate/Ripon road). Ripon 5 miles. Harrogate 7 miles.
⭎ Harrogate

HAWES

Bainbridge Ings Caravan & Camping Site, Hawes, North Yorkshire, DL8 3NU
Tel: 01969 667354
Email: janet@bainbridge-ings.co.uk
www.bainbridge-ings.co.uk
Pitches For ⛺ ⬛ 🚐 **Total** 80
Acreage 5 **Open** Apr **to** Oct
Access Good **Site** Level
Nearest Bus Stop (Miles) ½
A quiet, clean, family run site with beautiful views and only ½ mile from Hawes. Motorcycles are accepted but not in groups.
Facilities ✦ ⬆️ ⬆️ ⌐ ⊙ 🛢 🅿️ 🛒
🛢 ➕ 🅿️ ⬛
Directions Approaching Hawes from Bainbridge on the A684 turn left at the signpost marked Gayle and we are 300yds on at the top of the hill.
⭎ Garsdale

HAWES

Honeycott Caravan Park, Ingleton Road, Hawes, North Yorkshire, DL8 3LH
Tel: 01969 667310
Email: info@honeycott.co.uk
www.honeycott.co.uk
Pitches For ⬛ ⬛ **Total** 13
Acreage 1½ **Open** Mar **to** Oct
Access Good **Site** Sloping
Nearest Bus Stop (Miles) ¼
Peaceful Park with great views, just a 10 minute walk from Hawes. Ideal base from which to explore the Yorkshire Dales.
Facilities [symbols]
Nearest Town Hawes
Directions ½ a mile west of Hawes on the B6255 Ingleton road. 17 miles west of Leyburn and 20 miles east of the M6 junction 37.
⇌ Garsdale

HAWES

Shaw Ghyll, Simonstone, Hawes, North Yorkshire, DL8 3LY
Tel: 01969 667359
Email: infi@shawghyll.co.uk
www.yorkshirenet.co.uk/accgde/ ydcotts.htm
Pitches For ⬛ ⬛ ⬛ **Total** 30
Acreage 2½ **Open** Apr **to** Oct
Access Good **Site** Level
Quiet sheltered site, ideal for walks and families, pleasant aspect, river and lovely scenic walks.
Facilities [symbols]
Nearest Town Hawes
Directions 2 miles north of Hawes following the Muker road.

HELMSLEY

Foxholme Touring Caravan & Camping Park, Harome, Helmsley, North Yorkshire, YO62 5JG
Tel: 01439 772336
Pitches For ⬛ ⬛ ⬛ **Total** 60
Acreage 6 **Open** Easter **to** Oct
Access Good **Site** Level
Nearest Bus Stop (Miles) 1
ADULTS ONLY PARK in an ideal touring area. Near National Park, Abbeys and Herriot country.
Facilities [symbols]
Nearest Town Helmsley
Directions A170 towards Scarborough, after ½ mile turn right to Harome, turn left at church, through village, follow caravan signs.
⇌ Malton

HELMSLEY

Golden Square Caravan Park, Oswaldkirk, Helmsley, York, North Yorkshire, YO62 5YQ
Tel: 01439 788269
Email: reception@goldensquarecaravanpark.com
www.goldensquarecaravanpark.co.uk
Pitches For ⬛ ⬛ ⬛ **Total** 110
Acreage 10 **Open** 01-Mar **to** 31-Oct
Access Good **Site** Level
Nearest Bus Stop (Miles) Outside
Secluded site with magnificent views of North Yorkshire Moors. Ideal for visiting the city of York. Shop. Indoor/Outdoor play areas. Award winning facilities. Family/disabled bathroom. De-Lux all service pitches. Indoor/Outdoor swimming pool nearby. New development for holiday homes.
Facilities [symbols]

Nearest Town Helmsley
Directions 2 miles south of Helmsley. First right off the B1257 to Ampleforth.
⇌ Thirsk/Malton

HELMSLEY

Wombleton Caravan Park, Moorfield Lane, Wombleton, Kirkbymoorside, North Yorkshire, YO62 7RY
Tel: 01751 431684
Email: info@wombletoncaravanpark.co.uk
www.wombletoncaravanpark.co.uk
Pitches For ⬛ ⬛ ⬛ **Total** 118
Acreage 5 **Open** Mar **to** Oct
Access Good **Site** Level
Nearest Bus Stop (Miles) 1
Ideal for North Yorkshire Steam Railway, Duncombe Park, Nunnington Hall, Rievauly Abbey, Helmsley Castle and Flamingo Land.
Facilities [symbols]
Nearest Town Helmsley
Directions Leave Helmsley by A170 for 4 miles, turn right for Wombleton. Go through Wombleton and the Park is ½ a mile on the left.

HELMSLEY

Wrens of Ryedale, Gale Lane, Nawton, North Yorkshire, YO62 7SD
Tel: 01439 771260
Email: maria@wrensofryedale.co.uk
www.wrensofryedale.co.uk
Pitches For ⬛ ⬛ ⬛ **Total** 45
Acreage 3½ **Open** Apr **to** Oct
Access Good **Site** Level
Nearest Bus Stop (Miles) ¼
Attractive, quiet, family run site. Situated on edge of Yorkshire Moors National Park. Very good centre for touring.
Facilities [symbols]
Nearest Town Scarborough/York
Directions Leave Helmsley by the A170. 2½ miles to Beadlam, pass the church on left, in 20 yards turn right. Site is 500 yards down the lane.
⇌ Malton

INGLETON

The Trees Caravan Park, Westhouse, Ingleton, North Yorkshire, LA6 3NZ
Tel: 015242 41511
Email: stocks@greenwoodleghe.co.uk
www.caravancampingsites.co.uk/ northyorkshire/thetrees
Pitches For ⬛ ⬛ ⬛ **Total** 29
Acreage 3 **Open** Apr **to** Oct
Access Good **Site** Level
Set in beautiful country scenery. Ideal for walking and touring. Mountains, caves and waterfalls nearby.
Facilities [symbols]
Nearest Town Ingleton
Directions From Ingleton, travel 1¼ miles along the A65 towards Kirkby Lonsdale (about ¼ mile past the A687 junction - Country Harvest). Turn left at signpost for Lower Westhouse, site is on the left in 50yds.
⇌ Bentham

KNARESBOROUGH

Allerton Park Caravan Park, Allerton Mauleverer, Nr Knaresborough, North Yorkshire, HG5 0SE
Tel: 01423 330569
Email: enquiries@yorkshireholidayparks.co.uk
www.yorkshireholidayparks.co.uk
Pitches For ⬛ ⬛ ⬛ **Total** 20

Acreage 17 **Open** Feb **to** 03-Jan
Access Good **Site** Level
Nearest Bus Stop (Miles) ½
Woodland park with plenty of wildlife and walks. David Bellamy Silver Award for Conservation.
Facilities [symbols]
Nearest Town Knaresborough
Directions On the A59 York to Harrogate road, ½ mile east of Aim.
⇌ Harrogate

KNARESBOROUGH

Kingfisher Caravan & Camping Park, Low Moor Lane, Farnham, Knaresborough, North Yorkshire, HG5 9JB
Tel: 01423 869411
Pitches For ⬛ ⬛ ⬛ **Total** 50
Acreage 10 **Open** Mar **to** Oct
Access Good **Site** Level
Nearest Bus Stop (Miles) Outside
Ideal touring base for the Dales, convenient for Harrogate and York. Adjacent to a golf range.
Facilities [symbols]
Nearest Town Knaresborough
Directions From Knaresborough take the A6055. In 1¼ miles turn left to Farnham Village, in Farnham turn left, park is approx. 1 mile on the left.
⇌ Knaresborough

KNARESBOROUGH

Knaresborough Caravan Club Site, New Road, Scotton, Knaresborough, North Yorkshire, HG5 9HH
Tel: 01423 860196
www.caravanclub.co.uk
Pitches For ⬛ ⬛ ⬛ **Total** 74
Acreage 8 **Open** Mar **to** Jan
Access Good **Site** Lev/Slope
Nearest Bus Stop (Miles) ¼
Surrounded by mature trees and hedges. Riverside walks, tennis, pitch 'n' putt and boating in the local area. Close to Ripley Castle, Old Court House Museum and Old Mother Shiptons Cave. Non members welcome. Booking essential.
Facilities [symbols]
Nearest Town Knaresborough
Directions Leave A1 at junc 47 and take A59 sp Knaresborough. At roundabout turn right onto the A59 and continue through Knaresborough, at junction with traffic lights turn left and continue on A59. At next lights turn right onto B6165, at petrol station turn right into New Road, site is 50 yards on the right.
⇌ Knaresborough

LEYBURN

Constable Burton Hall Caravan Park, Constable Burton, Leyburn, North Yorkshire, DL8 5LJ
Tel: 01677 450428
Email: caravanpark@constableburton.com
www.cbcaravanpark.co.uk
Pitches For ⬛ ⬛ **Total** 120
Acreage 10 **Open** 07-Mar **to** Oct
Access Good **Site** Lev/Slope
Nearest Bus Stop (Miles) Outside
Ideal for walking and touring. Many castles, gardens and historic houses nearby. No childrens play area and strictly no games.
Facilities [symbols]
Nearest Town Leyburn
Directions On the A684 midway between Bedale and Leyburn.
⇌ Northallerton

LEYBURN
Lower Wensleydale Caravan Club Site, Harmby, Leyburn, North Yorkshire, DL8 5NU
Tel: 01969 623366
www.caravanclub.co.uk
Pitches For ⅄ ⬛ ⬛ **Total** 92
Acreage 10 **Open** Mar to Nov
Access Poor **Site** Level
Situated in the hollow of a disused quarry, now overrun with wild flowers and mosses. Ducks and rabbits roam the site freely. Ideal for walking. Close to Constable Burton Gardens, Bolton Castle and Middleham Castle. Non members welcome. Booking essential.
Facilities ⬛ ⫽ ⬛ ⬛ ⫞ ⌐ ⌐ ⬛ ⬛
⬛ ⬛ ⬛ ⬛
Nearest Town Leyburn
Directions From the A684, in Harmby turn off by the Pheasant Inn, cross the railway bridge and immediately turn left at brown caravan sign. Follow signs to the entrance. The immediate approach road to the site is narrow, with steep blind bends (look for traffic mirrors on bends).
⚏ Leyburn

MALTON
Ashfield Caravan Park, Kirby Misperton, Malton, Yorkshire (North), YO17 6UU
Tel: 01653 668555
Email: mail@ashfieldcaravanpark.co.uk
www.ashfieldcaravanpark.co.uk
Pitches For ⬛ ⬛ ⬛ **Total** 30
Acreage 2 **Open** Mar to Oct
Site Level
Nearest Bus Stop (Miles) ¼
Ideal for Flamingo Land, Castle Howard, Whitby,York,Scarborough.
Facilities ⬛ ⫽ ⬛ ⬛ ⫞ ⌐ ⌐ ⬛ ⬛
⬛ ⬛ ⬛ ⬛ ⬛ ⬛ ⫞ ⬛ ⬛
Nearest Town Pickering
Directions A169 to Kirbymisperton next left passed Flamingo land.

MUKER
Usha Gap Caravan & Camp Site, Usha Gap, Muker, Richmond, North Yorkshire, DL11 6DW
Tel: 01748 886214
Email: info@ushagap.co.uk
www.ushagap.co.uk
Pitches For ⅄ ⬛ ⬛ **Total** 24
Acreage 1 **Open** All Year
Access Good **Site** Level
Nearest Bus Stop (Miles) Outside
Alongside a small river. Shops and a pub ¼ mile. Ideal touring and good walking.
Facilities ⬛ ⬛ ⫞ ⌐ ⌐ ⬛ ⬛
Nearest Town Hawes
⚏ Darlington

PATELEY BRIDGE
Heathfield Caravan Park, Ramsgill Road, Pateley Bridge, Harrogate, Yorkshire (North), HG3 5PY
Tel: 01423 711652
Email: heathfieldcp1@gmail.com
www.heathfieldhp.co.uk
Pitches For ⅄ ⬛ ⬛ **Total** 0
Open Mar to Oct
Access Good **Site** Sloping
Nearest Bus Stop (Miles) 1
Alongside river superb scenic walks set in Nidderdale.
Facilities ⬛ ⫽ ⬛ ⬛ ⫞ ⌐ ⌐ ⬛ ⬛
⬛ ⬛ ⬛ ⬛ ⬛ ⬛ ⬛ ⬛
Nearest Town Pateley Bridge
Directions Follow Low Wath Road for 1 mile, turn left after Bridge Inn and follow signs.
⚏ Harrogate

PATELEY BRIDGE
Manor House Farm Caravan Site, Manor House Farm, Summerbridge, Harrogate, North Yorkshire, HG3 4JS
Tel: 01423 780322 mob0772324504
Pitches For ⅄ ⬛ ⬛ **Total** 40
Open Mar to Oct
Access Good **Site** Terraced
Close to the River Nidd and the Nidderdale Way. Ideal for walking. Sorry, Dogs by arrangement.
Facilities ⫽ ⬛ ⬛ ⫞ ⌐ ⌐ ⬛ ⬛ ⬛
⬛ ⬛ ⬛ ⬛
Nearest Town Harrogate/Pateley Bridge
Directions Situated on the B6165 between Harrogate and Pateley Bridge.
⚏ Harrogate

PICKERING
Black Bull Caravan Park, Malton Road, Pickering, North Yorkshire, YO18 8EA
Tel: 01751 472528
Email:
enquiries@blackbullcaravanpark.com
www.blackbullcaravanpark.com
Pitches For ⅄ ⬛ ⬛ ⬛ **Total** 72
Acreage 4 **Open** Mar to Oct
Access Good **Site** Level
Nearest Bus Stop (Miles) Outside
Central location for many attractions and the gateway to the North Yorks Moors and steam railway, Eden Camp, Flamingoland and much more. Holiday Caravans also available for hire.
Facilities ⫽ ⬛ ⬛ ⫞ ⌐ ⌐ ⬛ ⬛ ⬛
⬛ ⬛ ⬛ ⬛ ⬛ ⬛ ⬛ ⬛ ⬛ ⬛ ⬛ ⬛
Nearest Town Pickering
Directions 1 mile south of Pickering on the A169 Malton road.
⚏ Malton

PICKERING
Hutton Le Hole Caravan Park, Westfield Lodge, Hutton Le Hole, York, North Yorkshire, YO62 6UG
Tel: 01751 417261
Email: rwstrickland@farmersweekly.net
www.westfieldlodge.co.uk
Pitches For ⅄ ⬛ ⬛ ⬛ **Total** 47
Acreage 5 **Open** 22-Mar to Oct
Access Good **Site** Level
Nearest Bus Stop (Miles) 3
Excellent for the North Yorkshire Moors. Many local scenic walks. Centrally located for the coast and York.
Facilities ⬛ ⫽ ⬛ ⬛ ⫞ ⌐ ⌐ ⬛ ⬛
⬛ ⬛ ⬛ ⬛
Nearest Town Pickering
Directions Approx. 7 miles west of Pickering on the A170 turn right (north) at Keldholme signposted Hutton Le Hole. After approx 2 miles go over the cattle grid, site is on the left before the village.
⚏ Malton

PICKERING
Overbrook Caravan Park, Maltongate, Thornton-le-Dale, Nr Pickering, North Yorkshire, YO18 7SE
Tel: 01751 474417
Email:
enquiry@overbrookcaravanpark.co.uk
www.overbrookcaravanpark.co.uk
Pitches For ⬛ ⬛ ⬛ **Total** 50
Acreage 3½ **Open** Mar to 07-Jan
Access Good **Site** Sloping
Nearest Bus Stop (Miles) ½
ADULTS ONLY park in one of North Yorkshires prettiest villages. Peaceful, picturesque location.

Facilities ⫽ ⬛ ⬛ ⫞ ⌐ ⌐ ⬛ ⬛
⬛ ⬛ ⬛ ⬛
Nearest Town Pickering
Directions From the A1 follow the A64 onto the A169, then the A170 from Pickering.
⚏ Malton

PICKERING
Rosedale Caravan Park, Rosedale Abbey, Pickering, North Yorkshire, YO18 8SA
Tel: 01751 417272
Email: info@flowerofmay.com
www.flowerofmay.com
Pitches For ⅄ ⬛ ⬛ **Total** 0
Open Easter to Oct
Access Good **Site** Level
Nearest Bus Stop (Miles) ¼
Idyllic retreat. Ideal for walking and hiking through the beautiful North Yorkshire Moors. Pets welcome by arrangement.
Facilities ⬛ ⫽ ⬛ ⬛ ⫞ ⌐ ⌐ ⬛ ⬛ ⬛
⬛ ⬛ ⬛ ⬛ ⬛ ⬛ ⬛ ⬛ ⬛
Nearest Town Pickering
Directions Turn off the A170 towards Rosedale.
⚏ Malton

PICKERING
Spiers House Caravan & Camping Site, Cropton, Pickering, Yorkshire (North), YO18 8ES
Tel: 02476 423008
Email:
enquiries@campingintheforest.co.uk
www.campingintheforest.co.uk
Pitches For ⅄ ⬛ ⬛ **Total** 160
Open All Year
Access Good **Site** Level
For an exciting way to see the countryside, why not try the scenic 18 miles steam train journey from nearby Pickering. Within easy driving distance of York, Scarborough and Whitby.
Facilities ⬛ ⫽ ⬛ ⬛ ⬛ ⫞ ⌐ ⬛ ⬛
⬛ ⬛ ⬛ ⬛
Nearest Town Pickering
Directions From the A170 between Pickering and Kirkby Moorside, turn off at sign for Wrelton, Cropton and Rosedale Abbey (going north). 1½ miles after Cropton turn right sp Spiers House.
⚏ Malton

PICKERING
Vale of Pickering Caravan Park, Carr House Farm, Allerston, Pickering, North Yorkshire, YO18 7PQ
Tel: 01723 859280
Email: tony@valeofpickering.co.uk
www.valeofpickering.co.uk
Pitches For ⅄ ⬛ ⬛ **Total** 120
Acreage 8 **Open** 07-Mar to 02-Jan
Access Good **Site** Level
Nearest Bus Stop (Miles) 1
High standard of service and superb facilities. Peaceful play area and games area. ETB 5 Star Graded. AA 5 pennants, David Bellamy Gold.
Facilities ⬛ ⫽ ⬛ ⬛ ⫞ ⌐ ⌐ ⬛ ⬛ ⬛
⬛ ⬛ ⬛ ⬛ ⬛ ⬛ ⬛ ⬛ ⬛
Nearest Town Scarborough
Directions From Pickering take the A170 to Allerston, turn right opposite Cayley Arms Hotel, due south 1¼ miles.
⚏ Malton

RICHMOND
Brompton Caravan Park,
BromptononSwale, Easby, Richmond,
Yorkshire (North), DL10 7EZ
Tel: 01748 824629
Email:
brompton.caravanpark@btconnect.com
www.bromptoncaravanpark.com
Pitches For Å ⊕ ➡ ➡ Total 177
Acreage 14 **Open** Mid Mar **to** Oct
Access Good **Site** Level
Nearest Bus Stop (Miles) Outside
Along river, ideal touring and camping new
for 2012 camping pods.
Facilities ♿ ƒ ⊟ ⅏ ☏ ⊙ ⏚ ⚓ ◨ ☎
⚲ ⊘ ⊗ ✗ ⌂ ⎅ ⊟ ⊟ ✓ ⚡
Nearest Town Richmond
Directions Richmond follow signs from
centre for A1 south, Brompton on Swale.
⚞ Darlington

RICHMOND
Orchard Caravan Park, Reeth, Richmond,
North Yorkshire, DL11 6TT
Tel: 01748 884475
Email: peter.daly7@btinternet.com
Pitches For ⊕ ➡ Total 56
Acreage 3½ **Open** Apr **to** Oct
Access Good **Site** Level
Nearest Bus Stop (Miles) ½
All grassed area in an apple orchard, beside
the River Swale. Sports area adjacent. Ideal
for walkers.
Facilities ƒ ⅏ ☏ ⊙ ⚲ ⊘ ⊛ ⚓ ⊟ ✓ ⚡
Nearest Town Richmond
Directions Approx. 11½ miles from
Richmond.
⚞ Darlington

RICHMOND
**Richmond Hargill House Caravan Club
Site,** Gilling West, Richmond, North
Yorkshire, DL10 5LJ
Tel: 01748 822734
www.caravanclub.co.uk
Pitches For ⊕ ➡ Total 66
Acreage 4½ **Open** Mar **to** Nov
Access Good **Site** Lev/Slope
Nearest Bus Stop (Miles) Outside
Situated in Herriot country with wonderful
views of the Yorkshire Dales National Park.
Non members welcome. Booking essential.
Facilities ♿ ƒ ⊟ ⅏ ⚓ ⊟ ☎
⚲ ⎅ ⊘ ⚓⊟ ☎
Nearest Town Richmond
Directions Leave the A1 at Scotch Corner
and take the A66 signposted Penrith. At the
crossroads turn left signposted Gilling West,
site is 100 yards on the left.
⚞ Richmond

RIPON
River Laver Holiday Park, Studley Road,
Ripon, North Yorkshire, HG4 2QR
Tel: 01765 690508
Email: riverlaver@lineone.net
www.riverlaver.co.uk
Pitches For ⊕ ➡ Total 8
Acreage 5 **Open** Mar **to** Nov
Access Good **Site** Level

Ideal base for the Yorkshire Moors and Dales.
Easy access to Fountains Abbey and road
network.
Facilities ♿ ƒ ⊟ ⅏ ⅏ ☏ ⊙ ⏚ ⚓ ◨ ☎
⚲ ⊘ ⚓⊟ ⊟ ✓ ⚡
Nearest Town Ripon
Directions ½ mile from Ripon on the B6265
towards Fountains Abbey.
⚞ Harrogate

RIPON
**Riverside Meadows Country Caravan
Park,** Ure Bank Top (Dept No.1), Ripon,
North Yorkshire, HG4 1JD
Tel: 01765 602964
Email: info@flowerofmay.com
www.flowerofmay.com
Pitches For Å ⊕ ➡ Total 200
Acreage 28 **Open** Mar **to** Oct
Access Good **Site** Lev/Slope
Nearest Bus Stop (Miles) ½
Countryside park alongside a river. Ideal for
touring the Yorkshire Dales. Bar complex for
all the family. Pets are welcome by
arrangement.
Facilities ♿ ƒ ⅏ ⅏ ☏ ⊙ ⏚ ⚓ ◨ ☎
⚲ ⎅ ⊘ ⊛ ⊻ ⍑ ✗ ⌂ ⚓⊟ ⊟ ✓ ⚡
Directions Leave the A1 onto the A61 north
of Ripon town centre, ½ mile.
⚞ Harrogate

SCARBOROUGH
Arosa Caravan & Camping Park Ltd.,
Ratten Row, Seamer, Scarborough,
Yorkshire (North), YO12 4QB
Tel: 01723 862166
Email: info@arosacamping.co.uk
www.arosacamping.co.uk
Pitches For Å ⊕ ➡ Total 118
Acreage 4½ **Open** Mar **to** 04-Jan
Access Good **Site** Level
Nearest Bus Stop (Miles) ¼
Ideal Touring.
Facilities ♿ ƒ ⅏ ⅏ ☏ ⊙ ⏚ ⚓ ◨ ☎
⚲ ⎅ ⊘ ⊗ ✗ ⍑ ⌂ ⎅ ⚓⊟ ⊟ ✓
⚡ ⚲
Nearest Town Scarborough
Directions 3 miles from Scarborough just off
the A64, in the village of Seamer on B1261
⚞ Seamer

SCARBOROUGH
Cayton Village Caravan Park, Mill Lane,
Cayton Bay, Scarborough, North Yorkshire,
YO11 3NN
Tel: 01723 583171
Email: info@caytontouring.co.uk
www.caytontouring.co.uk
Pitches For Å ⊕ ➡ ➡ Total 310
Acreage 21 **Open** Mar **to** Oct
Access Good **Site** Level
Nearest Bus Stop (Miles) Outside
Luxurious facilities, playground, shop, dog
walk and bus service from park entrance.
Seasonal pitches, winter storage and
caravan sales. Grass, hard standing and
super sites. Low season supersaver & OAP
discounts. Scarborough 3 miles, Filey 4
miles, Beach ½ mile. Adjoining village with
pubs, chip shop and PO.

Facilities ♿ ƒ ⊟ ⅏ ⅏ ☏ ⊙ ⏚ ⚓ ◨ ☎
⚲ ⎅ ⊘ ⊛ ⍑ ✗ ⚓⊟ ⊙ ⚡ ⚲ ⚲ ⚲
Nearest Town Scarborough
Directions On the A165, 3 miles south of
Scarborough turn inland at Cayton Bay
roundabout. The park is ½ a mile on the right
hand side. From the A64 take the B1261 sp
Filey. At Cayton take the second left at the
Blacksmiths Arms on to Mill Lane, the park
is on the left.
⚞ Seamer

SCARBOROUGH
Crows Nest Caravan Park, Gristhorpe,
Filey, Yorkshire (North), YO14 9PS
Tel: 01723 582206
Email:
enquiries@crowsnestcaravanpark.com
www.crowsnestcaravanpark.com
Pitches For Å ⊕ ➡ Total 50
Acreage 20 **Open** Mar **to** Oct
Access Good **Site** Lev/Slope
Nearest Bus Stop (Miles) Outside
New super pitches and toilet block.
Facilities ♿ ƒ ⊟ ⅏ ⅏ ☏ ⊙ ⏚ ⚓ ◨ ☎
⚲ ⎅ ⊘ ⊻ ⍑ ✗ ⌂ ⚓⊟ ⊟ ✓ ⚡
Nearest Town Scarborough
Directions Just off the A165 Scarborough
to Filey coast road.
⚞ Scarborough

SCARBOROUGH
Flower of May Holiday Park, Lebberston
Cliff, Scarborough, North Yorkshire, YO11
3NU
Tel: 01723 584311
Email: info@flowerofmay.com
www.flowerofmay.com
Pitches For Å ⊕ ➡ Total 300
Acreage 13 **Open** Easter **to** Oct
Access Good **Site** Level
Nearest Bus Stop (Miles) Outside
Family run park with superb facilities. Exciting
playground, luxury leisure centre with indoor
pool. Family bars. Supermarket. Serviced
pitches now available with metered electric.
Pets are welcome by arrangement.
Facilities ♿ ⚡ ƒ ⊟ ⅏ ☏ ⊙ ⏚ ⚓
⚲ ⚲ ⊘ ⊻ ⍑ ✗ ⌂ ⎅ ⚓⊟ ⊟ ✓
⚲
Nearest Town Scarborough
Directions 3 miles south of Scarborough off
A165 signposted at roundabout.
⚞ Scarborough

SCARBOROUGH
Jasmine Park, Cross Lane, Snainton,
Scarborough, North Yorkshire, YO13 9BE
Tel: 01723 859240
Email: enquiries@jasminepark.co.uk
www.jasminepark.co.uk
Pitches For Å ⊕ ➡ Total 50
Acreage 5 **Open** Mar **to** Oct
Access Good **Site** Level
Nearest Bus Stop (Miles) ½
Super pitches as standard.
Facilities ♿ ⚡ ƒ ⊟ ⅏ ☏ ⊙ ⏚ ⚓ ◨ ☎
⚲ ⎅ ⊘ ⌂ ⊛ ⚓⊟ ⊟ ✓ ⚡ ⚲
Nearest Town Scarborough

Come touring or camping with us
and discover the gorgeous
Yorkshire coast and countryside...

FLOWER OF MAY
family holiday parks

SCARBOROUGH | YORK | PICKERING | RIPON
BOOK: FLOWEROFMAY.COM | 01723 584311

Directions Just off the A170 between Scarborough(8miles) and Pickering (8miles) well signposted.
⚐ Scarborough

SCARBOROUGH
Lebberston Touring Park, Filey Road, Lebberston, Scarborough, North Yorkshire, YO11 3PE
Tel: 01723 585723
Email: info@lebberstontouring.co.uk
www.lebberstontouring.co.uk
Pitches For ⚏ ⚎ **Total** 125
Acreage 7½ **Open** Mar **to** Oct
Access Good **Site** Lev/Slope
Quiet, country park. Well spaced pitches with extensive views over Vale of Pickering and the Yorkshire Wolds. All pets on a lead. Dog area. Trailer tents accepted. Visit Britain 5 Stars and AA 4 Pennants.
Facilities 🖿 ⅀ 🏕 🔥 🍴 ⊙ ⌁ 🖢 ▣ 🍴
⅀ ▣ 🏕 🏢 ▣ 🕮 🐾 🌢
Nearest Town Scarborough/Filey
Directions From A64 or A165 take B1261 to Lebberston and follow signs.
⚐ Scarborough/Filey

SCARBOROUGH
Scalby Close Park, Burniston Road, Scarborough, North Yorkshire, YO13 0DA
Tel: 01723 365908
Email: info@scalbyclosepark.co.uk
www.scalbyclosepark.co.uk
Pitches For ⚐ ⚏ ⚎ **Total** 42
Acreage 3 **Open** Mar **to** Oct
Access Good **Site** Level
Nearest Bus Stop (Miles) ½
Sheltered, tree lined, level pitches. Ideal for touring North Yorkshire Moors and the coast. Near to Scarborough.
Facilities 🖿 ⅀ 🔥 🏕 🖢 🍴 ⊙ ⌁ 🖢 🍴
🏢 ▣ ▣ 🕮
Nearest Town Scarborough
Directions 2 miles north of Scarboroughs North Bay, signed 400 yards.
⚐ Scarborough

SCARBOROUGH
Scarborough Camping & Caravanning Club Site, Field Lane, Burniston Road, Scarborough, North Yorkshire, YO13 0DA
Tel: 01723 366212
Email:
scarborough.site@thefriendlyclub.co.uk
www.campingandcaravanningclub.co.uk/scarborough
Pitches For ⚐ ⚏ ⚎ **Total** 300
Acreage 20 **Open** Apr **to** 10-Nov
Nearest Bus Stop (Miles) Outside

Near the beach and the North Yorks Moors National Park. Non members welcome. You can also call us on 0845 130 7633.
Facilities 🖿 ⅀ 🔥 🏕 🖢 🍴 ⊙ ⌁ 🖢 🍴
🏢 🏕 🌢 🍴 🖢 ▣ 🕮 🌢
Directions Located 1 mile north of Scarborough on the west side of the A165.
⚐ Scarborough

SCARBOROUGH
Spring Willows Leisure Park, c/o Blue Sky Resorts, Main Road, Staxton, Scarborough, Yorkshire (North), YO12 4SB
Tel: 01723 891505
Email: swreception@springwillows.co.uk
www.springwillows.co.uk
Pitches For ⚐ ⚏ ⚎ **Total** 40
Open 10-Feb **to** 02-Jan
Access Good **Site** Level
Nearest Bus Stop (Miles) ¼
Easy reach of Bridlington, Filey,Scarborough and Whitby.
Facilities 🖿 ⅀ 🔥 🍴 ⌁ 🖢 ▣ 🍴
⅀ ⅀ 🏢 🏕 🖢 ▣ 🐾 ⌁ 🍴 🖢 ▣ 🕮 🌢
Nearest Town Scarborough
Directions From Scarborough take the A64 then A1039
⚐ Seamer

SELBY
Oakmere Caravan Park, Hill Farm, Skipwith, Selby, North Yorkshire, YO8 5SN
Tel: 01757 288910
Email: oakmerecaravan@aol.com
www.oakmerecaravan.webeden.co.uk
Pitches For ⚏ ⚎ **Total** 30
Acreage 5 **Open** Mar **to** Nov
Access Good **Site** Level
Nearest Bus Stop (Miles) Outside
On site coarse fishery. Close to historic York, the market town of Selby and a designer outlet. 45 minutes form the East coast. Strictly no tents.
Facilities 🖿 ⅀ 🔥 🍴 ⊙ ⌁ 🖢 ▣ 🍴
⅀ ⅀ 🏢 🖢 ▣ 🍴 🕮 🔥
Nearest Town York
Directions From York take the A19 signposted Selby. At Escrick turn left signposted Skipwith, Oakmere is 3 miles on the left.
⚐ York

SETTLE
Langcliffe Park, Settle, North Yorkshire, BD24 9LX
Tel: 01729 822387
Email: info@langcliffe.com
www.langcliffe.com
Pitches For ⚐ ⚏ ⚎ ⚎⅀ **Total** 75
Acreage 13 **Open** Mar **to** 15-Jan
Access Good **Site** Level

Nearest Bus Stop (Miles) ¼
Peaceful site in a beautiful area, surrounded by the Yorkshire Dales. Located 1 mile from Settle to Carlisle railway.
Facilities 🖿 ⅀ 🔥 🏕 🖢 🍴 ⊙ ⌁ 🖢 ▣ 🍴
⅀ 🏢 ⊙ 🏕 🌢 🍴 🖢 ▣ 🕮 🌢
Nearest Town Settle
Directions From the A65 south, take the B6479 into Settle. Go through Market Square, under the viaduct, then turn first right to Horton in Ribblesdale, Park is on the left.
⚐ Settle

SKIPTON
Eshton Road Caravan Site, Eshton Road, Gargrave, Nr Skipton, North Yorkshire, BD23 3PN
Tel: 01756 749229
Pitches For ⚐ ⚏ ⚎ **Total** 0
Acreage 2 **Open** All Year
Access Good **Site** Level
Nearest Bus Stop (Miles) Outside
Alongside the Leeds Liverpool Canal, on the edge of the Yorkshire Dales National Park.
Facilities ⅀ 🔥 🏕 🖢 🍴 ⊙ ⌁ 🍴 🖢 🔥 🗶
Directions 4 miles from Skipton on the A65.
⚐ Gargrave

SLINGSBY
Robin Hood Caravan Park, Slingsby, York, North Yorkshire, YO62 4AP
Tel: 01653 628391
Email: info@robinhoodcaravanpark.co.uk
www.robinhoodcaravanpark.co.uk
Pitches For ⚐ ⚏ ⚎ **Total** 48
Acreage 4 **Open** Mar **to** Oct
Access Good **Site** Level
Nearest Bus Stop (Miles) ¼
In the heart of picturesque Ryedale, this privately owned park offers peace and tranquillity. An ideal centre for York, the Moors, Heartbeat country and the seaside resorts of Scarborough, Whitby and Filey.
Facilities 🖿 🗶 ⅀ 🔥 🏕 🖢 🍴 ⊙ ⌁ 🖢
▣ 🍴 ⅀ ⅀ 🏢 ⊙ 🏕 🌢 🍴 🖢 ▣ 🕮 🌢
Nearest Town Malton
Directions Direct access from the B1257 Malton to Helmsley road.
⚐ Malton

SLINGSBY
Slingsby Camping & Caravanning Club Site, Railway Street, Slingsby, North Yorkshire, YO62 4AN
Tel: 01653 628335
Email: slingsby.site@thefriendlyclub.co.uk
www.campingandcaravanningclub.co.uk/slingsby

Pitches For ▲ ⊞ ⊟ Total 60
Acreage 2 Open Apr to 10-Nov
Access Good Site Level
Nearest Bus Stop (Miles) ½
An ideal base to discover the North Yorkshire Moors. York with all its attractions is just a short drive away. BTB 5 Star Graded and AA 3 Pennants. Non members welcome. You can also call us on 0845 130 7633.
Facilities ⬧ ⓕ Ⓗ ⬚⬚ ⬚⬚ ⌐ ☺⬚ ⬚ ⬚ ⬚ ⬚
⬚⬚ ⓞ ⬚⬚⬚⬚ �≋ ⬚
Directions From the A64 turn left signposted Castle Howard, drive through Castle Howard Estate until you reach the Malton to Helmsly road. Go straight into Slingsby Village, go round the bend onto Railway Street and continue through the village ¼ mile to the site entrance.
⬌ Malton

SNEATON

North Yorkshire Moors Caravan Club Site, Sneaton, Whitby, North Yorkshire, YO22 5JE
Tel: 01947 810505
www.caravanclub.co.uk
Pitches For ⊞ ⊟ Total 92
Acreage 12 Open Mar to Nov
Access Good Site Level
Tranquil site in the North Yorks Moors National Park (Heartbeat country). 5 miles from a sandy beach. Ideal for walkers. Boules pitch and mini golf on site. Own sanitation required. Non members welcome. Booking essential.
Facilities ⓕ Ⓗ ⬚ ⬚⬚ ⬚⬚ ⓞ ⬚⬚⬚⬚ ⬚
Directions From the A171 take the B1416 signposted Ruswarp, after 3¾ miles on a sharp left hand bend continue through red gates signposted Maybeck (care required), site is ½ mile on the right.
⬌ Whitby

TADCASTER

Whitecote Caravan Park, Ryther Road, Ulleskelf, Nr Tadcaster, North Yorkshire, LS24 9DY
Tel: 01937 835231
www.whitecotecaravanpark.co.uk
Pitches For ▲ ⊞ ⊟ Total 0
Open Mar to Jan
Access Good Site Level
Nearest Bus Stop (Miles) ¼
Holiday caravan for hire.
Facilities ⓕ ⬚⬚ ⬚⬚ ⌐ ⬚
⬚⬚ ⓞ ⬚ ⬚⬚⬚⬚ �≋
Nearest Town York
⬌ Ulleskelf

THIRSK

Hillside Caravan Park, Canvas Farm, Knayton, Thirsk, North Yorkshire, YO7 4BR
Tel: 01845 537349
Email: info@hillsidecaravanpark.co.uk
www.hillsidecaravanpark.co.uk
Pitches For ⊞ ⊟ Total 50
Acreage 9 Open 04-Feb to 04-Jan
Access Good Site Level
Quiet family run site in a beautiful rural location at the foot of the Hambleton Hills. Ideally situated for exploring the Yorkshire Moors and Dales, and Herriot country. Good walking area.
Facilities ⬧ ⓕ ⬚ Ⓗ ⬚⬚ ⬚⬚ ⌐ ☺⬚ ⬚ ⬚ ⬚
⬚ ⬚⬚⬚⬚ ⬚ ✦ �≋ ⬚
Nearest Town Thirsk
Directions Exit the A19 dual carriageway signposted Knayton, and follow signs into Knayton Village. Pass the Dog & Gun Public House on the left and leave the village, go straight over the crossroads and the site entrance is 1 mile on the left.
⬌ Northallerton

THIRSK

Sowerby Caravan Park, Sowerby, Thirsk, North Yorkshire, YO7 3AG
Tel: 01845 522753
Email: sowerbycaravans@btconnect.com
www.ukparks.co.uk/sowerby
Pitches For ⊞ ⊟ Total 25
Acreage 1½ Open Mar to Oct
Access Good Site Level
Nearest Bus Stop (Miles) ½
Alongside a river. Ideal location for touring.
Facilities ⬧ ⬧ ⓕ Ⓗ ⬚⬚ ⌐ ☺⬚ ⬚ ⬚ ⬚
⬚⬚ ⓞ ⬚ ✦ ⬚⬚⬚⬚ ⬚ �≋
Nearest Town Thirsk
Directions From Thirsk go through Sowerby towards Dalton, the park is ½ mile south of Sowerby on the right.
⬌ Thirsk

THIRSK

Thirsk Racecourse Caravan Club Site, Thirsk, North Yorkshire, YO7 1QL
Tel: 01845 525266
www.caravanclub.co.uk
Pitches For ▲ ⊞ ⊟ Total 60
Acreage 3 Open 22-Mar to 07-Oct
Access Good Site Level
Situated in the racecourse, surrounded by the Dales and Moors. Just a 5 minute walk to Thirsk town centre. Close to Rievaulx Abbey. Non members welcome. Booking essential.
Facilities ⬧ Ⓗ ⬚⬚ ⌐ ⬚ ⌐ ⬚⬚ ⌐ ⬚
⬚ ⬚⬚ ⓞ ⬚⬚⬚⬚ ⬚
Nearest Town Thirsk
Directions Use following route only caravans are not allowed on A170 Sutton Bank. Leave A1 at Ripon-Thirsk junction onto A61 Signed Thirsk. Site entranceis on the left(just past racecourse buildings)
⬌ Thirsk

THORNABYONTEES

White Water Park Caravan Club Site, Tees Barrage, StocktononTees, North Yorkshire, TS18 2QW
Tel: 01642 634880
www.caravanclub.co.uk
Pitches For ▲ ⊞ ⊟ Total 115
Acreage 15 Open All Year
Access Good Site Level
Nearest Bus Stop (Miles) ½
Part of the largest white water canoeing and rafting course in Britain. Teeside Park nearby provides shopping, cinema and bowling alley. Just a short drive to the coast. Non members welcome. Booking essential.
Facilities ⬧ ⓕ ⬚ Ⓗ ⬚⬚ ⌐ ☺⬚ ⬚ ⬚
⬚ ⓞ ⬚ ⬚⬚ ✦ ⬚⬚⬚⬚ ⬚ �≋
Nearest Town Stockton-on-Tees
Directions From A19 take A66 sp Darlington. Follow sp for Teeside Retail Park, continue in n/side lane after 200yds take 1st exit sp Teeside Retail Park. At lights t rt over A66, cross r/way br straight over mini r/about cross Tees Barrage Bridge, site is on rt past Talpore Pub.
⬌ Stockton-on-Tees

WHITBY

Abbot's House Farm Camping & Caravan Site, Abbot's House Farm, Goathland, Whitby, North Yorkshire, YO22 5NH
Tel: 01947 896270
www.abbotshouse.org.uk
Pitches For ▲ ⊞ ⊟ Total 90
Acreage 2½ Open Mar to Oct
Access Good Site Level
Nearest Bus Stop (Miles) ½

The North Yorkshire Moors Steam Railway runs through the farm. Yorkshire Televisions Heartbeat country. 9 miles from Whitby, 25 miles from Scarborough and 40 miles from York.
Facilities ⬧ ⓕ Ⓗ ⬚⬚ ⬚⬚ ⌐ ☺⬚ ⬚ ⬚
⬚⬚ ⬚⬚ ⬚⬚⬚⬚ ⬚ ⬚
Nearest Town Whitby
Directions From Whitby take the A171 west for approx. 3 miles, turn south onto the A169, after approx. 6 miles turn right signposted Goathland. Turn left opposite Goathland Garage.
⬌ Goathland

WHITBY

Brow House Farm Caravan Site, Brow House Farm, Goathland, Whitby, Yorkshire (North), YO22 5NP
Tel: 01947 896274
Email: browhousefarm@btinternet.com
Pitches For ▲ ⊞ ⊟ Total 0
Acreage 2 Open Mar to Oct
Access Good Site Level
Nearest Bus Stop (Miles) ¼
Situated in Heartbeat Country near Greengrass Farm and the North Yorkshire Moors. Historic steam railway runs through the village.
Facilities ⓕ ⬚⬚ ⌐ ☺⬚ ⬚ ⬚⬚ ⓞ ⬚⬚⬚⬚ ⬚
Nearest Town Whitby
Directions Whitby A169 turn off for Goatland through village past church uphill on left.
⬌ Goatland

WHITBY

Grouse Hill Caravan & Camping Park, Nr Robin Hoods Bay, Fylingdales, Whitby, North Yorkshire, YO22 4QH
Tel: 01947 880543/881230
Email: info@grousehill.co.uk
www.grousehill.co.uk
Pitches For ▲ ⊞ ⊟ Total 198
Acreage 14 Open Mar to Oct
Access Good Site Level
Nearest Bus Stop (Miles) ¼
Friendly family run site, set in a tranquil moorland valley. Excellent base to explore the coast and country. 3 miles to the nearest beach (Boggle Hole), and a 5 minute walk to the local country inn.
Facilities ⬧ ⓕ Ⓗ ⬚⬚ ⌐ ☺⬚ ⬚ ⬚ ⬚
⬚⬚ ⬚⬚ ⓞ ⬚ ✗ ⬚⬚⬚⬚ ⬚ �≋ ✦ ☺
Nearest Town Whitby
Directions Signed just off the A171 Scarborough to Whitby road, behind the Flask Inn.
⬌ Whitby

WHITBY

Ladycross Plantation, Egton, Whitby, Yorkshire (North), YO21 1UA
Tel: 01947 895502
Email: enquiries@ladycrossplantation.co.uk
www.ladycrossplantation.co.uk
Pitches For ▲ ⊞ ⊟ ⬚ Total 140
Acreage 130 Open Mar to Nov
Access Good Site Level
Nearest Bus Stop (Miles) ¼
Ideal for exploring national park and the north east coast. David Bellamy Gold Award for Conservation.
Facilities ⬧ ⓕ ⬚ Ⓗ ⬚⬚ ⌐ ☺⬚ ⬚ ⬚
⬚⬚ ⬚ ⬚ ☺ ☺ ☺
Nearest Town Whitby
Directions Follow A171 From Whitby to Middlesborough for approx 4 miles turn left Towards Egton.
⬌ Egton Bridge

WHITBY

Middlewood Farm Holiday Park,
Middlewood Lane, Fylingthorpe, Robin
Hoods Bay, Whitby, North Yorkshire, YO22
4UF
Tel: 01947 880414
Email: info@middlewoodfarm.com
www.middlewoodfarm.com
Pitches For Å ⊕ ⊟ **Total** 120
Acreage 7 **Open** Mar to 04-Jan
Access Good **Site** Level
Nearest Bus Stop (Miles) ¼
Peaceful family park, 10 minutes walk to the
beach, pubs, shops and Robin Hoods Bay.
Disabled facilities, bath and parent and baby
room. Only 5 miles from Whitby. Magnificent
views and walks.
Facilities Symbols
Nearest Town Whitby
Directions Signposted. Take the A171
Scarborough to Whitby road, 3 miles south
of Whitby take the Fylingthorpe and Robin
Hoods Bay road. follow the browncaravan
and camping signs to guide you onto
Middlewood Lane. park is 500 yds on left.
⇌ Whitby

WHITBY

Northcliffe and Seaview Holiday Parks,
High Hawsker, Whitby, North Yorkshire,
YO22 4LL
Tel: 01947 880477
Email: enquiries@northcliffe-seaview.com
www.northcliffe-seaview.com
Pitches For ⊕ **Total** 62
Open 01-Mar to 07-Nov
Access Good
Nearest Bus Stop (Miles) ¼
Exclusive SEASONAL ONLY Touring Park.
Luxury Award Winning park with panoramic
sea views. All weather, all mains, individual
plots. Childrens play park. Coast cafe/bar,
farmstyle shop & deli, licensed bar. Holiday
Homes for sale or hire. David Bellamy Gold
award park.
Facilities Symbols
Nearest Town Whitby
Directions South from Whitby 3 miles, turn
left B1447 to Robin Hoods Bay.
⇌ Whitby

WHITBY

Ugthorpe Lodge Caravan Park,
Guisborough Road, Ugthorpe, Nr Whitby,
Yorkshire (North), YO21 2BE
Tel: 01947 840518
Pitches For Å ⊕ ⊟ **Total** 40
Open Apr to Oct
Access Good **Site** Level
Nearest Bus Stop (Miles) ¼

5 miles from the beach. Fishing nearby.
Facilities Symbols
Nearest Town Whitby
Directions On the A171, 9 miles from Whitby
and 8 miles from Guisborough.
⇌ Lealholme

YORK

Acomb Grange, Grange Lane, York, YO23
3QZ
Tel: 01904 797387
Email: info@acombgrange.co.uk
www.acombgrange.co.uk
Pitches For Å ⊕ ⊟ ⊟≤ **Total** 5
Acreage 1 **Open** All Year
Access Fair **Site** Level
Nearest Bus Stop (Miles) ½
Fishing on site in a restored Mediaeval moat.
Near the City of York and the Moors and
Dales.
Facilities Symbols
Nearest Town York
Directions Obtain directions by visiting web
site. In suburbs of a city.
⇌ York

YORK

Cawood Park, Ryther Road, Cawood, Vale
of York, North Yorkshire, YO8 3TT
Tel: 01757 268450
Email: enquiries@cawoodpark.com
www.cawoodpark.com
Pitches For ⊕ ⊟ **Total** 42
Acreage 10 **Open** All Year
Access Good **Site** Level
Nearest Bus Stop (Miles) ½
Here at Cawood Holiday Park, which is a
quiet rural park, we have worked hard to
create an environment which keeps its
natural simplicity to provide a trouble free
holiday. Some pitches have views over our
fishing lake. Ideal for York.
Facilities Symbols
Nearest Town York/Selby
Directions From the A19 take the B1222
signposted Cawood, oppositethe entrance to
Escrick Park Estate. Follow road and go over
the bridge, at the traffic lights turn right and
Cawood Park is ½ a mile on the left.
⇌ York/Selby

YORK

Chowdene Camping & Caravan Site,
Chowdene, Malton Road, York, YO32 9TD
Tel: 01904 289359
Email: touraco@talktalk.net
www.caravanstv.com
Pitches For Å ⊕ ⊟ ⊟≤ **Total** 20
Acreage 1½ **Open** Mar to Nov
Access Good **Site** Level

Nearest Bus Stop (Miles) Outside
Small, quiet, family run site. VW Camper
friendly and we welcome the smaller camper
vehicles. Excellent for York and its many
attractions. Adjacent to a Park & Ride. Some
hardstandings available.
Facilities Symbols
Directions From the A1 take the A64 for approx
17 miles. Ignoring the first turning, take the
A1036 at the roundabout for York. After 1 mile
(at the third roudabout with a large tile shop),
continue and drive slowly for 200 yards and
see our site sign on the right, after the bungalow
turn into our drive and go 100 yards to the site.
⇌ York

YORK

Goosewood Holiday Park, Sutton-on-the-
Forest, York, North Yorkshire, YO61 1ET
Tel: 01347 810829
Email: enquiries@goosewood.co.uk
www.flowerofmay.com
Pitches For ⊕ ⊟ **Total** 100
Acreage 15 **Open** Mar to 02-Jan
Access Good **Site** Level
Nearest Bus Stop (Miles) ¼
Wooded walks and a fishing lake. Ideal for
sightseeing in York and the Dales. Pets
welcome by arrangement.
Facilities Symbols
Nearest Town York
Directions From the A1237 York ring road,
take the B1363 to Helmsley, 4 miles to
Goosewood.
⇌ York

YORK

Home Farm Camping & Caravan Park,
Moreby, Stillingfleet, York, North Yorkshire,
YO19 6HN
Tel: 01904 728263
Email: home_farm@hotmail.co.uk
Pitches For Å ⊕ ⊟ **Total** 25
Acreage 3 **Open** Feb to Dec
Access Good **Site** Level
Nearest Bus Stop (Miles) Outside
Alongside the River Ouse. Ideal base to tour
York and surrounding Dales and North
Yorkshire Moors. 4 miles to the nearest shop
or supermarket.
Facilities Symbols
Nearest Town York
Directions On the B1222 between the village
of Naburn and Stllingfleet. 6 miles south of
York City walls.
⇌ York

YORK

Moor End Farm, Acaster Malbis, York, YO23 2UQ
Tel: 01904 706727
Email: roger@acaster99.fsnet.co.uk
www.moorendfarm.co.uk
Pitches For 🏕 ⊞ 🚐 **Total** 20
Acreage 1 **Open** Easter **to** Oct
Access Good **Site** Level
Nearest Bus Stop (Miles) ¼
Ideal for York and the York/Selby cycle track.
Facilities ⬚ 🚿 🖽 🚻 🍴 ⊙ ⊿ 🔌 ⊡ 🔥 🚻 🛒
Nearest Town York
Directions Follow signs from A64/1237 intersection at Copmanthorpe.
🚆 York

YORK

Moorside Caravan Park, Lords Moor Lane, Strensall, York, YO32 5XJ
Tel: 01904 491865/491208
www.moorsidecaravanpark.co.uk
Pitches For 🏕 ⊞ 🚐 **Total** 50
Open Mar **to** Oct
Access Good **Site** Level
NO CHILDREN. Fishing lake on site. Near York Golf Course.
Facilities ⬚ 🚿 🖽 🚻 🍴 ⊙ ⊿ 🔌 ⊡ 🛒 🍴 🛒 🔌 🔥 ♨ 🛒
Nearest Town York
Directions Take the A1237, then take the Strensall turn and head towards Flaxton.
🚆 York

YORK

Sheriff Hutton Camping & Caravanning Club Site, Bracken Hill, Sheriff Hutton, North Yorkshire, YO60 6QG
Tel: 01347 878660
Email: sheriff.hutton@thefriendlyclub.co.uk
www.campingandcaravanningclub.co.uk/sheriffhutton
Pitches For 🏕 ⊞ 🚐 **Total** 90
Acreage 10 **Open** Apr **to** 10-Nov
Access Good **Site** Level
Nearest Bus Stop (Miles) ¾
Close to the city of York. BTB 4 Star Graded, AA 3 Pennants and Loo of the Year Award. Non members welcome. You can also call us on 0845 130 7633.
Facilities ⬚ 🚿 🖽 🚻 🍴 ⊙ ⊿ 🔌 ⊡ 🛒 🍴 🔌 ⊙ 🔥 🚻 ⊡ 🛒 ♨ 🔌 🛒
Nearest Town York
Directions From York follow signposts for Earswick Strensall, keep left at the filling station and Ship Inn, site is second on the right.
🚆 York

YORK

The Ponderosa Caravan Park, East Moor, SuttonontheForest, Nr York, North Yorkshire, YO61 1ET
Tel: 01347 811233
Pitches For 🏕 ⊞ 🚐 **Total** 40
Acreage 3 **Open** All Year
Access Good **Site** Level
Nearest Bus Stop (Miles) Outside
Near to the historic city of York, North Yorkshire Moors and many local attractions.
Facilities 🚿 🖽 🚻 🍴 ⊙ ⊿ 🔌 ⊡ 🛒 🔌 🛒 🔥 🚻 🛒
Nearest Town York
Directions Signposted 800 yards off the B1363 Wigginton to Helmsley road, 6 miles from York.
🚆 York

YORK

Willow House Caravan Park, Wigginton Road, Wigginton, York, North Yorkshire, YO32 2RH
Tel: 01904 750060
Email: info@willowhouseyork.co.uk
www.willowhouseyork.co.uk
Pitches For 🏕 ⊞ 🚐 🚐 **Total** 32
Acreage 4 **Open** All Year
Access Good **Site** Level
Nearest Bus Stop (Miles) Outside
ADULTS ONLY SITE. 3 miles from the centre of York. Handy for the Yorkshire Moors, Wolds, Dales and the coast. Shopping centres nearby.
Facilities ⬚ 🚿 🖽 🚻 🍴 ⊙ ⊿ 🔌 ⊡ 🛒 ♨ 🔌 🍴 🔥 ⊡ 🛒 🔌 🛒 ♨
Nearest Town York
Directions From York take the A1237 bypass to the B1363 Wigginton Road, site is ½ a mile on the right.
🚆 York

YORK

York Beechwood Grange Caravan Club Site, Malton Road, York, YO32 9TH
Tel: 01904 424637
www.caravanclub.co.uk
Pitches For ⊞ 🚐 **Total** 115
Acreage 11 **Open** Mar **to** Jan
Access Good **Site** Level
Set in open countryside, yet only 3 miles from York. Boules pitch on site. Plenty to do and see in York from river cruises to the Jorvik Viking Centre and the National Railway Museum. Non members welcome. Booking essential.
Facilities ⬚ 🚿 🖽 🚻 🍴 ⊙ ⊡ 🛒 ♨ 🔌 ⊙ 🔥 🚻 ⊡ 🛒
Nearest Town York
Directions Turn off the A64 onto the A1237 signposted Thirsk. At roundabout turn right into road signposted local traffic only, site is at the end of the drive.
🚆 York

YORK

York Meadows Caravan Park York Road, Sheriff Hutton, York, YO60 6QP
Tel: 01347 878508
Email: reception@yorkmeadowscaravan.com
www.yorkmeadowscaravanpark.com
Pitches For 🏕 ⊞ 🚐 🚐 **Total** 70
Acreage 15 **Open** Mar **to** Oct
Access Good **Site** Level
Ideal for visiting York, coastal areas, North York Moors, Castle Howard. Centre of three major walking routes.
Facilities ⬚ 🚿 🖽 🖽 🚻 🍴 ⊙ ⊿ 🔌 ⊡ 🛒 ♨ 🔌 ⊙ 🔥 🚻 ⊡ 🛒 ♨ 🛒
Nearest Town York
Directions 8 miles from York. Take A64 to Scarborough. Turn left to Flaxton & Sheriff Hutton. Turn left to Strensall. Park is on the right
🚆 York

YORK

York Rowntree Park Caravan Club Site, Terry Avenue, York, YO23 1JQ
Tel: 01904 658997
www.caravanclub.co.uk
Pitches For 🏕 ⊞ 🚐 **Total** 102
Acreage 4 **Open** All Year
Access Good **Site** Level
Nearest Bus Stop (Miles) ½
On the banks of the River Ouse. Within walking distance of York. Close to York Minster, Jorvik Viking Centre, Castle Howard, York Castle Museum and The Shambles. Non members welcome. Booking essential.

Facilities ⬚ 🚿 🖽 🚻 🍴 ⊙ 🔌 ⊡ 🛒 🔌 🍴 ⊙ 🔥 🚻 ⊡ 🛒 ♨
Directions From A64 south of York take A19 sp York Centre, DO NOT turn onto A1237. After 2 mls take the one-way system sp City Centre, at Mecca Bingo keep It continue over bridge. T It immediately before Swan Pub after 250 yds t rt into Terry Ave, site on right.
🚆 York

YORK

York Touring Caravan Site, Towthorpe Moor Lane, Towthorpe, York, YO32 9ST
Tel: 01904 499275
Email: info@yorkcaravansite.co.uk
www.yorkcaravansite.co.uk
Pitches For 🏕 ⊞ 🚐 **Total** 28
Open All Year
Access Good **Site** Level
Golf range and 9 hole golf course on site. ETB 4 Star Graded and AA 4 Pennants.
Facilities ⬚ 🚿 🖽 🚻 🍴 ⊙ ⊿ 🔌 ⊡ 🛒 🔌 🍴 🔥 🚻 ⊡ 🛒 ♨ 🛒
Nearest Town York
Directions From the A64 take turnoff signposted Strensall and Haxby, site is 1½ miles on the left.
🚆 York

YORKSHIRE (SOUTH)

BARNSLEY

Greensprings Touring Park, Rockley Lane, Worsbrough, Barnsley, South Yorkshire, S75 3DS
Tel: 01226 288298
Pitches For 🏕 ⊞ 🚐 🚐 ⊟ **Total** 60
Acreage 4 **Open** Apr **to** Oct
Access Good **Site** Lev/Slope
Nearest Bus Stop (Miles) 1
Country site, well wooded with pleasant walks. Convenient for the M1. Ideal location for Sheffield venues.
Facilities 🚿 🖽 🚻 🍴 ⊙ ⊿ 🔌 ⊡ ♨ 🔌 ⊙ 🔥 🚻 ⊡ 🛒
Nearest Town Barnsley
Directions Junction 36 on M1. A61 to Barnsley, take left turn after ¼ mile signed to Pilley. Site is 1 mile along this road.
🚆 Barnsley

ROTHERHAM

Thrybergh Country Park, Doncaster Road, Thrybergh, Rotherham, South Yorkshire, S65 4NU
Tel: 01709 850353
www.rotherham.gov.uk
Pitches For ⊞ 🚐 **Total** 24
Acreage 1½ **Open** All Year
Access Good **Site** Level
Nearest Bus Stop (Miles) Outside
35 acre fly fishery with surfaced footpath on site. 35 acresof beautiful countryside, lakeside cafe.
Facilities ⬚ 🚿 🖽 🚻 🍴 ⊙ 🛒 ♨ 🔌 🚻 🔥 🚻 ⊡ 🛒 🔌
Nearest Town Rotherham
Directions 4 miles north of Rotherham on the A630 between Thrybergh and Hooton Roberts.
🚆 Rotherham

SHEFFIELD

Fox Hagg Farm, Lodge Lane, Rivelin, Sheffield, South Yorkshire, S6 5SN
Tel: 0114 230 5589
Pitches For 🏕 ⊞ 🚐 **Total** 60
Acreage 2 **Open** Apr **to** Oct
Access Good **Site** Level
Nearest Bus Stop (Miles) ¼
On the outskirts of the Peak District, scenic views and nature walks. Ideal touring. All new showers.

Facilities ♪ ⊞ 🄷 ⅏ ♉ ⌂ ⊙ ⅃ 🛁 ℣ ⚲ ⚐
Nearest Town Sheffield
Directions Off the A57, near Rivelin Post Office.
🚊 Sheffield

YORKSHIRE (WEST)

ELLAND

Elland Hall Farm Caravan Site, Exley Lane, Elland, West Yorkshire, HX5 0SL
Tel: 01422 372325
Email: enquiries@ellandhallfarm.co.uk
www.ellandhallfarm.co.uk
Pitches For ▲ ⌂ ⛟ **Total** 10
Acreage 1 **Open** Apr to Oct
Access Good **Site** Level
Facilities ♪ 🄷 ⅏ ⌂ ⊙ ℣ ⊙ 🄿
Directions From Elland take the Brighouse road, at the railway bridge turn left into Exley Lane.
🚊 Halifax

HAWORTH

Upwood Holiday Park, Blackmoor Road, Oxenhope, Haworth, West Yorkshire, BD22 9SS
Tel: 01535 644242
Email: info@upwoodpark.co.uk
www.upwoodpark.co.uk
Pitches For ▲ ⌂ ⛟ **Total** 100
Acreage 10 **Open** Mar to 04-Jan
Access Good **Site** Lev/Slope
Nearest Bus Stop (Miles) Outside
Pleasantly situated close to the Yorkshire Dales National Park. Beautiful, panoramic views over the surrounding countryside. One mile from the Bronte Village of Haworth and Worth Steam Railway. 12 Camping and Mega Pods available.
Facilities ♿ ♪ 🄷 ⅏ ⌂ ⊙ ⅃ 🄼 ⛽ 🄿
⚿ ⚑ ⚙ ✕ 🄣 ♨ 🄼 🄿⊞ 🄴 ⚲ ⚐
Nearest Town Keighley
Directions Situated off the A629 Keighley to Halifax road. Turn by the Flappit Pub onto the B6144 towards Haworth, after 1 mile turn left onto Blackmoor Road, and the site entrance is by the bus stop.
🚊 Keighley

HEBDEN BRIDGE

Hebden Bridge Caravan Club Site, Cragg Vale, Hebden Bridge, West Yorkshire, HX7 5RU
Tel: 01422 882531
www.caravanclub.co.uk
Pitches For ⌂ ⛟ **Total** 45
Acreage 2½ **Open** Mar to Nov
Access Good **Site** Level
Nearest Bus Stop (Miles) Outside
Screened site bordered by a stream. Three walks adjacent to the site. Visit Brontes Haworth Parsonage, walk the Moors and Pennine Way. Horse drawn canal boat rides available at Hebden Bridge (2½ miles). Own sanitation required. Non members welcome. Booking essential.
Facilities ♪ 🄷 ⅏ ⚿ ℣ ⊙ ⛽ 🄿 ⊟
Nearest Town Hebden Bridge
Directions Leave the A646 in Mytholmroyd Village and take the B6138 signposted Rochdale (care required, narrow bridge). Site is 1 mile on the right.
🚊 Hebden Bridge

LEEDS

Glenfield Caravan Park, 120 Blackmoor Lane, Bardsey, Leeds, West Yorkshire, LS17 9DZ
Tel: 01937 574657
Email: glenfieldcp@aol.com
www.ukparks.co.uk/glenfieldcp

Pitches For ▲ ⌂ ⛟ **Total** 30
Acreage 3½ **Open** All Year
Access Good **Site** Level
Nearest Bus Stop (Miles) Outside
Beautifully kept park. Lovely walks and places to eat nearby. Close to golf courses and a nature reserve for walking. Easy access and ideal touring base. New 5 Star heated shower block with toilets and laundry. Family room.
Facilities ♿ ♪ 🄷 ⅏ ⌂ ⅃ 🄼 ⛽
℣ ⊙ ⛽ ⚲ ⚐ ⚲
Directions From Leeds take the A58 towards Wetherby, after approx 8 miles turn left at Shadwell Harewood sign. After 1 mile take right hand fork, continue for 1 mile and site is on the left at the bottom of the hill.
🚊 Leeds

LEEDS

Moor Lodge Caravan Park, Blackmoor Lane, Bardsey, Leeds, West Yorkshire, LS17 9DZ
Tel: 01937 572424
Email: moorlodgecp@aol.com
www.moorlodgecaravanpark.co.uk
Pitches For ▲ ⌂ ⛟ **Total** 12
Acreage 8 **Open** All Year
Access Good **Site** Level
Nearest Bus Stop (Miles) ½
ADULTS ONLY. Immaculate countryside park.
Facilities ⚡ ♪ 🄷 ⅏ ⌂ ⊙ ⛽ 🄼 🄿
℣ ⊙ ⛽ 🄷 ⚐
Nearest Town Leeds
Directions Turn off the A1 at Wetherby and take the A58 towards Leeds for 4 miles, turn right after the New Inn Pub (Ling Lane). At the crossroads turn right and Moor Lodge is at the bottom of the hill on the right.
🚊 Leeds

OTLEY

Clarion Lodge Campsite, West Chevin Road, Menston, Nr Otley, West Yorkshire, LS29 6BG
Tel: 01943 876300
Email: clarionlodgecamp@aol.com
www.clarionlodgecampsite.co.uk
Pitches For ▲ ⌂ ⛟ **Total** 20
Acreage 2 **Open** Mar to Nov
Access Good **Site** Level
Nearest Bus Stop (Miles) ½
Small, quiet, family run with spectacular countryside views.
Facilities ♪ 🄷 ⅏ ⌂ ⊙ ⛽ 🄼 🄿
Nearest Town Otley
Directions From Otley take the A660 towards Guiseley. Turn left at the crossroads near the Hare & Hounds onto Buckle Lane, keep left at Chevin Inn and the Site is 200 yards on the right.
🚊 Guiseley

SHIPLEY

Dobrudden Caravan Park, Baildon Moor, Baildon, Shipley, West Yorkshire, BD17 5EE
Tel: 01274 581016
Email: liz@dobrudden.co.uk
www.dobrudden.co.uk
Pitches For ▲ ⌂ ⛟ 🚐≾ **Total** 30
Acreage 4 **Open** Feb to Jan
Access Good **Site** Level
Nearest Bus Stop (Miles) 3
In the middle of moorland, handy for the Dales and Moors. Local to Bronte Country. Ideal for touring and visiting Leeds.
Facilities ♪ 🄷 ⅏ ⌂ ⊙ ⛽ 🄼 🄿
℣ ⊙ ✕ 🄷 ⛽ 🄿 ⚐
Nearest Town Shipley
🚊 Baildon

SILSDEN

Brown Bank Caravan Park, Brown Bank Lane, Silsden, West Yorkshire, BD20 0NN
Tel: 01535 653241
Email: timlaycock@btconnect.com
Pitches For ▲ ⌂ ⛟ **Total** 15
Acreage 12 **Open** Apr to Oct
Access Good **Site** Level
Nearest Bus Stop (Miles) Outside
On the edge of Ilkley Moor with good views and excellent walks. Ideal base for touring. Many attractions within 15 miles.
Facilities ♿ ♪ 🄷 ⅏ ⌂ ⊙ ⅃ ⛽
⊙ ⚑ 🄼 ⛽ 🄿 ⛽ ⚲
Directions From Silsden take the A6034, turn right on the bend into Brown Bank Lane, site is 1½ miles on the right. Also signposted from Addingham on the A6034.
🚊 Steeton

SILSDEN

Dales Bank Holiday Park, Low Lane, Silsden, Keighley, West Yorkshire, BD20 9JH
Tel: 01535 653321/656523
Pitches For ▲ ⌂ ⛟ **Total** 52
Acreage 5 **Open** Apr to Oct
Access Good **Site** Level
Nearest Bus Stop (Miles) 1
Central for Ilkley, Craven Dales and Bronte Country. Bed & Breakfast available.
Facilities ♿ 🄷 ⅏ ⌂ ⊙ ⅃ ⛽
℣ ⊙ ⚑ ✕ ♈ ♨ 🄼 ⛽ 🄿 ⛽ ⚲ ⚲
Nearest Town Silsden
Directions In Silsden turn up one way street Briggate, after 100 yards turn into Bradley Road, after ¾ miles turn right, site entrance is third on the right.
🚊 Steeton

SILSDEN

Lower Heights Farm Camping Silsden, West Yorkshire, BD20 9HW
Tel: 01535 653035
Email: mmsrowling@aol.com
Pitches For ▲ ⌂ ⛟ 🚐≾ **Total** 5
Acreage 2 **Open** All year
Access Good **Site** Level
Nearest Bus Stop (Miles) ½
Quiet site with good views. Only 5 caravan pitches but any number of tents. Facebook.
Facilities ♪ 🄷 ⅏ ⌂ ⛽ 🛁 ℣ 🄿
Nearest Town Skipton
Directions 1 mile from Silsden off A6034.
🚊 Steeton

WETHERBY

Haighfield Caravan Park, 5 Blackmoor Lane, Bardsey, Leeds, West Yorkshire, LS17 9DY
Tel: 01937 574658
Email: haighfieldcp@aol.com
www.haighfieldcaravanpark.co.uk
Pitches For ▲ ⌂ ⛟ 🚐≾ **Total** 30
Acreage 3 **Open** All Year
Site Level
Nearest Bus Stop (Miles) ½
Small family run and owned Park. Close to Leeds, York and Harrogate. Ideal for touring Yorkshire.
Facilities ♿ ⚡ ♪ 🄷 ⅏ ⌂ ⊙ ⅃ 🄼
🄿 ℣ ⊙ 🄣 🄷 ⛽ 🄿 ⚐
Nearest Town Wetherby
Directions Exit the A1/M1 link at Wetherby and follow the A58 Wetherby and Leeds road. Go through Collingham and turn right onto Church Lane into Bardsey. Go past Bardsey Church and the Bingley Arms, the Park is at the top of the hill on the left.
🚊 Leeds

WALES

ANGLESEY

AMLWCH

Point Lynas Caravan Park, Llaneilian, Amlwch, Anglesey, LL68 9LT
Tel: 01407 831130
Email: enquiries@pointlynas.co.uk
www.pointlynas.co.uk
Pitches For Å 🚐 🚍 **Total** 12
Acreage 2 **Open** Apr **to** Oct
Site Lev/slope
Nearest Bus Stop (Miles) 1
Set in a quiet away from it all area. 250 metres from Porth Eilian Cove and Anglesey Coastal Path.
Facilities ƒ 📠🅿♒⊙♨🍴🔥🄳 📺
🏪🎯🍴🅿 ☼ 🎣
Nearest Town Amlwch
Directions From the A5025 at Cerrig Man follow signs for Llaneilian and then Porth Eilian. Park is on the left 400 metres past Llaneilian Church.
⇌ Holyhead

BEAUMARIS

Kingsbridge Caravan Park, Llanfaes, Beaumaris, Anglesey, LL58 8LR
Tel: 01248 490636
Email: info@kingsbridgecaravanpark.co.uk
www.kingsbridgecaravanpark.co.uk
Pitches For Å 🚐 🚍 **Total** 48
Acreage 14 **Open** Mar **to** Oct
Access Good **Site** Level
Nearest Bus Stop (Miles) ¼
4 Star Park with 2 underfloor heated shower blocks. 2 miles from historic Beaumaris. Telephone booking.
Facilities ƒ 📠🅿♒⊙♨🍴
🏪🎯🍴🔥🄳🄿
Nearest Town Beaumaris
Directions 1¼ miles past Beaumaris Castle. At crossroads turn left, 400yds to the site.
⇌ Bangor

BENLLECH

Ad Astra Caravan Park, Brynteg, Nr Benllech, Anglesey, LL78 7JH
Tel: 01248 853283
Email: brian@brynteg53.fsnet.co.uk
www.adastracaravanpark.co.uk
Pitches For Å 🚐 🚍 **Total** 40
Acreage 3 **Open** Mar **to** Oct
Access Good **Site** Level
Nearest Bus Stop (Miles) Outside
Scenic views, ideal base for touring.
Facilities 🛁 ƒ 📠🅿♒⊙♨🍴🔥🄳 📺
🏪🎯🍴🄳 ☼ 🎣
Nearest Town Benllech
Directions Turn left up the hill from Benllech Village square onto the B5108. Drive 1½ miles to California Inn, turn left onto the B5110. Park is 500 yards on right hand side.
⇌ Bangor

BENLLECH

Bodafon Caravan & Camping Park, Bodafon, Benllech, Anglesey, LL74 8RU
Tel: 01248 852417
Email: robert@bodafonpark.co.uk
www.bodafonpark.co.uk
Pitches For Å 🚐 🚍 **Total** 50
Acreage 5 **Open** Mar **to** Oct
Access Good **Site** Level
Nearest Bus Stop (Miles) ¼
Quiet family site with good views, ¾ miles from the beach. Ideal touring.
Facilities ƒ 📠🅿♒⊙♨🍴
🄳🎯🍴🔥🄳 ☼ 🎣 ♒
Nearest Town Benllech Bay

BENLLECH

Cae Mawr Caravan Club Site, Llangefni Road, Benllech, Anglesey, LL73 8NY
Tel: 01248 853737
www.caravanclub.co.uk
Pitches For 🚐 🚍 **Total** 76
Acreage 6½ **Open** Mar **to** Oct
Access Good **Site** Level
A sheltered site with cheerful hydrangers. 1 mile from the beach. Close to Beaumaris Castle, Butterfly Palace, Sea Zoo and NT Plas Newydd. Own sanitation required. Non members welcome. Booking essential.
Facilities ƒ 📠🅿🏪 🄳🎯🍴🔥🄳 📺
Nearest Town Benllech
Directions From A55 on approaching Bangor continue on A5 sp Holyhead. Cross Britannia Br. leave dual carriageway via second slip road t rt on A5025. In Benllech continue on A5025 (DO NOT turn left) then turn left on B5110. Site on the rt by Parciau Arms Pub.
⇌ Benllech

BENLLECH

Garnedd Touring Park, Lon Bryn Mair, Brynteg, Anglesey, LL78 8QA
Tel: 01248 853240
Email: mike@garnedd.com
www.garnedd.com
Pitches For Å 🚐 **Total** 20
Acreage 9 **Open** Mar **to** Oct
Access Good **Site** Level
Nearest Bus Stop (Miles) ¼
Five beaches within 5 minutes of the site. Wonderful views. Cottage and static caravan available for hire. You can also call us on Mobile: 07973 156371.
Facilities ƒ 📠🅿♒⊙♨🍴
🄳🎯🍴🄳 ☼
Nearest Town Benllech
Directions From Menai Bridge take the A5025 signposted Amlwch and Benllech. After entering Benllech turn left at Londis Garage, turn into the fourth lane, site is 600 yards on the right.

BENLLECH

Home Farm Caravan Park, Marianglas, Anglesey, LL73 8PH
Tel: 01248 410614
Email: enq@homefarm-anglesey.co.uk
www.homefarm-anglesey.co.uk
Pitches For Å 🚐 🚍 **Total** 0
Open Apr **to** Oct
Access Good **Site** Level
Nearest Bus Stop (Miles) ½
1 to 1½ miles from various beaches.
Facilities 🛁 ƒ 📠🅿♒⊙♨🍴🔥🄳 📺
🄳🎯🍴🔥🏪🍴🔥🄳🎣 📺
Nearest Town Benllech
Directions Follow the A5025 from bridge for 11 miles, go through Benllech, keep left at the roundabout towards Amlwch. Park is ½ mile on the left, 300 yards after the church.
⇌ Bangor

BENLLECH

Penrhos Caravan Club Site, Brynteg, Benllech, Anglesey, LL78 7JH
Tel: 01248 852617
www.caravanclub.co.uk
Pitches For 🚐 🚍 **Total** 90
Acreage 9 **Open** Mar **to** Oct
Access Good **Site** Lev/Slope
Nearest Bus Stop (Miles) Outside

2 miles from a safe sandy beach. Near a farm trail, bird sanctuary, Beaumaris Castle and Sea Zoo. Take a trip on Snowdons rack and pinion mountain railway for breathtaking views. Non members welcome. Booking essential.
Facilities 🛁 ƒ 📠🅿♒🏪 🄳🎯🍴🔥🄳🄿 📺
Nearest Town Benllech
Directions Continue on A5025 sp Amlwch. Turn left onto B5510, continue straight on at crossroads with California Pub site is ½ mile on the right.
⇌ Benllech

BENLLECH

Plas Uchaf Caravan Park, Benllech Bay, Benllech, Anglesey, LL74 8NU
Tel: 01407 763012
Pitches For Å 🚐 🚍 **Total** 100
Acreage 18 **Open** Mar **to** Oct
Access Good **Site** Level
Nearest Bus Stop (Miles) ½
Family room, tarmac roads and perimeter parking, 30 plus picnic tables and 3 heated toilet blocks. Near the beach.
Facilities 🛁 ƒ 📠🅿♒⊙♨🍴🔥🄳 📺
🄳🎯🍴🔥🏪🍴🔥🄳 ☼
Nearest Town Benllech
Directions ½ a mile from Benllech, signposted on the B5108 up the hill after the fire station.
⇌ Bangor

BENLLECH

St. Davids Park, Red Wharf Bay, Anglesey, LL75 8RJ
Tel: 01248 852341
Email: info@stdavidspark.com
www.stdavidspark.com
Pitches For Å 🚐 🚍 **Total** 100
Open Mid Mar **to** Sept
Site Sloping
Nearest Bus Stop (Miles) ½
Private beach, On site gastro pub, Direct access to coastal path.
Facilities 🛁 ƒ 📠🅿♒⊙♨🍴🔥🄳 📺
🄳🎯🍴🔥🏪 🄳🍴🔥🄳 ⚓ ☼ 📺
Nearest Town Benllech
Directions On the A5025 1 mile south of Benllech.
⇌ Bangor

BRYNSIENCYN

Fron Caravan & Camping Site, Brynsiencyn, Anglesey, LL61 6TX
Tel: 01248 430310
Email: mail@froncaravanpark.co.uk
www.froncaravanpark.co.uk
Pitches For Å 🚐 🚍 **Total** 70
Acreage 5¼ **Open** Easter **to** Sept
Access Good **Site** Level
Nearest Bus Stop (Miles) Outside
Ideal for touring Anglesey and North Wales. Wales Tourist Board 4 Star Grading.
Facilities 🛁 ƒ 📠🅿♒⊙♨🍴🔥🄳 📺
🄳🎯🍴🔥🄳
Nearest Town Llanfairpwllgwyn
Directions At start of Llanfairpwllgwyn turn left onto A4080 to Brynsiencyn follow road through village site is on the right ¼ mile after village.
⇌ Bangor

LLANFWROG

Penrhyn Bay Caravan Park, Llanfwrog, Holyhead, Anglesey, LL65 4YG
Tel: 01407 730496/730411
Email: info@penrhynbay.com
www.penrhynbay.com
Pitches For Å 🚐 🚍 **Total** 170
Acreage 15 **Open** 15-Mar **to** Oct

ANGLESEY

Access Good **Site** Level
Nearest Bus Stop (Miles) 2
On the coast overlooking the beach on one side and Holyhead Harbour on the other. Fishing, sailing, cycling and plenty of walks.
Facilities
Nearest Town Valley/Holyhead
Directions Take the A55 to Anglesey, take exit 3 to Valley, turn right at the traffic lights onto the A5025 and go through Llanfachraeth. Take the first turn left signposted Llanfwrog, Sandy Beach and Penrhyn, Site is on this road.
⇌ Valley/Holyhead

LLANGEFNI

Mornest Caravan Park, Pentre Berw, Gaerwen, Anglesey, LL60 6HU
Tel: 01248 421725
Email: heulwen@ygors.plus.com
www.mornestcaravanpark.co.uk
Pitches For Å ⊕ ⊕ **Total** 45
Open Mar **to** Oct
Access Good **Site** Lev/Slope
Nearest Bus Stop (Miles) ¼
Facilities
Nearest Town Llangefni
Directions Go over Menai Bridge and take exit 7 off and follow signs through Gaerwen.
⇌ Bangor

MOELFRE

Creigiau Camping Site, Creigiau, Dulas, Amlwch, Anglesey, LL70 9HJ
Tel: 01248 410243
Email: debbiepeni@hotmail.co.uk
Pitches For Å ⊕ **Total** 50
Open Nov **to** Sept
Access Good **Site** Lev/Slope
Nearest Bus Stop (Miles) Outside
3 miles to beach, alongside river.
Facilities
Nearest Town Moelfre
Directions On the A5025. 2 miles from Moelfre Roundabout heading towards Amlwch.
⇌ Bangor

MOELFRE

Melin Rhos Caravan Park, Lligwy, Moelfre, Anglesey, LL24 8RU
Tel: 01248 852417
Email: robert@bodafonpark.co.uk
www.bodafonpark.co.uk
Pitches For Å ⊕ ⊕ **Total** 40
Acreage 4 **Open** Mar **to** Oct
Access Good **Site** Level
Quarter of an hours walk to the lovely beach at Lligwy.
Facilities
Nearest Town Benllech
Directions From Benllech continue along the A5025, at the roundabout turn left, after 2 miles go down a three lane hill and back up, at the top of the hill turn right and the site is approx. ½ a mile on the left.
⇌ Bangor

MOELFRE

Tyddyn Isaf Camping & Caravan Park, Lligwy Bay, Dulas, Anglesey, LL70 9PQ
Tel: 01248 410203
Email: mail@tyddynisaf.co.uk
www.tyddynisaf.co.uk
Pitches For Å ⊕ ⊕ **Total** 80
Acreage 16 **Open** Mar **to** Oct
Access Good **Site** Sloping

Family run park with a private footpath to a fine, sandy beach. Loo of the Year Winner, AA 5 Pennant Premier Park, David Bellamy Gold Award, Welcome Host Award, WTB 5 Star Graded and Finalist of Practical Caravan Top 100 Parks in 2013.
Facilities
Nearest Town Benllech
Directions Take the A5025 from Britannia Bridge, go through Benllech approx. 8 miles, continue to Moelfre Island via left staying on the main road to Brynrefail Village. Turn right opposite the telephone box and International camping sign, we are ½ mile on the right down the lane.
⇌ Bangor

MOELFRE

Tyn Rhos Caravan Park, Moelfre, Anglesey, LL72 8NL
Tel: 01248 852417
Email: robert@bodafonpark.co.uk
www.bodafonpark.co.uk
Pitches For Å ⊕ ⊕ **Total** 50
Acreage 10 **Open** Mar **to** Oct
Access Good **Site** Level
Near Lligwy Beach. Surrounded by numerous footpaths, including coastal path, fishing and ancient monuments.
Facilities
Nearest Town Benllech
Directions From Benllech proceed along the A5025 to the roundabout, turn right to Moelfre and at MDM Design turn left for 2 miles, site is on the road.
⇌ Bangor

PENTRAETH

Clai Mawr Caravan Park, Park Lodge, Pentraeth, Anglesey, LL75 8DX
Tel: 01248 450467
Email: claimawr@onetel.net
www.claimawr-holidays-anglesey.co.uk
Pitches For ⊕ ⊕ **Total** 14
Acreage 4 **Open** Mar **to** Oct
Access Good **Site** Lev/slope
Nearest Bus Stop (Miles) Entrance
Quiet, family run site overlooking Red Wharf Bay and the Snowdon mountains.
Facilities
Nearest Town Benllech
Directions On the A55, cross Britannia Bridge then take the second exit, turn right onto the A5025. Go through Pentraeth until the 40mph sign, entrance is on the right.
⇌ Bangor

RHOSNEIGR

Bodfan Farm, Rhosneigr, Anglesey, LL64 5XA
Tel: 01407 810706
Email: wap@llynfor.freeserve.co.uk
www.bodfanfarm.co.uk
Pitches For Å ⊕ ⊕ **Total** 120
Acreage 15 **Open** Easter **to** Sept
Access Good **Site** Sloping
Nearest Bus Stop (Miles) ½
Excellent beaches. Ideal for touring Anglesey and Snowdonia. Plenty of open spaces for children to play.
Facilities
Nearest Town Rhosneigr
Directions Leave the A55 at junction 5 and follow the A4080 to Rhosneigr. We are next to the school on Sandy Lane.
⇌ Rhosneigr

RHOSNEIGR

Shoreside Camp & Caravan Park, Station Road, Rhosneigr, Anglesey, LL64 5QX
Tel: 01407 810279
Email: shoresidecamping@gmail.com
www.shoresidecamping.co.uk
Pitches For Å ⊕ ⊕ **Total** 100
Acreage 6 **Open** Easter **to** Oct
Access Good **Site** Lev/Slope
Nearest Bus Stop (Miles) Outside
Bowling and tennis. Near the beach and opposite a golf club. 10 miles from Holyhead, day trips to Dublin.
Facilities
Nearest Town Rhosneigr
Directions Take the A55 to junction 5, then take the A4080 to Rhosneigr, opposite the golf club.
⇌ Rhosneigr

RHOSNEIGR

Tyn Llidiart Camping Site, Tyn Llidiart, Tywyn Trewan, Bryngwran, Anglesey, LL65 3SW
Tel: 01407 810678
Email: ruthtynllidiart@aol.com
Pitches For Å ⊕ ⊕ **Total** 5
Acreage ¾ **Open** All Year
Access Fair **Site** Level
Pleasant, quiet site near the beach.
Facilities
Nearest Town Rhosneigr
Directions Take the A5 to Bryngwran, turn by the Post Office, after approx. 1 mile you will pass a garage on the left and three white cottages on the right, at the third cottage turn right, then fork right, go over the cattle grid and the site is on the left.
⇌ Holyhead

TREARDDUR BAY

Tyn Rhos Camping Site, Ravenspoint Road, Trearddur Bay, Holyhead, Anglesey, LL65 2AX
Tel: 01407 860369
Pitches For Å ⊕ ⊕ **Total** 200
Acreage 20 **Open** Mar **to** Oct
Access Good **Site** Lev/Slope
Nearest Bus Stop (Miles) ½
Well established family run site, rural location with modern facilities. Views of Snowdonia, coastal walks, sandy beaches (Blue Flag Award) 10 minutes. Ideal touring base, Holyhead port town to Ireland - 3 miles. Separate rally field also available. Visit Wales 3 Star Graded.
Facilities
Nearest Town Holyhead
Directions Follow the A55 across Anglesey, leaving at junction 2. First left off roundabout and follow signs for Trearddur Bay B4545. After approx. 1½ miles turn right onto Ravenspoint Road (after the Spar shop on the left), ¾ miles to the shared entrance, take left hand branch.
⇌ Holyhead

TREARDDUR BAY

Valley of the Rocks, Porthdafarch Road, Trearddur Bay, Holyhead, Anglesey, LL65 2LL
Tel: 01407 765787
Pitches For Å ⊕ ⊕ **Total** 40
Open Mar **to** Oct
Access Good **Site** Lev/Slope
Nearest Bus Stop (Miles) 1
Near to the beach, boating, fishing, Southstack Lighthouse, Holyhead Mountain and many nice walks.

Facilities ⚡ ⟟ 🏕🚿⌂🏐⌁🍴⛺
♿ 🏴 🅿 🏪 ♉ 🛒🚐 🌣
Nearest Town Holyhead
Directions Follow A55 across Anglesey to where the road terminates at the roundabout. Take 1st left at roundabout then take immediate right between 2 pubs. follow road for approx 1 mile until you see the sign for Valley of the Rocks Caravan Park .
🚆 Holyhead

VALLEY

Bodowyr Caravan & Camping Park,
Bodowyr, Bodedern, Anglesey, LL65 3SS
Tel: 01407 741171
Email: bodowyr@yahoo.com
www.bodowyrcaravansite.co.uk
Pitches For 🛆 🚐 🚌 **Total** 45
Acreage 2 **Open** Mar to Oct
Access Good **Site** Level
Nearest Bus Stop (Miles) ½
Peaceful farm 3 miles from beaches and close to a wide range of sporting facilities. Convenient for touring Anglesey and ferries to Ireland.
Facilities ♿ ⟟ 🏕🚿⌂🏐🍴⛺
🏴 ✕ ⛚🚐🍴🚐 🌣
Nearest Town Holyhead
Directions From Holyhead take the A55, turn off at the Bodedern exit (junction 4) and turn left for Bodedern. Bodowyr is the first turning on the left. Site has international camping signs from the A5 junction.
🚆 Valley

VALLEY

Pen-Y-Bont Farm Caravan & Camping Site, Four Mile Bridge, Valley, Anglesey, LL65 3EY
Tel: 01407 740481
Email: post@penybontfarm.co.uk
www.penybontfarm.co.uk
Pitches For 🛆 🚐 🚌 **Total** 20
Acreage 4 **Open** Easter to Oct
Access Good **Site** Level
Nearest Bus Stop (Miles) ¼
Small, quiet, family site in an idyllic scenic location, near to beautiful beaches and the coastal path for walking. Ideal location for wind surfing, canoeing and cycling.
Facilities 🏕⌂🚐⌂🍴⛺ 🌣
Nearest Town Holyhead/Trearddur Bay
Directions Leave the A55 at exit 3 following signs for Valley and Trearddur Bay (approx 2 miles). Site is on the right before approaching Four Mile Bridge.
🚆 Valley/Holyhead

BRIDGEND

PORTHCAWL

Brodawel Camping Park, Brodawel House, Moor Lane, Nottage, Porthcawl, Bridgend, CF36 3EJ
Tel: 01656 783231
www.brodawelcamping.co.uk
Pitches For 🛆 🚐 🚌 **Total** 100
Acreage 5 **Open** Apr to Oct
Access Good **Site** Level
Nearest Bus Stop (Miles) ¼
Convenient to all beaches, very central for touring area. Off Licence. Designer Village Wales 3 miles.
Facilities ♿ ⟟ 🏕🚿⌂⌁🍴⛺
♿ 🏴 🅿 🎳🚐🍴🚐 🌣 ⚘ 📶
Nearest Town Porthcawl
Directions Leave the M4 at junction 37, turn onto the A4229 for Porthcawl for 2 miles, signposted Moor Lane.
🚆 Pyle

CAERPHILLY

ABERCARN

Cwmcarn Forest Campsite, Cwmcarn Forest Visitor Centre, Nantcarn Road, Cwmcarn, Crosskeys, Caerphilly, NP11 7FA
Tel: 01495 272001
Email: cwmcarn-vc@caerphilly.gov.uk
www.cwmcarnforest.co.uk
Pitches For 🛆 **Total** 20
Open 02-Jan to 23-Dec
Access Good
Nearest Bus Stop (Miles) ½
Beautiful valley setting. Good local walks and fishing. 17km mountain bike trail. Glamping pods 7 family plus 3 standard
Facilities ⟟ 🏕🚿⌂🏐🍴🍴⛺
✕🚐🚐🍴 ⌁⟋
Nearest Town Crosskeys
Directions Leave the M4 at junction 28 (signposted Risca Brynmawr) and take the A467 north for approx 7 miles. Forest Drive is well signposted with brown tourism signs.
🚆 Crosskeys

BARGOED

Parc Cwm Darran, Deri, Bargoed, Caerphilly, CF81 9NR
Tel: 01443 875557
Email: countryside@Caerphilly.gov.uk
www.caerphilly.gov.uk/countryside
Pitches For 🛆 **Total** 30
Acreage 2 **Open** Apr to Sept
Access Good **Site** Sloping
Nearest Bus Stop (Miles) Outside
Close to Brecon Beacons.
Facilities ♿ ⟟ 🏕🚿⌂⌁🍴⛺
🏴 ✕⛚🚐🍴🚐⟋ 🌣
Nearest Town Bargoed
Directions Midway between Deri and Fochriw north of Bargoed on A469
🚆 Bargoed

CARMARTHENSHIRE

CARMARTHEN

Coedhirion Farm Park, Coedhirion, Llanddarog, Carmarthen, Carmarthenshire, SA32 8BQ
Tel: 01267 275666
Email: welshfarmhouse@hotmail.com
www.welshfarm.co.uk
Pitches For 🛆 🚐 🚌 ♉ **Total** 10
Acreage 1½ **Open** Mar to Oct
Access Good **Site** Level
Nearest Bus Stop (Miles) Outside
A small Park on a working farm amidst woodland and countryside. 5 minutes from the National Botanic Garden of Wales and 15 minutes from Ffos Las Racecourse. B&B and self catering cottage also available.
Facilities ⟟ 🏕🚿⌂⌁🍴🚐⛺
🏴 🅿 ⛚🚐🅿
Nearest Town Carmarthen
Directions From Carmarthen take the A48 east for 6 miles, turn right then immediately right again into our driveway.
🚆 Carmarthen

CARMARTHEN

Pant Farm Caravan & Camping Park, Llangunnor Road, Carmarthen, Carmarthenshire, SA31 2HY
Tel: 01267 235665
Pitches For 🛆 🚐 🚌 **Total** 0
Open Mar to Nov
Access Good **Site** Level
Nearest Bus Stop (Miles) Outside
ADULTS ONLY SITE. Central and convenient location for touring South Wales.

Facilities ✕ ⟟ 🏕🚿⌂🍴🚐🅿⟋🌣
Nearest Town Carmarthen
Directions Carmarthen 1 mile east on B4300.
🚆 Carmarthen

CLYNDERWEN

Derwenlas, Clynderwen, Carmarthenshire, SA66 7SU
Tel: 01437 563504
Pitches For 🛆 🚐 🚌 **Total** 4
Open Apr to Sept
Access Good **Site** Level
Facilities ⟟ 🏕🚿⌂⌁🍴🅿⛺
🏴 🅿 🏪⛚🚐🅿
Nearest Town Narberth
Directions 3 to 3½ miles north of Narberth on the A478.
🚆 Clynderwen

KIDWELLY

Tanylan Farm Holidays, Tanylan Farm, Kidwelly, Carmarthenshire, SA17 5HJ
Tel: 01267 267306
Email: tanylanfarm@gmail.com
www.tanylanfarmholidays.co.uk
Pitches For 🛆 🚐 🚌 **Total** 100
Acreage 8 **Open** Mar to Sept
Access Good **Site** Level
Level ground on a former dairy farm. 400 yards from the beach. Membership to Park Resorts.
Facilities ♿ ⟟ 🏕🚿⌂⌁🍴🚐🅿⛺
♿ 🏴 🅿 🏪⛚🚐🅿 🌣 📶
Nearest Town Kidwelly
Directions In Kidwelly turn left at the Spar Supermarket, take the coastal road to Ferryside for approx. 1 mile and turn left at the duck pond.
🚆 Kidwelly

LAUGHARNE

Broadway Caravan Park, Broadway, Laugharne, Carmarthenshire, SA33 4NU
Tel: 01994 427272
Pitches For 🛆 🚐 🚌 **Total** 6
Access Good **Site** Level
Nearest Bus Stop (Miles) Outside
Disabled toilet & shower.
Facilities ⟟ 🏕🍴⌂🅿🚐🅿 🌣
Directions Take the A4066 from St. Clears to Laugharne, continue to Pendine and site is ½ mile on the left.
🚆 Carmarthen

LLANDDEUSANT

Blaenau Farm, Llanddeusant, Llangadog, Carmarthenshire, SA19 9UN
Tel: 01550 740277
Email: patrickofllynyfan@yahoo.co.uk
Pitches For 🛆 🚐 🚌 **Total** 0
Acreage 20 **Open** Easter to Oct
Access Poor **Site** Level
Nearest Bus Stop (Miles) 7
Isolated mountain farm, spectactular scenery, rich in wildlife.
Facilities 🏕 🚐 🅿⟋ 🌣
Nearest Town Llandovery
Directions A4069 to Llangadog and onto Three Horseshoes, turn left over river bridge. Follow signs to farm.
🚆 Llangadog

LLANDOVERY

Rhandirmwyn Camping & Caravanning Club Site, Rhandirmwyn, Llandovery, Carmarthenshire, SA20 0NT
Tel: 01550 760257
Email:
rhandirmwyn.site@thefriendlyclub.co.uk
www.campingandcaravanningclub.co.uk/rhandirmwyn

Pitches For ⚊ ⚊ ⚊ **Total** 90
Acreage 11 **Open** 14-Mar **to** 10-Nov
Access Good **Site** Level
Set in the beautiful Welsh countryside on the banks of the Afon Tywi. Ideal for fishing. Lodges available for hire. WTB 4 Star Graded, AA 3 Pennants, David Bellamy Gold Award and Loo of the Year Award. Non members welcome. You can also call us on 0845 130 7633.
Facilities ♿ ∮ 🅗 🆖 🖛 🏠 ⊙ ⊒ 🍴 ◻ 📶
🔭 🛒 🎵 ✕ 🖾 🔲 ⚡ ✉ 📶
Nearest Town Llandovery
Directions From Llandovery take the A483, turn left signposted Rhandirmwyn. Turn left at the Post Office in Rhandirmwyn, site is on the left before the river.
✈ Llandovery

LLANWRDA

Maesbach Caravan & Camping Park, Horseshoe Valley, Ffarmers, Llanwrda, Carmarthenshire, SA19 8EX
Tel: 01558 650650
Email: admin@maesbach.com
Pitches For ⚊ ⚊ ⚊ **Total** 20
Acreage 5 **Open** Mar **to** Oct
Access Good **Site** Lev/Slope
Nearest Bus Stop (Miles) 1
Tranquil family run peace lovers' retreat with magnificent countryside views, ideal for a relaxing holiday escape. Quiet lanes are perfect for walking, cycling and horse riding, or explore sandy beaches at the coast. Ideally placed for touring West Wales. Visit Llyn Brianne Reservoir, Roman Dolaucothi Gold Mines, Aberglasny or National Botanical Gardens, RSPB Reserve or Red Kite feeding station at Llanddeusant, Abergorlech mountain bike trail at Brechfa Forest or the village of Llandewi Brefi as featured in the TV series 'Little Britain', or why not just stay on the park and enjoy the silence!!
Facilities ∮ 🅗 🆖 🖛 🏠 ⊒ ◻ 📶
🔭 🛒 🖛 🔲 ⚡
Nearest Town Lampeter
Directions Turn right off A482 (Llanwrda to Lampeter road) pass through Pumpsaint, continue for 1 mile, take right turn signed Ffarmers and Maesbach. Continue for approx 1 mile to Ffarmers, turn right Drovers Arms pub, Maesbach is 1 mile on the left.
✈ Llanwrda

NEWCASTLE EMLYN

Afon Teifi Caravan & Camping Park, Pentrecagal, Newcastle Emlyn, Carmarthenshire, SA38 9HT
Tel: 01559 370532
Email: afonteifi@btinternet.com
www.afonteifi.co.uk
Pitches For ⚊ ⚊ ⚊ **Total** 110
Acreage 6½ **Open** Mar **to** Oct
Access Good **Site** Level
Nearest Bus Stop (Miles) Outside
Situated by the River Teifi in the beautiful Teifi Valley. Only 20 minutes from numerous Cardigan Bay beaches. Swimming nearby. Ideal touring centre. AA 4 Pennants.
Facilities ♿ ∮ 🅗 🆖 🖛 🏠 ⊙ ⊒ 🍴 ◻ 📶
🔭 🛒 🛒 ✕ 🖾 🔲 ✗ 🎵 ⚡
Nearest Town Newcastle Emlyn
Directions On the A484 2 miles east of Newcastle Emlyn.
✈ Carmarthen

NEWCASTLE EMLYN

Dolbryn Farm, Capel Iwan Road, Newcastle Emlyn, Carmarthenshire, SA38 9LP
Tel: 01239 710683

Email: enquiries@dolbryn.co.uk
www.dolbryn.co.uk
Pitches For ⚊ ⚊ ⚊ **Total** 60
Acreage 13 **Open** Mar **to** Oct
Access Good **Site** Lev/Slope
Nearest Bus Stop (Miles) 2
Idyllic country site with stream, lakes, hills, etc..
Facilities ∮ 🅗 🆖 🖛 🏠 ⊙ ⊒ 🍴 ◻ 📶
🔭 🔲 ♀ 🖛 🖾 🔲 🎵 ✗ 🎵
Nearest Town Newcastle Emlyn
Directions Turn left off the A484 Carmarthen to Cardigan road at Newcastle Emlyn signposted leisure centre & swimming pool. Follow camping signs for 2 miles.
✈ Carmarthen

NEWCASTLE EMLYN

Moelfryn Caravan & Camp Park, Pant-Y-Bwlch, Newcastle Emlyn, Carmarthenshire, SA38 9JE
Tel: 01559 371231
Email: moelfryn@moelfryncaravanpark.co.uk
www.moelfryncaravanpark.co.uk
Pitches For ⚊ ⚊ ⚊ **Total** 25
Acreage 3 **Open** Mar **to** 10-Jan
Access Good **Site** Level
Situated in a tranquil, rural setting with panoramic views for relaxation. Perfect base for exploring the beauty of West Wales.
Facilities ∮ 🅗 🆖 🖛 🏠 ⊒ ◻ 📶
🔭 🔲 🖾 🖛 🔲 🎵 ✗ 🎵
Nearest Town Newcastle Emlyn
Directions From Carmarthen take the A484 to Cynwyl Elfed. Pass the Blue Bell Inn and take the left fork after approx. 200 yards B4333 towards Hermon and stay on this road for 7 miles. There is a brown sign on your left, take that turn and site is ¼ mile on the right.
✈ Carmarthen

PEMBREY

Pembrey Country Park Caravan Club Site, Pembrey, Llanelli, Carmarthenshire, SA16 0EJ
Tel: 01554 834369
www.caravanclub.co.uk
Pitches For ⚊ ⚊ **Total** 130
Acreage 12 **Open** Mar **to** Jan
Access Good **Site** Level
Set on the edge of a 520 acre country park. Vast range of outdoor sporting activities available including horse riding, dry slope skiing and toboggan riding, putt 'n' putt and sea fishing. Ideal for walkers and bird/butterfly watchers. Only 1 mile from a Blue Flag sandy beach. Non members welcome. Booking essential.
Facilities ∮ 🅗 🆖 🖛 🏠 ⊙ ⊒ 📶
🔭 🔲 🔲 🖾 🖛 🔲 🎵 🎵
Nearest Town Llanelli
Directions Leave M4 at junc 48 and take A4138 sp Llanelli, on the outskirts of Llanelli turn right onto A484. In Pembrey Village turn left at signpost Pembrey Country Park and follow signs to Country Park, site is on the right before park gates.
✈ Llanelli

CEREDIGION (CARDIGANSHIRE)
ABERAERON

Aeron Coast Caravan Park, North Road, Aberaeron, Ceredigion, SA46 0JF
Tel: 01545 570349
Email: enquiries@aeroncoast.co.uk
www.aeroncoast.co.uk
Pitches For ⚊ ⚊ ⚊ **Total** 100

Acreage 8 **Open** Mar **to** Oct
Access Good **Site** Level
Nearest Bus Stop (Miles) ¼
Good family facilities. Aberaeron is a recognised beauty spot. Picturesque harbour, coastal and river walks. Only 200yds from shops. 5 Star Graded.
Facilities ♿ ∮ 🅗 🆖 🖛 🏠 ⊙ ⊒ 🍴 ◻ 📶
🔭 🖾 🔲 🛒 ✕ ♀ 🖾 🖛 🖾 ✗ 🖾 🔲 🔲
Nearest Town Aberaeron
Directions Main coastal road A487 on northern edge of Aberaeron, follow brown tourism signs. Filling station at entrance.
✈ Aberystwyth

ABERAERON

Cwmsaeson Caravan Park, Oakford, Aberaeron, Ceredigion, SA47 0RY
Tel: 01545 581067
Email: elin@cwmsaeson.co.uk
www.cwmsaeson.co.uk
Pitches For ⚊ ⚊ **Total** 25
Acreage 3 **Open** Mar **to** Oct
Access Good **Site** Level
Quiet family site set in open countryside with wonderful views. Ideal touring location for the West Wales coastline.
Facilities ♿ ∮ 🅗 🆖 🖛 🏠 ⊙ ⊛ 🖛 🎵
Directions From the A487 at Llwyncelyn (from the south) turn right towards Oakford. After 1¼ miles at the T-Junction in Oakford Village turn left, site is 800 yards on the left.
✈ Aberystwyth

ABERPORTH

Caerfelin Caravan Park, Aberporth, Nr Cardigan, Ceredigion, SA43 2BZ
Tel: 01239 810540
Pitches For ⚊ ⚊ **Total** 5
Open Mid Mar **to** Oct
Access Good **Site** Level
Nearest Bus Stop (Miles) ¼
Well sheltered park nestled in a woodland valley. Just a 5 minute walk to sandy beaches and the village of Aberporth. Friendly welcome assured.
Facilities ♿ ∮ 🆖 🖛 🏠 ⊙ ⊒ 🍴 ◻ 📶
🔭 🖾 🔲
Directions Turn north off the A487 at Blaenannerch onto the B433 to Aberporth. Enter the village of Aberporth and turn right at St. Cynwyls Church, park is 200 yards on the left.
✈ Carmarthen

ABERPORTH

Dolgelynen Holiday Park, Aberporth, Nr Cardigan, Ceredigion, SA43 2HS
Tel: 01239 811095
Pitches For ⚊ ⚊ ⚊ **Total** 24
Access Good **Site** Lev/Slope
Nearest Bus Stop (Miles) Outside
Quiet site overlooking the sea. 1 mile from the beach. Many eating places close by.
Facilities ♿ ∮ 🆖 🖛 🏠 ⊙ ◻ 🖾 🔲 🔲 🔲
Nearest Town Cardigan
Directions From Cardigan take the A487, then take the B4333, second turning. From Aberystwyth take the A487 towards Cardigan, before Cardigan take the first turning onto the B4333 sp Aberporth, site is 1 mile on the right.
✈ Cardigan

ABERYSTWYTH

Morfa Bychan Holiday Park, Aberystwyth, Ceredigion, SY23 4QQ
Tel: 01970 617254
Email: morfa@hillandale.co.uk
www.hillandale.co.uk
Pitches For ⚊ ⚊ ⚊ ⚊ **Total** 75

Acreage 6 **Open** Mar **to** Oct
Access Good **Site** Sloping
100 acre park overlooking Cardigan Bay with our own private beach. Heated swimming pool, water hook-ups.
Facilities ♿ ∮ 🖳 🕭 🎢 ⟳ ⊙ � 🔟 🛒
🖩 🛠 🎢 ⚓ ⟋ 🌲 ⟶ 🖃 🖳 ✉ ☂ ﹋ ⚲ 🗢
Nearest Town Aberystwyth
Directions Take the A487 south from Aberystwyth, after ½ mile signposted to the right, but this is NOT suitable for touring caravans who should continue for 2½ miles and turn right at the second sign. Follow signs for 1½ miles.
⚑ Aberystwyth

BORTH
Glanlerry Caravan Park, Borth, Ceredigion, SY24 5LU
Tel: 01970 871413
Email: enquiries@glanlerrycaravanpark.co.uk
www.glanlerrycaravanpark.co.uk
Pitches For ⋀ 🚐 🚍 **Total** 0
Open Apr **to** Oct
Access Good **Site** Level
Nearest Bus Stop (Miles) Outside
Family only camping site. Sheltered touring area, alongside a river bank with spectacular scenery. ½ a mile from the beach.
Facilities
✗ ∮ 🖳 🕭 🎢 ⟳ ⊙ ⌐ 🔟 🛒 🛠 ♿ ⟶ 🖃 🖳 ﹋
🗢
Nearest Town Borth
⚑ Borth

CARDIGAN
Brongwyn Touring Caravan & Camping Park, Brongwyn Mawr, Penparc, Cardigan, Ceredigion, SA43 1SA
Tel: 01239 613644
Email: enquiries@cardiganholidays.co.uk
www.tentsandtourers.co.uk
Pitches For ⋀ 🚐 🚍 **Total** 20
Acreage 3 **Open** May **to** Sept
Access Good **Site** Level
Nearest Bus Stop (Miles) ½
3 miles from Mwnt (seals and dolphins) ideal base for exploring Cardigan Bay and North Pembrokeshire.
Facilities ♿ ∮ 🖳 🕭 🎢 ⟳ ⊙ ⌐ 🔟 🛒
🖩 ⚓ ⟶ 🖃 🖳 ﹋
Nearest Town Cardigan
Directions A487 from Cardigan towards Aberystwyth follow brown tourist signsin Penpar. Turn left towards Mwnt for ½ mile then tirn right opposite our sign.
⚑ Aberystwyth

CARDIGAN
Penralltllyn Caravan Park, Cilgerran, Cardigan, Pembrokeshire, SA43 2PP
Tel: 01239 682350
Pitches For ⋀ 🚐 🚍 **Total** 20
Acreage 1 **Open** Easter **to** Oct
Site Level
Approx. 15 minutes from lots of beaches. Plenty of woodland walks and lakes in the valley.
Facilities ∮ 🖳 🕭 🎢 ⟳ ⌐ ⟶
Nearest Town Cardigan
Directions 3 miles south east of Cardigan on the A484 (Cardigan to Carmarthen road). Turn over the bridge at Llechryd, go straight on for 1½ miles, after crossroads Site is second entrance on the right. Wide farm lane which is kept in good condition.
⚑ Carmarthen

CARDIGAN
TyGwyn Caravan Park, MinYMor, Mwnt, Cardigan, Ceredigion, SA43 1QH
Tel: 01239 614518
Email: info@campingatmwnt.co.uk
www.www.campingatmwnt.co.uk
Pitches For ⋀ 🚐 🚍 **Total** 30
Acreage 6 **Open** April **to** October
Site Lev/Slope
Beach 10 Mins walk. Near coastal path.
Facilities ♿ ∮ 🖳 🕭 🎢 ⟳ ⌐ 🔟 🛒 🖩 ﹋
Nearest Town Cardigan
Directions Take the B4548 for Gwbert off the A487. At the Cardigan bypass, follow signs to Mwnt.
⚑ Carmarthen

DEVILS BRIDGE
Woodlands Caravan Park, Devils Bridge, Aberystwyth, Ceredigion, SY23 3JW
Tel: 01970 890233
Email: enquiries@woodlandsdevilsbridge.co.uk
www.woodlandsdevilsbridge.co.uk
Pitches For ⋀ 🚐 🚍 **Total** 50
Acreage 8 **Open** Easter **to** Oct
Access Good **Site** Level
Quiet country site adjoining a farm. Within walking distance of the famous Devils Bridge & Waterfalls and steam train. Excellent mountain bike trail nearby and bike shelter on site. Ideal for walking, bird watching, fishing and touring, or just relaxing!
Facilities ♿ ∮ 🖳 🕭 🎢 ⟳ ⊙ ⌐ 🔟 🛒
🖩 🖩 ⊙ ⚓ ⚓ ⟶ 🖃 🖳 🗢
Nearest Town Aberystwyth
Directions 12 miles East of Aberystwyth on A4120 in Devils Bridge village and 300yds from bridge. Or 3 miles south west of Ponterwyd, turn off A44 at Ponterwyd.
⚑ Aberystwyth

LAMPETER
Hafod Brynog Caravan Park, Ystrad Aeron, Felinfach, Lampeter, Ceredigion, SA48 8AE
Tel: 01570 470084
Email: hafod@brynog.wanadoo.co.uk
Pitches For ⋀ 🚐 🚍 **Total** 30
Acreage 8 **Open** Easter **to** Sept
Access Good **Site** Lev/Slope
Nearest Bus Stop (Miles) ¼
A quiet site with beautiful views. 6 miles from Cardigan Bay. Ideal for coastal and inland touring, or just relaxing.
Facilities ∮ 🖳 🕭 🎢 ⟳ ⊙ ⌐ 🔟 🛒
🖩 ⊙ ⟶ 🖃 🖳 ﹋
Nearest Town Aberaeron
Directions On the main A482 Lampeter to Aberaeron road, 6 miles from both. Site entrance is opposite the church and next to the pub in the village of Ystrad Aeron.
⚑ Aberystwyth

LLANARTH
Shawsmead Caravan Club Site, Oakford, Llanarth, Ceredigion, SA47 0RN
Tel: 01545 580423
www.caravanclub.co.uk
Pitches For 🚐 🚍 **Total** 50
Acreage 4 **Open** Mar **to** Oct
Access Good **Site** Level
Peaceful meadowland site with pleasant views of the coast and Cardigan Bay. 4 miles from the coast. Ideal for bird watching including Red Kites. Local craft centres. Non members welcome. Booking essential.
Facilities ♿ ∮ 🖳 🕭 🎢 ⟳ ⌐ 🔟 🛒
🖩 🖩 ⊙ ⟶ 🖃 🖳 🗢
Nearest Town Llanarth

Directions From the A487, in Llwyncelyn turn onto the B4342 signposted Ystrad Aeron. At the crossroads go straight on, site is 1¼ miles on the right.
⚑ Llanarth

LLANGRANNOG
Maes Glas Caravan Park, Penbryn, Sarnau, Llandysul, Ceredigion, SA44 6QE
Tel: 01239 654268
Email: enquiries@maesglascaravanpark.co.uk
www.maesglascaravanpark.co.uk
Pitches For ⋀ 🚐 🚍 **Total** 10
Acreage 4 **Open** Mar **to** Oct
Access Good **Site** Level
Nearest Bus Stop (Miles) Outside
Near Penbryn beach. David Bellamy Gold Award for Conservation. Buses in summer only.
Facilities ∮ 🖳 🕭 🎢 ⟳ ⊙ ⌐ 🔟 🛒
🖩 ⊙ 🛠 ⚓ 🎢 ♿ ⟶ 🖃 🗢
Nearest Town Llangrannog
Directions Turn off the A487 between Cardigan and New Quay in the village of Sarnau by the old church, signposted Penbryn. Follow the road down for ¾ miles to the telephone box, at next junction bear left and the park entrance is on the right.
⚑ Aberystwyth

LLANON
Woodlands Holiday Park, Llanon, Ceredigion, SY23 5LX
Tel: 01974 202342
Email: info@woodlandsholidayparkllanon.co.uk
www.woodlandsholidayparkllanon.co.uk
Pitches For ⋀ 🚐 🚍 **Total** 40
Acreage 4 **Open** Mar **to** Oct
Access Good **Site** Level
Nearest Bus Stop (Miles) ¼
Ideal for a quiet, relaxing break. 200 metres from the beach. 3 miles from the quaint harbourside town of Aberaeron.
Facilities ♿ ∮ 🖳 🕭 🎢 ⟳ ⊙ ⌐ 🔟 🛒
🖩 ⊙ ⟶ 🖃 🖳 ﹋ 🗢
Nearest Town Aberaeron
Directions 3 miles north of Aberaeron on the A487, in the village of Llanon, turn left at the International sign towards the sea.
⚑ Aberystwyth

LLANRHYSTUD
Morfa Caravan Park, Morfa, Llanrhystud, Ceredigion, SY23 5BU
Tel: 01974 202253
Email: morfa@morfa.net
www.morfa.net
Pitches For ⋀ 🚐 🚍 **Total** 20
Open Apr **to** Oct
Access Good **Site** Level
Nearest Bus Stop (Miles) 1
Situated on seafront of sandy beach.
Facilities ♿ ∮ 🖳 🕭 🎢 ⟳ ⊙ ⌐ 🔟 🛒
🖩 🖩 ⊙ ⚓ ⟶ 🖃 ⟋
Nearest Town Aberaeron
Directions From Aberystwyth take the A487 towards Aberaeron. In Llanrhystud turn right opposite the petrol station.
⚑ Aberystwyth

LLANRHYSTUD
Pengarreg Caravan Park, Llanrhystud, Ceredigion, SY23 5DJ
Tel: 01974 202247
Email: miller_i@btconnect.com
www.utowcaravans.co.uk
Pitches For ⋀ 🚐 🚍 **Total** 0
Open Mar **to** Jan
Access Good **Site** Level

Nearest Bus Stop (Miles) ¼
On the beach and by a river. Ideal for hillside walks. Two play areas.
Facilities ⚹ ∱ ▣ ▣ ▦ ∱ ∩ ☉ ⌣ ▣ ☏
⅀ ℔ ◯ ⚊ ✕ ♈ ⛏ ▣ ◾ ✈ ⚡ ❄
Nearest Town Aberystwyth
Directions 9 miles south of Aberystwyth on the A487, opposite the Texaco Garage.
⚹ Aberystwyth

NEW QUAY

Cardigan Bay Camping & Caravanning Club Site, Llwynhelyg, Cross Inn, Llandysul, Ceredigion, SA44 6LW
Tel: 01545 560029
Email:
cardigan.baysite@thefriendlyclub.co.uk
www.campingandcaravanningclub.co.uk/cardiganbay
Pitches For ⛺ ⚑ ⚐ **Total** 90
Acreage 14 **Open** Apr **to** 03-Nov
Access Difficult **Site** Lev/Slope
Nearest Bus Stop (Miles) 1
Near to golden beaches, forests and lakes. 3 miles from horse racing and close to many attractions. WTB 4 Star Graded and AA 3 Pennants. Non members welcome. You can also call us on 0845 130 7633.
Facilities ⚹ ∱ ▣ ▣ ▦ ∱ ∩ ☉ ⌣ ▣ ☏
℔ ◯ ⚊ ♈ ⛏ ✈ ▣ ⚡ ❄
Directions From the A487 Cardigan to Aberystwyth road, at Synod Inn turn left onto the A486 signposted New Quay. After 2 miles in the village of Cross Inn turn left after the Penrhiwgated Arms Pub, site is on the right after approx. ¾ miles.
⚹ Aberystwyth

NEW QUAY

Tydu Vale Caravan Park, Pantrhyn, Cwmtodu, Llwyndafydd, Ceredigion, SA44 6LH
Tel: 07852 469335
Pitches For ⛺ ⚑ ⚐ **Total** 6
Acreage 2 **Open** Mar **to** Oct
Access Good **Site** Sloping
Nearest Bus Stop (Miles) Outside
Coastal path 100 yards away.
Facilities ∱ ∩ ☉ ⌣ ☏ ℔ ◯ ✕ ♈ ✈ ⛏
Nearest Town Cardigan
Directions A487 main road.
⚹ Aberystwyth

NEW QUAY

Wern Mill Camping Site, Gilfachreda, New Quay, Ceredigion, SA45 9SP
Tel: 01545 580699
Pitches For ⛺ ⚑ ⚐ **Total** 50
Acreage 2½ **Open** Easter **to** Oct
Access Good **Site** Level
Very sheltered, family site. ½ mile from two sandy beaches. Idyllic walks. Ideal centre for touring Mid Wales.
Facilities ∱ ▣ ▦ ∩ ☉ ⌣ ☏
℔ ◯ ⚊ ✈ ▣
Nearest Town New Quay
Directions From Aberystwyth take the A487 via Aberaeron to Llanarth. Gilfachrheda is located 1½ miles from Llanarth on the B4342 to New Quay road.
⚹ Aberystwyth

NEWCASTLE EMLYN

Cenarth Falls Holiday Park, Cenarth, Newcastle Emlyn, Ceredigion, SA38 9JS
Tel: 01239 710345
Email: enquiries@cenarth-holipark.co.uk
www.cenarth-holipark.co.uk
Pitches For ⛺ ⚑ ⚐ **Total** 30
Acreage 2 **Open** Mar **to** Mid Nov
Access Good **Site** Level
Nearest Bus Stop (Miles) ¼

Ideal touring location for the coast and countryside. Near Coastal National Park. Indoor swimming pool with sauna, steam rooms, jacuzzi and leisure suite. Holders of numerous awards including Wales in Bloom, Calor Gas Best Park in Britain Award and David Bellamy Gold Award.
Facilities ⚹ ∱ ▣ ▦ ∩ ☉ ⌣ ☏
℔ ◯ ⚊ ✕ ♈ ♨ ⛏ ✈ ▣ ▣ ⚡
Nearest Town Newcastle Emlyn
Directions 3 miles west of Newcastle Emlyn on the A484. Cross Cenarth Bridge and travel for ¼ mile, turn right at directional signs for the park.
⚹ Carmarthen

SARNAU

Brynawelon Touring & Camping Park, Sarnau, Llandysul, Ceredigion, SA44 6RE
Tel: 01239 654584
Email: info@brynaweloncp.co.uk
www.brynaweloncp.co.uk
Pitches For ⛺ ⚑ ⚐ **Total** 40
Acreage 4 **Open** Mar **to** Oct
Access Good **Site** Level
Nearest Bus Stop (Miles) ¼
Quiet family site with rural surroundings. 2 miles from Penbryn Beach.
Facilities ⚹ ∱ ▣ ▣ ▦ ∩ ☉ ⌣ ☏ ⚡ ❄
Nearest Town Cardigan
Directions Travelling north on A487 take a right turn at Sarnau crossroads, site is 600 yards on the left.
⚹ Carmarthen

SARNAU

Treddafydd Farm, Treddafydd, Sarnau, Llandysul, Ceredigion, SA44 6PZ
Tel: 01239 654551
Pitches For ⛺ ⚑ ⚐ **Total** 10
Acreage 1 **Open** May **to** Sept
Access Good **Site** Sloping
Nearest Bus Stop (Miles) ½
1 mile from sandy Penbryn beach.
Facilities ∱ ▦ ∩ ☉ ⌣ ☏ ℔ ◯ ✈ ▣ ☏
Nearest Town Cardigan
Directions 1 mile from the A487, in the village of Sarnau turn by the church then first left.
⚹ Carmarthen/Aberystwyth

CONWY
ABERGELE

Henllys Farm Camping & Touring Site, Henllys, Towyn, Abergele, Conwy, LL22 9HF
Tel: 01745 351208
www.henllys.com
Pitches For ⛺ ⚑ ⚐ **Total** 280
Acreage 14 **Open** Mar **to** Oct
Access Good **Site** Level
Nearest Bus Stop (Miles) ¼
Level site adjoining farm land, yet close to attractions.
Facilities ⚹ ∱ ▦ ∩ ☉ ⌣ ☏ ⚡ ▣
℔ ◯ ⚊ ✈ ▣ ▣
Nearest Town Rhyl
Directions 3 miles west of Rhyl on the A548 coast road.
⚹ Rhyl

ABERGELE

Hunters Hamlet Touring Caravan Park, Sirior Goch Farm, BetwsYnRhos, Abergele, Conwy, LL22 8PL
Tel: 01745 832237
Email: huntershamlet@aol.com
www.huntershamlet.co.uk
Pitches For ⚑ ⚐ **Total** 30

Acreage 2½ **Open** Mar **to** Oct
Access Good
Nearest Bus Stop (Miles) ½
Within easy distance to Llandudno, Snowdonia, Anglesey, Bodnamt Gardens and Welsh Food Emporium.
Facilities ⚹ ∱ ▣ ▣ ▦ ∩ ☉ ⌣ ☏ ⚡ ▣
℔ ◯ ♨ ▣ ▣ ▣
Nearest Town Abergele
Directions Junc 24 off A55. A547 into Abergele. turn left onto the A548 to Llanrwst. Right, B5381 towards Betws-yn Rhos we are on the left.
⚹ Abergele

ABERGELE

Owen's Caravan Park, Gainc Bach, Towyn Road, Towyn, Abergele, Conwy, LL22 9ES
Email: info@owenscp.co.uk
www.owenscaravanpark.co.uk
Pitches For ⚑ ⚐ **Total** 12
Open Mar **to** Oct
Access Good **Site** Level
Nearest Bus Stop (Miles) Outside
Near the coast, within walking distance of local amenities and entertainment.
Facilities ∱ ▦ ∩ ☉ ⌣ ☏
⚊ ✈ ▣ ❄
Nearest Town Towyn
Directions From Rhyl, follow A548 coast road first park on right afterTowyn Church.
⚹ Rhyl

ABERGELE

Roberts Caravan Park, Waterloo Service Station, Penrefail Cross Roads, Abergele, Conwy, LL22 8PN
Tel: 01745 833265
Email:
waterlooservicestation@hotmail.co.uk
Pitches For ⚑ ⚐ **Total** 60
Open Mid Mar **to** Oct
Access Good **Site** Lev/Slope
Nearest Bus Stop (Miles) Outside
A quiet, tidy site with a well stocked shop. Near the beach and within easy reach of the Snowdonia mountain range.
Facilities ∱ ▦ ∩ ☉ ⌣ ☏
⅀ ℔ ◯ ⚊ ✈ ▣ ⛏
Nearest Town Abergele
Directions From Abergele take the A548 Llanrwst road for 2 miles, at the crossroads of the B5381 turn left towards St. Asaph. site is 100 yards on the right of the junction.
⚹ Rhyl

BETWSYCOED

Cwmlanerch Caravan Park, BetwsyCoed, Conwy, LL24 0BG
Tel: 01492 642770
Email: info@delinorthwales.co.uk
www.cwmlanerchsnowdonia.co.uk
Pitches For ⛺ ⚐ **Total** 40
Open Mar **to** Nov
Access Good **Site** Level
Nearest Bus Stop (Miles) 1
In the heart of the Snowdonia National Park and alongside the River Conwy. Ideal location for walking and mountain biking (Marin Trail close by). Many attractions nearby.
Facilities ∱ ▣ ▣ ▦ ∩ ☉ ⌣ ☏ ▣
⚊ ▣ ▣ ⛏
Nearest Town BetwsyCoed
Directions From BetwsyCoed take the B5106 and the park is 1 mile on the right.
⚹ BetwsyCoed

BETWS-Y-COED

Rynys Farm Camping Site, Rynys Farm, Nr Betws-y-Coed, Llanrwst, Conwy, LL26 0RU
Tel: 01690 710218
Email: carol@rynys-camping.co.uk
www.rynys-camping.co.uk
Pitches For ▲ ♥ ♥ **Total** 0
Acreage 6 **Open** All Year
Access Good **Site** Level
Nearest Bus Stop (Miles) ¼
Very scenic and peaceful site with excellent clean facilities. Central for touring.
Facilities ∮ �Ⅲ⌐ ⊙ ⚊ ♥ ☎ ⊬ ▣
Nearest Town Betws-y-Coed
Directions 2 miles south of Betws-y-Coed Left by Conway Falls, 200yds from A5.
⚞ Betws-y-Coed

BETWS-Y-COED

Y Giler Arms, Rhydlydan, Pentrefoelas, Conwy, LL24 0LL
Tel: 01690 770612
Email: gilerarms@hotmail.co.uk
www.giler.co.uk
Pitches For ▲ ♥ ♥ ≋ **Total** 20
Acreage 4 **Open** All Year
Access Good **Site** Level
On the edge of Snowdonia National Park.
Facilities Ⅲ⌐ ⊙ ⚊ ▣ ♥
▤ ✗ ♀ Ⅲ ♣ ⊬ ▣ ▣ ✐ ⋇ ☎
Nearest Town Betws-y-Coed
Directions On the A5 between Glasfryn and Pentrefoelas.
⚞ Betws-y-Coed

COLWYN BAY

Bron-Y-Wendon Touring Caravan Park, Wern Road, Llanddulas, Colwyn Bay, Conwy, LL22 8HG
Tel: 01492 512903
Email: stay@northwales-holidays.co.uk
www.northwales-holidays.co.uk
Pitches For ♥ ♥ **Total** 130
Acreage 8 **Open** All Year
Access Good **Site** Lev/Slope
Nearest Bus Stop (Miles) ¼
Pitches have coastal views. Just a short walk to the beach. Site is ideal for seaside and touring. Visit Wales 5 Star Graded, AA 5 Pennants and Premier Park. Super pitches available.
Facilities ∮ ∮ ▣ Ⅲ ⌐ ⊙ ⚊ ♥
▣ ♥ ℓ ⊙ ☎ Ⅲ ♣ ⊬ ▣ ▣ ⋇ ☎
Nearest Town Colwyn Bay
Directions Follow the A55 into North Wales and take the Llanddulas junction (A547), junction 23. Follow tourist information signs to the park.
⚞ Colwyn Bay

CONWY

Tyn Terfyn Touring Caravan Park, Tal Y Bont, Conwy, LL32 8YX
Tel: 01492 660525
www.tynterfyn.co.uk
Pitches For ▲ ♥ ♥ **Total** 15
Acreage 2 **Open** 14-Mar to Oct
Access Good **Site** Level
Nearest Bus Stop (Miles) Outside
Scenic views, good walking, fishing and boating. Ideal touring location.
Facilities ∮ ∮ Ⅲ ⌐ ⊙ ⚊ ⚊ ♥
ℓ ⊙ ♥ ⊬ ▣
Nearest Town Conwy
Directions From Conwy travel approx 5 miles on the B5106 until road sign for Tal-y-Bont. First house on the left after sign.

CONWY

Wern Farm Caravan Park, Wern Farm, Tyn-Y-Groes, Conwy, LL32 8SY
Tel: 01492 650257
Email: gsutcliffe007@btinternet.com
Pitches For ♥ ♥ **Total** 24
Acreage 2½ **Open** 15-Mar to Nov
Access Good **Site** Sloping
Nearest Bus Stop (Miles) Outside
Facilities ∮ ▣ Ⅲ ⌐ ⌐ ⊙ ⚊ ♥ ⊬ ▣
Nearest Town Conwy
Directions Take the A55 to Conwy then the B5106 signposted Trefriw. Site is 4 miles (1 mile past the Groes Inn).
⚞ Llandudno Junction

LLANRWST

Bron Derw Touring Caravan Park, Bron Derw, Llanrwst, Conwy, LL26 0YT
Tel: 01492 640044
Email: bronderw@aol.com
www.bronderw-wales.co.uk
Pitches For ♥ ♥ **Total** 48
Acreage 4 **Open** Mar to Oct
Access Good **Site** Level
Nearest Bus Stop (Miles) ½
Ideal for exploring the Snowdonia mountain range and the North Wales coast. Adults Only field separate from the main touring site.
Facilities ∮ ∮ Ⅲ ⌐ ⌐ ⊙ ⚊ ♥
ℓ ⊙ ♥ ⊬ ▣ ⋇ ✎ ☎
Nearest Town Llanrwst
Directions From the A5 or A55 take the A470 into Llanrwst. Turn into Parry Road (sp Llanddoged) and go to T-Junction, turn left and the Park entrance is on the right.
⚞ Llanrwst

LLANRWST

Glyn Farm Caravans, Trefriw, Llanrwst, Conwy, LL27 0RZ
Tel: 01492 640442
Pitches For ♥ ♥ **Total** 33
Open Mar to Oct
Access Good **Site** Level
Nearest Bus Stop (Miles) Outside
Beautiful walking country. Centrally situated for Snowdonia attractions and the coastal resorts of Llandudno, Colwyn Bay and the Isle of Anglesey.
Facilities ∮ ∮ ▣ Ⅲ Ⅲ ⌐ ⊙ ♥ ℓ ✗ ⊬ ▣ ⋇
Nearest Town Llanrwst
Directions On the B5106 BetwsyCoed to Conwy road, Trefriw Village is 4 miles from BetwsyCoed and 8 miles from Conwy. Turn right into the village car park opposite Trefriw Woollen Mills, site is 200 yards from the main road.
⚞ Llanrwst

PENMAENMAWR

Trwyn Yr Wylfa Farm, Trwyn Yr Wylfa, Penmaenmawr, Conwy, LL34 6SF
Tel: 01492 622357
Pitches For ▲ ♥ **Total** 100
Acreage 10 **Open** Apr to Sept
Site Sloping
Nearest Bus Stop (Miles) ½
Secluded site in Snowdonia National Park. Overlooking the sea.
Facilities Ⅲ ⌐ ⊙ ⚊ ♥ ⊬ ▣ ⋇
Nearest Town Penmaenmawr
Directions Leave the A55 at junction 16 for Penmaenmawr. Turn by Mountain View Hotel, farm is ¼ mile east.
⚞ Penmaenmawr

PENMAENMAWR

Tyddyn Du Touring Park, Conwy Old Road, Penmaenmawr, Conwy, LL34 6RE
Tel: 01492 622300
Email: stay@tyddyndutouringpark.co.uk
www.tyddyndutouringpark.co.uk
Pitches For ▲ ♥ ♥ **Total** 100
Acreage 5 **Open** 22-Mar to Oct
Access Good **Site** Lev/Slope
Nearest Bus Stop (Miles) ¼
ADULTS ONLY site overlooking Conwy Bay to Llandudno and Anglesey. Heated toilet and shower block with disabled facilities and laundry. Close to the A55 so ideal for touring Snowdonia. 5 star WTB.
Facilities ♿ ∮ ▣ Ⅲ ⌐ ⊙ ⚊ ⚊ ▣ ♥
ℓ ⊙ ♥ ⊬ ▣ ▣ ☎ ♥
Nearest Town Penmaenmawr
Directions 1 mile east of Penmaenmawr. Take the A55 from Conwy and at junction 16 turn left at the roundabout after the Shell Garage and sharp left again. Site access is on the right after The Gladstone.
⚞ Penmaenmawr

TY-NANT

Glan Ceirw Caravan Park, Ty Nant, Corwen, Conwy, LL21 0RF
Tel: 01490 420346
Email:
glanceirwcaravanpark@yahoo.co.uk
www.glanceirwcaravanpark.com
Pitches For ▲ ♥ ♥ **Total** 12
Acreage 5 **Open** Mar to Aug
Access Good **Site** Lev/Slope
Nearest Bus Stop (Miles) ½
Ideal for cycling, walking, canoeing, white water rafting and sailing.
Facilities ∮ ▣ Ⅲ ⌐ ⊙ ⚊ ▣ ♥
ℓ ⊙ ♀ ♣ ⊬ ✐ ⋇
Nearest Town Corwen
Directions On the A5 between Corwen and Betws-Y-Coed.
⚞ Betws-Y-Coed

DENBIGHSHIRE

LLANGOLLEN

Ddol Hir Caravan Park, Pandy Road, Glyn Ceiriog, Llangollen, Denbighshire, LL20 7PD
Tel: 01691 718681
www.ukparks.com
Pitches For ▲ ♥ ♥ **Total** 25
Acreage 6 **Open** Mar to Oct
Access Good **Site** Level
Nearest Bus Stop (Miles) ¼
Pretty riverside Park in a scenic valley with mountain walks. Trout fishing and pony trekking. Within walking distance of shops and pubs.
Facilities ♿ ∮ Ⅲ Ⅲ ⌐ ⊙ ⚊ ♥
ℓ ⊙ ♥ ⊬ ▣ ▣ ✐ ⋇
Nearest Town Llangollen
Directions Turn off the A5 at Chirk onto the B4500, park is on the left approx. 6 miles, just through the village of Glyn Ceiriog.
⚞ Chirk

LLANGOLLEN

Wern Isaf Caravan & Camping Park, Wern Isaf Farm, Llangollen, Denbighshire, LL20 8DU
Tel: 01978 860632
Email: wernisaf@btopenworld.com
www.wernisaf.co.uk
Pitches For ▲ ♥ ♥ **Total** 40
Acreage 2 **Open** Easter to Oct
Access Good **Site** Lev/Slope
Nearest Bus Stop (Miles) 1

Quiet and very scenic site overlooking Llangollen. Ideal for touring North Wales. Nearby we have horse riding, a steam railway, white water rafting and very scenic walks. You can also contact us on Mobile: 07974 797828.
Facilities ⫪ 🗗 🅷 ♨️🖧 ⌢ ☉ ⌟ 🟊 🛒 🌊
📶 ☉ 🛆 ✈️ 🖪 🛒
Nearest Town Llangollen
Directions In Llangollen turn up behind Bridge End Hotel, go over the canal bridge and turn right into Wern Road, site is ½ a mile on the right.
🚆 Ruabon

PRESTATYN

Nant Mill Farm Caravan & Tenting Park, Nant Mill, Prestatyn, Denbighshire, LL19 9LY
Tel: 01745 852360
Email: nantmilltouring@aol.com
www.nantmilltouring.co.uk
Pitches For ⚊ ⚊ ⚊ **Total** 150
Acreage 5 **Open** Easter **to** Oct
Access Good **Site** Lev/Slope
Nearest Bus Stop (Miles) Outside
Near town shops. ½ a mile from the beach. Ideal for touring North Wales. Restaurant and bar 200 yards away.
Facilities ♿ ⫪ 🆚 🖧 ⌢ 🛒 🛆 🛒
🛆 ✈️ 🖪
Nearest Town Prestatyn
Directions ½ mile east of Prestatyn on A548 coast road.
🚆 Prestatyn

RUTHIN

Dyffryn Ial Caravan Site, Troell Yr Alun, LlanarmonYnIal, Near Mold, Denbighshire, CH7 5TA
Tel: 01824 780286
Pitches For ⚊ ⚊ **Total** 18
Acreage ½ **Open** Mar **to** Oct
Access Good **Site** Level
Nearest Bus Stop (Miles) Outside
ADULTS ONLY SITE alongside the River Alyn in an area of outstanding natural beauty. Near Clwydian Hills, Offas Dyke walk and Country Park Loggerheads. Over 100 walks in the area. Ideal for touring North Wales.
Facilities ⫪ 🆚 🖧 ⌢ 🛒 📶 ✈️ 🛆 🅰️
Nearest Town Mold/Ruthin
Directions 6 miles from both Mold and Ruthin on the A494, take the B5430 towards Llanarmon-Yn-Ial, site is on the right 1 mile before Llanarmon Village.
🚆 Wrexham

ST. ASAPH

Penisar Mynydd Caravan Park, Caerwys Road, Rhuallt, St Asaph, Denbighshire, LL17 0TY
Tel: 01745 582227
Email: contact@penisarmynydd.co.uk
www.penisarmynydd.co.uk
Pitches For 🅰️ ⚊ ⚊ ⚊ **Total** 75
Acreage 6 **Open** Mar **to** 15-Jan
Access Good **Site** Lev/Slope
Quiet, rural park. Large flat tent area. Close to Rhyl and Prestatyn. Ideal for touring the main A55 coastal route to Holyhead. Adults Only field. Superpitches available.
Facilities ⫪ 🗗 🅷 🆚 🖧 ⌢ 🛒 ☉ 🛒
📶 ☉ ✈️ 🖪 🌊 🌿 🔥
Nearest Town Prestatyn
Directions Leave the A55 Chester to Bangor road at junction 29, park is 500 yards on the right.
🚆 Prestatyn

FLINTSHIRE

GRONANT

Greenacres Caravan Park, Shore Road, Gronant, Flintshire, LL19 9SS
Tel: 01745 854061
Email: info@greenacrescaravanpark.co.uk
Pitches For ⚊ ⚊ **Total** 40
Open Mar **to** Oct
Access Good **Site** Level
Nearest Bus Stop (Miles) Outside
500 yards from the beach. Two licensed premises with live entertainment. Health suite and swimming pool.
Facilities ♿ ⫪ 🅷 🆚 ⌢ 🛒 🛒
📶 ☉ ✖️ 🍴 📺 🛆 ⚽ 🖪
Nearest Town Prestatyn
Directions 2 miles from Prestatyn off the main A548 coast road.
🚆 Prestatyn

MOLD

Fron Farm Caravan Park, Fron Farm, Rhes-Y-Cae Road, Hendre, Mold, Flintshire, CH7 5QW
Tel: 01352 741482
Email: stay@fronfarmcaravanpark.co.uk
www.fronfarmcaravanpark.co.uk
Pitches For 🅰️ ⚊ ⚊ **Total** 120
Acreage 5 **Open** Apr **to** Oct
Access Good **Site** Level
Nearest Bus Stop (Miles) ½
Farm site with animals to see and scenic views.
Facilities ♿ ⫪ 🆚 ⌢ 🛒
📶 ☉ 🛆 ✈️ 🖪 🌿
Nearest Town Mold
Directions From Mold take the A541 towards Denbigh, pass through Rhydymwyn and Hendre, turn right at the next crossroads for Rhes-Y-Cae.
🚆 Flint

MOLD

Pantymwyn Caravan Park, Erw Goed, Pantymwyn, Mold, Flintshire, CH7 5EF
Tel: 01352 740365
Email: info@pantymwyncaravanpark.co.uk
www.pantymwyncaravanpark
Pitches For ⚊ ⚊ **Total** 0
Acreage 19 **Open** Apr **to** Oct
Nearest Bus Stop (Miles) ½
Loggerheads National Park, Theatre Clwyd.
Facilities ⫪ 🛒 📶 🔥 🛆 ⚽ 🖪 🌿
Nearest Town Mold
Directions 2½ miles from Mold. Near Mold Golf Club.
🚆 Buckley

GWYNEDD

ABERDARON

Bryn Ffynnon Caravan Site,
Rhoshirwaun, Pwllheli, Gwynedd, LL53 8LF
Tel: 01758 730643
Pitches For ⚊ ⚊ **Total** 28
Open Mar **to** Oct
Access Good **Site** Level
Nearest Bus Stop (Miles) 1
Near to the beach and the village. Also Mobile 07989170441
Facilities ⫪ 🆚 🖧 ⌢ 🛒 🛆 🛒
📶 🛆 ✈️ 🖪 🌿
Nearest Town Pwllheli
Directions From the A499 take the B4413, go through Sarn and continue to Aberdaron.
🚆 Pwllheli

ABERDARON

Dwyros Campsite, Aberdaron, Pwllheli, Gwynedd, LL53 8BS
Tel: 01758 760295
Email: dwyroscamp@aol.com
Pitches For 🅰️ ⚊ ⚊ **Total** 60
Acreage 4 **Open** Mar **to** Oct
Site Level
Nearest Bus Stop (Miles) ¼
Near the beach,within walking distance of beach and village.
Facilities ♿ ⫪ 🆚 🖧 ⌢ ☉ 🛆 🛒 📶
Nearest Town Aberdaron
🚆 Pwllheli

ABERDARON

Mur Melyn Camping Site, Mur Melyn, Aberdaron, Pwllheli, Gwynedd, LL53 8LW
Tel: 01758 760522
Email: murmelyn@hotmail.co.uk
www.murmelyncamping.co.uk
Pitches For 🅰️ ⚊ ⚊ **Total** 60
Acreage 2½ **Open** Easter **to** Oct
Access Good **Site** Level
Nearest Bus Stop (Miles) 1
Near the beach and a river with scenic views. Ideal for touring Wales.
Facilities ⫪ 🆚 ⌢ 🛒 📶
Nearest Town Pwllheli
Directions Take A499 west from Pwllheli, then fork onto to B4413 at Llanbedrog about 3 miles before Aberdaron take Whistling Sand road. Turn left at Pen-y-Bont House to site ½ mile.
🚆 Pwllheli

ABERDARON

Tir Glyn Caravan Park, Tir Glyn Farm, Uwchmynydd, Aberdaron, Pwllheli, Gwynedd, LL53 8DA
Tel: 01758 760248
Email: tirglyn@btconnect.com
www.tirglyn.com
Pitches For 🅰️ ⚊ ⚊ **Total** 40
Acreage 3 **Open** May **to** Oct
Access Good **Site** Lev/Slope
Nearest Bus Stop (Miles) ½
Surrounded by National Trust land, overlooking the sea for scenic views. Near beaches. Local authority licence. Static caravan for hire.
Facilities ⫪ 🅷 🆚 ⌢ ☉ 🛒 📶 ✈️ 🖪 🌿
Nearest Town Pwllheli
Directions Pwllheli B4413 to Aberdaron. In Aberdaron Village turn right on the bridge signed Uwchmynydd, keep left then turn first left, we are first farm on the left.
🚆 Pwllheli

ABERSOCH

Beach View Caravan Park, Bwlchtocyn, Abersoch, Gwynedd, LL53 7BT
Tel: 01758 712956
Pitches For 🅰️ ⚊ ⚊ **Total** 47
Acreage 5 **Open** Mid Mar **to** Mid Oct
Access Good **Site** Level
Nearest Bus Stop (Miles) ¼
Just a very short walk to the beach. Ideal touring area.
Facilities ⫪ 🆚 ⌢ ☉ 🛆 🛒
📶 ☉ 🛆 ✈️ 🖪 🌿
Nearest Town Abersoch
Directions Drive through Abersoch and Sarn Bach, go over the crossroads and turn next left signposted Bwlchtocyn and Porthtocyn Hotel. Go past the chapel and take left turn following signs for Porthtocyn Hotel, Beach View Park is on the left.
🚆 Pwllheli

ABERSOCH

Bryn Bach Caravan & Camping Site, Tyddyn Talgoch Uchaf, Bwlchtocyn, Abersoch, Gwynedd, LL53 7BT
Tel: 01758 712285
Email: brynbach@abersochcamping.co.uk
www.abersochcamping.co.uk
Pitches For **Total** 65
Acreage 3 **Open** Mar **to** Oct
Access Good **Site** Level
Nearest Bus Stop (Miles) ¼
Close to 2 sandy beaches, golf course and trekking centre.
Facilities
Nearest Town Abersoch
Directions Take the Sarn Bach road from Abersoch,go through Sarn Bach and take the next left turn to Bwlchtocyn.
Pwllheli

ABERSOCH

Deucoch Touring & Camping Park, Sarn Bach, Abersoch, Gwynedd, LL53 7LD
Tel: 01758 713293
Email: info@deucoch.com
www.deucoch.com
Pitches For **Total** 70
Acreage 5 **Open** Mar **to** Oct
Access Good **Site** Level
Nearest Bus Stop (Miles) Outside
Overlooking Abersoch beach and the Snowdonia mountain range. Within walking distance of Abersoch Village and the beach.
Facilities
Nearest Town Abersoch
Directions Take the Bwlchtocyn road out of Abersoch, at the crossroads in Sarn Bach turn right, go past the school on the left and the Site is on the right.
Pwllheli

ABERSOCH

Trem Y Mor, Sarn Bach, Abersoch, Pwllheli, Gwynedd, LL53 7ET
Tel: 01758 712052
Email: tremymor@btconnect.com
www.tgholidays@leisure
Pitches For **Total** 75
Acreage 5 **Open** Mar **to** Oct
Access Good **Site** Sloping
Nearest Bus Stop (Miles) Outside
ADULTS ONLY SITE. 10 minutes walk to the beach.
Facilities
Nearest Town Abersoch
Directions From Abersoch take the road to Sarn Bach. In Sarn Bach turn left at the square, Trem Y Mor is the first site on the right.
Pwllheli

ABERSOCH

Tyn-y-Mur Touring & Camping Park, Lon Garmon, Abersoch, Gwynedd, LL53 7UL
Tel: 01758 713223/712328
Email: info@tyn-y-mur.co.uk
www.tyn-y-mur.co.uk
Pitches For **Total** 59
Open Apr **to** Oct
Access Good **Site** Lev/slope
Nearest Bus Stop (Miles) ¼
Near the beach with superb, uninterrupted, panoramic coastal views of Abersoch Bay and Hells Mouth.
Facilities
Nearest Town Abersoch
Directions On the A499 Pwllheli to Abersoch road, on approaching Abersoch turn right at Land & Sea Services Garage, site is then ¾ miles on the left hand side.
Pwllheli

ARTHOG

Garthyfog Camping Site, Garthyfog Farm, Arthog, Gwynedd, LL39 1AX
Tel: 01341 250338
Email: abcjohnson@btinternet.com
www.garthyfog.co.uk
Pitches For **Total** 20
Acreage 5 **Open** All Year
Site Lev/Slope
2 miles from Fairbourne, safe bathing, sandy beach and shops. Beautiful scenery, panoramic views. 300 yards from main road, sheltered from wind. Mains cold water. Plenty of room for children to play around the farm, rope-swing, little stream, etc. Two log cabins available to let.
Facilities
Nearest Town Barmouth/Dolgellau
Directions A493, 6 miles from Dolgellau, left by Village hall, look for signs on right hand side.
Morfa Mawddach

BALA

Bala Camping & Caravanning Club Site, Crynierth Caravan Park, Cefn-Ddwysarn, Bala, Gwynedd, LL23 7LN
Tel: 01678 530324
Email: bala.site@thefriendlyclub.co.uk
www.campingandcaravanningclub.co.uk/bala
Pitches For **Total** 50
Acreage 4 **Open** 15-Mar **to** 04-Nov
Access Good **Site** Level
Situated on the edge of Snowdonia National Park. 4 miles from Bala Lake. Good for watersports. Ideal touring site. WTB 4 Star Graded and AA 3 Pennants. Non members welcome. You can also call us on 0845 130 7633.
Facilities
Nearest Town Bala
Directions From the A5 turn onto the A494 to Bala. At signpost Cefn-Ddwysarn turn right before the red phone box, site is 400 yards on the left.
Ruabon

BALA

Bryn Gwyn Caravan & Camping Park, Godrer Aran, Llanuwchllyn, Bala, Gwynedd, LL23 7UB
Tel: 01678 540687
Pitches For **Total** 8
Acreage 2 **Open** End Mar **to** Oct
Access Good **Site** Level
Nearest Bus Stop (Miles) 1
Small, peaceful riverside park within easy walking distance of the village inn (excellent reasonable meals available). Country walks and bird watching along the lanes. Ideal touring centre for North and Mid Wales. Good for cycling tours and hill walking. Six seasonal touring pitches with electric and hard standings.
Facilities
Nearest Town Bala
Directions From Bala take the A494 and travel alongside Bala Lake for approx. 5 miles. Turn right immediately after 40mph speed limit sign on approaching Llanuwchllyn Village.
Wrexham

BALA

Glanllyn-Lakeside Caravan & Camping Park, Bala, Gwynedd, LL23 7SS
Tel: 01678 540227
Email: info@glanllyn.com
www.glanllyn.com
Pitches For **Total** 100
Acreage 14 **Open** Easter **to** Oct
Access Good **Site** Level
Nearest Bus Stop (Miles) Outside
Level parkland with trees. Alongside a lake and river, large launching area for sailing.
Facilities
Nearest Town Bala
Directions 3 miles south west of Bala on the A494, situated on the left alongside Bala Lake.
Wrexham

BALA

Pen Y Bont Touring & Camping Park, Llangynog Road, Bala, Gwynedd, LL23 7PH
Tel: 01678 520549
Email: penybont-bala@btconnect.com
www.penybont-bala.co.uk
Pitches For **Total** 95
Acreage 6 **Open** Mar **to** Oct
Access Good
Nearest Bus Stop (Miles) ½
100 yards from Bala Lake and just a 15 minute walk into Bala. Motor home service point.
Facilities
Nearest Town Bala
Directions ½ a mile from Bala on the B4391 to Llangynog.
Wrexham

BALA

Tylsaf Camping Site, Llangynog Road, Bala, Gwynedd, LL23 7PP
Tel: 01678 520574
www.tyisafbala.co.uk
Pitches For **Total** 30
Acreage 2 **Open** Mar **to** Oct
Access Good **Site** Level
Working farm alongside a stream for fishing. Log fires. Ideal touring.
Facilities
Nearest Town Bala
Directions 2½ miles southeast of Bala on the B4391, near the telephone kiosk and post box.
Ruabon

BALA

Tyn Cornel Camping & Caravan Park, Frongoch, Bala, Gwynedd, LL23 7NU
Tel: 01678 520759
Email: tyncornel@mail.com
www.tyncornel.co.uk
Pitches For **Total** 67
Acreage 10 **Open** Easter **to** Oct
Access Good **Site** Level
Nearest Bus Stop (Miles) ¼
Quiet and clean 4 Star site beside the River Tryweryn. Next door to the National White Water Centre, watch the thrills and spills of the white water rafting, or take part! Ideally situated for touring North Wales. Indoor swimming pool nearby.
Facilities
Nearest Town Bala
Directions 4 miles from Bala on the A4212 Porthmadog road.
Ruabon

GWYNEDD

BANGOR

Dinas Farm Camping & Touring Site,
Dinas Farm, Halfway Bridge, Bangor,
Gwynedd, LL57 4NB
Tel: 01248 364227
Email: dinasfarmcamping@btinternet.com
www.dinasfarmcamping.co.uk
Pitches For ▲ ⬜ ⬛ ⬛ **Total** 35
Acreage 4 **Open** Easter **to** Oct
Access Good **Site** Level
Nearest Bus Stop (Miles) 50 yards
Sheltered site on the banks of the River
Ogwen. Centrally situated for beaches and
mountains. Open on site with a permit.
Facilities symbols
Nearest Town Bangor
Directions Leave the A55 at junc 11 and take
the A5 towards Bethesda for 1 mile. Turn right
at Halfway Bridge towards Tregarth then turn
first left.
⚏ Bangor

BARMOUTH

Benar Beach Camping & Touring Site,
Talybont, Barmouth, Gwynedd, LL44 2RX
Tel: 01341 247001/247571
Pitches For ▲ ⬜ ⬛ ⬛ **Total** 0
Acreage 9 **Open** Mar **to** Oct
Access Good **Site** Level
Nearest Bus Stop (Miles) 1
Friendly family site 100 yards from miles of
golden sand dunes. By the Taith Arddudwy
Way which is a 24 mile pathway. Ideal base
for touring Snowdonia with its gardens,
castles, caverns, railways and much more.
On and by the all Wales coastal path.
Facilities symbols
Nearest Town Barmouth
Directions 5 miles north of Barmouth on the
A496 turn left by Llanddwywe Church ½ mile
after Talybont Village, site is 100 yards from
the beach on the left.
⚏ Dyffryn Arddudwy

BARMOUTH

**Hendre Mynach Touring Caravan &
Camping Park,** Barmouth, Gwynedd, LL42
1YR
Tel: 01341 280262
Email: mynach@lineone.net
www.hendremynach.co.uk
Pitches For ▲ ⬜ ⬛ **Total** 240
Acreage 10 **Open** Mar **to** 09-Jan
Access Good **Site** Level
Nearest Bus Stop (Miles) Outside
100yds from a safe, sandy beach, 20 minutes
walk down the promenade to Barmouth town
centre. An excellent base for estuary and
mountain walks. Pubs nearby with childrens
room. Near to cycle route 8.
Facilities symbols
Nearest Town Barmouth
Directions ½ a mile north of Barmouth on
the A496 Barmouth to Harlech road.
⚏ Barmouth

BARMOUTH

Islawrffordd Caravan Park, E G Evans &
Sons Ltd, Tal-y-Bont, Nr Barmouth,
Gwynedd, LL43 2AQ
Tel: 01341 247269
Email: eige@islawrffordd.co.uk
www.islawrffordd.co.uk
Pitches For ▲ ⬜ ⬛ ⬛ **Total** 105
Acreage 10 **Open** Mar **to** 01-Nov
Access Good **Site** Level
Nearest Bus Stop (Miles) ¼
Next to the beach with no roads or railway
lines to cross.
Facilities symbols
Nearest Town Barmouth
Directions Just off the A496 approx. 4 miles
north of Barmouth in the village of Tal-y-Bont.
⚏ Tal-y-Bont

BARMOUTH

Parc Isaf Farm, Dyffryn Ardudwy,
Gwynedd, LL44 2RJ
Tel: 01341 247447
Email: post@parcisaf.co.uk
www.parcisaf.co.uk
Pitches For ▲ ⬜ ⬛ **Total** 30
Acreage 3 **Open** Mar **to** Oct
Access Good **Site** Lev/Slope
Nearest Bus Stop (Miles) ½
Overlooking Cardigan Bay. Plenty of
mountain and woodland walks. Harlech
Castle and Portmeirion (Italian village) close
by.
Facilities symbols
Nearest Town Barmouth
Directions From Barmouth take the A496
north for 5 miles, go through the small village
of Talybont, ¼ mile on, opposite the church
on the left there is a right hand turn through
pillar gateway. Second farm on the right,
signposted.
⚏ Dyffryn Ardudwy/Talybont

BEDDGELERT

Beddgelert Caravan & Camping Site,
Beddgelert, Gwynedd, LL55 4UU
Tel: 02476 423008
Email:
enquiries@campingintheforest.co.uk
www.campingintheforest.co.uk
Pitches For ▲ ⬜ ⬛ **Total** 190
Open All Year
Access Good **Site** Level
In the heart of Snowdonia, excellent for
exploring Portmeirion Village, the castles of
Caernarfon, Harlech, Conwy and Beaumaris,
and the Ffestiniog Railway.
Facilities symbols
Nearest Town Beddgelert
Directions A487 towards Caernarfon turn
right onto A4085, campsite on right.
⚏ Porthmadog

CAERNARFON

Bryn Gloch Caravan & Camping Park,
Betws Garmon, Caernarfon, Gwynedd,
LL54 7YY
Tel: 01286 650216
Email: eurig@bryngloch.co.uk
www.northwalescamping.co.uk
Pitches For ▲ ⬜ ⬛ ⬛ **Total** 150
Acreage 28 **Open** Mar **to** Oct
Access Good **Site** Level
Nearest Bus Stop (Miles) Outside
Award winning site with scenic views. Plenty
of flat and mountain walks in the area. Ideal
touring centre and only 2 miles from
Snowdon. AA 4 Pennants and AA Best
Campsite in Wales.
Facilities symbols
Nearest Town Caernarfon
Directions 4½ miles south west of
Caernarfon on A4085. Site on right opposite
Betws Garmon church.
⚏ Bangor

CAERNARFON

**Cwm Cadnant Valley Camping &
Caravan Park,** Llanberis Road,
Caernarfon, Gwynedd, LL55 2DF
Tel: 01286 673196
Email: cades@cwmcadnant.co.uk
www.cwmcadnant.co.uk
Pitches For ▲ ⬜ ⬛ **Total** 69
Open Mar **to** Oct
Access Good **Site** Sloping
Nearest Bus Stop (Miles) Outside
Cafe/restaurant and indoor swimming pool
nearby. You can also call us on FreePhone:
0800 043 5941.
Facilities symbols
Nearest Town Caernarfon
Directions On the A4086, 1km from the town
centre.
⚏ Bangor

CAERNARFON

Llys Derwen Camping & Caravan Site,
Ffordd Bryngwyn, Llanrug, Nr Caernarfon,
Gwynedd, LL55 4RD
Tel: 01286 673322
Email: llysderwen@aol.com
www.llysderwen.co.uk
Pitches For ▲ ⬜ ⬛ **Total** 20
Acreage 4½ **Open** Mar **to** Oct
Access Good **Site** Level
Nearest Bus Stop (Miles) ¼
Small family run site. 2 miles from Llanberis
and the foot of Mount Snowdon. Static
caravans also available for hire.
Facilities symbols
Nearest Town Caernarfon
Directions From Caernarfon take the A4086
towards Llanberis. In the village of Llanrug
turn right at the Glyntwrog Public House, site
entrance is 100 yards on the right.
⚏ Bangor

CAERNARFON

Plas Gwyn Caravan & Camping Park,
Plas Gwyn, Llanrug, Caernarfon,
Gwynedd, LL55 2AQ
Tel: 01286 672619
Email: info@plasgwyn.co.uk
www.plasgwyn.co.uk
Pitches For Å 🚐 🚐 🚐 **Total** 40
Acreage 4 **Open** Mar **to** Oct
Access Good **Site** Level
Nearest Bus Stop (Miles) Outside
Small, peaceful park. 3 miles from
Snowdonia Mountains and 5 miles from the
beach. Award winning hire caravans. En-
suite bed and breakfast available in the
house.
Facilities ⚡ 🗇 🖽 🕼🖰 🏲 ⊙ 🖴 🗵 🛋
🕏 ⊙🕀🖾🖸 🖾 ⅍ 🤶
Nearest Town Caernarfon
Directions 3 miles from Caernarfon on the
A4086, signposted on right.
🚊 Bangor

CAERNARFON

Rhyd-y-Galen Caravan & Camping Park,
Bethel, Caernarfon, Gwynedd, LL55 1UL
Tel: 01286 650216
Email: info@copacamping.co.uk
www.wales-camping.co.uk
Pitches For Å 🚐 🚐 **Total** 56
Acreage 4 **Open** Mar **to** Oct
Access Good **Site** Level/Sloping
Nearest Bus Stop (Miles) Outside
1½ miles from Plas Menai Watersports
Centre. Snowdon Footpath only 15 minutes
away.
Facilities ⚡ 🗇 🗇 🖽 🕼🖰 🏲 ⊙ 🖴 🗵 🛋
🕏 ⊙ 🖾 ⅍🕂🖾🖸 🖾 🐾🤶
Nearest Town Caernarfon
Directions 2 miles east of Caernarfon on the
B4366.
🚊 Bangor

CAERNARFON

Silver Birches Camping, Betws Garmon,
Caernarfon, Gwynedd, LL54 7YR
Tel: 01286 650707
Email: camping@silverbirches.org.uk
www.silverbirches.org.uk
Pitches For Å **Total** 13
Open Mar **to** Oct
Site Level
Nearest Bus Stop (Miles) ¼
Silver Birches is a small, peaceful, ADULTS
ONLY site, situated in the Snowdonia
National Park. An ideal place to relax and
enjoy the dramatic scenery, and a good base
for many outdoor pursuits.
Facilities ⚡ 🕼🏲 ⊙ 🖴 🗵 🛋🗨🅰🤶
Nearest Town Caernarfon
Directions Take the A4085 towards
Beddgelert, go straight through Caeathro and
Waunfawr, Silver Birches is 0.2 miles after
the sign for Betws Garmon, just 80 metres
on the left after red phone box.
🚊 Bangor

CAERNARFON

Tyn Rhos Farm Caravan Park, Tyn Rhos
Farm, Saron, Llanwnda, Caernarfon,
Gwynedd, LL54 5UH
Tel: 01286 830362
www.tynrhosfarm.co.uk
Pitches For Å 🚐 🚐 **Total** 25
Acreage 2 **Open** Mar **to** Mid Jan
Access Good **Site** Level
Nearest Bus Stop (Miles) Outside
2½ miles from the beach, 1 mile from steam
railway and cycle track. All pitches are hard
standing.
Facilities ⚡ 🗇 🗇 🖽 🕼🖰 🏲 ⊙ 🖴 🗨🗵🔧

Nearest Town Caernarfon
Directions From Caernarfon take the A487,
after passing Tesco go straight on at the
roundabout, turn first right to Saron
Llanfaglan, entrance is 3 miles on the left.
🚊 Bangor

CAERNARFON

White Tower Caravan Park, Llandwrog,
Caernarfon, Gwynedd, LL54 5UH
Tel: 01286 830649
Email: whitetower@supanet.com
www.whitetowerpark.co.uk
Pitches For Å 🚐 🚐 **Total** 60
Acreage 6 **Open** Mar **to** Nov
Access Good **Site** Level
Nearest Bus Stop (Miles) Outside
2½ miles from the beach, 3¼ miles from
Caernarfon. Splendid views of Snowdon.
Central for touring Llyn Peninsula, Anglesey
and Snowdonia.
Facilities ♿🛁 ⚡ 🗇 🖽 🕼🖰 🏲 ⊙🖴 🛋
🖾 🕏 ⊙ 🖀 🗨🛡 🖎 🐾 🖎 ⅍🕂🖾🖸
🖾 ⅍🤶
Nearest Town Caernarfon
Directions From Caernarfon follow the A487
Porthmadog road for approx ¼ mile, go past
McDonalds, straight ahead at the roundabout
and take the first turning on the right. We
are 3 miles on the right.
🚊 Bangor

CHWILOG

Tyddyn Heilyn Caravan Park, Chwilog,
Pwllheli, Gwynedd, LL53 6SW
Tel: 01766 810441
Email: tyddynh@btinternet.com
Pitches For Å 🚐 🚐 **Total** 5
Access Good **Site** Level
Beautiful tree lined public footpath near the
site to the beach. 15 minutes from Pwllheli,
Porthmadog and Snowdonia. Wi-Fi available
on request.
Facilities ⚡ 🗇 🕼🖰 🏲 ⊙🖴 🗨
🖾🕂🖾🖸 🖾 🤶
Nearest Town Pwllheli
Directions From the A497 take the B4354,
in Chwilog Village turn right opposite Madryn
Arms, second site on the right, signpost at
entrance.
🚊 Criccieth

CLYNNOG FAWR

Aberafon Camping & Caravan Site, Gyrn
Goch, Caernarfon, Gwynedd, LL54 5PN
Tel: 01286 660295
Email: hugh@maelor.demon.co.uk
www.aberafon.co.uk
Pitches For Å 🚐 🚐 **Total** 65
Acreage 10 **Open** Apr **to** Oct
Access Poor **Site** Level
Nearest Bus Stop (Miles) Outside
Near the beach. Site shop only open during
the summer holidays.
Facilities ⚡ 🗇 🖽 🏲 ⊙🖴 🗵 🛋
🖾 ⊙ 🖀 🗨 🛡 🖾🕂🖾🖸 🖎 ⅍
Nearest Town Caernarfon
Directions From Caernarfon take the A499
towards Pwllheli, site is 1 mile after Clynnog
Fawr on the right hand side.
🚊 Bangor

CRICCIETH

Eisteddfa Caravan & Camping Site,
Eisteddfa Lodge, Pentrefelin, Criccieth,
Gwynedd, LL52 0PT
Tel: 01766 522696
Email: eisteddfa@criccieth.co.uk
www.eisteddfapark.co.uk
Pitches For Å 🚐 🚐 **Total** 120
Acreage 22 **Open** Mar **to** Oct

Access Good **Site** Lev/Slope
Nearest Bus Stop (Miles) Outside
Spectacular views of Cardigan Bay and the
mountains. Plenty of footpaths for walking.
Facilities ⚡ 🗇 🖽 🕼🖰 🏲 ⊙🖴 🗵 🛋
🖾 ⊙ 🖀 🗨🗙 🖾 🖾🕂🖾🖸 🖎 ⅍
Nearest Town Criccieth
Directions On the A497 Porthmadog to
Criccieth road, 1½ miles north east of Criccieth.
Entrance is at the west end of Pentrefelin
beside the Plas Gwyn Nursing Home.
🚊 Criccieth

CRICCIETH

**Llanystumdwy Camping & Caravanning
Club Site,** Tyddyn Sianel, Llanystumdwy,
Criccieth, Gwynedd, LL52 0LS
Tel: 01766 522855
Email:
llanystumdwy.site@thefriendlyclub.co.uk
www.campingandcaravanningclub.co.uk/
llanystumdwy
Pitches For Å 🚐 🚐 **Total** 70
Acreage 4 **Open** 21-Mar **to** 04-Nov
Access Good **Site** Sloping
Nearest Bus Stop (Miles) Outside
Situated just outside Criccieth with scenic
coastal views. Nearby attractions include
Ffestiniog Railway and Snowdonia National
Park. WTB 4 Star Graded and AA 3
Pennants. Non members welcome. You can
also call us on 0845 130 7633.
Facilities ♿ ⚡ 🗇 🖽 🕼🖰 🏲 ⊙🖴 🗵 🛋
🖾 ⊙ 🖀 🗨🖾🕂🖾🖸 🖎 🤶
Directions From Criccieth take the A497 and
turn second right signposted Llanstumdwy,
site is on the right.
🚊 Criccieth

CRICCIETH

Llwynbugeilydd Caravan Park,
Llwynbugeilydd Farm, Criccieth, Gwynedd,
LL52 0PN
Tel: 01766 523140
Pitches For Å 🚐 🚐 **Total** 36
Acreage 5 **Open** Apr **to** Oct
Access Good **Site** Lev/slope
Nearest Bus Stop (Miles) Outside
Views of Snowdonia from the site. Situated
away from traffic noise. Very clean facilities.
1 mile from the beach and charming town of
Criccieth. ½ a mile from first class sea trout
and salmon fishing on the River Dwyfor.
Facilities ⚡ 🕼🖰 🏲 ⊙🖴 🗵 🛋 🖾🕂🖾 ⅍
Nearest Town Criccieth
Directions Take Caernarfon road from main
Cricceth/ Pwllheli road, park is on right
approx 1½
miles.
🚊 Criccieth

DOLGELLAU

Dolgamedd Camping & Caravan Site,
Dolgamedd, Bontnewydd, Dolgellau,
Gwynedd, LL40 2DG
Tel: 01341 450221
Email: mair@dolgamedd.co.uk
www.dolgamedd.co.uk
Pitches For Å 🚐 🚐 🚐 **Total** 76
Acreage 12 **Open** Easter **to** Oct
Access Good **Site** Level
Nearest Bus Stop (Miles) Outside
Situated alongside the River Wnion, where
campfires are allowed.The river allows for
swimming, canoeing and fishing.
Facilities ⚡ 🗇 🖽 🕼🖰 🏲 ⊙🖴 🗵 🛋 🖾
🖾🕂🖾🖸 🛡 ⅍ 🐾🤶
Nearest Town Dolgellau
Directions 3 miles from Dolgellau on the
A494 towards Bala, turn right at Bontnewydd
onto the B4416 towards Brithdir. Continue
over the bridge and Dolgamedd is on the left.
🚊 Machynlleth

DOLGELLAU

Llwyn-Yr-Helm Farm, Brithdir, Dolgellau, Gwynedd, LL40 2SA
Tel: 01341 450254
Email: info@llwynyrhelmcaravanpark.co.uk
www.llwynyrhelmcaravanpark.co.uk
Pitches For Å ⊕ ➡ **Total** 25
Acreage 2½ **Open** Easter **to** Oct
Access Good **Site** Lev/Slope
Nearest Bus Stop (Miles) ¼
Seasides, hills, mountains, rivers, lakes and slate mines. Ideal for walking and mountain biking at Coed Y Brenin.
Facilities ᕃ ∮ ⊟ ⚇ ♠ ⌂ ⊙ ⊒ ⨄ ⬚ ☎
ℙ ⊙ ⤸ ⊒ ⅍
Nearest Town Dolgellau
Directions Turn off the A470 or the A494 onto the B4416 to Brithdir. At the phonebox and village hall turn into a minor road, Park is ½ a mile on the left.
⇌ Machynlleth

DOLGELLAU

Tanyfron Camping & Caravan Park, Arran Road, Dolgellau, Gwynedd, LL40 2AA
Tel: 01341 422638
Email: info@tanyfron.co.uk
www.campsitesnowdonia.co.uk
Pitches For Å ⊕ ➡ **Total** 43
Acreage 2 **Open** All year
Access Good **Site** Level
Nearest Bus Stop (Miles) ¼
Small 5 Star Holiday Park, just a few minutes walk from Dolgellau and the supermarket. 8 miles to beaches. Ideal base for touring, walking, cycling, fishing and golf. All hard standing pitches with hook ups. 4 Star B&B available. Internet connection.
Facilities ∮ ⊟ ⚇ ♠ ⌂ ⊙ ⊒ ⨄ ⬚ ☎
ℙ ⊙ ✗ ⊒ ⅍ ☍
Nearest Town Dolgellau
Directions From Welshpool take the A470, after the Little Chef turn off for Dolgellau, site is ½ a mile on the left, by the 30mph sign.
⇌ Barmouth

DOLGELLAU

Tyddyn Farm, Islawrdref, Dolgellau, Gwynedd, LL40 1TL
Tel: 01341 422472
Pitches For Å ⊕ ➡ **Total** 0
Open All Year
Access Good **Site** Lev/Slope
Beautiful views of Cader Idris Mountain and alongside a river. Plenty of walks and fishing locally. ¼ of a mile from Lake Hotel.
Facilities ☎ ➤ ⊒
Nearest Town Dolgellau
Directions 2 miles from Dolgellau on the Cader road. Pass Gwernan Lake Hotel, ¼ of a mile turn right through a wooden gate, go over the cattle grid and turn left.
⇌ Machynlleth

DOLGELLAU

Vanner Caravan & Camping Site, Vanner, Llanelltyd, Dolgellau, Gwynedd, LL40 2HE
Tel: 01341 422854
Email: enquiries@vanner.co.uk
www.vanner.co.uk
Pitches For Å ⊕ ➡ **Total** 30
Acreage 2 **Open** Apr **to** Oct
Access Good **Site** Level
Nearest Bus Stop (Miles) ½
Ancient monument (ruin), alongside river, ideal for walking and cycling.
Facilities ᕃ ∮ ⚇ ♠ ⌂ ⊙ ⊒ ☎
ℙ ⊙ ➤ ⊒ ⅍
Nearest Town Dolgellau

Directions Take A470 west towards Barmouth for 1½ miles turn right at Cymer Abbey sign and follow signs to site.
⇌ Barmouth

DYFFRYN ARDUDWY

Murmur-yr-Afon Touring Caravan & Camping Site, Dyffryn Ardudwy, Gwynedd, LL44 2BE
Tel: 01341 247353
Email: mills@murmuryrafon25.freeserve.co.uk
www.murmuryrafon.co.uk
Pitches For Å ⊕ ➡ **Total** 77
Acreage 4 **Open** Mar **to** Oct
Access Good **Site** Level
Nearest Bus Stop (Miles) Outside
1 mile from beach. Set in sheltered and natural surroundings, 100yds from village and shops, petrol stations and licensed premises.
Facilities ᕃ ∮ ⊟ ⚇ ♠ ⌂ ⊙ ⊒ ⨄ ⬚ ☎
ℙ ⊙ ⊠ Ѧ ➤ ⊒ ⅍
Nearest Town Barmouth
Directions Take the A496 coast road from Barmouth towards Harlech. Caravan Site is located 100yds on the right after the Spar shop.
⇌ Dyffryn

FFESTINIOG

Llechrwd Riverside Campsite, Maentwrog, Blaenau Ffestiniog, Gwynedd, LL41 4HF
Tel: 01766 Maentwrog 590240
Email: llechrwd@hotmail.com
www.llechrwd.co.uk
Pitches For Å ⊕ ➡ **Total** 45
Acreage 5 **Open** Easter **to** Oct
Access Good **Site** Level
Nearest Bus Stop (Miles) Outside
Riverside camp within Snowdonia National Park, with meadow walk. Fully furnished bell tent for hire.
Facilities ᕃ ∮ ⚇ ♠ ⌂ ⊙ ⊒ ⬚ ☎ ➤ ⊒
Directions On the A496. Blaenau Ffestiniog 3 miles, Porthmadog 8 miles.
⇌ Blaenau Ffestiniog

HARLECH

Woodlands Caravan Park, Harlech, Gwynedd, LL46 2UE
Tel: 01766 780419
Email: info@woodlandparkharlech.co.uk
www.woodlandsparkharlech.com
Pitches For Å ⊕ ➡ **Total** 18
Open Mar **to** Oct
Access Good **Site** Level
Nearest Bus Stop (Miles) ¼
Walking distance to Harlech town centre, beach,railway station, wonderful views of Harlech Castle.
Facilities ∮ ⊟ ⚇ ♠ ⌂ ⊙ ⊒ ⨄ ☎
ℙ ⊙ ➤ ⊒ ⅍ ☍
Nearest Town Harlech
⇌ Harlech

LLANBEDROG

Wern Newydd Tourer Park, Llanbedrog, Pwllheli, Gwynedd, LL53 7PG
Tel: 01758 740220
Email: office@wern-newydd.co.uk
www.wern-newydd.co.uk
Pitches For Å ⊕ ➡ ➡⟨ **Total** 25
Acreage 2½ **Open** Mar **to** Oct
Access Good **Site** Level
Nearest Bus Stop (Miles) ¼
Peaceful location on the beautiful Lleyn Peninsula. Near the beach and village with its country pubs and bistro. The area offers many walks, watersports activities and attractions.

Facilities ∮ ⊟ ⚇ ♠ ⌂ ⊙ ⊒ ☎
ℙ ➤ ⊒ ⅍ ⚲
Nearest Town Abersoch
Directions From Pwllheli take the A499 towards Abersoch, in Llanbedrog turn right onto B4413 sp Aberdaron. Continue through the village, go past the chemists (on the right) then take the first turning right onto an unclassified road, site is 700 yards on the right.
⇌ Pwllheli

MORFA NEFYN

Graeanfryn Farm, Morfa Nefyn, Gwynedd, LL53 6YQ
Tel: 01758 720455
Email: jan@campingnorthwales.co.uk
www.campingnorthwales.co.uk
Pitches For Å ⊕ ➡ **Total** 40
Acreage 1½ **Open** Mar **to** Oct
Access Good **Site** Level
Nearest Bus Stop (Miles) ¼
Rural location, 1 mile from the beach. Barbecue area. Cafe/Restaurant nearby. One static caravan for hire. Camping and Caravan Club 3 Star Site and WTB 3 Star Graded. Jumbo tent pitches available.
Facilities ∮ ⚇ ♠ ⌂ ⊙ ⊒ ℙ ➤ ⊒ ⚲
Nearest Town Pwllheli
Directions From Pwllheli take the A497 for 5 miles, at the roundabout turn left and then turn next left. Entrance to the site is 50 yards on the right.
⇌ Pwllheli/Bangor

PORTHMADOG

Black Rock Sands Camping & Touring Park, Morfa Bychan, Porthmadog, Gwynedd, LL49 9YH
Tel: 01766 513919
www.blackrocksands.webs.com
Pitches For Å ⊕ ➡ **Total** 140
Acreage 9 **Open** Mar **to** Oct
Access Good **Site** Level
Nearest Bus Stop (Miles) ½
Adjacent to a 7 mile sandy beach.
Facilities ᕃ ∮ ⚇ ♠ ⌂ ⊙ ⊒ ⬚ ☎
ℙ ⊙ Ѧ ➤ ⊒ ⅍
Nearest Town Porthmadog
Directions From Porthmadog take the road to Morfa Bychan, turn right just before the beach.
⇌ Porthmadog

PORTHMADOG

GlanYMor Camping Park, Morfa Bychan, Porthmadog, Gwynedd, LL49 9YH
Tel: 01766 514640
www.glanymor.webs.com
Pitches For Å ⊕ ➡ **Total** 60
Acreage 5 **Open** Easter **to** Oct
Site Level
Nearest Bus Stop (Miles) ½
Adjacent to a 7 mile sandy beach.
Facilities ∮ ⚇ ♠ ⌂ ⊙ ⊒ ℙ ➤ ⊒ ⅍
Nearest Town Porthmadog
Directions From Porthmadog take the road to Morfa Bychan, continue to the beach, entrance is on the left.
⇌ Porthmadog

PORTHMADOG

Gwyndy Caravan Park, Black Rock Sands, Morfa Bychan, Porthmadog, Gwynedd, LL49 9YB
Tel: 01766 512047
Email: joan.gwyndy@btinternet.com
Pitches For ⊕ ➡ **Total** 24
Acreage 5 **Open** Mar **to** Oct
Access Good **Site** Level
Nearest Bus Stop (Miles) ¼

Select family run park, just a few minutes from the beach, with backdrop of mountain views. Ideal for touring the Snowdonia area. All super pitches.
Facilities ⨍ ▯ ▢ ⬚ ▢ ⌐ ⊙ ⬦ ▢ ▤ ▢ ⋇
📶

Nearest Town Porthmadog
Directions In Porthmadog turn towards Black Rock Sands follow the road into the village of Morfa Bychan past the Spar Supermarket, turn first left and then second right into road leading into caravan park. Exactly 2 miles from Porthmadog.
➤ Porthmadog

PORTHMADOG
Tyddyn Adi Caravan & Camping Park,
Tyddyn Adi, Morfa Bychan, Nr Black Rock Sands, Porthmadog, Gwynedd, LL49 9YW
Tel: 01766 512933
Email: tyddynadi@btconnect.com
www.tyddynadi.co.uk
Pitches For ⚑ ⛺ ⬚ ⬚ **Total** 50
Acreage 28 **Open** Mar to Sept
Access Good **Site** Level
Nearest Bus Stop (Miles) Outside
At the foot of Moel-y-Gest Mountain and near Black Rock Sands. Perfect base from which to explore Snowdonia.
Facilities ⨍ ▯ ▢ ⬚ ⌐ ⊙ ⬦ ▢ ▤ ▢
⬚ ▢ ⋇ ⬚ ▢ ⋇

Nearest Town Porthmadog
Directions Take the A487 from Caernarfon, turn right at The Factory Shop and follow signs for Morfa Bychan. We are opposite Greenacres (Haven).
➤ Porthmadog

PWLLHELI
Abererch Sands Holiday Centre, Pwllheli, Gwynedd, LL53 6PJ
Tel: 01758 612327
www.abererchsands.co.uk
Pitches For ⚑ ⛺ ⬚ **Total** 0
Open Mar to Oct
Access Good **Site** Level
Nearest Bus Stop (Miles) ¼
Adjacent to the beach. Heated indoor swimming pool.
Facilities ⬚ ⨍ ▢ ▢ ⌐ ⊙ ⬦ ▢ ▤ ▢
⬚ ▢ ⬚ ⬚ ▢ ⋇ 📶

Nearest Town Pwllheli
Directions From Pwllheli take the A497 towards Porthmadog for 1 mile, turn right at first roundabout and follow road to the Site.
➤ Pwllheli

PWLLHELI
Hendre Caravan Park, Efailnewydd, Near Pwllheli, Gwynedd, LL53 8TN
Tel: 01758 613416
Email: enq@hendrecaravanpark.co.uk
www.hendrecaravanpark.co.uk
Pitches For ⚑ ⛺ ⬚ **Total** 12
Acreage 10 **Open** Mar to Oct
Access Good **Site** Level
Nearest Bus Stop (Miles) ¼
Nefyn and Pwllheli beaches, Pwllheli marina, 7½ miles from Abersoch.
Facilities ⨍ ▢ ▢ ⌐ ⊙ ⬦ ▢ ▤ ▢
⬚ ▢ ⬚ ▢ ▢ ⋇

Nearest Town Pwllheli
Directions From Pwllheli take the A497 after 1 mile turn left in Efailnewydd on B4415 we are 500 metres on left.
➤ Pwllheli

PWLLHELI
Hirdre Fawr Caravan & Camping, Hirdre Fawr Farm, Edern, Pwllheli, Gwynedd, LL53 8YY
Tel: 01758 770309
Email: annwenw@yahoo.com
www.hirdrefawr.co.uk
Pitches For ⚑ ⛺ ⬚ **Total** 80
Acreage 7 **Open** End Mar to Oct
Access Good **Site** Level
Nearest Bus Stop (Miles) Outside
Pebly beach on site which also adjoins the coastal path. Central to the Llyn Peninsula. 2 miles from a golf coarse and beach access. Fishing off the rocks.
Facilities ⨍ ▢ ⌐ ⊙ ⬦ ▢ ▤ ▢
⬚ ⬚ ▢ ▢ ⬦ ⚲

Nearest Town Pwllheli
Directions On the B4417, 1½ miles out of Edern towards Tudweiliog.
➤ Pwllheli

TALSARNAU
Barcdy Touring Caravan & Camping Park, Talsarnau, Gwynedd, LL47 6YG
Tel: 01766 770736
Email: anwen@barcdy.co.uk
www.barcdy.co.uk
Pitches For ⚑ ⛺ ⬚ **Total** 98
Acreage 12 **Open** May to Sept
Access Good **Site** Lev/Slope
Walks from site to nearby mountains and lakes. Ideal touring Snowdonia.
Facilities ⨍ ▯ ▢ ▢ ⌐ ⊙ ⬦ ▢ ▤ ▢
⬚ ▢ ⬚ ⬚ ▢ ⋇ 📶

Nearest Town Harlech
Directions From Bala A4212 to Trawsfynydd. A487 to Maentwrog. At Maentwrog left onto A496, signposted Harlech. Site 4 miles.
➤ Talsarnau

TYWYN
Caethle Chalet & Caravan Park, Aberdyfi Road, Tywyn, Gwynedd, LL36 9HS
Tel: 01654 712116
Pitches For ⚑ ⛺ ⬚ **Total** 50
Acreage 15 **Open** Apr to Oct
Access Good **Site** Lev/Slope
Nearest Bus Stop (Miles) Outside
Set in the countryside with great views. Near the beach.
Facilities ⨍ ▢ ⌐ ⊙ ⬦ ▢ ▤ ▢
Nearest Town Tywyn
Directions On the A493 coast road, 1½ miles couth of Tywyn.
➤ Tywyn

TYWYN
Dol Einion, Tal-y-Llyn, Tywyn, Gwynedd, LL36 9AJ
Tel: 01654 761312
Email: marianrees@tiscali.co.uk
www.tal-y-llynheritagecentre.co.uk
Pitches For ⚑ ⛺ ⬚ ⬚ **Total** 0
Acreage 3 **Open** All Year
Access Good **Site** Level
Nearest Bus Stop (Miles) ¼
Flat, grassy site with a stream in Snowdonia National Park. At the start of the popular Minffordd Path to the summit of Cader Idris. Heritage Centre on site with full summer programme on Welsh history, traditions and music. Ideal for walking and touring. Fly fishing ½ mile, narrow gauge railway 3 miles and beach 11 miles. B&B and self catering cottage on site. Hotel restaurant and bar nearby. Public telephone nearby. Good bus service.
Facilities ⨍ ▢ ▢ ⌐ ⊙ ⬦
⬚ ⬦ ▢ ▢ ⚲ ⋇ ⬚
Nearest Town Dolgellau

Directions From Dolgellau take the A470 for 2 miles, turn right onto the A487 and continue for 4 miles. Turn right onto the B4405, site is 300 metres.
➤ Machynlleth

TYWYN
ErwWen Caravan Park, Mill Lane, Bryncrug, Tywyn, Gwynedd, LL36 9NU
Tel: 01654 710374
Pitches For ⚑ ⛺ **Total** 20
Acreage 2 **Open** Mar to Oct
Access Good **Site** Level
Nearest Bus Stop (Miles) ¼
Ideal touring.
Facilities ▢ ⌐ ⬚ ▤ ▢
Nearest Town Tywyn
Directions 2 miles from Tywyn on the road to Dolgellau in the village of Bryncrug, turn first left after the playing field.
➤ Tywyn

TYWYN
Pall Mall Farm Caravan Park, Pall Mall Farm, Tywyn, Gwynedd, LL36 9RU
Tel: 01654 710384
Email: richardmvaughan@gmail.com
www.pallmallfarmcaravanpark.co.uk
Pitches For ⚑ ⛺ ⬚ **Total** 50
Open Easter to Oct
Nearest Bus Stop (Miles) Outside
½ a mile to the town and safe sandy beach which is ideal for watersports. Leisure centre in the town plus a cinema, cafes, tennis courts, bowling green and putting green. Tal-y-Llyn Steam Railway nearby.
Facilities ⬚ ⨍ ▢ ⌐ ⊙ ⬦ ▤ ▢
⬚ ▢ ⬚ ⬚ ▢ ⋇
Nearest Town Tywyn
Directions Park is the first on the left when leaving Tywyn on the A493 Dolgellau road.
➤ Tywyn

TYWYN
Waenfach Caravan Site, Waenfach, Llanegryn, Tywyn, Gwynedd, LL36 9SB
Tel: 01654 711052
Pitches For ⚑ ⛺ ⬚ **Total** 10
Open Easter to Oct **Access** Good
Small site on a working farm. 3 miles from the sea.
Facilities ⬚ ⚲ ⨍ ▯ ▢ ▢ ⌐ ⊙ ⬦ ▢ ▢
⬚ ▢ ⬚ ⬚ ▢ ⋇
Nearest Town Tywyn
Directions 4 miles north of Tywyn on the A493.
➤ Tywyn

TYWYN
Ynsymaengwyn Caravan Park, The Lodge, Tywyn, Gwynedd, LL36 9RY
Tel: 01654 710684
Email: rita@ynysy.co.uk
www.ynysy.co.uk
Pitches For ⚑ ⛺ ⬚ **Total** 80
Acreage 4 **Open** Apr to Oct
Access Good **Site** Level
Nearest Bus Stop (Miles) Outside
In the grounds of an old manor house with a river at the bottom of the site for fishing. Near the beach and shops. Superpitches. Woodland walks open to the public. Secure storage for cycles. WTB 4 Star Grading and AA 4 Pennants.
Facilities ⬚ ⨍ ▢ ⌐ ⊙ ⬦ ▢ ▤ ▢
⬚ ▢ ⬚ ▢ ⬚ ▢ ⋇
Nearest Town Tywyn
Directions Take the A493 from Tywyn to Dolgellau, we are the second caravan park on the left.
➤ Tywyn

MONMOUTHSHIRE

ABERGAVENNY

Blossom Touring Park Tredillion, Llantillio, Pertholey, Abergavenny, Monmouthshire, NP7 8BG
Tel: 01873 850444
Email: james.harris27@btinternet.com
www.blossompark.co.uk
Pitches For ⅄ ⊞ 🚐 🚃 ⋚ **Total** 90
Acreage 7½ **Open** Mar **to** Oct
Access Good **Site** Sloping
Nearest Bus Stop (Miles) 1½
Set in a south facing pear and plum orchard located 1.5 miles on the out skirts of Abergavenny.

With an abundance of activities for all the family Abergavenny is a fantastic choice for your well earned holiday.

Sugar Loaf Mountain. Skirrid Mountain walks.
Facilities 🖎 ⚡ 🖵 🕻 🚽 ⇌ 🖙 🔌 🖳 🗑
🖳🚾🖭🖪 🛒 ⚡ 🛜
Nearest Town Abergavenny
Directions Hardwick Roundabout at Abertale, take A465 towards Hereford for 1 mile. Turn right, then left in to Oldcross Road (B4521), then right B4233.
🚃 Abergavenny

ABERGAVENNY

Pandy Caravan Club Site, Pandy, Abergavenny, Monmouthshire, NP7 8DR
Tel: 01873 890370
www.caravanclub.co.uk
Pitches For ⊞ 🚐 **Total** 53
Acreage 5 **Open** 15-Mar **to** 04-Nov
Access Good **Site** Level
Nearest Bus Stop (Miles) ½
Pleasant site scattered with mature trees and bounded by the River Honddu. Near Offas Dyke Path. 50 yards from the Old Pandy Hotel and there are several pubs in the vicinity. Close to the Brecon Beacons and Tintern Abbey. Non members welcome. Booking essential.
Facilities 🖎 ⚡ 🖵 🕻 🚾 ⇌ 🖙 🗑
🖳 🖭 🖪 ⊙ 🚽 🖭 🛜
Nearest Town Abergavenny
Directions From the A465, DO NOT go into Abergavenny but continue on the A465 following signs for Hereford. After 6¼ miles turn left by the Pandy Inn into a minor road, site is on the left immediately after passing under the railway bridge.
🚃 Abergavenny

ABERGAVENNY

Pyscodlyn Farm Caravan & Camping Site, Llanwenarth Citra, Abergavenny, Monmouthshire, NP7 7ER
Tel: 01873 853271
Email: pyscodlyn.farm@virgin.net
www.pyscodlyncaravanpark.com
Pitches For ⅄ ⊞ 🚐 **Total** 60
Acreage 4½ **Open** Apr **to** Oct
Access Good **Site** Level
Nearest Bus Stop (Miles) Outside
Ideal for walking, cycling and exploring the Black Mountains and Brecon Beacons National Park.
Facilities 🖎 ⚡ 🖵 🖙 🖎 ⊙ ⇌ 🔌 🖳 🗑
🖭 🖭 🖪 🛜
Nearest Town Abergavenny
Directions Situated on A40 (Brecon road), 1½ miles from Nevill Hall Hospital, on the left 50 yards past the telephone box.
🚃 Abergavenny

MONMOUTH

Bridge Caravan Park & Camping Site, Dingestow, Monmouth, Monmouthshire, NP25 4DY
Tel: 01600 740241
Email: info@bridgecaravanpark.co.uk
www.bridgecaravanpark.co.uk
Pitches For ⅄ ⊞ 🚐 **Total** 123
Acreage 4 **Open** Easter **to** Oct
Access Good **Site** Level
Nearest Bus Stop (Miles) Outside
Riverside site. Easy access.
Facilities 🖎 ⚡ 🖵 🕻 🚾 ⇌ ⊙ ⇌ 🔌 🖳 🗑
🖳 🖭 🖪 🖪 🖙 🛒 ❄
Nearest Town Monmouth
Directions 4 miles west of Monmouth.
🚃 Abergavenny

MONMOUTH

Glen Trothy Caravan Park, Mitchel Troy, Monmouth, Monmouthshire, NP25 4BD
Tel: 01600 712295
Email: enquiries@glentrothy.co.uk
www.glentrothy.co.uk
Pitches For ⅄ ⊞ 🚐 **Total** 130
Acreage 6½ **Open** Mar **to** Oct
Access Good **Site** Level
Nearest Bus Stop (Miles) Outside
Quiet level Park set in beautiful countryside on the edge of Forest of Dean and Wye Valley. Alongside a river for fishing. 1½ miles from the historic town of Monmouth. Plenty of castles and attractions nearby. No arrivals before 2pm.
Facilities 🖎 ⚡ 🖵 🕻 🚾 ⇌ 🖙 🔌 🖳 🗑
🖭 🖪 🖭 🖪 🛒 ❄
Nearest Town Monmouth
Directions From North & North East M5, M50 to Ross on Wye then A40 to Monmouth. After traffic lights, 150yds, turn lt
(before Tunnel), 150 yds to T junc. Turn lt and follow signs to Mitchel Troy- 1½ miles The park is on the rt as you enter village. From East & South Gloucester A4136 and Cheptow A466 to Monmouth over River Wye bridge. Turn lt at traffic lights onto A40, then as above. From South West Newport M4 junction 24 then A449 to Raglan.
🚃 Newport

NEWPORT

NEWPORT

Pentre-Tai Farm, Rhiwderin, Newport, NP10 8RQ
Tel: 01633 893284
Email: sue@pentretai.f9.co.uk
www.pentretaifarm.co.uk
Pitches For ⅄ ⊞ 🚐 **Total** 5
Acreage 3 **Open** All Year
Access Good **Site** Lev/Slope
Nearest Bus Stop (Miles) ½
Ideal for visiting Cardiff and the Welsh castles. Useful stopover for Irish ferry. Good pub nearby. B&B also available (WTB 4 Star).
Facilities ⚡ 🚾 ⇌ 🖙 ⊙ 🖙 🗑 🖪 🕻 🔌
Nearest Town Newport
Directions Leave the M4 at junction 28 and take the A467, at the next roundabout take the A468 for approx. 1 mile. Turn right immediately after Rhiwderin Inn and go straight through the village and straight down the lane to the Farm. Go past the farmhouse then turn into yard.
🚃 Newport

NEWPORT

Tredegar House Country Park Caravan Club Site, Coedkernew, Newport, NP10 8TW
Tel: 01633 815600
www.caravanclub.co.uk
Pitches For ⅄ ⊞ 🚐 **Total** 79
Acreage 7 **Open** All Year
Access Good **Site** Level
Nearest Bus Stop (Miles) ¼
Bordered by an ornamental lake by Tredegar House. Tea rooms on site. Adventure playground adjacent. 7 miles from Cardiff. Non members welcome. Booking essential.
Facilities 🖎 ⚡ 🖵 🕻 🚾 ⇌ 🖙 🖙 🖳 🗑
🖳 🖭 🖪 🛒 🛜
Nearest Town Newport
Directions Leave the M4 at junction 28 and take the A48 signposted Tredegar House. At the roundabout turn left into the site entrance and follow site signs.
🚃 Newport

PEMBROKESHIRE

AMROTH

Little Kings Park, Amroth Road, Ludchurch, Narberth, Pembrokeshire, SA67 8PG
Tel: 01834 831330
Email: littlekingspark@btconnect.com
www.littlekings.co.uk
Pitches For ⅄ ⊞ 🚐 🚃 ⋚ **Total** 121
Acreage 16 **Open** Mar **to** Oct
Access Good **Site** Level
Quiet family park in a country setting with an excellent outlook towards the sea. Perfectly placed for easy access to explore all that Pembrokeshire has to offer.
Facilities 🖎 ⚡ 🖵 🕻 🚾 ⇌ 🖙 🔌 🖳 🗑
🖳 🖭 🖪 ✕ 🍴 🗛 🖙 🖭 🖪 🛒 ⚑ 🛜
Nearest Town Amroth
Directions 5 miles south east of Narberth. From the A477 in Llanteg Village, 2 miles after the petrol station turn left towards Amroth and Wisemans Bridge, turn first right signposted Ludchurch and the Park is 300 metres on the left.
🚃 Kilgetty

AMROTH

Pantglas Farm, Tavernspite, Pembrokeshire, SA34 0NS
Tel: 01834 831618
Email: pantglasfarm@btinternet.com
www.pantglasfarm.co.uk
Pitches For ⅄ ⊞ 🚐 🚃 ⋚ **Total** 86
Acreage 14 **Open** Mid Mar **to** Mid Oct
Access Good **Site** Lev/Slope
Nearest Bus Stop (Miles) ¼
A family caravan and camping park, quiet and secluded. Super play area for children. High standard toilet and shower facilities, disabled wet room facility. Year round caravan storage available. Within easy reach of Tenby, Saundersfoot and Amroth. Indoor swimming pool only 1 mile away.
Facilities 🖎 ⚡ 🖵 🕻 🚾 ⇌ 🖙 ⇌ 🔌 🖳 🗑
🖳 🖭 🖪 🍴 🗛 🖙 🖭 🖪 🛒 ⚑ 🛜
Nearest Town Whitland/Narberth
Directions A477 towards Tenby take the B4314 at Red Roses crossroads to Tavernspite 1¼ miles, take the middle road at the village pump. Pantglas is ½ mile down on the left.
🚃 Whitland

ANGLE

Castle Farm Camping Site, Castle Farm, Angle, Nr Pembroke, Pembrokeshire, SA71 5AR
Tel: 01646 641220
Pitches For ▲ ⛟ ⛺ **Total** 25
Acreage 2½ **Open** Easter **to** Oct
Access Good **Site** Lev/Slope
Overlooking East Angle Bay and directly behind the church in the village. Approx. 1 mile from a safe, sandy beach. Near to 2 public houses, Beach Cafe, a good shop and childrens play area. Pets are welcome if kept on leads.
Facilities ƒ ⬚⬚⬚⬚⬚⬚⬚⬚
Nearest Town Pembroke
Directions Approx. 10 miles from Pembroke.
⚞ Pembroke

BROAD HAVEN

Creampots Touring Caravan & Camping Park, Broadway, Broad Haven, Littlehaven, Haverfordwest, Pembrokeshire, SA62 3TU
Tel: 01437 781776
Email: creampots@btconnect.com
www.creampots.co.uk
Pitches For ▲ ⛟ ⛺ **Total** 72
Acreage 7 **Open** Mar **to** Nov
Access Good **Site** Level
Nearest Bus Stop (Miles) ¼
Family run park thats quiet, peaceful and well maintained. Ideal for couples and families. 1½ miles from safe sandy beach and coastal path at Broad Haven. 21 hardstanding pitches. Near Haverfordwest, Broad Haven and Littlehaven. WTB 4 Star Graded.
Facilities ♿ ƒ ⬚⬚⬚⬚⬚⬚⬚⬚⬚
Nearest Town Haverfordwest
Directions Take the B4131 Broad Haven road from Haverfordwest to Broadway (5 miles). Turn left and Creampots is 600 yards on the right.
⚞ Haverfordwest

FISHGUARD

Fishguard Bay Caravan Park, Garn Gelli, Fishguard, Pembrokeshire, SA65 9ET
Tel: 01348 811415
Email: enquiries@fishguardbay.com
www.fishguardbay.com
Pitches For ▲ ⛟ ⛺ **Total** 50
Acreage 5 **Open** Mar **to** Dec
Access Good **Site** Lev/Slope
Superb cliff top location offering excellent views and walks along this Heritage coast of Pembrokeshire.
Facilities ƒ ⬚⬚⬚⬚⬚⬚⬚⬚⬚
Nearest Town Fishguard
Directions Take the A487 Cardigan road from Fishguard for 1½ miles, turn left at sign.
⚞ Fishguard

FISHGUARD

Gwaun Vale Touring Park, Llanychaer, Fishguard, Pembrokeshire, SA65 9TA
Tel: 01348 874698
Email: margaret.harries@talk21.com
www.gwaunvale.co.uk
Pitches For ▲ ⛟ ⛺ **Total** 29
Acreage 1½ **Open** Apr **to** Oct
Access Good **Site** Level
Nearest Bus Stop (Miles) 1
Beautiful views of Gwaun Valley. Ideal for walking on Pembrokeshire Coast National Park.
Facilities ƒ ⬚⬚⬚⬚⬚⬚⬚
Nearest Town Fishguard
Directions From Fishguard take the B4313, site is 1½ miles on the right hand side.
⚞ Fishguard

FISHGUARD

Rosebush Caravan & Camping Park, Rhoslwyn, Rosebush, Narberth, Pembrokeshire, SA66 7QT
Tel: 01437 532206
Pitches For ▲ ⛟ ⛺ **Total** 45
Acreage 15 **Open** Mar **to** Oct
Access Good **Site** Level
ADULTS ONLY PARK in the centre of Pembrokeshire, 800ft above sea level. 3 acre lake for coarse fishing. Mountain walks. David Bellamy Gold Award for Conservation.
Facilities ƒ ⬚⬚⬚⬚⬚⬚⬚⬚
⬚⬚⬚⬚⬚⬚⬚
Nearest Town Fishguard
Directions From the A40 take the B4313 near Narberth to Fishguard. 1 mile from the B4329 Haverfordwest to Cardigan road.
⚞ Clynderwen

HAVERFORDWEST

Dunston Hill Caravan & Camping, Dunston Hill Farm, Pelcomb, Haverfordwest, Pembrokeshire, SA62 6ED
Tel: 01437 710525
Email: kenjenkins@hotmail.com.uk
Pitches For ▲ ⛟ ⛺ **Total** 40
Acreage 4 **Open** Apr **to** Sept
Nearest Bus Stop (Miles) Outside
Great views from the site. Close to a Blue Flag beach. 10 miles from Europes smallest city of St. Davids.
Facilities ƒ ⬚⬚⬚⬚⬚⬚⬚⬚⬚
Nearest Town Haverfordwest
Directions From Haverfordwest take the A487 towards St Davids for 3 miles, site is 200 yards past the first petrol station on the right.
⚞ Haverfordwest

HAVERFORDWEST

Nolton Cross Caravan Park, Nolton, Haverfordwest, Pembrokeshire, SA62 3NP
Tel: 01437 710701
Email: info@noltoncross-holidays.co.uk
www.noltoncross-holidays.co.uk
Pitches For ▲ ⛟ ⛺ **Total** 15
Acreage 1½ **Open** Mar **to** Dec
Access Good **Site** Level
Nearest Bus Stop (Miles) 1½
Coarse fishing lake on site. 1½ miles from sandy beaches. Central location for touring Pembrokeshire.
Facilities ƒ ⬚⬚⬚⬚⬚⬚⬚
⬚⬚⬚⬚⬚⬚
Nearest Town Haverfordwest
Directions Take the A487 from Haverfordwest towards St Davids, after 5 miles at the village of Simpson Cross turn left for Nolton, follow for 1 mile to the next crossroads and turn left, entrance is 100 yards on the right.
⚞ Haverfordwest

HERMON

The Lamb Inn Touring Caravan Park, Hermon, Glogue, Pembrokeshire, SA36 0DS
Tel: 01239 831864
Email: street867@btinternet.com
www.thelambinnhermon.co.uk
Pitches For ⛟ ⛺ **Total** 28
Acreage 2 **Open** Easter **to** 03-Jan
Access Good **Site** Level
Nearest Bus Stop (Miles) Outside
Quiet and secluded ADULTS ONLY Park at the rear of The Lamb Inn Pub. Ideal for walking and cycling. Close to Cardigan.
Facilities ƒ ⬚⬚⬚⬚⬚⬚⬚⬚
⬚⬚⬚⬚⬚⬚⬚⬚⬚⬚⬚
Nearest Town Cardigan

Directions From Carmarthen take the A40 west, turn right onto the A478 Cardigan road. At Crymmych turn right and follow signs to Hermon for 2 miles.
⚞ Clunderwen

KILGETTY

Stone Pitt Caravan Park, Begelly, Kilgetty, Pembrokeshire, SA68 0XE
Tel: 01834 811086
Email: info@stonepitt.co.uk
www.stonepitt.co.uk
Pitches For ⛟ ⛺ **Total** 36
Acreage 6 **Open** Mar **to** 09-Jan
Access Good **Site** Lev/Slope
Nearest Bus Stop (Miles) Outside
Quiet, peaceful, family run park. Within easy reach of Pembrokeshires wonderful beaches, Folly Farm, Heatherton, Oakwood, Tenby and Saundersfoot. Ideal touring. All pitches are hardstanding with grey water waste.Online booking available.
Facilities ƒ ⬚⬚⬚⬚⬚⬚⬚⬚
⬚⬚⬚⬚⬚⬚⬚⬚
Nearest Town Saundersfoot/Tenby
Directions From St. Clears take the A477, at the next roundabout turn onto the A478 for Narberth. Go over the next roundabout in Begelly Village, site is ½ a mile on the left.
⚞ Kilgetty

LITTLE HAVEN

Redlands Touring Caravan & Camping Park, Hasguard Cross, Nr Little Haven, Haverfordwest, Pembrokeshire, SA62 3SJ
Tel: 01437 781300
Email: info@redlandscamping.co.uk
www.redlandstouring.co.uk
Pitches For ▲ ⛟ ⛺ ≼ **Total** 60
Acreage 5 **Open** Mar **to** Dec
Access Good **Site** Level
Nearest Bus Stop (Miles) ¼
4 Star Park set in Pembrokeshire National Park, within easy reach of coastal path and superb sandy beaches.Sea views, Immaculate facilities. Extra large tent pitches. Special Offers for couples in Low Season.
Facilities ƒ ⬚⬚⬚⬚⬚⬚⬚⬚
⬚⬚⬚⬚⬚⬚⬚⬚
Nearest Town Little Haven
Directions 6½ miles southwest of Haverfordwest, on B4327 Dale Road.
⚞ Haverfordwest

LITTLE HAVEN

South Cockett Caravan & Camping Park, Broadway, Little Haven, Haverfordwest, Pembrokeshire, SA62 3TU
Tel: 01437 781296
Email: esmejames@hotmail.co.uk
www.southcockett.co.uk
Pitches For ▲ ⛟ ⛺ **Total** 73
Acreage 6 **Open** Easter **to** Oct
Access Good **Site** Level
Nearest Bus Stop (Miles) ¼
1 mile from the beach. Ideal for touring.
Facilities ƒ ⬚⬚⬚⬚⬚⬚⬚⬚⬚
Nearest Town Broad Haven
Directions From Haverfordwest take the B4341 for Broad Haven for about 6 miles, turn left at sign post and the Site is ¼ of a mile.
⚞ Haverfordwest

MILFORD HAVEN

Sandy Haven Caravan Park, Herbrandston, Nr Milford Haven, Pembrokeshire, SA73 3ST
Tel: 01646 698844
www.sandyhavencampingpark.co.uk
Pitches For ▲ ⛟ ⛺ **Total** 26

Open Whitsun **to** Sept
Access Good **Site** Lev/Slope
Nearest Bus Stop (Miles) ¼
Very quiet and uncommercialised site, alongside a beautiful beach and sea estuary. Ideal for a family holiday.
Facilities ♿ ⌂ ⬇ 🚿 ⚡🌭🔌 ✏
Nearest Town Milford Haven
Directions Take the Dale Road from Milford Haven, turn left at Herbrandston School and follow the village road down to the beach.
⚏ Milford Haven

NARBERTH

Wood Office Caravan & Tent Park, Cold Blow, Narberth, Pembrokeshire, SA67 8RR
Tel: 01834 860565
Email: barbara_morris@btconnect.com
Pitches For ▲ 🚐 🚛 **Total** 30
Access Good **Site** Level
Nearest Bus Stop (Miles) Outside
Close to Oakwood Park, Bluestone & Blue Lagoon and Folly Farm. Please telephone prior to bringing a dog.
Facilities ♿ ∱ 🚾⌂⌐🍴⊙⬇ 📦 🖵 ☎
♨ 🚻 🕅 🚲 🏧 ♨ ✄
Nearest Town Narberth
Directions Leave the M4 and take the A40, then the A478, at the top of Templeton turn left onto the B4315 to Cold Blow.
⚏ Narberth

NEWPORT

Llwyngwair Manor Holiday Park, Newport, Pembrokeshire, SA42 0LX
Tel: 01239 820498
www.pembrokeshireholidaypark.co.uk
Pitches For ▲ 🚐 🚛 **Total** 0
Acreage 55 **Open** Mar **to** 02-Jan
Access Good **Site** Level
Nearest Bus Stop (Miles) Outside
1 mile from a sandy beach. Alongside the River Nevern in 55 acres of wood and parkland in Pembrokeshire Coast National Park.
Facilities ♿∱ 🚾⌂⌐🍴⊙⬇ 📦 🖵 ☎
♨ 🚻 🕅 🍴 🗙 🍷 ⟨⟩ 🚲 🏧 ♨🌭🔌 🖵 🖵 ✄ ♨
Nearest Town Newport
Directions 1 mile from Newport on the A487 to Cardigan.
⚏ Fishguard

NEWPORT

Morawelon Caravan & Camping Site, Morawelon, The Parrog, Newport, Pembrokeshire, SA42 0RW
Tel: 01239 820565
Email: carreg@morawelon.fsnet.co.uk
Pitches For ▲ 🚐 🚛 **Total** 90
Acreage 5 **Open** Mar **to** Oct
Access Good **Site** Sloping
Nearest Bus Stop (Miles) ½
Ideal family site. Near to the beach with a slipway for boat launching just outside the entrance. On the Pembrokeshire Coastal Path.
Facilities ∱ 🚾⌂⌐🍴⊙ ☎ 🗙 🖵 🖵
Nearest Town Newport
Directions A487 from Fishguard, 7 miles to Newport. A487 from Cardigan, 12 miles to Newport. Turn right after the garage, continue into Newport, turn left down Parrog Road. Go down to the bottom and Morawelon is the house by the slipway.
⚏ Fishguard

NEWPORT

Tycanol Farm Camp Site, Newport, Pembrokeshire, SA42 0ST
Tel: 01239 820264
Email: sharonjackson70@hotmail,co.uk
www.caravancampingsites.co.uk

Pitches For ▲ 🚐 🚛 🚛 **Total** 40
Acreage 6 **Open** All Year
Access Good **Site** Level
Nearest Bus Stop (Miles) ¼
Organic farm, situated on a coastal path with easy access to beaches and the town. barbecue nightly. Bunk house accommodation.
Facilities ✿ ∱ 🚾⌂⌐⊙⬇ 🖵 ♨ 🌭🔌 ✏
Nearest Town Newport
⚏ Fishguard

PEMBROKE

Freshwater East Caravan Club Site, Trewent Hill, Freshwater East, Pembroke, Pembrokeshire, SA71 5LJ
Tel: 01646 672341
www.caravanclub.co.uk
Pitches For ▲ 🚐 🚛 **Total** 128
Acreage 12½ **Open** Mar **to** Oct
Access Good **Site** Lev/Slope
Nearest Bus Stop (Miles) ¼
Situated at the bottom of a hill in Pembrokeshire Coast National Park. Just a few minutes from the beach with clifftop views and coastal walks. Close to the castles of Pembroke, Carew and Manorbier. Near Folly Farm and Oakwood Theme Park. Non members welcome. Booking essential.
Facilities ♿ ∱ 🚾⌂⌐🍴⊙⬇ 🖵 ☎
♨ 🚻 🕅 🚲 🌭🔌 🖵 ☎ ♑
Nearest Town Pembroke
Directions From A477 take A4075 sp Pembroke. Immediately after passing under railway bridge turn left on A4139. In Lamphey at left hand bend continue onto B4584 sp Freshwater East. After 1¾ miles turn right sp Stackpole, at foot of hill turn right at Club site.
⚏ Pembroke

PEMBROKE

Windmill Hill Caravan Park, St Daniels Hill, Pembroke, Pembrokeshire, SA71 5BT
Tel: 01646 682392
Email: wjgibby@btconnect.com
www.windmillhillcaravanpark.co.uk
Pitches For ▲ 🚐 🚛 **Total** 30
Open Mar **to** Dec
Access Good **Site** Level
Ideal base for surfing, hiking and rock climbing.
Facilities ♿ ∱ 🚾⌂⌐🍴⊙⬇ 🖵 ☎ 🌭🔌 🖵
Nearest Town Pembroke
Directions From Pembroke take the B4319, site is ½ a mile on the right hand side.
⚏ Pembroke

SAUNDERSFOOT

Mill House Caravan Park, Pleasant Valley, Stepaside, Saundersfoot, Pembrokeshire, SA67 8LN
Tel: 01834 812069
Email: holiday@millhousecaravan.co.uk
www.millhousecaravan.co.uk
Pitches For ▲ 🚐 🚛 **Total** 12
Acreage 2½ **Open** Mar **to** Oct
Access Good **Site** Level
Nearest Bus Stop (Miles) Outside
Beautiful and sheltered setting in a wooded valley, next to an old water mill. 15 minute walk to the beach and coastal path. Holiday caravans for hire.
Facilities ∱ 🚾⌂⌐🍴⊙⬇ 📦 🖵 ☎
🕅 🚲 ♨ 🌭🔌 ♑
Directions 13 miles west of St. Clears on the A477 turn left signposted Stepaside. After crossing the bridge turn sharp left then immediately left again signed Pleasant Valley. Site is approx, 500 metres on the left hand side.
⚏ Kilgetty

SAUNDERSFOOT

Moysland Farm Camping Site, Narberth Road, Saundersfoot, Pembrokeshire, SA69 9DS
Tel: 01834 812455
Pitches For ▲ 🚐 🚛 **Total** 17
Acreage 2 **Open** July **to** 01-Sep
Access Good **Site** Level
Nearest Bus Stop (Miles) ¼
On cycle route for touring local area.
Facilities ∱ 🚾⌂⌐🍴 🖵 🖵
Nearest Town Saundersfoot
Directions On A478 near Twycross roundabout, 1½ miles north of Tenby.
⚏ Tenby

ST. DAVIDS

Caerfai Bay Caravan & Tent Park, St Davids, Pembrokeshire, SA62 6QT
Tel: 01437 720274
Email: info@caerfaibay.co.uk
www.caerfaibay.co.uk
Pitches For ▲ 🚐 🚛 **Total** 105
Acreage 10 **Open** Mar **to** Mid Nov
Site Lev/Slope
Nearest Bus Stop (Miles) 1
A family run park with panoramic coastal views. AA Welsh Campsite of the year 2013 Adjacent to the Pembrokeshire Coastal Path and a bathing beach. Within walking distance of St Davids, Britians smallest city. Holiday hire caravans available. No dogs allowed in the tent fields during school summer holidays (July/August).
Facilities ♿ ∱ 🚾⌂⌐🍴⊙⬇ 📦 🖵 ☎
🕅 🚲 ♨ 🌭🔌 🖵 🖵 ♑
Nearest Town St Davids
Directions Turn off the A487 (Haverfordwest to St. Davids road) at St. Davids Visitor Centre signposted Caerfai. At the end of the road, ¾ miles, turn right into park.
⚏ Haverfordwest

ST. DAVIDS

Hendre Eynon Camp Site, Hendre Eynon, St Davids, Pembrokeshire, SA62 6DB
Tel: 01437 720474
Email: hendreeynon@gmail.com
www.hendreeynon.co.uk
Pitches For ▲ 🚐 🚛 **Total** 72
Open Apr **to** Sept
Access Good **Site** Level
Nearest Bus Stop (Miles) Outside
Ideal family site, spotlessly clean facilities, sheltered pitches, close to coast path.
Facilities ∱ 🚾⌂⌐🍴⊙⬇ 📦 🖵 ☎
♨ 🚻 🕅 ♨ 🌭🔌 ♨
Nearest Town St Davids
Directions At St Davids take the Fishguard road and fork left at the rugby club signposted Llanrhian. Keep going straight and after approx. 2 miles Hendre Eynon is on the right hand side.
⚏ Haverfordwest

ST. DAVIDS

Nine Wells Caravan & Camping Park, Nine Wells, Solva, Nr Haverfordwest, Pembrokeshire, SA62 6UH
Tel: 01437 721809
Email: ocean6@clara.co.uk
www.ninewellscamping.com
Pitches For ▲ 🚐 🚛 **Total** 70
Acreage 4½ **Open** Easter **to** Oct
Access Good **Site** Lev/Slope
Nearest Bus Stop (Miles) Outside
Sandy beach ¾ mile. Walk the coastal footpath to Solva. About 5 minute walk to cove and coastal footpath and Iron Age Fort, down National Trust Valley. You can also call us on Mobile 07974 516461.

Facilities ✱ ▥♻️🅿️☉⌫🍴 ♨📶♿🅿️🔥♨

Nearest Town Haverfordwest

Directions From Haverfordwest take A487 to Solva. ½ mile past Solva turn left at Nine Wells. Site clearly signposted.

≢ Haverfordwest

ST. DAVIDS

Park Hall Camping Park, Maerdy Farm, Penycwm, Haverfordwest, Pembrokeshire, SA62 6LS

Tel: 01437 721606/721282

Pitches For ▲ ⚏ 🚐 ⚏ Total 100

Acreage 7 **Open** Mar **to** Oct

Access Good **Site** Level

Near the beach with scenic views. Ideal touring. Disabled toilet and shower. Dish washing facilities.

Facilities ♿ ✱ ▥♻️🅿️☉⌫🍴 🔥♨
♨🅿️♿🔥♨

Nearest Town Haverfordwest

Directions 12 miles from Haverfordwest on the A487 and 6 miles from St. Davids. Turn at the 14th Signal Regiment Brawdy.

≢ Haverfordwest

ST. DAVIDS

St Davids Lleithyr Meadow Caravan Club Site, Whitesands, St Davids, Pembrokeshire, SA62 6PR

Tel: 01437 720401

www.caravanclub.co.uk

Pitches For ⚏ 🚐 Total 118

Acreage 8 **Open** Mar **to** Oct

Access Good **Site** Level

Nearest Bus Stop (Miles) ½

Just a short walk to Whitesands Bay. Shop adjacent. Non members welcome. Booking essential.

Facilities ♿ ✱ ▥♻️🅿️ 🅾️ 🔥
♨♨🅾️♻️🅿️♿

Nearest Town St. Davids

Directions From Haverfordwest take A487, before entering St Davids t rt on B4583 sp Whitesands, t lt still on B4583. At second xroads (DO NOT follow Lleithyr Meadow signs at first xroads) t sharp right opposite St Davids Golf Club, site is 500 yards on left.

≢ St. Davids

TENBY

Buttyland Camping Park, Manorbier, Tenby, Pembrokeshire, SA70 7SX

Tel: 01834 871278

Email: stay@buttyland.com

www.buttyland.com

Pitches For ▲ ⚏ 🚐 ⚏ Total 50

Acreage 10 **Open** 15-Mar **to** 15-Nov

Access Good **Site** Level

Nearest Bus Stop (Miles) ¼

Perfect location for Tenby, close to beach, 2 country pubs serving food, station next to park.

Facilities ✱ ▥♻️🅿️☉⌫🅾️🔥
♨♨☓♨🖥️🅿️♿🔥♨ 🛜

Nearest Town Tenby

Directions After Tenby follow A4139 towards Pembroke, then after approx 4 miles, follow signs for Manorbier Railway station.

≢ Manorbier

TENBY

Hazelbrook Caravan Park, Sageston, Nr Tenby, Pembrokeshire, SA70 8SY

Tel: 01646 651351

Email: hazbrook12@hotmail.co.uk

www.hazelbrookcaravan.co.uk

Pitches For ▲ ⚏ 🚐 Total 70

Acreage 7½ **Open** 14-Mar **to** 05-Nov

Access Good **Site** Level

Nearest Bus Stop (Miles) ¼

Quiet family site, 1 mile from Carew Castle and Mill, 2 miles from Dinosaur Park and 7 miles from Oakwood Theme Park.

Facilities ✱ ▥♻️🅿️☉⌫🅾️🔥
♨🅾️♨🔥🅿️♿🔥♨

Nearest Town Tenby

Directions Turn off the A477 at the roundabout turning onto the B4318 for Tenby. Caravan park is 20 yards on the right (60 foot entrance).

≢ Tenby

TENBY

Milton Bridge Caravan Park, Milton, Nr Tenby, Pembrokeshire, SA70 8PH

Tel: 01646 651204

Email:
enquiries@miltonbridgecaravanpark.co.uk

www.miltonbridgecaravanpark.co.uk

Pitches For ⚏ 🚐 Total 12

Acreage 3 **Open** Mar **to** Oct

Access Good **Site** Lev/Slope

Nearest Bus Stop (Miles) Outside

Small, friendly park situated on a tidal river. Ideal base for exploring the many attractions in the area.

Facilities ✱ 🅿️▥♻️🅿️☉⌫🔥🔥
🔥🅾️♨🅿️♿🖊️🛜

Nearest Town Tenby

Directions Half way between Kilgetty and Pembroke Dock on the A477.

≢ Lamphey

TENBY

Red House Farm, Twy Cross, Tenby, Pembrokeshire, SA69 9DP

Tel: 01834 813918

Pitches For ▲ ⚏ 🚐 Total 10

Acreage 2 **Open** May **to** Sept

Access Good **Site** Lev/Slope

Nearest Bus Stop (Miles) ¼

Very quiet, small, ADULTS ONLY site. Most appreciated by those seeking peace rather than entertainment. Not suitable for small children. Sorry No pets.

Facilities ✱ ▥♻️🅿️ ♨♨🅿️A

Nearest Town Tenby

Directions Situated just off the A478, 1½ miles from both Tenby and Saundersfoot. Regular bus service.

≢ Tenby

TENBY

Tudor Glen Caravan Park, Jameston, Nr Tenby, Pembrokeshire, SA70 7SS

Tel: 01834 871417

Email: info@tudorglencaravanpark.com

www.tudorglencaravanpark.com

Pitches For ⚏ 🚐 Total 0

Acreage 6 **Open** Mar **to** Oct

Access Good **Site** Lev/Slope

Nearest Bus Stop (Miles) ¼

1 mile from Manorbier.

Facilities ✱ ▥♻️🅿️☉⌫🅾️🔥
♨♨🅾️♨🔥🅿️♿

Nearest Town Tenby

Directions From Tenby take the A4139 Coast Road west for 6 miles. Site is on the right before entering village of Jameston.

≢ Tenby

TENBY

Well Park Caravans, Tenby, Pembrokeshire, SA70 8TL

Tel: 01834 842179

Email: enquiries@wellparkcaravans.co.uk

www.wellparkcaravans.co.uk

Pitches For ▲ ⚏ 🚐 ⚏ Total 100

Acreage 10 **Open** Mar **to** Oct

Access Good **Site** Lev/Slope

Nearest Bus Stop (Miles) Outside

Ideally situated between Tenby 1 mile and Saundersfoot 1½. A family run Park with excellent facilities, very central and convenient for the beautiful beaches and places of interest, along the Pembrokeshire coast. AA 4 Pennant and Wales in Bloom award winning park.

Facilities ✱ ▥♻️🅿️☉⌫🔥🅾️🔥
♨🅾️♨🅿️🔥🖊️♿🔥🅿️♿🔥♨ 🛜

Nearest Town Tenby

Directions On righthand side of main Tenby (A478) road 1 mile north of Tenby.

≢ Tenby

TENBY

Windmills Camping Park, Tenby, Pembrokeshire, SA70 8TJ

Tel: 01834 842200

Pitches For ▲ ⚏ 🚐 Total 25

Acreage 4 **Open** Easter **to** Oct

Access Good **Site** Level

Nearest Bus Stop (Miles) ½

Situated on a hill above Tenby with sea views. Footpath and cycle track down to the town and north beach.

Facilities ✱ ▥♻️🅿️☉🔥 ♨♨🔥

Nearest Town Tenby

Directions Approaching Tenby turn left up the lane just past New Hedges Village.

≢ Tenby

TENBY

Wood Park Caravan Park, New Hedges, Tenby, Pembrokeshire, SA70 8TL

Tel: 01834 843414

Email: info@woodpark.co.uk

www.woodpark.co.uk

Pitches For ▲ ⚏ 🚐 Total 60

Acreage 2 **Open** Apr **to** Oct

Access Good **Site** Lev/Slope

Nearest Bus Stop (Miles) Outside

Quiet, family park ideally situated between Tenby and Saundersfoot. Advanced bookings are not taken for Motor Caravans. No Groups permitted. No dogs allowed Bank Holidays and school holidays, one small pet only at all other times. No dogs in hire caravans.

Facilities ✱ ▥♻️🅿️☉⌫🔥🅾️🔥
♨🅾️♨🔥🅿️🔥🅿️♿🔥♨ 🛜

Nearest Town Tenby

Directions At the roundabout 2 miles north of Tenby, take the A478 towards Tenby. Take the second turn right and right again.

≢ Tenby

POWYS

BALA

Henstent Park, Llangynog, Nr Oswestry, Powys, SY10 0EP

Tel: 01691 860479

Email: henstent@mac.com

www.henstent.co.uk

Pitches For ▲ ⚏ 🚐 Total 35

Acreage 1½ **Open** All Year

Access Good **Site** Sloping

Nearest Bus Stop (Miles) Outside

Spectacular mountain views with frontage to the River Tanat. Rural location popular with bird watchers and walkers.

Facilities ✱ ▥♻️🅿️☉⌫🔥🅾️🔥
♨🅾️♨🔥🅿️🔥🖊️🔥♨🔥🛜

Nearest Town Bala

Directions Situated on the B4391. Follow signs for Bala from Oswestry. 18 miles from Oswestry, 12 miles from Bala.

≢ Gobowen

BRECON

Anchorage Caravan Park, Bronllys, Brecon, Powys, LD3 0LD
Tel: 01874 711246
www.anchoragecp.co.uk
Pitches For **Total** 110
Acreage 8 **Open** All Year
Access Good **Site** Lev/Slope
Nearest Bus Stop (Miles) Outside
Overlooking the Brecon Beacons National Park. Ideally situated for touring and walking mid and South Wales.
Facilities
Nearest Town Brecon
Directions 8 miles north east of Brecon in the village of Bronllys.
≠ Abergavenny

BRECON

Bishops Meadow Caravan Park, Bishops Meadow, Hay Road, Brecon, Powys, LD3 9SW
Tel: 01874 610000
Email: info@bishops-meadow.co.uk
www.bishops-meadow.co.uk
Pitches For **Total** 30
Acreage 6 **Open** Mar **to** Oct
Access Good **Site** Level
Nearest Bus Stop (Miles) ¼
Set in idyllic open countryside with spectacular views over the Brecon Beacons. Ideal for walking, cycling, fishing and canoeing on the River Wye.
Facilities
Nearest Town Brecon
Directions On the B4602 1 mile form the town centre.
≠ Abergavenny

BRECON

Lakeside Caravan Park, Llangorse Lake, Llangorse, Brecon, Powys, LD3 7TR
Tel: 01874 658226
Email: lakesidereception@tiscali.co.uk
www.llangorselake.co.uk
Pitches For **Total** 80
Open 20-Mar **to** Oct
Access Good **Site** Level
Llangorse Lake, mountains and beautiful scenery.
Facilities
Nearest Town Brecon
Directions From Brecon take the B4560 and follow signs to Llyn Lake. 6 miles from Brecon.
≠ Abergavenny

BRECON

Pencelli Castle Caravan & Camping Park, Pencelli Castle, Pencelli, Brecon, Powys, LD3 7LX
Tel: 01874 665451
Email: pencelli@tiscali.co.uk
www.pencelli-castle.com
Pitches For **Total** 80
Acreage 10 **Open** Feb **to** 28-Nov
Access Good **Site** Level
Nearest Bus Stop (Miles) Outside
Multi award winning park in the heart of the Brecon Beacons and adjoining Brecon Canal. Plenty of good walking and cycling in the area.
Facilities
Nearest Town Brecon
Directions Leave Brecon on the A40 heading east, after 2 miles turn onto the B4558 signposted Pencelli and follow brown tourism signs.
≠ Abergavenny

BUILTH WELLS

Irfon River Caravan Park, Upper Chapel Road, Garth, Builth Wells, Powys, LD4 4BH
Tel: 01792 391203
Email: info@irfonriver.co.uk
www.irfonriver.co.uk
Pitches For **Total** 24
Acreage 6½ **Open** Easter **to** October
Access Good **Site** Lev/Slope
Nearest Bus Stop (Miles) ½
Quiet ADULTS ONLY site alongside a river with scenic views. Fly fishing on site. Ideal touring in the beauty of the mountains and forest. Convenient for events at the Royal Welsh Showground. Static holiday vans for sale. You can also contact us on Mobile: 07817 283449.
Facilities
Nearest Town Builth Wells
Directions 500 yards along the B4519 on entering Garth (Garth is 6 miles west of Builth Wells along the A483).
≠ Garth

BUILTH WELLS

White House Campsite, Hay Road, Builth Wells, Powys, LD2 3BP
Tel: 01982 552255
Email: info@whitehousecampsite.co.uk
www.whitehousecampsite.co.uk
Pitches For **Total** 30
Acreage 3 **Open** Apr **to** Sept
Access Good **Site** Level
Nearest Bus Stop (Miles) ¼
On the banks of the River Wye. Just a ten minute walk from the Royal Welsh Showground. WTB 3 Star Graded.
Facilities
Nearest Town Builth Wells
Directions Adjacent to the A470 at the eastern edge of Builth Wells.
≠ Builth Road

CLYRO

Borders Hideaway Holiday Home Park, Painscastle Road, Clyro, Hay-on-Wye, Herefordshire, HR3 5SG
Tel: 01497 820156
Email: bhhhp@hotmail.co.uk
www.bhhhp.co.uk
Pitches For **Total** 35
Acreage 4 **Open** Mar **to** 07-Jan
Access Good **Site** Lev/Slope
Nearest Bus Stop (Miles) ½
Close to Hay-on-Wye, the second hand book capital of the world! Near to Golden Valley, Brecon Beacons and the Black Mountains.
Facilities
Nearest Town Hay-on-Wye
Directions Upon entering Clyro on the A438 (Leominster to Brecon road), turn at the brown tourism caravan sign and follow the road and signs for 1 mile.
≠ Hereford

CRICKHOWELL

Riverside Caravan & Camping Park New Road, Crickhowell, Powys, NP8 1AY
Tel: 01873 810397
www.riversidecaravanscrickhowell.co.uk
Pitches For **Total** 65
Acreage 3½ **Open** Mar **to** Oct
Access Good **Site** Level
Nearest Bus Stop (Miles) ¼
River, mountain and canal walks.
Facilities
Nearest Town Crickhowell
Directions Between the A40 and the A4077 at Crickhowell.
≠ Abergavenny

LLANBRYNMAIR

Cringoed Caravan Park, The Birches, Llanbrynmair, Powys, SY19 7DR
Tel: 01650 521237
Email: enquiries@cringoed.co.uk
www.cringoed.co.uk
Pitches For **Total** 35
Acreage 10 **Open** Mar **to** Nov
Site Level
Nearest Bus Stop (Miles) 1
nearest beaches Aberbovey, Twywn, Barmouth, Borth, all within 45 minutes.
Facilities
Nearest Town Machynlleth
Directions 12 miles inland towards Newtown.
≠ Machynlleth

LLANBRYNMAIR

GwernyBwlch Caravan Club Site, Llanbrynmair, Powys, SY19 7EB
Tel: 01650 521351
www.caravanclub.co.uk
Pitches For **Total** 34
Acreage 5 **Open** Mar **to** Oct
Access Good **Site** Lev/Slope
Lovely setting with views to the mountains across a valley. Bird hide and feeding station on site, watch for Red Kites. Own sanitation required. Non members welcome. Booking essential.
Facilities
Nearest Town Llanbrynmair
Directions From the A470, 1 mile past Llanbrynmair turn right at Caravan Club sign, site is 50 yards up the hill on the left.
≠ Llanbrynmair

LLANDRINDOD WELLS

Bryncrach Farm Caravan Site, Bryncrach, Hundred House, Llandrindod Wells, Powys, LD1 5RY
Tel: 01982 570291
Email: stella@midwalescaravanpark.co.uk
www.midwalescaravanpark.co.uk
Pitches For **Total** 15
Acreage 1¾ **Open** All Year
Access Good **Site** Level
Nearest Bus Stop (Miles) ¼
Quiet site with splendid views and walks. Fishing and riding can be arranged. River nearby. You can also contact us on Mobile: 07534 509104.
Facilities
Nearest Town Builth Wells
Directions Hundred House is on the A481 between Builth Wells and the A44. Turn left signposted Franks Bridge immediately before the public house, after 250 yards turn left into farm road.
≠ Llandrindod Wells

LLANDRINDOD WELLS

Dalmore Caravan Park, Howey, Llandrindod Wells, Powys, LD1 5RG
Tel: 01597 822483
Pitches For **Total** 20
Acreage 2 **Open** Mar **to** Oct
Access Good **Site** Lev/Gentle Slope
Nearest Bus Stop (Miles) Outside
EXCLUSIVELY FOR ADULTS. Ideal base for hiking and touring Mid Wales, scenic views.
Facilities
Nearest Town Llandrindod Wells
Directions 2½ miles south of Llandrindod Wells, adjoining the main A483, at the top of the hill and towards Builth Wells.
≠ Llandrindod

LLANSANTFFRAID

Bryn-Vyrnwy Caravan Park, Bryn-Vyrnwy, Llansantffraid, Powys, SY22 6AY
Tel: 01691 828252
Email: brynvyrnwyholidaypark@btconnect.com
www.brynvyrnwyholidaypark.co.uk
Pitches For **Total** 10
Acreage 3 **Open** Apr **to** 01-Nov
Access Good **Site** Level
Nearest Bus Stop (Miles) ½
On the banks of the River Vyrnwy. Good eating places close by. ¾ of an hour from seaside resorts.
Facilities
Nearest Town Welshpool
Directions From Oswestry take the A483 towards Welshpool, at Llynclys take the A495 for 3 miles.
Welshpool

LLANSANTFFRAID

Vyrnwy Caravan Park, Llansantffraid, Powys, SY22 6SY
Tel: 01691 828217
Email: info@vyrnwycaravansltd.co.uk
www.vyrnwycaravanpark
Pitches For **Total** 40
Acreage 40 **Open** Apr **to** Sept
Access Good **Site** Level
Nearest Bus Stop (Miles) Outside
Alongside a river.
Facilities
Nearest Town Oswestry
Directions Take the A483 then the B4393 to Llansantffraid.
Gobowen

MACHYNLLETH

Morben Isaf Holiday Home & Touring Park, Derwenlas, Machynlleth, Powys, SY20 8SR
Tel: 01654 781473
Email: manager@morbenisaf.co.uk
www.morbenisaf.co.uk
Pitches For **Total** 35
Open Mid Mar **to** Oct
Access Good **Site** Level
Nearest Bus Stop (Miles) Outside
Next door to Dyfi Osprey Project at Cors Dyfi. 8 miles from Ynyslas Beach and 3 miles from Ynys-Hir Nature Reserve.
Facilities
Nearest Town Machynlleth
Directions 2½ miles south of Machynlleth on the A487 Aberystwyth road.
Machynlleth

MIDDLETOWN

Bank Farm Caravan Park, Middletown, Welshpool, Powys, SY21 8EJ
Tel: 01938 570526
Email: bankfarmcaravans@yahoo.co.uk
www.bankfarmcaravans.co.uk
Pitches For **Total** 20
Acreage 2 **Open** Mar **to** Oct
Access Good **Site** Lev/Slope
Nearest Bus Stop (Miles) ¼
Scenic views, ideal touring area.
Facilities
Nearest Town Welshpool
Directions On A458 5½ miles east of Welshpool and 13¼ miles west of Shrewsbury.
Welshpool

NEW RADNOR

Old Station Caravan Park, New Radnor, Powys, LD8 2SS
Tel: 01544 350543
Email: info@oldstationcaravanpark.co.uk
www.oldstationcaravanpark.co.uk
Pitches For **Total** 12
Acreage 1¾ **Open** All Year
Access Good **Site** Level
Nearest Bus Stop (Miles) ¼
Ideal base for walking and cycling. Easy access to Offa's Dyke, Elan Valley Dams and the attractions of Mid Wales. You can also contact us on Mobile: 07917 846508. Field available for small rallies. 2 statics & cottage for hire.
Facilities
Nearest Town Kington
Directions 6 miles from Kington on the A44 to Rhayader.
Leominster

NEWTOWN

Smithy Park, Abermule, Newtown, Montgomery, Powys, SY15 6ND
Tel: 01584 711280
Email: info@smithypark.co.uk
www.smithypark.co.uk
Pitches For **Total** 30
Acreage 5 **Open** Mar **to** Oct
Access Good **Site** Level
Nearest Bus Stop (Miles) Outside
Set between the River Mule and the River Severn, with a branch of the Shropshire Union Canal nearby.
Facilities
Nearest Town Newtown
Directions Abermule is off the A483 between Welshpool and Newtown.
Newtown

PENYBONTFAWR

Parc Farm, Penybontfawr, Powys, SY10 0PD
Tel: 01691 860204
Email: deal@tinyworld.co.uk
www.parcfarm-minafon.co.uk
Pitches For **Total** 12
Open Easter **to** Oct
Access Good **Site** Level
Nearest Bus Stop (Miles) Outside
River frontage with beautiful scenery.
Facilities
Nearest Town Oswestry/Welshpool
Directions On the B4391.
Welshpool

PRESTEIGNE

Rockbridge Park, Presteigne, Powys, LD8 2NF
Tel: 01568 708326
Email: info@bestparks.co.uk
www.rockbridgepark.co.uk
Pitches For **Total** 53
Acreage 13 **Open** Mar **to** Nov
Access Good **Site** Level
Nearest Bus Stop (Miles) Outside
Picturesque and peaceful site alongside the River Lugg. Park homes for sale.
Facilities
Nearest Town Presteigne
Directions 1 mile west of Presteigne on the B4356.
Knighton

PRESTEIGNE

Walton Court Caravan Site, Walton Court, Walton, Presteigne, Powys, LD8 2PY
Tel: 01544 350259
Email: jeanandglyn@hotmail.co.uk
www.waltoncourtcaravanandcampingsite.co.uk
Pitches For **Total** 30
Acreage 7 **Open** Mar **to** Oct
Access Good **Site** Level
Nearest Bus Stop (Miles) Outside
Many walks and rides into the hills. The Harp Inn (15 mins walk) serves excellent food.
Facilities
Nearest Town Kington
Directions On the A44 Kington to Aberystwyth road, in the village of Walton opposite the Crown Hotel.
Knighton

WELSHPOOL

Carmel Caravan Park, Tynewydd, Cefncoch, Welshpool, Powys, SY21 0AJ
Tel: 01938 810542
Email: carmelcaravanpk@aol.com
www.carmelcaravanpark.com
Pitches For **Total** 120
Open 15-Mar **to** Oct
Access Good **Site** Level
Farm site set alongside a river for walks.
Facilities
Nearest Town Newtown
Directions From Welshpool take the A458 to Llanfair Caereinion, turn left over the bridge and follow signs for Cefncoch. Turn left at the pub and follow caravan signs.
Newtown

WELSHPOOL

Rhyd-Y-Groes Touring Caravan & Camping Park, Pont Rhyd-Y-Groes, Marton, Welshpool, Powys, SY21 8JJ
Tel: 01938 561228
Email: hldavies@hotmail.co.uk
www.rhyd-y-groes.co.uk
Pitches For **Total** 40
Acreage 4½ **Open** All Year
Access Good **Site** Lev/Slope
ADULTS ONLY PARK set among natural beauty with outstanding views. Near Offas Dyke footpath. Ideal for touring and bird watching. Some fully serviced pitches available. 5 star rated.
Facilities
Nearest Town Welshpool
Directions From the A490 Welshpool to Churchstoke road, turn left for Marton approx 5 miles from Welshpool.
Welshpool

WELSHPOOL

Riverbend Caravan Park, Llangadfan, Nr Welshpool, Powys, SY21 0PP
Tel: 01938 820356
Email: riverbend@hillandale.co.uk
www.hillandale.co.uk
Pitches For **Total** 50
Acreage 4 **Open** All Year
Access Good **Site** Level
Nearest Bus Stop (Miles) ½
The best of both worlds! - In unspoilt rural Wales, yet close to the Welsh coast. On the River Banwy with 1 mile of private fishing. Local pub.
Facilities
Nearest Town Llanfair Caereinion
Directions Take the A458 from Welshpool westbound towards the coast. After 17 miles you enter the village of Llangadfan, turn left at Gann Office (pub), and the Park is 300 metres on the right.
Welshpool

SWANSEA

GOWERTON

Gowerton Caravan Club Site, PontyCob Road, Gowerton, Swansea, SA4 3QP
Tel: 01792 873050
www.caravanclub.co.uk
Pitches For ⊕ ⊕ **Total** 132
Acreage 17 **Open** Mar **to** Nov
Access Good **Site** Level
Nearest Bus Stop (Miles) ½
Easy drive to many safe sandy beaches. Inland theres the Vale of Neath and Aberdulais Falls. Non members welcome. Booking essential.
Facilities ƒ 🅷 ℍ𝔹 ♠ ℾ ◫ 🌡
🆂ℚ 🅻£ 🅾 🛁 ✖ 🗄 ♣ 🛜
Nearest Town Swansea
Directions Leave M4 at junc 47 take A483 sp Swansea. At r/about t rt on A484, at next r/about go straight over, next r/about t lt on B4296 sp Gowerton. After passing under railway bridge at lights t rt, next lights t rt into Pont-y-Cob Rd, site ¼ mile on rt.
⚏ Swansea

HORTON

Bank Farm, Horton, Gower, Swansea, SA3 1LL
Tel: 01792 390228
Email: enquires@bankfarmleisure.co.uk
www.bankfarmleisure.co.uk
Pitches For ⋀ ⊕ ⊕ **Total** 230
Acreage 80 **Open** Mar **to** 18-Nov
Access Good **Site** Sloping
Nearest Bus Stop (Miles) ¼
Overlooking the beach. Heated swimming pool.
Facilities ƒ 🅷 ℍ𝔹 ℾ ◫ 🍴 🛁 🌡 🍺
🆂ℚ 🅾 🛁 ✖ 🍴 🗄 🍴 ♣ ◫ 🗄
Nearest Town Swansea
Directions Take the A4118 from Swansea towards Port Eynon, turn left for Horton 1 mile before Port Eynon, turn right at the site entrance after 200 yards.
⚏ Swansea

OXWICH

Oxwich Camping Park, Oxwich, Gower, Swansea, SA3 1LS
Tel: 01792 390777
Pitches For ⋀ **Total** 180
Acreage 10 **Open** Apr **to** Sept
Site Lev/Slope
Nearest Bus Stop (Miles) ¼
Wooded site near the beach with great cliff walks.
Facilities 🛁 🅷 ℍ𝔹 ℾ ◫ 🍴 🛁 🅻£ 🍴 🗄
Nearest Town Swansea
Directions Leave the M4 at junction 42 and follow signs for the A4118. Turn left at Oxwich signpost then right at the crossroads.
⚏ Swansea

RHOSSILI

Pitton Cross Caravan & Camping Park, Rhossili, Swansea, SA3 1PT
Tel: 01792 390593
Email: admin@pittoncross.co.uk
www.pittoncross.co.uk
Pitches For ⋀ ⊕ ⊕ **Total** 100
Acreage 6 **Open** All Year
Access Good **Site** Level
Nearest Bus Stop (Miles) Outside
Quiet, family friendly park, with a mix of sea views and sheltered areas. Within walking distance of beaches. Ideal for surfing and kiting.
Facilities 🛁 🅷 ℍ𝔹 ℾ ◫ 🍴 🛁 🌡 🅾 🍺
🆂ℚ 🅻 🅾 🛁 🗄 🍴 ◫ 🗄
Nearest Town Swansea

Directions Leave the M4 at junc 42 and take the A483 to Swansea. Follow signs for A4067 to Mumbles, turn right onto the B4436 to South Gower and follow to Kittle, turn right at Pennard Church. Turn left at the T-Junction onto the A4118, go through Scurlage and turn right, Park is 2 miles.
⚏ Swansea

WREXHAM

WREXHAM

Plassey Leisure Park, Eyton, Wrexham, LL13 0SP
Tel: 01978 780277
Email: enquiries@plassey.com
www.plassey.com
Pitches For ⋀ ⊕ ⊕ **Total** 120
Acreage 10 **Open** All Year
Access Good **Site** Level
Nearest Bus Stop (Miles) ½
On site facilities include a 9 hole golf course, a craft centre with 16 workshops and boutiques, garden centre, hair and beauty studio, restaurant and coffee shop. We even have our own on-site mini real ale brewery!
Facilities 🛁 ♿ ƒ 🅷 ℍ𝔹 ℾ ◫ 🍴 🛁 🌡
🆂ℚ 🅻£ 🅾 ✖ 🍴 🍴 ♣ 🍴 ♣ ✖ 🗄 ◫ 🗄 ⚏ 🌡
♣ 🛜
Nearest Town Wrexham
⚏ Wrexham

WREXHAM

Trench Farm Touring Caravan Park & Fisheries, Trench Farm, Redhall Lane, Penley, Wrexham, LL13 0NA
Tel: 01978 710098
Email: mail@trenchfarmfisheries.co.uk
www.trenchfarmfisheries.co.uk
Pitches For ⋀ ⊕ ⊕ ⊕£ **Total** 20
Acreage 5 **Open** Mar **to** Nov
Access Good **Site** Level
Nearest Bus Stop (Miles) ½
Set in 160 acres of farmland. Lovely long country walks. Fishing on site.
Facilities ♿ ƒ 🅷 ℍ𝔹 ℾ ◫ 🍴 🅾 🗄 🅾 🍺
📧 🗄 🍴
Nearest Town Ellesmere
Directions Appeox 3 miles from Ellesmere on the A528 towards Wrexham. On the Shropshire and Wrexham border.
⚏ Wrexham

SCOTLAND

ABERDEENSHIRE

ABERDEEN

Deeside Holiday Park, South Deeside Road, Maryculter, Aberdeen, Aberdeenshire, AB12 5FX
Tel: 01224 733860
Email: deeside@holiday-parks.co.uk
www.holiday-parks.co.uk
Pitches For ⋀ ⊕ ⊕ ⊕£ **Total** 0
Acreage 10 **Open** All Year
Access Good **Site** Level
Nearest Bus Stop (Miles) ¼
A tranquil retreat set in the southern valley of the River Dee, yet only a few miles from the lively city of Aberdeen, and at the gateway to the spectacular scenery of Royal Deeside.
Facilities ƒ 🅷 ℍ𝔹 ℾ ◫ 🍴 ⊙ 🛁 🅾 🍺
🆂ℚ 🅾 🛁 ♣ 🍴 📧 ◫ 🗄 ✖ 🛜
Nearest Town Aberdeen
Directions From Aberdeen take the B9077 at Bridge of Dee roundabout for 6 miles. From Stonehaven take the B979.
⚏ Aberdeen

ABOYNE

Aboyne Loch Caravan Park, Aboyne, Royal Deeside, Aberdeenshire, AB34 5BR
Tel: 013398 86244
Email: heatherreid24@yahoo.co.uk
Pitches For ⋀ ⊕ ⊕ **Total** 32
Open Mar **to** Oct
Access Good **Site** Level
Nearest Bus Stop (Miles) Outside
By Aboyne Loch. Beside two golf courses and within walking distance of two restaurants. Boats available to hire. Good area for walking. Dog walk. David Bellamy Gold Award.
Facilities ♿ ƒ 🅷 ℍ𝔹 ℾ ◫ 🍴 🛁 🅾 🍺
🅻 🅾 🛁 ♣ 🍴 ◫ 🗄 ♣
Nearest Town Banchory
Directions Take the A96 to Ballater.

ABOYNE

Tarland Camping & Caravanning Club Site, Tarland By Deeside, Tarland By Aboyne, Aberdeenshire, AB34 4UP
Tel: 01339 881388
Email: tarland.site@thefriendlyclub.co.uk
www.campingandcaravanningclub.co.uk/tarland
Pitches For ⋀ ⊕ ⊕ **Total** 52
Acreage 8 **Open** Mar **to** 05-Jan
Access Good **Site** Level
Nearest Bus Stop (Miles) ¼
Close to the village of Tarland and approx. 6 miles from Aboyne. STB 5 Star Graded and AA 3 Pennants. Non members welcome. You can also call us on 0845 130 7633.
Facilities ƒ 🅷 ℍ𝔹 ℾ ◫ 🍴 ⊙ 🛁 🅾 🍺
🅻 🅾 🛁 🍴 ◫ 🗄 ♣ 🛜 🅾 🍺
Nearest Town Aboyne
Directions Take the A93 from Aberdeen, in Aboyne turn right at the Struan Hotel onto the B9094. After 6 miles take the next turn right and then fork left before the bridge, site is on the left in 600 yards.
⚏ Aberdeen

BANCHORY

Feughside Caravan Park, Mount Battock, Strachan, Banchory, Aberdeenshire, AB31 6NT
Tel: 01330 850669
Email: info@feughsidecaravanpark.co.uk
www.feughsidecaravanpark.co.uk
Pitches For ⋀ ⊕ ⊕ ⊕£ **Total** 27
Open Apr **to** Oct
Access Good **Site** Level

Set in the heart of Royal Deeside. Relax in this beautiful and picturesque part of the Scottish countryside. Visit Scotland 4 Star, AA 4 Pennant, David Bellamy Gold and near The Deeside Way.
Facilities
Nearest Town Banchory
Directions From Banchory take the B974 for 3 miles to Strachan, then take the B976 for 2 miles to the Feughside Inn, turn right and the Park entrance is 100 metres.
Aberdeen

BANFF

Wester Bonnyton Caravan & Camping Park, Wester Bonnyton, Gamrie, Banff, Aberdeenshire, AB45 3EP
Tel: 01261 832470
Email: westerbonnyton@fsmail.net
www.wester-bonnyton.co.uk
Pitches For **Total** 8
Acreage 2 **Open** 31-Mar **to** Oct
Access Good **Site** Lev/Slope
Nearest Bus Stop (Miles) Outside
Quiet farm site in open countryside with panoramic views of the Moray Firth. Located on the North East Scotland Coastal Trail.
Facilities
Nearest Town Banff
Directions 2 miles east of Macduff on the B9031 coastal trail, approx 1 mile from the A98 Banff to Fraserburgh road.
Keith

BRAEMAR

Braemar The Invercauld Caravan Club Site, Glenshee Road, Braemar, Ballater, Aberdeenshire, AB35 5YQ
Tel: 01339 741373
www.caravanclub.co.uk
Pitches For **Total** 97
Acreage 9½ **Open** Dec **to** Oct
Access Good **Site** Level
Nearest Bus Stop (Miles) ¼
Abundant wildlife can be seen at this gateway to the Cairngorms, ideal for walking and cycling. Near a dry ski slope. Open in December for winter sports. Ski racks, drying room and community room (winter only) on site. Non members welcome. Booking essential.
Facilities
Nearest Town Braemar
Directions Just off the A93 on the outskirts of Braemar Village.

CRUDEN BAY

Craighead Caravan & Camping Park, Cruden Bay, Peterhead, Aberdeenshire, AB42 0PL
Tel: 01779 812251
Email: stephen@craigheadcamping.co.uk
www.craigheadcamping.com
Pitches For **Total** 17
Acreage 5 **Open** All Year
Access Good **Site** Level
Nearest Bus Stop (Miles) ½
1 mile from the beach. Close to castles and the Whisky Trail.
Facilities
Nearest Town Peterhead
Directions 6 miles south of Peterhead on the A90, signposted from main road.
Aberdeen

KINTORE

Hillhead Caravan Park, Kintore, Aberdeenshire, AB51 0YX
Tel: 01467 632809
Email: enquiries@hillheadcaravan.co.uk
www.hillheadcaravan.co.uk
Pitches For **Total** 29
Acreage 1½ **Open** All Year
Access Good **Site** Level
Nearest Bus Stop (Miles) 1
Quiet, sheltered park. Easy access to Castle and Malt Whisky Trails, Aberdeen and Royal Deeside.
Facilities
Nearest Town Kintore
Directions From south leave A96 at Broomhill roundabouts third exit. From north stay on A96 past Kintore (DO NOT enter Kintore), leave at Broomhill roundabouts first exit. Follow brown & white caravan signs onto B994, in ¼ mile turn left onto the B994 sp Kemnay. After 2 miles turn right sp Kintore and Hillhead Caravan Park is 1 mile on the right.
Inverurie

LAURENCEKIRK

Brownmuir Caravan Park, Fordoun, Laurencekirk, Aberdeenshire, AB30 1SJ
Tel: 01561 320786
Email: brownmuircaravanpark@talk21.com
www.brownmuircaravanpark.co.uk
Pitches For **Total** 10
Acreage 7 **Open** Apr **to** Oct
Access Good **Site** Level
Nearest Bus Stop (Miles) Outside
Quiet site. Ideal for cycling and walking. Golf course in the village.
Facilities
Nearest Town Laurencekirk
Directions On the A90, 4 miles north of Laurencekirk, turn left at the junction marked Fordoun and Auchenblae. After 150 yards turn left and go over the bridge, the Park is 1 mile on the right.
Stonehaven

LAURENCEKIRK

Dovecot Caravan Park, Northwaterbridge, By Laurencekirk, Aberdeenshire, AB30 1QL
Tel: 01674 840630
Email: adele@dovecotcaravanpark.co.uk
www.dovecotcaravanpark.co.uk
Pitches For **Total** 25
Acreage 6 **Open** Apr **to** 28-Oct
Access Good **Site** Level
Nearest Bus Stop (Miles) ¼
Alongside the River North Esk. 8 miles from a sandy beach and 10 miles from the Angus Glens. Static caravans and a cottage available for hire.
Facilities
Nearest Town Laurencekirk
Directions From the A90 at Northwaterbridge, turn to Edzell Woods and the Site is signposted 300 metres on the left.
Laurencekirk

PORTSOY

Sandend Caravan Park, Sandend, Portsoy, Aberdeenshire, AB45 2UA
Tel: 01261 842660
Email: sandendholidays@aol.com
www.sandendcaravanpark.co.uk
Pitches For **Total** 52
Acreage 4½ **Open** Apr **to** 04-Oct
Access Good **Site** Level
Nearest Bus Stop (Miles) ¼
In a conservation village overlooking a sandy beach. Ideal for touring and The Whisky Trail.
Facilities
Nearest Town Portsoy
Directions 3 miles from Portsoy on the A98.
Keith

ST. CYRUS

East Bowstrips Holiday Park, St Cyrus, Nr Montrose, Aberdeenshire, DD10 0DE
Tel: 01674 850328
Email: tully@bowstrips.freeserve.co.uk
www.ukparks.co.uk/eastbowstrips
Pitches For **Total** 33
Acreage 4 **Open** Apr **to** Oct
Access Good **Site** Lev/Slope
Nearest Bus Stop (Miles) ½
Quiet park by the coast. Ideal touring base. Beautiful sandy beach and nature reserve approx 1 mile.
Facilities
Nearest Town Montrose
Directions Approx 6 miles north of Montrose. Follow A92, enter village of St. Cyrus, first left after Hotel, second right.
Montrose

TURRIFF

East Balthangie Caravan Park, East Balthangie, Cuminestown, Turriff, Aberdeenshire, AB53 5XY
Tel: 01888 544261/544280
Email: ebc@4horse.co.uk
www.eastbalthangie.co.uk
Pitches For **Total** 12
Acreage 5 **Open** Mar **to** Oct
Access Good **Site** Level
Nearest Bus Stop (Miles) 5
Good base for touring, Banff and Buchan.
Facilities
Nearest Town Turriff
Directions From Ellon take New Deer Road, pass New Deer and take 1st road to right.
Inverurie

ANGUS

ARBROATH

Elliot Caravan Park, Dundee Road, Arbroath, Angus, DD11 2PH
Tel: 01241 873466
Pitches For **Total** 8
Acreage 2 **Open** Apr **to** Sept
Access Good **Site** Level
Nearest Bus Stop (Miles) Outside
Near the beach, across from a golf club. Ideal for touring and sea fishing.
Facilities
Nearest Town Arbroath
Directions On the A92, ½ a mile from town.
Arbroath

ARBROATH

Red Lion Holiday Park, Dundee Road, Arbroath, Angus, DD11 2PT
Tel: 01241 872038
Email: red-lion@btconnect.com
www.redlion-holidaypark.com
Pitches For **Total** 300
Acreage 4 **Open** Mid Mar **to** Oct
Access Good **Site** Level
Nearest Bus Stop (Miles) Outside

ANGUS, ARGYLL & BUTE

Adjacent to the seaside and beach.
Facilities ♿ ✉ 🚻 🅿 🛁 ⛽ 🔥 ⊙ 🍴 📶
🛒 🎮 🏪 🐕 ✕ 🛍 🔥 🛒 ➡🅿 🍴 💺 ⛄ 📶
Nearest Town Arbroath
Directions From Dundee take the A92, when entering Arbroath the park is on the left past the first mini roundabout.
⚏ Arbroath

CARNOUSTIE

Woodlands Caravan Site, Newton Road, Carnoustie, Angus, DD7 6GR
Tel: 01241 854430
Email: info@woodlandscaravanpark.net
www.woodlandscaravanpark.net
Pitches For ▲ ♦ ♦ **Total** 58
Open Mid Mar to Oct
Access Good **Site** Level
Nearest Bus Stop (Miles) Outside
Near the beach, leisure centre, golf courses and a bowling green.
Facilities ♿ ✉ 🚻 🅿 🛁 ⛽ 🔥 ⊙ 🍴 📶 ⊡
🛒 🎮 🏪 ➡🅿 🍴 💺 📶
Nearest Town Carnoustie
Directions Well signposted from all directions of the town.
⚏ Carnoustie

FORFAR

Foresterseat Caravan Park, Arbroath Road, Forfar, Angus, DD8 2RY
Tel: 01307 818880
Email: emma@foresterseat.co.uk
www.foresterseat.co.uk
Pitches For ▲ ♦ ♦ ♦ ⛺ **Total** 76
Acreage 16 **Open** Mar to Nov
Access Good **Site** Level
Nearest Bus Stop (Miles) Outside
Modern Park on the edge of Forfar, with 42 Super Pitches. Ideal base for touring the Angus Glens and scenic coast. 1 mile from a golf course and fishing loch. Walking path networks on the site. Fully licensed restaurant on site.
Facilities ♿ ✉ 🚻 🅿 🛁 ⛽ 🔥 ⊙ 🍴 📶 ⊡
🛒 ✕ 🍴 💺 ➡🅿 🍴 💺 📶
Nearest Town Forfar
Directions From Forfar take the A932 towards Arbroath, Foresterseat is 1 mile after Cunninghill Golf Course on the right.
⚏ Arbroath

KIRRIEMUIR

Drumshademuir Caravan Park,
Roundyhill, By Glamis, Forfar, Angus, DD8 1QT
Tel: 01575 573284
Email: holidays@drumshademuir.com
www.drumshademuir.com
Pitches For ▲ ♦ ♦ **Total** 60
Acreage 15 **Open** All Year
Access Good **Site** Level
Nearest Bus Stop (Miles) Outside
Panoramic views. Central location for towns, cities and Angus Glens.
Facilities ♿ ✉ 🚻 🅿 🛁 ⛽ 🔥 ⊙ 🍴 📶 ⊡
🛒 🎮 🏪 ✕ 🍴 ➡🅿 🍴 💺 ⛄ 🔥
Nearest Town Kirriemuir
Directions From the A94 or the A90 take the A928, park is 3 miles north of Glamis Castle.
⚏ Dundee

ARGYLL & BUTE

CAMPBELTOWN

Peninver Sands Holiday Park, Peninver, By Campbeltown, Argyll & Bute, PA28 6QP
Tel: 01586 552262
Email: info@peninver-sands.com
www.peninver-sands.com

Pitches For ♦ **Total** 25
Acreage 2¾ **Open** 15-Mar to 15-Jan
Access Good **Site** Lev/Slope
Nearest Bus Stop (Miles) Outside
Situated right on the beach.
Facilities ⛽ 🚻 🅿 🛁 ⊙ 🍴 📶 ⊡
🔥 🛒 ➡🅿
Nearest Town Campbeltown
Directions From Campbeltown take the B842 north for 4½ miles. Park is on the right as you enter the village of Peninver.
⚏ Oban

CONNEL

Oban Camping & Caravanning Club Site, Barcaldine By Connel, Argyll & Bute, PA37 1SG
Tel: 01631 720348
Email: oban.site@thefriendlyclub.co.uk
www.campingandcaravanningclub.co.uk/oban
Pitches For ▲ ♦ ♦ **Total** 75
Acreage 4½ **Open** 21-Mar to 28-Oct
Access Good **Site** Level
Nearest Bus Stop (Miles) Outside
Set in a delightful walled garden. Superb forest walks are just 5 minutes from the site. A perfect base to explore the Highlands and Islands. STB 4 Star Graded and AA 3 Pennants. Non members welcome. You can also call us on 0845 130 7633.
Facilities ⛽ 🚻 🅿 🛁 ⛽ 🔥 ⊙ 🍴 📶 ⊡
🛒 🎮 🏪 ✕ 🍴 🐕 ➡🅿 🍴 🔥 📶
Nearest Town Loch Linnhe
Directions Heading North on the A828, 7 miles from the Connel bridge turn right at the Camping & Caravanning Club sign opposite the Marine Resource Centre, proceed through the large iron gates.
⚏ Oban

DUNOON

Cot House Caravan Park, Sandbank Road, Kilmun By Dunoon, Argyll & Bute, PA23 8QS
Tel: 01369 840351
Pitches For ▲ ♦ ♦ ♦ ⛺ **Total** 14
Acreage 1 **Open** Mar to Oct
Access Good **Site** Level
Nearest Bus Stop (Miles) Outside
Alongside river.
Facilities ⛽ 🚻 🅿 🛁 ⊙ 🍴 📶 ⊡
🛒 ➡🅿 💺
Nearest Town Dunoon
Directions A815 Dunoon to Strachur road.
⚏ Gourock

GLENBARR

Killegruer Caravan Site, Woodend, Glenbarr, Tarbert, Argyll & Bute, PA29 6XB
Tel: 01583 421241
Email: anne.littleson@btinternet.com
www.killegruercaravansite.com
Pitches For ▲ ♦ ♦ **Total** 25
Acreage 1¼ **Open** Apr to Oct
Access Good **Site** Level
Nearest Bus Stop (Miles) Outside
Overlooking a sandy beach with views of the Inner Hebrides and the Mull of Kintyre. Site facilities have recently been upgraded. Hair dryers available. Close to the ferry link to Arran and Islay Jura & Gigha.
Facilities ♿ ⛽ 🚻 🅿 🛁 ⊙ 🍴 📶
🛒 🎮 🏪 ➡🅿 💺
Nearest Town Campbeltown
Directions 12 miles north of Campbeltown on the A83.
⚏ Oban

ISLE OF COLL

Garden House Camp Site, Garden House, Isle of Coll, Argyll, Argyll & Bute, PA78 6TB
Tel: 01879 230374
Email: collcampsite@hotmail.com
www.visitcoll.com
Pitches For ▲ ♦ ♦ **Total** 25
Acreage 2 **Open** Apr to 15-Sep
Access Good **Site** Level
In the middle of a nature reserve and only 5 minutes to the beach.
Facilities ⛽ 🚻 🅿 🛁 ⊙ 🍴 📶
Nearest Town Arinagour
Directions Take the airport road west and before the airport take the track on the left at Uig to Walled Garden.
⚏ Oban

LOCHGILPHEAD

Tayvallich Caravan Site, Leachive Farm, Tayvallich, By Lochgilphead, Argyll & Bute, PA31 8PL
Tel: 01546 870206
Email: fiona@leachive.co.uk
www.leachive.co.uk
Pitches For ▲ ♦ ♦ **Total** 15
Acreage 4 **Open** Apr to Oct
Access Good **Site** Level
Nearest Bus Stop (Miles) ¼
Set beside a sheltered sea loch, ideal for canoeing and sailing. Nearby the Beaver Trail Loch and nature reserve.
Facilities ♿ ⛽ 🚻 🅿 🛁 ⊙ 🍴 📶 🎮 🐕 ➡🅿 💺
Nearest Town Lochgilphead
Directions From Lochgilphead follow signs for Oban for 3 miles, then follow signs for Tayvallich.
⚏ Oban

LUSS

Luss Camping & Caravanning Club Site, Luss, Loch Lomond, Alexandria, Nr Glasgow, Argyll & Bute, G83 8NT
Tel: 01436 860658
Email: luss.site@thefriendlyclub.co.uk
www.campingandcaravanningclub.co.uk/luss
Pitches For ▲ ♦ ♦ **Total** 90
Acreage 12 **Open** 21-Mar to 28-Oct
Access Good **Site** Level
Nearest Bus Stop (Miles) ¼
On the banks of Loch Lomond with good views of Ben Lomond. Fishing (permit required) and watersports. STB 4 Star Graded, AA 3 Pennants, Loo of the Year Award and Babychange Winner 2002. CLUB MEMBER CARAVANNERS & MOTORHOMES ONLY. Non member tents welcome. You can also call us on 0845 130 7633.
Facilities ♿ ⛽ 🚻 🅿 🛁 ⊙ 🍴 📶 ⊡
🎮 🏪 🐕 ✕ ➡🅿 💺 📶
Nearest Town Luss
Directions Take the A82 from the Erskine Bridge and head north towards Tarbet. Ignore first signpost for Luss. After the bagpipe and kiltmakers workshop take the next turn right sp Lodge of Loch Lomond and international camping sign, site approx. 200 yards.
⚏ Balloch

MUASDALE

Muasdale Holiday Park, Muasdale, Tarbert, Argyll & Bute, PA29 6XD
Tel: 01583 421207
Email: enquiries@muasdaleholidays.com
www.muasdaleholidays.com
Pitches For ▲ ♦ ♦ **Total** 10
Open Apr to 23-Oct
Access Good

Nearest Bus Stop (Miles) 100 Yards
Adjoining the beach with stunning views of Islay, Jura and Gigha. Sea fishing on site (bring your own equipment). Convenient for ferries to Islay, Jura, Gigha and Arran.
Facilities
Nearest Town Campbeltown/Tarbert
Directions On the A83 at the southern end of Muasdale Village, approx. 22 miles from Tarbert.

OBAN

Caravans at Highfield, 3 Kiel Croft, Benderloch, Oban, Argyll & Bute, PA37 1QS
Tel: 07766 303136
Email: elaine.clsite@gmail.com
www.clsite.co.uk
Pitches For Total 10
Acreage 1 **Open** Apr to Oct
Access Good **Site** Level
Nearest Bus Stop (Miles) ½
Country location only 500 metres from Tralee beach. 1 mile to the village for shop and cafe. Ideal for walking and touring, only 10 miles from Oban. Fort William and Inveraray within 1 hours drive.
Facilities
Nearest Town Oban
Directions Turn off the A828 in Benderloch signposted Tralee and South Shian. Highfield is approx 800 metres on the right (its the second gate on the right after Hawthorn Cottage Restaurant).
⚏ Connel

OBAN

Oban Caravan & Camping Park,
Gallanachmore Farm, Gallanach Road, Oban, Argyll & Bute, PA34 4QH
Tel: 01631 562425
Email: info@obancaravanpark.com
www.obancaravanpark.com
Pitches For Total 150
Acreage 15 **Open** Apr to 07-Oct
Access Good **Site** Level
Nearest Bus Stop (Miles) Outside
On the coast with beautiful views. Close to a diving centre and ferry to islands.
Facilities
Nearest Town Oban
Directions 2½ miles south of Obanon Gallanach road.
⚏ Oban

SOUTHEND

Machribeg Caravan Site, Southend, By Campbeltown, Argyll & Bute, PA28 6RW
Tel: 01586 830249
Pitches For Total 80
Acreage 4 **Open** Easter to Sept
Access Good **Site** Level
Nearest Bus Stop (Miles) Outside
Near the beach with good views, very quiet location. 18 hole golf course.
Facilities
Nearest Town Campbeltown
Directions Take the B843 from Campbeltown for 10 miles. Site is situated 250yds through Southend Village on the left by the beach.

TAYINLOAN

Point Sands Holiday Park, Tayinloan, Argyll & Bute, PA29 6XG
Tel: 01583 441263
Email: info@pointsands.co.uk
www.pointsands.co.uk

Pitches For Total 30
Acreage 15 **Open** Apr to Oct
Access Good **Site** Level
Nearest Bus Stop (Miles) Outside
Peaceful site on a safe sandy beach with terrific scenery. Near to island ferries. Ideal for touring and visiting the Isles of Gigha, Arran and Islay. Holiday homes to let. On site Takeaway.
Facilities
Nearest Town Tarbert
Directions On the A83 Glasgow to Campbeltown road, 17 miles south of Tarbert.
⚏ Arrochar

AYRSHIRE (NORTH)
ISLE OF ARRAN

Lochranza Caravan & Camping Site,
Lochranza, Isle of Arran, North Ayrshire, KA27 8HL
Tel: 01770 830273
Email: info@arran-campsite.com
www.arran-campsite.com
Pitches For Total 60
Acreage 2½ **Open** Mar to Oct
Access Good **Site** Level
Nearest Bus Stop (Miles) Outside
Beautiful mountain scenery and abundant wildlife. Red Deer and Red Squirrels are often seen on site, aswell as Golden Eagles overhead. Adjacent to a golf course.
Facilities
Nearest Town Brodick
Directions Follow the road north for 14 miles to the north end of the island. Site entrance is opposite the Isle of Arran Distillery.
⚏ Ardrossan

ISLE OF ARRAN

Middletons Caravan & Camping Park,
Cordon, Lamlash, Isle of Arran, North Ayrshire, KA27 8NQ
Tel: 01770 600251
Email: info@middletonscamping,com
www.middletonscamping.com
Pitches For Total 40
Acreage 3½ **Open** Mar to Oct
Access Good **Site** Level
Nearest Bus Stop (Miles) ¼
Centrally located on the Island, near the beach and village.
Facilities
Nearest Town Lamlash
Directions From Brodick ferry terminal turn left onto the A841, 4 miles to Lamlash. Pass the Police Station on the left, go over the bridge then sharp left, site is ¼ of a mile.
⚏ Ardrossan

Isle of Arran

Seal Shore Camping & Touring, Seal Shore, Kildonan, Isle of Arran, North Ayrshire, KA27 8SE
Tel: 01770 820320
Email: enquiries@campingarran.com
www.campingarran.com
Pitches For Total 43
Acreage 2¾ **Open** Mar to Oct
Access Good **Site** Sloping
Nearest Bus Stop (Miles) Outside
Situated on our own private beach.
Facilities
Nearest Town Whiting Bay
Directions From the Brodick ferry turn left, we are situated 12 miles, along the coast.
⚏ Ardrossan

LARGS

South Whittlieburn Farm, Brisbane Glen, Largs, North Ayrshire, KA30 8SN
Tel: 01475 675881
Email: largsbandb@southwhittlieburnfarm.freeserve.co.uk
www.smoothhound.co.uk/hotels/whittlie
Pitches For Total 5
Acreage 5 **Open** All Year
Access Good **Site** Level/Sloping
Nearest Bus Stop (Miles) ½
Situated on a working sheep farm with 4 Star Farmhouse B&B accommodation also available. Great for hill walking. Close to Largs for ferries, shops, restaurants, pubs, swimming pool, putting green and theatre.
Facilities
Nearest Town Largs
Directions From the A78 in Largs, turn off just past Vikingar Complex (sp Brisbane Glen), Park is approx 2¼ miles on the left.
⚏ Largs

AYRSHIRE (SOUTH)
AYR

Ayr Craigie Gardens Caravan Club Site,
Craigie Road, Ayr, South Ayrshire, KA8 0SS
Tel: 01292 264909
www.caravanclub.co.uk
Pitches For Total 90
Acreage 7 **Open** 22-Mar to 04-Nov
Access Good **Site** Level
Nearest Bus Stop (Miles) ½
Situated in a beautiful park, just a ten minute walk from Ayr seaside resort. Open March then all year. 40 golf courses in the area. Close to Burns Heritage Trail, Culzean Castle, Vikingar and The Tam OShanter Experience. Non members welcome. Booking essential.
Facilities
Nearest Town Ayr
Directions From the A77 Ayr bypass take the A719 signposted Ayr. Just past the racecourse at the traffic lights turn left into Craigie Road, on right bend turn left into Craigie Gardens, keep right and site is 400 yards.
⚏ Ayr

AYR

Heads of Ayr Caravan Park, Dunure Road, Ayr, South Ayrshire, KA7 4LD
Tel: 01292 442269
Email: stay@headsofayr.com
www.headsofayr.com
Pitches For Total 36
Open Mar to Oct
Access Good **Site** Level
Nearest Bus Stop (Miles) Outside
Just a 10 minute walk to the beach.
Facilities
Nearest Town Ayr
Directions 5 miles south of Ayr on the A719. coast road.
⚏ Ayr

AYR

Sundrum Castle Holiday Park - Parkdean, By Ayr, South Ayrshire, KA6 5JH
Tel: 0344 335 3740
Email: enquiries@parkdeanholidays.com
www.parkdeantouring.com
Pitches For Total 45
Acreage 32 **Open** Mar to Nov
Access Good **Site** Level

Nearest Bus Stop (Miles) 1
Set in glorious rolling countryside, just 4 miles from Ayr's sandy beach.
Facilities ♦ 🖃 🏠 �📶 �🎱 ⌂ 🏪 ⊙ ↻ 🍴
🏕 🛢 🆚 ✕ 🍺 📞 ⚓ 🔥 ⊕ 🐾 ✕ ⛵ 🛰
Nearest Town Ayr
Directions A70 towards Ayr, the park is 4 miles before Ayr, through village of Coylton on right hand side.
🚲 Ayr

BARRHILL
Barrhill Holiday Park, Millers Holiday Parks, Barrhill, Girvan, South Ayrshire, KA26 0PZ
Tel: 01465 821355
Email: barrhillholidaypark@gmail.com
www.barrhillholidaypark.com
Pitches For 🅰 ⬛ ⊟ ⊟ ⊱ **Total** 30
Acreage 1 **Open** Mar **to** Jan
Access Good **Site** Level
Nearest Bus Stop (Miles) Outside
Close to the border of Dumfries & Galloway and Ayrshire, Ideal for exploring both counties and SW Scotland.
Facilities ♦ ♦ 🖃 🏠 ⌂ 🎱 ⌂ ⊙ ↻ ⚓ ⊕ 🛰
🏕 🛢 ⊙ 🆚 ⛵ 🔥 ↻ 🍴 ✕
Nearest Town Girvan
Directions Situated on the A714 between Newton Stewart and Girvan, 1 mile north of Barrhill.
🚲 Barrhill

BARRHILL
Queensland Holiday Park, Barrhill, Girvan, South Ayrshire, KA26 0PZ
Tel: 01465 821364
Email: info@queenslandholidaypark.co.uk
www.queenslandholidaypark.co.uk
Pitches For 🅰 ⬛ ⊟ **Total** 64
Acreage 9 **Open** Mar **to** Jan
Access Good **Site** Level
Nearest Bus Stop (Miles) Outside
Ideal location for walking and cycling in Galloway Forest, or for touring South Scotland. Good local rivers.
Facilities ♦ ♦ 🖃 🏠 ⌂ 🎱 ⌂ ⊙ ↻ ⚓ ⊕ 🛰
🏕 🛢 ⊙ 🆚 ⛵ 🔥 ↻ 🍴 ✕ 🛰
Nearest Town Girvan
Directions 10 miles south east of Girvan on the A714.
🚲 Barrhill

MAYBOLE
Culzean Castle Camping & Caravanning Club Site, Culzean Castle, Maybole, South Ayrshire, KA19 8JX
Tel: 01655 760627
Email:
culzean.castlesite@thefriendlyclub.co.uk
www.campingandcaravanningclub.co.uk

Pitches For 🅰 ⬛ ⊟ **Total** 90
Acreage 10 **Open** 21-Mar **to** 28-Oct
Access Good **Site** Lev/Slope
Nearest Bus Stop (Miles) Outside
Set in the grounds of historic Culzean Castle with excellent views and country walks. STB 4 Star Graded and AA 3 Pennants. Non members welcome. You can also call us on 0845 130 7633.
Facilities ♦ ♦ 🖃 🏠 ⌂ 🎱 ⌂ ⊙ ↻ ⚓ ⊕ 🛰
🏕 🛢 🔥 🆚 ⛵ 🔥 ↻ 🍴 ✕ 🛰
Nearest Town Maybole
Directions In Maybole turn right onto the B7023 signposted Culzean and Maidens. After 100 yards turn left, site is 4 miles on the right.
🚲 Maybole

PRESTWICK
Prestwick Holiday Park, Prestwick, Ayrshire (South), KA9 1UH
Tel: 01292 479261
Email:
prestwickholidaypark@Hotmail.co.uk
Pitches For 🅰 ⬛ ⊟ **Total** 20
Acreage 11 **Open** Mar **to** Oct
Access Good **Site** Level
Nearest Bus Stop (Miles) Outside
Near the beach.
Facilities ♦ 🏠 ⌂ 🎱 ⌂ ⊙ ↻ 🍴 ⚓ ⊕ 🛰
🏕 🛢 ⊙ 🍺 🆚 ⚓ 🔥 ↻ ✕
Nearest Town Prestwick
Directions Signposted off the A79 1 mile north of Prestwick.
🚲 Prestwick

CLACKMANNAN
ALLOA
The Woods Caravan Park, Diverswell Farm, Fishcross, Alloa, Clackmannan, FK10 3AN
Tel: 01259 762802
Email: woodscaravan@btconnect.com
www.thewoodscaravanpark.co.uk
Pitches For ⬛ ⊟ ⊟ ⊱ **Total** 105
Acreage 14 **Open** All Year
Access Good **Site** Level
Nearest Bus Stop (Miles) ½
Central for Glasgow, Edinburgh, Perth, The Trossachs and Stirling.
Facilities ♦ ♦ 🖃 🏠 ⌂ 🎱 ⌂ ⊙ ↻ 🍴 ⚓ ⊕ 🛰
🏕 🛢 ⊙ ✕ 🔥 ↻ 🍴 ⊕ ✕ 🛰
Nearest Town Alloa
Directions From Alloa, head for Fishcross and follow signs for the Woods Caravan Park.
🚲 Alloa

DUMFRIES & GALLOWAY
CROCKETFORD
Park of Brandedleys, Crocketford, Dumfries & Galloway, DG2 8RG
Tel: 01387 266700
Email: brandedleys25@yahoo.co.uk
www.brandedleys.co.uk
Pitches For 🅰 ⬛ ⊟ ⊟ ⊱ **Total** 47
Acreage 10 **Open** All Year
Access Good **Site** Level
Nearest Bus Stop (Miles) Outside
Ideal for touring the south west of Scotland.
Facilities ♦ ♦ ♦ 🖃 🏠 ⌂ 🎱 ⌂ ⊙ ↻ ⚓ 🛰
🏕 🛢 🔥 ✕ 🍺 📞 ⚓ 🔥 🎱 ↻ 🍴 ⊕ ✕ ⚓
Nearest Town Dumfries
Directions A75 9 miles from Dumfries, 6 miles from Castle Douglas
🚲 Dumfries

DALBEATTIE
Glenearly Caravan Park, Dalbeattie, Dumfries & Galloway, DG5 4NE
Tel: 01556 611393
Email: glenearlycaravan@btconnect.com
Pitches For 🅰 ⬛ ⊟ **Total** 39
Acreage 10 **Open** All Year
Access Good **Site** Level
Nearest Bus Stop (Miles) ¼
Peaceful site situated centrally for all local attractions.
Facilities ♦ ♦ 🖃 🏠 ⌂ 🎱 ⌂ ⊙ ↻ ⚓ ⊕ 🛰
🏕 🛢 ⊙ ⚓ 🔥 ↻ 🍴 ✕
Nearest Town Dalbeattie
Directions From Dumfries take the A711 towards Dalbeattie. On approaching Dalbeattie see signs for Glenearly on the right hand side.
🚲 Dumfries

DALBEATTIE
Mossband Caravan Park, Kirkgunzeon, Dumfries, Dumfries & Galloway, DG2 8JP
Tel: 01387 760208
Email: mossbandcp@btconnect.com
www.mossbandcaravanpark.co.uk
Pitches For ⬛ ⊟ **Total** 37
Acreage 5 **Open** Mar **to** Oct
Access Good **Site** Level
Nearest Bus Stop (Miles) Outside
Ideal touring, mountain biking,walking.
Facilities ♦ 🏠 ⌂ 🎱 ⌂ ⊙ ↻ ⚓ ⊕ 🛰
🔥 ↻ 🍴 ✕
Nearest Town Dalbeattie
Directions From Dumfries take the A711 Dalbeattie road for approx. 10 miles. We are on the right hand side at Kirgunzeon.
🚲 Dumfries

ECCLEFECHAN

Cressfield Caravan Park, Ecclefechan, Lockerbie, Dumfries & Galloway, DG11 3LG
Tel: 01576 300702
Email: info@cressfieldcaravanpark.co.uk
www.cressfieldcaravanpark.com
Pitches For 🏕 ⛺ 🚐 🚍 **Total** 200
Acreage 40 **Open** All Year
Access Good **Site** Level
Nearest Bus Stop (Miles) Outside
Lovely rural Scottish countryside.
Facilities (symbols)
Nearest Town Lockerbie
Directions From the M6 head north on the M74 to junction 19, then follow signs for Cressfield.
➤ Lockerbie

ECCLEFECHAN

Hoddom Castle Caravan Park, Hoddom, Lockerbie, Dumfries & Galloway, DG11 1AS
Tel: 01576 300251
Email: hoddomcastle@aol.com
www.hoddomcastle.co.uk
Pitches For 🏕 ⛺ 🚐 **Total** 89
Open Apr **to** Oct
Access Good **Site** Lev/Slope
Nearest Bus Stop (Miles) ¼
Facilities (symbols)
Nearest Town Annan
Directions Signposted 4 miles from Annan 2 miles from Ecclefechan junction 19 M74.
➤ Annan

GATEHOUSE OF FLEET

Anwoth Holiday Park, Garden Street, Gatehouse of Fleet, Castle Douglas, Dumfries & Galloway, DG7 2JU
Tel: 01557 814333
Email: paul@auchenlarie.co.uk
www.anwothholidaypark.co.uk
Pitches For 🏕 ⛺ 🚐 **Total** 28
Open Mar **to** Oct
Access Good **Site** Level
Nearest Bus Stop (Miles) ¼
Quiet 5 Star Park in the village of Gatehouse of Fleet.
Facilities (symbols)
Nearest Town Gatehouse of Fleet
Directions From Dumfries take the A75 towards Stranraer, 16 miles from Castle Douglas.
➤ Dumfries

GATEHOUSE OF FLEET

Auchenlarie Holiday Park, Gatehouse of Fleet, Castle Douglas, Dumfries & Galloway, DG7 2EX
Tel: 01556 506200
Email: enquiries@auchenlarie.co.uk
www.swalwellholidaygroup.co.uk
Pitches For 🏕 ⛺ 🚐 **Total** 109
Acreage 20 **Open** Mar **to** Oct
Access Good **Site** Sloping
Nearest Bus Stop (Miles) Outside
Our own sandy cove. Restaurant, 3 bars on site, as well as a pool, gym, crazy golf and a shop. Good centre for touring.
Facilities (symbols)
Nearest Town Gatehouse of Fleet
Directions On the main A75 5 miles west of Gatehouse of Fleet heading towards Stranraer, Park is on the left hand side.
➤ Dumfries

GATEHOUSE OF FLEET

Mossyard Caravan Park, Mossyard, Gatehouse of Fleet, Castle Douglas, Dumfries & Galloway, DG7 2ET
Tel: 01557 840226
Email: enquiry@mossyard.co.uk
www.mossyard.co.uk
Pitches For 🏕 ⛺ 🚐 **Total** 30
Open Apr **to** Oct
Access Good **Site** Level
Nearest Bus Stop (Miles) ½
Situated on a working farm and set in a coastal location with a back drop of the Galloway Hills. Family run business.
Facilities (symbols)
Nearest Town Gatehouse of Fleet
Directions 4 miles west of Gatehouse of Fleet on the A75, turn left at Mossyard sign and follow for 800 yards to reception.
➤ Dumfries

GRETNA

Braids Caravan Park, Annan Road, Gretna, Dumfries & Galloway, DG16 5DQ
Tel: 01461 337409
Email:
enquiries@thebraidscaravanpark.co.uk
www.thebraidscaravanpark.co.uk
Pitches For ⛺ 🚐 **Total** 84
Acreage 5 **Open** All Year
Access Good **Site** Lev/Slope
Nearest Bus Stop (Miles) ¼
Ideal touring centre. Good area for bird watching. On board tank waste disposal point. Small trailers welcome, rally building available. STB 4 Star Graded Park.
Facilities (symbols)
Directions From the M6 run straight onto the A74. Take the A75 signposted Dumfries/Stranraer. In 1 mile take the second left for Gretna (B721), park is 600yds on the left.
➤ Gretna Green

ISLE OF WHITHORN

Burrowhead Holiday Village, Tonderghie Road, Isle of Whithorn, Newton Stewart, Dumfries & Galloway, DG8 8JB
Tel: 01988 500252
Email: burrowheadhv@aol.com
www.burrowheadholidayvillage.co.uk
Pitches For 🏕 ⛺ 🚐 🚍 **Total** 90
Acreage 20 **Open** Mar **to** 01-Nov
Access Good **Site** Level
Beathtaking views over the Solway Firth and across to the Isle of Man.
Facilities (symbols)
Nearest Town Newton Stewart
Directions From the A75 at Newton Stewart take the A714 to Wigtown, then take the A746 to Whithorn. Then take the B7004 to the Isle of Whithorn and Burrowhead is signposted.
➤ Stranraer

KIPPFORD

Kippford Holiday Park, Kippford, Dalbeattie, Kirkcudbrightshire, DG5 4LF
Tel: 01556 620636
Email: info@kippfordholidaypark.co.uk
www.kippfordholidaypark.co.uk
Pitches For 🏕 ⛺ 🚐 **Total** 50
Acreage 8 **Open** All Year
Access Good **Site** Lev/Slope
Nearest Bus Stop (Miles) Outside
Just ½ a mile from the truly beautiful seaside village and pubs. Level pitches, many separately screened. Enjoy woodland walks to the sea and watch the Red Squirrels. Golf, fishing, biking, childrens play area and a shop on site. No on site entertainment.

Facilities (symbols)
Nearest Town Kippford
Directions From Dumfries take the A711 to Dalbeattie, then turn left onto the A710 signposted Colvend Coast. In 3½ miles, just beyond Kippford road end, turn right.
➤ Dumfries

KIRKPATRICK FLEMING

King Robert the Bruces Cave Caravan & Camping Site, Cove Farm, Kirkpatrick Fleming, By Lockerbie, Dumfries & Galloway, DG11 3AT
Tel: 01461 800285
Email: jan534@btinternet.co.uk
www.brucescave.co.uk
Pitches For 🏕 ⛺ 🚐 **Total** 40
Acreage 80 **Open** All Year
Access Good **Site** Level
Nearest Bus Stop (Miles) ¼
In the grounds of an 80 acre estate, peaceful, quiet and secluded. Famous ancient monument of King Robert the Bruces cave in the grounds. Free fishing on 3 miles of river for Trout and Salmon, or fish on the pond. Disabled toilet block and family shower rooms. Under 5's park. Holiday apartments available.
Facilities (symbols)
Nearest Town Gretna
Directions Turn off A74 M74 at Kirkpatrick Fleming, then in Kirkpatrick follow all signs to Bruces Cave.
➤ Annan

LANGHOLM

Whitshiels Caravan Park, Langholm, Dumfries & Galloway, DG13 0HG
Tel: 01387 380494
Email: whitshielscafe@btconnect.com
Pitches For 🏕 ⛺ 🚐 **Total** 4
Acreage ½ **Open** All Year
Access Good **Site** Level
Nearest Bus Stop (Miles) Outside
Ideal area for fishing, golf, Hadrians Wall, Gretna Green, Borders region and Armstrong Clan Museum. Scenic route to Edinburgh. 3 x 6 berth holiday caravans available to let.
Facilities (symbols)
Nearest Town Langholm
Directions 200 yards north of Langholm on the A7.
➤ Carlisle

MOFFAT

Moffat Camping & Caravanning Club Site, Hammerlands Farm, Moffat, Dumfries & Galloway, DG10 9QL
Tel: 01683 220436
Email: moffat.site@thefriendlyclub.co.uk
www.campingandcaravanningclub.co.uk/moffat
Pitches For 🏕 ⛺ 🚐 **Total** 180
Acreage 8 **Open** All Year
Site Level
Nearest Bus Stop (Miles) ¼
Set in the Scottish lowlands, the site is perfect for touring Scotland. The local village of Moffat has won awards for The Best Kept Village in Scotland. STB 4 Star Graded and AA 3 Pennants. Non members welcome. You can also call us on 0845 130 7633.
Facilities (symbols)
Nearest Town Moffat
Directions Take the Moffat sign off the A74, in 1 mile turn right by the Bank of Scotland, right again in 200 yards, signposted on the right, follow road round to the site.
➤ Lockerbie

MONREITH

Knock School Caravan Park, Monreith, Newton Stewart, Dumfries & Galloway, DG8 8NJ
Tel: 01988 700414
Email: pauline@knockschool.co.uk
www.knockschool.co.uk
Pitches For ⛺ 🚐 🚙 **Total** 15
Acreage 1 **Open** Easter **to** Oct
Access Good **Site** Lev/Slope
Nearest Bus Stop (Miles) Outside
Near sandy beaches and golf. Four hard standing pitches available.
Facilities 🚿 ⚽ 🅿
Nearest Town Port William
Directions 3 miles south on the A747 at crossroads to golf course.

NEWTON STEWART

Glentrool Holiday Park, Glentrool, Nr Newton Stewart, Dumfries & Galloway, DG8 6RN
Tel: 01671 840280
Email: enquiries@glentroolholidaypark.co.uk
www.glentroolholidaypark.co.uk
Pitches For ⛺ 🚐 🚙 **Total** 14
Acreage 7½ **Open** Mar **to** Oct
Access Good **Site** Level
Nearest Bus Stop (Miles) Outside
On the edge of a forest, ideal touring.
Facilities 🚿 ⚽ 🅿
Nearest Town Newton Stewart
Directions Situated off the A714, 9 miles north of Newton Stewart, ½ mile south of Glentrool Village.
🚂 Barhill

NEWTON STEWART

Kings Green Caravan Park, South Street, Port William, Newton Stewart, Dumfries & Galloway, DG8 9SH
Tel: 01988 700489
Email: kingsgreencaravanpark@gmail.com
www.portwilliam.com/kingsgreen
Pitches For ⛺ 🚐 🚙 **Total** 30
Open Mid-Mar **to** Oct
Access Good **Site** Level
Nearest Bus Stop (Miles) ¼
Located on the sea shore, sandy beaches within a mile of site.
Facilities 🚿 ⚽ 🅿
Nearest Town Newton Stewart
Directions Leave A75 at Newton Stewart on to A714 for approx 9 miles then B7085 to Port William.
🚂 Stranraer

PORT LOGAN

New England Bay Caravan Club Site, Port Logan, Stranraer, Dumfries & Galloway, DG9 9NX
Tel: 01776 860275
www.caravanclub.co.uk
Pitches For 🚐 🚙 **Total** 159
Acreage 17 **Open** Mar **to** Nov
Access Good **Site** Level
Set on the edge of Luce Bay with sea views. Direct access to a shingle and sand beach. Boat storage on site. Near a sports centre, bowling green and swimming pool. Close to Mull of Galloway RSPB Sanctuary, Castle Kennedy, Ardwell House and Port Logan Botanic Gardens. Non members welcome. Booking essential.
Facilities 🚿 ⚽ 🅿
Nearest Town Stranraer

Directions Approaching Stranraer on the A77 follow signs for Portpatrick A77, approx. 1½ miles past Stranraer continue on the A716 sp Drummore. Site is 2½ miles past Ardwell on the left.
🚂 Stranraer

PORTPATRICK

Castle Bay Holiday & Residential Park, Portpatrick, Stranraer, Dumfries & Galloway, DG9 9AA
Tel: 01776 810462
Email: castle.bay@btconnect.com
www.castlebayholidaypark.co.uk
Pitches For ⛺ 🚐 🚙 **Total** 40
Access Good **Site** Lev/Slope
Nearest Bus Stop (Miles) ½
Fine views across the Irish Sea. Coastal walk to nearby Portpatrick.
Facilities 🚿 ⚽ 🅿
Nearest Town Portpatrick
Directions From Stranraer take the A77 south. In Portpatrick turn first left after the 30mph sign, the Park is ¾ miles on the right after the railway bridge.
🚂 Stranraer

PORTPATRICK

Sunnymeade Caravan Park, Portpatrick, Nr Stranraer, Dumfries & Galloway, DG9 8LN
Tel: 01776 810293
Email: info-sunnymeade@btconnect.com
www.sunny-meade.co.uk
Pitches For ⛺ 🚐 🚙 **Total** 0
Open May **to** Sept
Access Good **Site** Lev/Slope
Nearest Bus Stop (Miles) ¼
Near the beach, a golf course, bowling and fishing.
Facilities 🚿 ⚽ 🅿
Nearest Town Portpatrick
Directions A77 to Portpatrick. First left on entering village, park is ¼ mile on the left.
🚂 Stranraer

SANDHEAD

Sands of Luce Holiday Park, Sandhead, Stranraer, Dumfries & Galloway, DG9 9JN
Tel: 01776 830456
Email: info@sandsofluceholidaypark.co.uk
www.sandsofluceholidaypark.co.uk
Pitches For ⛺ 🚐 🚙 **Total** 32
Acreage 8 **Open** Mar **to** Jan
Access Good **Site** Level
Nearest Bus Stop (Miles) Outside
Our spectacular beach and facilities.
Facilities 🚿 ⚽ 🅿
Directions Follow directions to Mull of Galloway, ¼ mile before the village of Sandhead.
🚂 Stranraer

SOUTHERNESS

Southerness Holiday Village - Parkdean, Southerness, By Dumfries, Dumfries & Galloway, DG2 8AZ
Tel: 0844 335 3740
Email: enquiries@parkdeanholidays.co.uk
www.parkdeantouring.com
Pitches For ⛺ 🚐 🚙 **Total** 99
Acreage 58 **Open** Mar **to** Nov
Access Good **Site** Level
Nearest Bus Stop (Miles) Outside
Beside 2 miles of sandy beach on the Solway Firth.

Facilities 🚿 ⚽ 🅿
Nearest Town Dumfries
Directions From Dumfries follow the A710 Solway coast road 1 mile after village of Kirkbean you'll see signpost to turn left take 1st left after entering Southerness Village.
🚂 Dumfries

STRANRAER

Aird Donald Caravan Park, Stranraer, Dumfries & Galloway, DG9 8RN
Tel: 01776 702025
Email: enquiries@aird-donald.co.uk
www.aird-donald.co.uk
Pitches For ⛺ 🚐 🚙 **Total** 75
Acreage 12 **Open** All Year
Access Good **Site** Level
Only 1 mile east of Stranraer town centre. Ideal touring. Tarmac hard standing for touring caravans in wet weather. Ideal site for ferry to Ireland. Good toilets and facilities. Leisure centre nearby.
Facilities 🚿 ⚽ 🅿
Nearest Town Stranraer
Directions Off A75 entering Stranraer. Signposted.
🚂 Stranraer

EDINBURGH (CITY)
EDINBURGH

Drum Mohr Caravan Park, Levenhall, Musselburgh, Edinburgh, EH21 8JS
Tel: 0131 665 6867
Email: admin@drummohr.org
www.drummohr.org
Pitches For ⛺ 🚐 🚙 🚴 **Total** 120
Acreage 10 **Open** All Year
Access Good **Site** Lev/Slope
Nearest Bus Stop (Miles) ¼
Camping Bothy and Octolodges now available for hire by the night! Close to Edinburgh with an excellent bus service. 12 holiday lodges available to rent some with hot tub.
Facilities 🚿 ⚽ 🅿
Directions From south on the A1, take the A199 to Musselburgh then the B1361 and follow park signs. From west on the A1, exit at the Wallyford slip road and follow park signs.
🚂 Wallyford

EDINBURGH

Edinburgh Caravan Club Site, 3537 Marine Drive, Edinburgh, City Of Edinburgh, EH4 5EN
Tel: 01313 126874
www.caravanclub.co.uk
Pitches For ⛺ 🚐 🚙 **Total** 146
Acreage 12 **Open** All Year
Access Good **Site** Level
Nearest Bus Stop (Miles) 1
Situated on the Firth of Forth with easy access to Edinburgh. Visit the castle which houses the Scottish Crown Jewels, Holyroodhouse Palace, Princes Street Gardens, Edinburgh Zoo, Whisky Heritage Centre and Deep Sea World. Non members welcome. Booking essential.
Facilities 🚿 ⚽ 🅿
Nearest Town Edinburgh

Directions At end of M8 turn left onto A720, at Gogar rndbt (end of bypass) turn right sp City Centre A8. After about 200yds turn left onto A902, at Barnton junc lights turn right, at Blackhall junc lights fork left into Telford Rd. At Crewe Toll rndbt left sp Davidsons Mains, at T-junc lights turn right sp Granton, at next T-junc lights turn left, at rndbt turn right into Marine Drive, site is ½m on the left.
⚞ Edinburgh

EDINBURGH

Mortonhall Caravan & Camping Park, 38 Mortonhall Gate, Frogston Road, Edinburgh (City), EH16 6TJ
Tel: 0131 664 1533
Email: mortonhall@meadowhead.co.uk
www.meadowhead.co.uk
Pitches For Å ⛺ 🚐 **Total** 250
Open All year
Access Good **Site** Level
Nearest Bus Stop (Miles) Outside
Set in 200 acres of parkland with views to the Pentland Hills. Arboretum with specimen trees. 15 minutes to the city centre.
Facilities ⬙ ℱ 🅵 🅷 🆄🅱 ℗ ⊙🚶 ▣ 🗑 🞷
♋ ▣ 🅾 🏤 ✕ 🍷 🕅 🛅 Å 🎁 🏳 🗠 🛜
Nearest Town Edinburgh
Directions Five minutes from the A720 city by-pass. Exit the by-pass at Straiton or Lothianburn junctions and follow signs for Mortonhall.
⚞ Edinburgh

FIFE
GLENROTHES

Balbirnie Park Caravan Club Site, Markinch, Glenrothes, Fife, KY7 6NR
Tel: 01592 759130
www.caravanclub.co.uk
Pitches For Å ⛺ 🚐 **Total** 81
Acreage 8 **Open** 22-Mar **to** 04-Nov
Access Good **Site** Lev/Slope
Nearest Bus Stop (Miles) ¼
Set in 400 acres of parkland. Many sporting facilities available in Glenrothes. Near to St. Andrews Golf Course, Royal Palace of Falkland, Deep Sea World Centre, The Secret Bunker, Tarvit House and Anstruther Fisheries Museum. Non members welcome. Booking essential.
Facilities ⬙ ℱ 🅷 🆄🅱 ℗ ▣ 🗑 🞷
♋ 🕅 🅾 ⚸ 🏤 🛅 🗠 🞷
Directions From south on the A90, after crossing bridge continue onto M90, leave at junction 2A and take A92 sp Kirkcaldy. Follow signs for Tay Road Bridge staying on A92, at end of dual carriageway turn right onto B9130, after ¾ miles turn left into Balbirnie Park.
⚞ Glenrothes

LEVEN

Monturpie Caravan Park, Monturpie, Upper Largo, By Leven, Fife, KY8 5QS
Tel: 01333 360254
Email: enquiries@monturpie.co.uk
www.monturpie.co.uk
Pitches For ⛺ 🚐 🚐 **Total** 28
Open 31-Mar **to** Oct
Access Good **Site** Level
Nearest Bus Stop (Miles) Outside
ADULTS ONLY SITE ideally situated for access to the East Neuk of Fife. Numerous golf courses in the area. Excellent for the Fife coastal path and St Andrews.
Facilities ⬙ ℱ 🅷 🆄🅱 ℗ ℗ ⊙🚶 🗑 🞷
🕅 ✕ 🏤 🛅 🏳 🅾 🛜
Nearest Town Leven

Directions From Leven take the A915, when in Upper Largo follow signs for St Andrews, the Park is on the right after approx ¾ miles.
⚞ Markinch

ST. ANDREWS

Craigtoun Meadows Holiday Park, Mount Melville, St Andrews, Fife, KY16 8PQ
Tel: 01334 475959
Email: craigtoun@aol.com
www.craigtounmeadows.co.uk
Pitches For Å ⛺ 🚐 🚐🔅 **Total** 58
Open 15-Mar **to** Oct
Access Good **Site** Level
Nearest Bus Stop (Miles) Outside
Only 1½ miles from beaches and golf course. Large childrens play area also with putting green, All weather football pitch and Flying Fox slide. Woodland walks.
Facilities ⬙ ℱ 🅵 🅷 🆄🅱 ℗ ℗ ⊙🚶 🞤 🗑 🞷
🕅 🅾 ⚸ ✕ 🏤 ♋ 🛅 🏳 🗠 🞷
Nearest Town St Andrews
Directions 1½ miles south west of St Andrews town centre. Head westwards from West Port along Hepburn Gardens.
⚞ Leuchars

HIGHLANDS
ACHARACLE

Resipole Holiday Park, Loch Sunart, Acharacle, Highlands, PH36 4HX
Tel: 01967 431235
Email: info@resipole.co.uk
www.resipole.co.uk
Pitches For Å ⛺ 🚐 🚐🔅 **Total** 60
Acreage 8 **Open** Apr **to** Oct
Access Good **Site** Level
Nearest Bus Stop (Miles) Outside
Loch side location, spectacular views, central for touring.
Facilities ⬙ ℱ 🅷 🆄🅱 ℗ ℗ ⊙🚶 🗑 🞷
♋ 🕅 🅾 🏤 🛅 🏳 🗠 🛜
Nearest Town Acharacle
Directions From Fort William take the A82 south for 8 miles, across Corran Ferry, then take the A861 to Strontian and Salen. Site is 8 miles west of Strontian on the roadside.
⚞ Fort William

ARISAIG

Camusdarach Campsite, Camusdarach, Arisaig, Highlands, PH39 4NT
Tel: 01687 450221
Email: stuartofcolliston@gmail.com
www.camusdarach.co.uk
Pitches For Å ⛺ 🚐 **Total** 42
Acreage 5 **Open** Mid Mar **to** Mid Oct
Access Good **Site** Level
Nearest Bus Stop (Miles) Outside
Just a short walk to the superb beaches as featured in the films Highlander and Local Hero. 1 mile from Traigh Golf Club (9 hole).
Facilities ⬙ ℱ 🅷 🆄🅱 ℗ ℗ ⊙🚶 🗑 🞷
🕅 🅾 ✕ 🏤 🛅 🏳 🗠 🛜
Nearest Town Mallaig
Directions From Mallaig (or Fort William) follow A830 to Camusdarach sign at B8008 follow signs to site.
⚞ Morar

ARISAIG

Portnardoran Caravan Site, Arisaig, Highlands, PH39 4NT
Tel: 01687 450267
www.arisaigcampsite.co.uk
Pitches For Å ⛺ 🚐 **Total** 30
Acreage 5 **Open** Easter **to** 15-Oct

Access Good **Site** Level
Nearest Bus Stop (Miles) Outside
Beside silver sands, scenic views of inner Hebrides, safe for swimming. Sea
Facilities ℱ 🆄🅱 ℗ ℗ ⊙🚶 🗑 🞷
♋ 🏤 🏳 🗠 🛜
Nearest Town Arisaig
Directions 2 miles north of Arisaig village, on Fort William - Arisaig road A830.
⚞ Arisaig

AVIEMORE

Dalraddy Holiday Park, Aviemore, Highlands, PH22 1QB
Tel: 01479 810330
Email: dhp@alvieestate.co.uk
www.dalraddy.co.uk
Pitches For Å ⛺ 🚐 **Total** 80
Acreage 93 **Open** All year
Access Good **Site** Level
Nearest Bus Stop (Miles) Outside
-Near Loch Aivie, Loch Insh, River Spey (ideal for fishing)near to Cairngorne Mountain Resort.
Facilities ⬙ ℱ 🅷 🆄🅱 ℗ ℗ ⊙🚶 🗑
♋ 🕅 🅾 🏤 🛅 🏳 🗠 🞷 �’ 🛜
Nearest Town Aviemore
Directions 2 miles south of Aviemore on the B9152.
⚞ Aviemoor

AVIEMORE

Glenmore Caravan & Camping Park, Glenmore, Aviemore, Highlands, PH22 1QU
Tel: 02476 423008
Email: enquiries@campingintheforest.co.uk
www.campingintheforest.co.uk
Pitches For Å ⛺ 🚐 **Total** 206
Open All Year
Access Good **Site** Level
In the heart of The Cairngorms with Loch Morlich adjoining the site. Close to Scotlands largest ski area.
Facilities ⬙ ℱ 🅷 🆄🅱 ℗ ⊙🗑 🞷🏤🛅
Directions From the A9 turn off for Aviemore, at the roundabout take the B9152 and follow signs for Glenmore Village and Cairngorm Mountain National Park for 7 miles, Site is on the right.
⚞ Aviemore

AVIEMORE

High Range Touring Caravan Park, Grampian Road, Aviemore, Highlands, PH22 1PT
Tel: 01479 810636
Email: info@highrange.co.uk
www.highrange.co.uk
Pitches For Å ⛺ 🚐🔅 **Total** 72
Acreage 2 **Open** Dec **to** Oct
Access Good **Site** Level
Nearest Bus Stop (Miles) ¼
Winter ski resort 9 miles from village/River Spey nearby/within Cairngorns National Park.
Facilities ⬙ ℱ 🅷 ℗ ℗ ⊙🚶 🗑 🞷
✕ 🏤 🛅 🏳 🗠 🞷
Nearest Town Aviemore
Directions Off the B9152 at the south end of Aviemore, directly opposite the B970.
⚞ Aviemore

BALLACHULISH

Glencoe Camping & Caravanning Club Site, Glencoe, Ballachulish, Argyll, Highlands, PH49 4LA
Tel: 01855 811397
Email: glencoe.site@thefriendlyclub.co.uk
www.campingandcaravanningclub.co.uk/glencoe
Pitches For Å ⛺ 🚐 **Total** 102

Acreage 11 **Open** 21-Mar **to** 28-Oct
Access Good **Site** Lev/Slope
Surrounded by mountains, this quiet site is situated next to forests. Non members welcome. You can also call us on 0845 130 7633.
Facilities ♿ ✆ 🅿 ⅏ ⌂ 🅿 ⊙ 🚿 🔥 📮 🖭
🏧 🛈 🛁 🚽 🗑 ❄
Nearest Town Fort William
Directions On the A82, 1 mile south east of Glencoe Village, follow signs for Glencoe Visitor Centre.
🚏 Fort William

BALMACARA

Reraig Caravan Site, Balmacara, Kyle of Lochalsh, Highlands, IV40 8DH
Tel: 01599 566215
Email: warden@reraig.com
www.reraig.com
Pitches For ⅄ 🚐 🚙 **Total** 45
Acreage 2 **Open** May **to** Sept
Access Good **Site** Level
Forest walks and a hotel adjacent to the site. Dishwashing sinks and hairdryers. No bookings. No large tents. Not suitable for units longer than 7½ metres. No awnings during July and August.
Facilities ✆ 🅿 🅿 ⅏ ⊙ 🖭 ⚊ 🏧 📮 🗑 🛜
Nearest Town Kyle of Lochalsh
Directions On the A87, 1¾ miles west of junction with A890. 4 miles east of the bridge to the Isle of Skye.
🚏 Kyle of Lochalsh

BETTYHILL

Craigdhu Caravan Site Bettyhill, Nr Thurso, Highlands, KW14 7SP
Tel: 01641 521273
Pitches For ⅄ 🚐 🚙 **Total** 40
Acreage 4½ **Open** Apr **to** Sept
Access Good **Site** Level
Nearest Bus Stop (Miles) ¼
Near beautiful beaches and a river for fishing. Scenic views. Ideal touring. Rare plants. New swimming pool, telephone, 2 hotels and restaurant nearby.
Facilities ✆ 🅿 🅿 ⊙ ⚊ 🖭 🏧 🛖 🗑
Nearest Town Bettyhill
Directions Main Thurso/Tongue road. Site can be seen Adjacent to road.
🚏 Thurso

BRORA

Brora Caravan Club Site, Dalchalm, Brora, Highlands, KW9 6LP
Tel: 01408 621479
www.caravanclub.co.uk
Pitches For ⅄ 🚐 🚙 **Total** 52
Acreage 5 **Open** Apr **to** Oct
Access Good **Site** Level
300 yards from a safe, sandy beach where Arctic Tern nest and you can see seals and dolphins. Play golf directly from the site. Many picturesque lochs and mountains nearby. Close to the Clynelish Distillery. Non members welcome. Booking essential.
Facilities ♿ ✆ 🅿 ⅏ 🅿 ⌂ 🖭
🏧 🛈 🛁 🚽 🗑
Nearest Town Brora
Directions From south on the A9, in Brora 1½ miles past the bridge, ignore Dalchalm sign and turn right at brown caravan sign. After 350 yards at the T-junction turn left, site is 150 yards on the right.
🚏 Brora

CULLODEN

Culloden Moor Caravan Club Site, Newlands, Culloden Moor, Inverness, Highlands, IV2 5EF
Tel: 01463 790625
www.caravanclub.co.uk
Pitches For ⅄ 🚐 🚙 **Total** 97
Acreage 7 **Open** Mar **to** Jan
Access Good **Site** Lev/Slope
Nearest Bus Stop (Miles) Outside
Breathtaking views over the Nairn Valley. 1 mile from the Culloden battlefield. Only 6 miles from Inverness with its superb shopping, Whisky trails and Loch Ness. Basic provisions available on site. Non members welcome. Booking essential.
Facilities ♿ ✆ 🅿 ⅏ 🅿 ⌂ 🖭
🏧 🛈 🛁 🛁 🚽
Nearest Town Inverness/Culloden
Directions From south on the A9 turn off signposted Hilton (ignoring previous signs for Culloden Moor), at roundabout turn left onto the B9006, site is 5 miles on the left.
🚏 Inverness

DINGWALL

Dingwall Camping & Caravanning Club Site, Jubilee Park Road, Dingwall, Highlands, IV15 9QZ
Tel: 01349 862236
Email: dingwall.site@thefriendlyclub.co.uk
www.campingandcaravanningclub.co.uk/dingwall
Pitches For ⅄ 🚐 🚙 **Total** 83
Acreage 6½ **Open** 21-Mar **to** 28-Oct
Access Difficult **Site** Level
Nearest Bus Stop (Miles) ½
Central for touring the Highlands. Train and ferry links to the Isle of Skye. Close to the city of Inverness. STB 4 Star Graded and AA 3 Pennants. Non members welcome. You can also call us on 0845 130 7633.
Facilities ♿ ✆ 🅿 ⅏ 🅿 ⌂ ⊙ ⚊ 🖭
🏧 🛈 🛁 🚽 📮 🖭 🗑 🛜
Nearest Town Dingwall
Directions From the northwest on the A862 in Dingwall turn right into Hill Street (past the Shell Filling Station), turn right into High Street then turn first left after the railway bridge, site is ahead.
🚏 Dingwall

DORNIE

Ardelve, Dornie, Kyle, RossShire, IV40 8DY
Tel: 01599 555231
www.ardelvecaravanandcampingpark.co.uk
Pitches For ⅄ 🚐 🚙 **Total** 35
Open Easter **to** Oct
Access Good **Site** Lev/Slope
Nearest Bus Stop (Miles) ¼
Overlooking a loch with views of Eilean Donan Castle. Static caravans for hire.
Facilities ✆ 🅿 ⅏ 🅿 ⊙ 🔥 🛖 📮
Nearest Town Dornie
Directions Just off the A87.
🚏 Kyle

DORNOCH

Dornoch Links Caravan & Camping Park, River Street, Dornoch, Highlands, IV25 3LX
Tel: 01862 810423
Email: info@dornochcaravans.co.uk
www.dornochcaravans.co.uk
Pitches For ⅄ 🚐 🚙 🚙⌁ **Total** 120
Acreage 25 **Open** Apr **to** 22-Oct
Access Good **Site** Level
Nearest Bus Stop (Miles) ¼
Facilities ♿ ✆ 📮 🅿 ⅏ 🅿 ⌂ ⊙ ⚊ 🖭
🏧 🛈 🔥 🛖 🗑 🛁 🚽 🖭 🖭 ❄ 🛜

Nearest Town Dornoch
Directions Dornoch is 2 miles off the A9 6 miles north of Tain.
🚏 Tain

DORNOCH

Grannie's Heilan' Hame Holiday Park - Parkdean, Embo, Dornoch, Highlands, IV25 3QD
Tel: 0844 335 3740
Email: enquiries@parkdeanholidays.co.uk
www.parkdeantouring.com
Pitches For ⅄ 🚐 🚙 **Total** 125
Acreage 60 **Open** Mar **to** Nov
Access Good **Site** Level
Nearest Bus Stop (Miles) Outside
Overlooking Embo Beach and close to the village of Dornoch.
Facilities ✆ 📮 🅿 ⅏ 🅿 ⌂ ⊙ ⚊
🖭 🏧 ✗ ♀ 🛖 ♨ 🔥 🛁 🎣 🛎 🚽 📮 🖭 🛜
Directions Follow A9, take exit A949 for Dornoch go through village, past cathedral and turn left. follow road for 3 miles, take a right for Embo and continue to end of road.
🚏 Tain

DUNBEATH

Inver Caravan Park, Houstry Road, Dunbeath, Highlands, KW6 6EH
Tel: 01593 731441
Email: rhonagwillim@yahoo.co.uk
www.inver-caravan-park.co.uk
Pitches For ⅄ 🚐 🚙 🚙⌁ **Total** 15
Acreage 1 **Open** All Year
Access Good **Site** Sloping
Nearest Bus Stop (Miles) ½
Quiet small site. Excellent location for exploring the far north of Scotland, walking and cycling. Visit Scotland 4* site.
Facilities ♿ ✆ 🅿 ⅏ 🅿 ⌂ ⊙ ⚊ 🖭 🏧
🛖 ✗ 🚽 🖭 🗑 🛜
Nearest Town Wick
Directions Adjacent to the A9, just north of Dunbeath. Take the turning signposted Houstry 3, Park entrance is 40 metres on the left hand side. 21 miles south west of Wick and 16 miles north east of Helmsdale.
🚏 Helmsdale

DUNDONNELL

Badrallach Bothy & Campsite, Croft 9, Badrallach, Dundonnell, Highlands, IV23 2QP
Tel: 01854 633281
Email: mail@badrallach.com
www.badrallach.com
Pitches For ⅄ 🚐 🚙 **Total** 15
Acreage 1 **Open** All Year
Access Poor **Site** Level
Lochshore site on a working croft, overlooking Anteallach on the Scoraig Peninsular. Bothy, peat stove. Otters, porpoises, Golden Eagles and wild flowers galore. Total peace and quiet - Perfect! Caravans by prior booking only. Airstream for hire. STB 4 Star Graded.
Facilities ♿ ✆ 🅿 ⌂ ⊙ ⚊ ♨ 🛖 🖭 🗑 ✐
Nearest Town Ullapool/Gairloch
Directions Off the A832, 1 mile east of the Dundonnell Hotel take a left turn onto a single track road to Badrallach, 7 miles to lochshore site.
🚏 Garve/Inverness

DUNDONNELL

Northern Lights Campsite, Croft 9, Badcaul, Dundonnell, Highlands, IV23 2QY
Tel: 01697 371379
Pitches For ⅄ 🚐 🚙 **Total** 12
Acreage 2 **Open** Apr **to** Aug
Access Good **Site** Lev/Slope
Nearest Bus Stop (Miles) ½

Overlooking Loch Broom and in close proximity of several Muras.
Facilities ⚡ 🚻 🚽 👤 🍴 📶 🅿
Nearest Town Ullapool
Directions On the A832, 19 miles south west of the junction with the A835 and 12 miles south east of Ullapool.
🚆 Garve

DURNESS

Sango Sands Caravan & Camping Site, Durness, Sutherland, Highlands, IV27 4PP
Tel: 01971 511262/511222
Email: keith.durness@btinternet.com
www.sangosands.com
Pitches For ⛺ 🚐 🚙 🚌 **Total** 82
Acreage 12 **Open** Apr to 15-Oct
Access Good **Site** Level
Nearest Bus Stop (Miles) ¼
Overlooking Sango Bay.
Facilities & ⚡ 🚻 🚽 🚿 👤 ☉ 🍴 🔥 🔲 🛒
📶 🅿 ✕ ⓣ ⚓ 🍴 🚙 ✗ 🌊 📶
Nearest Town Durness
Directions On the A838 in the centre of Durness Village.
🚆 Lairg

DUROR

Achindarroch Touring Park, Duror, Highlands, PA38 4BS
Tel: 01631 740329
Email: stay@achindarrochtp.co.uk
www.achindarrochtp.co.uk
Pitches For ⛺ 🚐 🚙 🚌 **Total** 0
Acreage 5 **Open** 24-Jan to 16-Jan
Access Good **Site** Level
Nearest Bus Stop (Miles) ¼
Friendly, family run site in a quiet, well sheltered, picturesque location at the foot of Glen Duror. Camping Pods available for hire.
Facilities & ⚡ 🚻 🚽 👤 ☉ 🍴 🔲 🛒
📶 🅿 🚙 ✗ 🌊 ⚓ 📶
Nearest Town Fort William
Directions Off the A828 north of Appin and south of Fort William and Ballachulish, signposted.
🚆 Fort William

EVANTON

Black Rock Caravan Park, Balconie Street, Evanton, Highlands, IV16 9UN
Tel: 01349 830917
Email: enquiries@blackrockscotland.co.uk
www.blackrockscotland.co.uk
Pitches For ⛺ 🚐 🚙 🚌 **Total** 56
Acreage 4½ **Open** Apr to Oct
Access Good **Site** Level
Nearest Bus Stop (Miles) Outside
Central location with a river beside the site. Ideal for fishing and forest walks.
Facilities & ⚡ 🚻 🚽 🚿 👤 ☉ 🍴 🔲 🛒
📶 🅿 ⚓ 🍴 🚙 🌊 📶
Nearest Town Dingwall
Directions From Dingwall take the A862 then the A9 to Evanton, approx 5 miles.
🚆 Dingwall

FORTROSE

Fortrose Caravan Park, Wester Greengates, Fortrose, Highlands, IV10 8RX
Tel: 01381 621927
Email: fortrosecaravanpark@hotmail.co.uk
www.fortrosecaravansite.co.uk
Pitches For ⛺ 🚐 🚙 🚌 **Total** 50
Acreage 4 **Open** Apr to Oct
Access Good **Site** Level
Nearest Bus Stop (Miles) ¼
On the shores of the Black Isle, overlooking Moray Firth. Near to Chanonry Point, one of the best places to view bottlenose dolphins.
Facilities ⚡ 🚻 👤 🍴 ☉ 🍴 🔲 🛒 🅿

🚻 ☉ 🚐 🔲 🛒 🌊
Nearest Town Inverness
Directions From the A9 follow signs to Fortrose. Turn right into Academy Street and the Park is on the right hand side.
🚆 Inverness

FORTROSE

Rosemarkie Camping & Caravanning Club Site, Ness Road East, Rosemarkie, Fortrose, Highlands, IV10 8SE
Tel: 01381 621117
Email:
rosemarkie.site@thefriendlyclub.co.uk
www.campingandcaravanningclub.co.uk/rosemarkie
Pitches For ⛺ 🚐 🚙 **Total** 60
Acreage 4 **Open** 21-Mar to 28-Oct
Access Good **Site** Level
Nearest Bus Stop (Miles) 1
On the shores of the Black Isle, overlooking Moray and Cromarty Firths. The spectacular coastline is famous for its bottle nosed dolphins. STB 4 Star Graded, AA 3 Pennants and Loo of the Year Award. Non members welcome. You can also call us on 0845 130 7633.
Facilities & ⚡ 🚻 🚽 🚿 👤 ☉ 🍴 🔲 🛒 🌊
📶 🅿 🚐 🔲 🛒 ☉ 🌊
Nearest Town Rosemarkie
Directions From the A9 at Tore roundabout take the A832 Fortrose to Cromarty road. Go through Avoch, in Fortrose turn right at the Police House into Ness Road signposted golf course and leisure centre. Turn first left and the site is 400 yards.
🚆 Inverness

GAIRLOCH

Gairloch Caravan & Camping Holiday Park, Strath, Gairloch, Highlands, IV21 2BX
Tel: 01445 712373
Email: info@gairlochcaravanpark.com
www.gairlochcampsite.co.uk
Pitches For ⛺ 🚐 🚙 🚌 **Total** 75
Acreage 6 **Open** Apr to Oct
Access Good **Site** Level
Near the beach. In the village centre for shops, hotels and restaurants. AA 3 Pennants.
Facilities ⚡ 🚻 🚽 👤 ☉ 🍴 🔲 🛒 🅿
📶 🅿 🚐 🔲 🛒 🌊 🌊
Nearest Town Gairloch
Directions Turn off the A832 at Auchtercairn onto the B8021. In approx. ½ mile turn right by Millcroft Hotel then immediately right into the site.
🚆 Achnasheen

GLENCOE

Invercoe Caravan & Camping Park, Glencoe, Ballachulish, Highlands, PH49 4HP
Tel: 01855 811210
Email: holidays@invercoe.co.uk
www.invercoe.co.uk
Pitches For ⛺ 🚐 🚙 🚌 **Total** 60
Acreage 5 **Open** All Year
Access Good **Site** Level
Lochside site with beautiful scenery. Slipway access to the loch. Ideal centre for touring West Highlands. Wi-Fi available for a charge.
Facilities & ⚡ 🚻 🚽 🚿 👤 ☉ 🍴 🔲 🛒
📶 ☉ 🚐 🔲 🛒 🚙 ✗ 📶
Nearest Town Fort William
Directions Heading north on the A82 turn right at Glencoe crossroads onto the B863.
🚆 Fort William

GLENCOE

Red Squirrel Campsite, Leacantuim Farm, Glencoe, Highlands, PH49 4HX
Tel: 01855 811256
www.redsquirrelcampsite.co.uk
Pitches For ⛺ 🚐 **Total** 0
Acreage 22 **Open** All Year
Site Lev/Slope
Casual and very different Three Star Site in the centre of the mountains. River for swimming. Kids under 12 years £1, adults £10. Gazebos during July and August for £7 per night. Group discounts available.
Facilities 🚻 🚽 👤 🍴 ☉ 🍴 🅿 🔲 🛒
Nearest Town Fort William
Directions Turn off the main A82 into Glencoe Village, turn up main street, go over the humpback bridge and park is 1½ miles.
🚆 Fort William

INVERGARRY

Faichemard Farm Caravan & Camping Park, Faichemard Farm, Invergarry, Highlands, PH35 4HG
Tel: 01809 501314
Email: enquires@faichemard-caravancamping.co.uk
www.faichemard-caravancamping.co.uk
Pitches For ⛺ 🚐 🚙 **Total** 35
Acreage 10 **Open** Apr to Oct
Access Good **Site** Lev/Slope
Nearest Bus Stop (Miles) 1
ADULTS ONLY SITE with plenty of space and quiet. Ideal for hill walking and bird watching. Pitch price £6.50-£15. Every pitch has its own picnic table.
Facilities ⚡ 🚻 🚽 👤 ☉ 🍴 🔲 🛒 🅿
📶 🅿 🔲 🛒 🍴 🌊
Nearest Town Fort William
Directions Take A82 to Invergarry (25 miles) travel west on A87 for 1 mile, take side road on right at sign for Faichem, proceed to the sign for A & D Grant Faichemard Farm.
🚆 Spean Bridge

INVERNESS

Auchnahillin Holiday Park, Daviot East, Inverness, Highlands, IV2 5XQ
Tel: 01463 772286
Email: info@auchnahillin.co.uk
www.auchnahillin.co.uk
Pitches For ⛺ 🚐 🚙 **Total** 50
Acreage 10 **Open** Apr to Oct
Access Good **Site** Level
Nearest Bus Stop (Miles) Outside
Ideal touring area for the Highlands, many attractions within easy reach.
Facilities & ⚡ 🚻 🚽 🚿 👤 ☉ 🍴 🔲 🛒
🚻 ☉ 🚐 🔲 🛒 🌊
Nearest Town Inverness
Directions Approx. 8 miles south of Inverness off the A9 take the turning onto the B9154 towards Daviot East and Moy.
🚆 Inverness

INVERNESS

MacDonalds Bught Caravan & Tent Park, Bught Lane, Inverness, Highlands, IV3 5SR
Tel: 01463 236920
Email: john@invernesscaravanpark.com
www.invernesscaravanpark.com
Pitches For ⛺ 🚐 🚙 🚌 **Total** 140
Acreage 4¾ **Open** Easter to 01-Oct
Access Good **Site** Level
Nearest Bus Stop (Miles) Outside
Alongside the River Ness and canal, and next to an Aquadome. Just a 20 minute walk into the town centre. Kitchen shed in the tent area. Ice rink and childrens park in the immediate vicinity and two sports stadiums.

Facilities ⚙ ⚡ 🅿 📶 📞 ☉ 🍴 🚮 ▣ 🍷 🏊 🐕 🎮 ⊙ ⚓ ✕ 🛒 ▣ 🔲

Nearest Town Inverness

Directions Situated inside Inverness city limits on the A82 Loch Ness road, beside the canal bridge and Aquadome.

🚆 Inverness

ISLE OF SKYE

Glen Brittle Camp Site Glen Brittle, Carbost, Isle of Skye, Highlands,

Tel: 01478 640404

Pitches For 🏕 ⛺ 🚐 **Total** 220

Acreage 10 **Open** Apr **to** Sept

Access Poor **Site** Lev/slope

Nearest Bus Stop (Miles) 7 Beach

Facilities ⚡ ▣ 📶 📞 ☉ 🍷 🏊 🐕 ⚓ 🛒 ▣ 📠 ✏ 📶

Nearest Town Carbost

Directions From Carbost take small road signed Glenbrittle Campsite, follow single track road 9 miles.

🚆 Kyle of Lochalsh

ISLE OF SKYE

Skye Camping & Caravanning Club Site, Borve, Arnisort, Edinbane, Portree, Isle of Skye, Highlands, IV51 9PS

Tel: 01470 582230

Email: skye.site@thefriendlyclub.co.uk

www.campingandcaravanningclub.co.uk/skye

Pitches For 🏕 ⛺ 🚐 **Total** 105

Acreage 7 **Open** 21-Mar **to** 04-Nov

Access Good **Site** Lev/Slope

Nearest Bus Stop (Miles) Outside

Situated on a working croft with Highland cows, sheep, ducks and chickens. Within easy reach of a variety of attractions including boat trips and a distillery. Restaurants and pubs close by. Camping Pods available for hire. Non members welcome. You can also call us on 0845 130 7633.

Facilities ⚙ ⚡ ▣ 📶 📞 ☉ ⚓ 🚮 🍷 🏊 ⊙ 🐕 🛒 ▣ 📠 ✏ 📶

Nearest Town Portree

Directions From Inverness head NW on A82 towards Fairfield Lane. At Telford Street roundabout take the third exit onto A82, go over 3 roundabouts and at Longman roundabout take the first exit onto A9. Do a slight left at Millbank, at the roundabout take second exit, turn left, turn left again, then turn left again.

🚆 Kyle of Lochalsh

Nearest Town Gairloch

Directions On the A832, 15 miles north of Gairloch.

🚆 Inverness

JOHN O'GROATS

John O'Groats Caravan & Camping Site, John O'Groats, Nr Wick, Highlands, KW1 4YR

Tel: 01955 611329

Email: info@johnogroatscampsite.co.uk

www.johnogroatscampsite.co.uk

Pitches For 🏕 ⛺ 🚐 **Total** 90

Acreage 4 **Open** Apr **to** Sept

Access Good **Site** Level

Nearest Bus Stop (Miles) Outside

On sea shore with clear view of Orkney Islands. Day trips to Orkney by passenger ferry, jetty nearby. Hotel and snack bar 600 yards. Cliff scenery and sea birds 1½ miles. STB 3 Star Graded.

Facilities ⚙ ⚡ ▣ 📶 📞 ☉ 🍷 🏊 🐕 ⚓ 🛒 ▣

Nearest Town John O'Groats

Directions End of A99 beside last house.

🚆 Wick

KINLOCHEWE

Kinlochewe Caravan Club Site, Kinlochewe, Achnasheen, Highlands, IV22 2PA

Tel: 01445 760239

www.caravanclub.co.uk

Pitches For ⛺ 🚐 **Total** 56

Acreage 5 **Open** Mar **to** Oct

Access Good **Site** Level

Peaceful location at the foot of Ben Eighe, surrounded by lochs, woodland and mountains. Close to Victoria Falls and Inverewe Gardens. Butcher calls into site twice a week. Adjacent to a service station and theres a general shop and cafe in the village. Non members welcome. Booking essential.

Facilities ⚙ ⚡ ▣ 📶 📞 ☉ ▣ 🍷 🏊 🐕 ⊙ ⚓ 🛒 ▣

Directions From Inverness take A9, in Tore at roundabout turn onto A835 sp Maryburgh, in Maryburgh at roundabout continue on A835 sp Ullapool. In Gorstan turn left onto A832, in Achnasheen at roundabout follow signs for Kinlochewe, site is 10 miles on the left.

LAIDE

Gruinard Bay Caravan Park, Laide, Ross-Shire, IV22 2ND

Tel: 01445 731225

Email: gruinard@ecosse.net

www.gruinardbay.co.uk

Pitches For 🏕 ⛺ 🚐 **Total** 35

Acreage 3 **Open** Apr **to** Oct

Access Good **Site** Level

Beach front location.

Facilities ⚡ ▣ 📞 ☉ 🍴 🚮 🍷 🏊 🏊 🐕 🛒 ▣ ▣

LAIRG

Dunroamin Caravan Park, Main Street, Lairg, Sutherland, IV27 4AR

Tel: 01549 402447

Email: enquiries@lairgcaravanpark.co.uk

www.lairgcaravanpark.co.uk

Pitches For 🏕 ⛺ 🚐 **Total** 30

Acreage 30 **Open** Apr **to** Oct

Access Good **Site** Level

Ideal for touring, fishing and sight seeing. Close to Loch Shin and all amenities. Secure Storage during Winter only.

Facilities ⚡ ▣ 📶 📞 ☉ 🍴 🚮 ▣ 🍷 🏊 🐕 ⊙ ✕ 🛒 📠 ▣ 📶

Nearest Town Lairg

Directions 300 yards east of Loch Shin on the A839 on Main Street Lairg. Site entrance in the village.

🚆 Lairg

LAIRG

Woodend Caravan & Camping Park, Woodend, Achnairn, Lairg, Highlands, IV27 4DN

Tel: 01549 402248

Pitches For 🏕 ⛺ 🚐 **Total** 45

Acreage 4 **Open** Apr **to** Sept

Access Good **Site** Lev/Slope

Overlooking Loch Shin for fishing and scenic views. Campers Kitchen is a small building where campers can take their cooking stores to prepare food, with table, chairs and a dish washing area. Ideal touring centre for north west. AA 3 Pennants and a Gold Award for Quality & Service from International Caravan & Camping Guide.

Facilities ⚡ 📶 📞 ☉ 🍴 🚮 ▣ 🍷 🏊 🍴 📠

Nearest Town Lairg

Directions From Lairg take the A836, then take the A838 and follow site signs.

🚆 Lairg

LOCHINVER

Clachtoll Campsite, Croft 134, Clachtoll, Lochinver, Highlands, IV27 4JD

Tel: 01571 855377

Email: mail@clachtollbeachcampsite.co.uk

www.clachtollbeachcampsite.co.uk

Pitches For 🏕 ⛺ 🚐 **Total** 40

Acreage 3 **Open** Easter **to** Sept

Access Good **Site** Level

200 yards from a sandy beach. Beautiful scenery. Ideal location for hillwalkers and children who enjoy rockpools.

Facilities ♿ ⚡ 🚽 ⬛ 🚿 🅿 ☉ ⬚ 🔲 🛒
🇮 🐕 🚻 ⬚

Nearest Town Lochinver
Directions 5 miles outside of Lochinver.
🚉 Inverness

MELVICH

Halladale Inn Caravan Park, Halladale
Inn, Melvich, Sutherland, KW14 7YJ
Tel: 01641 531282
Email: mazfling@tinyworld.co.uk
www.halladaleinn.co.uk
Pitches For ⛺ 🚐 🚍 **Total** 11
Acreage ½ **Open** Apr to Oct
Access Good **Site** Level
Nearest Bus Stop (Miles) 1
10 minutes walk from a lovely sandy beach.
Ideal for surfers. 14 miles from Forsinard
RSPB Reserve. Fishing on the Halladale
River.
Facilities ⚡ 🚽 ⬛ 🚿 🅿 ☉ ⬚ 🔲 🛒
🇮 ✕ 🚻 🔲 ⬚

Nearest Town Thurso
Directions 16 miles west of Thurso on the
A836 following the North Highlands Tourist
Route.
🚉 Forsinard

NAIRN

**Nairn Camping & Caravanning Club
Site,** Delnies Wood, Nairn, Inverness,
Highlands, IV12 5NX
Tel: 01667 455281
Email: nairn.site@thefriendlysite.co.uk
www.campingandcaravanningclub.co.uk/
nairn
Pitches For ⛺ 🚐 🚍 **Total** 75
Acreage 14 **Open** Mar to 28-Oct
Access Good **Site** Level
Nearest Bus Stop (Miles) Outside
Wooded setting just 2 miles from the beach,
close to the town of Nairn. STB 4 Star Graded
and AA 3 Pennants. Non members welcome.
You can also call us on 0845 130 7633.
Facilities ⚡ 🚽 🚿 🅿 ☉ ⬚ 🔲 🛒
🇮 🐕 ⬚ 🚻 🔲 ⬚ ⛷ ⬚

Nearest Town Nairn
Directions Off the A96 Inverness to
Aberdeen road 2 miles west of Nairn.
🚉 Nairn

NAIRN

Nairn Lochloy Holiday Park - Parkdean,
East Beach, Nairn, Highlands, IV12 4PH
Tel: 0344 335 3740
Email: enquiries@parkdeanholidays.co.uk
www.parkdeantouring.com
Pitches For ⛺ 🚐 🚍 **Total** 13
Acreage 15 **Open** Mar to Nov
Access Good **Site** Level
Nearest Bus Stop (Miles) ½
Situated next to the harbour, nestled in the
sand dunes of Nairn east Beach and the
lovely village of Nairn. Indoor pool.
Facilities ⚡ 🚿 🅿 ☉ ⬚ 🛒
🔲 🇮 ✕ 🍺 🍴 🐕 🎣 ⬚ 🚻 🔲 ⬚ ⬚

Nearest Town Nairn
Directions Take the A96 from Inverness or
Aberdeen. In Nairn follow signs, adjacent to
the harbour.
🚉 Nairn

NEWTONMORE

Invernahavon Caravan Site, Glentruim,
Newtonmore, Highlands, PH20 1BE
Tel: 01540 673534/673219
www.caravanclub.co.uk
Pitches For ⛺ 🚐 🚍 ⬚ **Total** 67
Acreage 10 **Open** Mar to Oct
Access Good **Site** Level

Tranquil and spacious family run site with
spectacular views of the Monarch of the Glen
country. Heather covered mountains, ideal
for walking and wildlife spotting. Adjacent to
the Rivers Spey and Truim, fishing permits
available. Booking essential.
Facilities ♿ ⚡ 🚽 ⬛ 🚿 🅿 ☉ ⬚ 🔲 🛒
🇮 🐕 ☉ 🚻 🔲 ⬚ ⬚

Nearest Town Newtonmore
Directions 2 miles south of Newtonmore on
the A9 turn right onto Glentruim road, site is
400 yards on the right.
🚉 Newtonmore

ONICH

Bunree Caravan Club Site, Onich, Fort
William, Highlands, PH33 6SE
Tel: 01855 821283
www.caravanclub.co.uk
Pitches For 🚐 🚍 **Total** 99
Acreage 7 **Open** Mar to Nov
Access Good **Site** Level
Nearest Bus Stop (Miles) ½
Situated at the edge of Loch Linnhe with
mountain views. Visit Ben Nevis or take a
cable car 2300 feet to Aonach Mor Mountain
for fabulous views of the whole mountain
range, the Great Glen and islands of Skye
and Rhum. Non members welcome. Booking
essential.
Facilities ♿ ⚡ 🚽 ⬛ 🚿 🅿 ⬚ 🔲 🛒
🇮 🐕 ☉ 🚻 🔲 ⬚

Nearest Town Onich
Directions From south east on the A82, just
past Onich turn left at Caravan Club sign into
a narrow track with traffic lights and passing
places, site is in ¼ mile.

POOLEWE

**Inverewe Gardens Camping &
Caravanning Club Site,** Inverewe
Gardens, Poolewe, Achnasheen,
Highlands, IV22 2LF
Tel: 01445 781249
Email:
inverewe.site@thefriendlyclub.co.uk
www.campingandcaravanningclub.co.uk/
inverewe
Pitches For ⛺ 🚐 🚍 **Total** 55
Acreage 3 **Open** 18-Apr to 28-Oct
Site Level
Nearest Bus Stop (Miles) ½
Close to Inverewe Gardens and Loch Ewe.
National Trust Ranger Walks ¼ mile. Diving
nearby. STB 4 Star Graded and AA 3
Pennants. Non members welcome. You can
also call us on 0845 130 7633.
Facilities ⚡ 🚽 ⬛ 🚿 🅿 ☉ ⬚ 🔲 🛒
🇮 🐕 🚻 🔲 ⬚ ⬚

Directions Site entrance is on the A832,
north of the village of Poolewe.
🚉 Achnasheen

PORTREE

Torvaig Caravan & Campsite, 8 Torvaig,
Portree, Isle of Skye, Highlands, IV51 9HU
Tel: 01478 611849
Email: torvaigcampsite@aol.com
www.portreecampsite.co.uk
Pitches For ⛺ 🚐 🚍 **Total** 90
Acreage 4½ **Open** April to 20-Oct
Access Good **Site** Sloping
Nearest Bus Stop (Miles) Outside
Ideal for touring the Isle of Skye.
Facilities ⚡ 🚽 ⬛ 🚿 🅿 ☉ 🔲 🛒 🚻 🐕 ⬚

Nearest Town Portree
Directions 1 mile north of Portree on the
main A855 road.
🚉 Kyle of Lochalsh

ROY BRIDGE

Bunroy Camping & Caravanning Site,
Bunroy Park, Roy Bridge, Highlands, PH31
4AG
Tel: 01397 712332
Email: info@bunroycamping.co.uk
www.bunroy.co.uk
Pitches For ⛺ 🚐 🚍 **Total** 25
Acreage 7 **Open** Apr to Oct
Access Good **Site** Level
Nearest Bus Stop (Miles) ½
Peaceful, secluded, riverside site. Ideal for
touring the Highlands and outdoor pursuits.
Facilities ⚡ 🚽 ⬛ 🚿 🅿 ☉ ⬚ 🔲 🛒
🇮 🐕 🚻 🔲 ⬚ ✓ ⬚

Nearest Town Fort William
Directions From the A86 in Roy Bridge, turn
off opposite the Stronlossit Inn, go past the
school on the left, over the railway bridge and
go straight on.
🚉 Roy Bridge

SHIEL BRIDGE

Morvich Caravan Club Site, Inverinate,
Shiel Bridge, Kyle, Highlands, IV40 8HQ
Tel: 01599 511354
www.caravanclub.co.uk
Pitches For ⛺ 🚐 🚍 **Total** 106
Acreage 7 **Open** Mar to Nov
Access Good **Site** Level
Set on a valley floor surrounded by hills and
mountains on National Trust land. Daily
guided walks July and August. Close to
Eilean Castle, Dunvegan Castle, Falls of
Glomach, Talisker Distillery and Isle of
Skye. Non members welcome. Booking
essential.
Facilities ♿ ⚡ 🚽 ⬛ 🚿 🅿 ⬚ 🔲 🛒
🇮 🐕 🚻 🔲 ⬚

Nearest Town Shiel Bridge
Directions From the A87, 1¼ miles past
Shiel Bridge at the head of Loch Duich, turn
right by the restaurant into loop road
signposted Morvich, after 1 mile turn right
into road to the site.

SHIEL BRIDGE

Shiel Bridge Caravan Park, Shiel Bridge,
Glenshiel, Kyle of Lochalsh, Ross-Shire,
IV40 8HW
Tel: 01599 511221
Email: johnfivesisters@btinternet.com
www.shielbridgecaravanpark.co.uk
Pitches For ⛺ 🚐 🚍 **Total** 75
Acreage 3 **Open** 16-Mar to 16-Oct
Access Good **Site** Level
Nearest Bus Stop (Miles) ¼
Alongside a river with spectacular scenery.
Ideal for walking and touring the Isle of Skye
and the North West Highlands.
Facilities ⚡ 🚽 ⬛ 🚿 🅿 ☉ ⬚ 🛒
🇮 🐕 🚻 🔲 ⬚ ⛷

Nearest Town Kyle of Lochalsh
Directions 16 miles east of Kyle of Lochalsh
on the A87.
🚉 Kyle of Lochalsh

SPEAN BRIDGE

Gairlochy Holiday Park, Old Station,
Gairlochy Road, Spean Bridge, Highlands,
PH34 4EQ
Tel: 01397 712711
Email: theghp@talk21.com
www.theghp.co.uk
Pitches For ⛺ 🚐 🚍 **Total** 10
Acreage 1½ **Open** Apr to Oct
Site Level
Ideal touring area.Self catering lodges and
Holiday caravans for hire.
Facilities ⚡ 🚽 ⬛ 🚿 🅿 ☉ ⬚ 🔲 🛒
🍴 🚻 🔲 ⬚ ✓ ⬚ ⬚

Nearest Town Spean Bridge

Directions 1 mile north of Spean Bridge on the A82 turn onto the B8004 signposted Gairlochy
⇌ Spean Bridge

SPEAN BRIDGE

Stronaba Caravan Camp Site, Stronaba, Spean Bridge, InvernessShire, PH34 4DX
Tel: 01397 712259
Pitches For ▲ ⊞ ⛟ **Total** 20
Acreage 3 **Open** Apr to Oct
Access Good **Site** Lev/Slope
Nearest Bus Stop (Miles) Outside
Outdoor activities, mountain bike trails and mountain gondola all nearby.
Facilities ⨍ ⬚ 🅿 ⌂ ⊙ 🅿
Nearest Town Fort William
Directions On the main A82, 2 miles north of Spean Bridge, on the left hand side (if travelling north).
⇌ Spean Bridge

STRATHPEFFER

Riverside Chalet & Caravan Park, Contin, Strathpeffer, Highlands, IV14 9ES
Tel: 01463 513599
Email: contact@lochnesschalets.co.uk
www.lochnesschalets.co.uk
Pitches For ▲ ⊞ ⛟ **Total** 30
Acreage 1½ **Open** Apr to Oct
Site Level
Nearest Bus Stop (Miles) ¼
Riverside location ideal for walking, mountain biking and fishing.
Facilities ⨍ ⬚ 🅿 ⌂ ⊙ ▥ 🅿
Nearest Town Strathpeffer
⇌ Dingwall

STRONTIAN

Sunart Camping Park Strontian, Highlands, PH36 4HZ
Tel: 01967 402080
Email: sunartcamping@orangehome.co.uk
www.sunartcamping.co.uk
Pitches For ▲ ⊞ ⛟ 🚐 **Total** 29
Acreage 3 **Open** Mar to 01-Feb
Access Good **Site** Level
Nearest Bus Stop (Miles) ¼
On Loch Sunart at the edge of small village with shop, resturants.
Facilities ⨍ ⬚ 🅿 ⌂ ⊙ 🅿
Nearest Town Fort William
Directions From A82 Corran Ferry turn left 12 miles to Strontian.
⇌ Fort William

THURSO

Dunnet Bay Caravan Club Site, Dunnet, Thurso, Highlands, KW14 8XD
Tel: 01847 821319
www.caravanclub.co.uk
Pitches For ▲ ⊞ ⛟ **Total** 57
Acreage 5 **Open** Apr to Oct
Access Good **Site** Level
Nearest Bus Stop (Miles) Outside
Situated on the beach above the sand dunes. Ideal for bird watching, walking, guided walks and day trips to the Orkney Islands. Climb Dunnet Head for magnificent views over Pentland Firth to Orkney and the north coast to Ben Loyal and Ben Hope. Non members welcome. Booking essential.
Facilities ⨍ ⬚ 🅿 ⌂ ⊙ 🅿
Nearest Town Thurso
Directions From Thurso take the A836, site is on the left approx. 2½ miles past Castletown Village.
⇌ Thurso

UIG

Uig Bay Camping & Caravan Site, 10 Idrigill, Uig, Isle of Skye, Highlands, IV51 9XU
Tel: 01470 542714
Email: lisa.madigan@btopenworld.com
www.uig-camping-skye.co.uk
Pitches For ▲ ⊞ ⛟ **Total** 50
Acreage 2¼ **Open** All Year
Access Good **Site** Level
Nearest Bus Stop (Miles) Outside
Close to a pebble beach. Near ferry terminal to the Western Isles. Ideal for touring the Highlands. Cycle hire locally.
Facilities ⨍ ⬚ 🅿 ⌂ ⊙ 🅿
Nearest Town Uig
Directions From Portree take the A87 to Uig, pass the ferry terminal and turn right just before the pier to the site.
⇌ Fort William

ULLAPOOL

Broomfield Holiday Park, Shore Street, Ullapool, Highlands, IV26 2UT
Tel: 01854 612020
Email: sross@broomfieldhp.com
www.broomfieldhp.com
Pitches For ▲ ⊞ ⛟ **Total** 140
Acreage 11 **Open** Easter to Sept
Access Good **Site** Level
Nearest Bus Stop (Miles) ¼
On the sea front. Beside a cafe/restaurant and adjacent to a golf course.
Facilities ⨍ ⬚ 🅿 ⌂ ⊙ 🅿
Nearest Town Ullapool
Directions Turn right past Ullapool Harbour.
⇌ Garve

WICK

Wick Caravan & Camping Site, Riverside Drive, Janetstown, Wick, Highlands, KW1 5SP
Tel: 01955 605420
Email: wickcaravansite@hotmail.co.uk
www.wickcaravansite.co.uk
Pitches For ▲ ⊞ ⛟ **Total** 90
Acreage 6½ **Open** Mid Apr to Mid Oct
Access Good **Site** Level
Nearest Bus Stop (Miles) ¼
Sheltered site overlooking the River Wick and surrounded by trees. Just a 10 minute walk to the town centre and 3 miles from the beach.
Facilities ⨍ ⬚ 🅿 ⌂ ⊙ 🅿
Nearest Town Wick
Directions From the A99, turn left into Thurso Street (A882), after ½ a mile turn right into Riverside Drive.
⇌ Wick

LANARKSHIRE (SOUTH)
ABINGTON

Mount View Caravan Park, Abington, South Lanarkshire, ML12 6RW
Tel: 01864 502808
Email: info@mountviewcaravanpark.co.uk
www.mountviewcaravanpark.co.uk
Pitches For ▲ ⊞ ⛟ **Total** 50
Acreage 5½ **Open** Mar to Oct
Access Good **Site** Lev/Slope
Nearest Bus Stop (Miles) ¼
Ideal for walking, touring and a quiet family holiday. Well situated for exploring Clyde Valley. One hour from Glasgow, Edinburgh and the Ayrshire coast.
Facilities ⨍ ⬚ 🅿 ⌂ ⊙ 🅿
Nearest Town Biggar
Directions Leave the M74 at junction 13 and take the A702 south into Abington Village, then follow signs down Station Road.
⇌ Lanark

LOTHIAN (EAST)
ABERLADY

Aberlady Caravan Park, Aberlady Station, Haddington Road, Aberlady, Lothian (East), EH32 0PZ
Tel: 01875 870666
Email: aberladycaravanpark@hotmail.com
www.aberladycaravanpark.co.uk
Pitches For ▲ ⊞ ⛟ 🚐 **Total** 30
Acreage 2 **Open** All Year
Access Good **Site** Level
Nearest Bus Stop (Miles) ¼
Ideal for touring East Lothian, Edinburgh 15 minutes by train.
Facilities ⨍ ⬚ 🅿 ⌂ ⊙ 🅿
Nearest Town Aberlady
Directions From Haddington take the A6137 to Aberlady site is approx 4½ on the left hand side.
⇌ Longniddry

DUNBAR

Belhaven Bay Caravan & Camping Park, Edinburgh Road, Dunbar, East Lothian, EH42 1TS
Tel: 01368 865956
Email: belhaven@meadowhead.co.uk
www.meadowhead.co.uk
Pitches For ▲ ⊞ ⛟ **Total** 128
Open 08-Mar to Oct
Access Good **Site** Level
Nearest Bus Stop (Miles) Outside
Set within the John Muir Country Park, and right on one side of East Lothians beautiful sandy beaches.
Facilities ⨍ ⬚ 🅿 ⌂ ⊙ 🅿
Nearest Town Dunbar
Directions From the A1 north or south, exit at Thistly Cross roundabout west of Dunbar and take the A1087 towards Dunbar, Park is approx. 1 mile.
⇌ Dunbar

NORTH BERWICK

Station Park Caravan Site East Fortune Farm, East Fortune, North Berwick, East Lothian, EH39 5JU
Tel: 01620 880231
Email: jane@brandleisure.co.uk
www.brandleisure.co.uk
Pitches For ⊞ ⛟ **Total** 15
Acreage 2 **Open** All Year
Access Good **Site** Level/Sloping
Facilities ⨍ ⬚ 🅿
Nearest Town North Berwick
Directions Turn off A1 at Haddington-Abbotsview junction on to A199. Turn left on to B1347. At T-junction turn right on to B1377. Site on left at farm entrance.
⇌ Drem

NORTH BERWICK

Tantallon Caravan & Camping Park, Dunbar Road, North Berwick, East Lothian, EH39 5NJ
Tel: 01620 893348
Email: tantallon@meadowhead.co.uk
www.meadowhead.co.uk
Pitches For ▲ ⊞ ⛟ **Total** 0
Open 08-Mar to Oct
Access Good **Site** Level

Nearest Bus Stop (Miles) ¼
Spectacular views over the Firth of Forth to the Bass Rock. Scotlands golfing capital.
Facilities ⬡
Nearest Town North Berwick
Directions From the A1, 3 miles west of Dunbar take the A198 and follow to North Berwick. Tantallon Park is on the right.
⚬ North Berwick

NORTH BERWICK
Yellowcraig Caravan Club Site, Dirleton, North Berwick, East Lothian, EH39 5DS
Tel: 01620 850217
www.caravanclub.co.uk
Pitches For ⬡ ⬡ **Total** 116
Acreage 7½ **Open** Mar to Nov
Access Good **Site** Level
Attractive site with grass covered sandy dunes and shrubs. Golden sands and rock pools nearby. Close to the Scottish Seabird Centre, Hailes Castle and East Fortune Museum of Flight. Non members welcome. Booking essential.
Facilities ⬡ ⬡ ⬡ ⬡ ⬡ ⬡ ⬡ ⬡ ⬡ ⬡ ⬡ ⬡ ⬡
Nearest Town North Berwick
Directions From A1 approaching East Linton turn right onto A198. After approx. 8¾ miles turn left past railway station, at junction turn left (still on A198). After 2½ miles turn right signposted Dirleton, turn right at site sign, site is 1 mile.
⚬ North Berwick

LOTHIAN (WEST)
BLACKBURN
Mosshall Farm Caravan Park, Mosshall Farm, Blackburn, West Lothian, EH47 7DB
Tel: 01501 762318
Pitches For ⬡ ⬡ ⬡ **Total** 25
Acreage ¾ **Open** All Year
Access Good **Site** Level
Nearest Bus Stop (Miles) ¼
Situated half way between Edinburgh and Glasgow.
Facilities ⬡ ⬡ ⬡ ⬡ ⬡ ⬡ ⬡ ⬡ ⬡ ⬡
Nearest Town Blackburn
Directions Leave the M8 at junction 4 and take the road for Whitburn. At T-Junction A705 take a left turn towards Blackburn, we are 300 yards on the right.
⚬ Bathgate

EAST CALDER
Linwater Caravan Park, West Clifton, East Calder, West Lothian, EH53 0HT
Tel: 0131 333 3326
Email: linwater@supanet.com
www.linwater.co.uk
Pitches For ⬡ ⬡ ⬡ **Total** 60
Acreage 5 **Open** 18-Mar to Oct
Access Good **Site** Level
Lovely amenities and walks nearby. Ideal for visiting Edinburgh, Royal Highland Showground and Falkirk Wheel.
Facilities ⬡ ⬡ ⬡ ⬡ ⬡ ⬡ ⬡ ⬡ ⬡ ⬡ ⬡ ⬡
Nearest Town Edinburgh
Directions From junction 1, Newbridge on the M9 or Wilkieston on the A71, park is signposted along the B7030.
⚬ Kirknewton

LINLITHGOW
Beecraigs Caravan & Camping Site,
Beecraigs Country Park, Nr Linlithgow, West Lothian, EH49 6PL
Tel: 01506 844516
Email: mail@beecraigs.com
www.beecraigs.com
Pitches For ⬡ ⬡ ⬡ ⬡ **Total** 48
Acreage 6½ **Open** All Year
Access Good **Site** Level
Within a 913 acre Country Park which offers a wide range of leisure and recreational interests - fly fishing, play area, Red Deer attraction, Highland cattle, restaurant and many woodland walks. Discounts for Caravan and Camping club members.
Facilities ⬡ ⬡ ⬡ ⬡ ⬡ ⬡ ⬡ ⬡ ⬡ ⬡ ⬡ ⬡ ⬡ ⬡ ⬡ ⬡ ⬡ ⬡ ⬡
Nearest Town Linlithgow
Directions From Linlithgow High Street follow signs for Beecraigs Country Park, taking you approx. 2 miles up Preston Road. At the top of the hill turn left and then first right, take the next right into reception within the Beecraigs Restaurant.
⚬ Linlithgow

LINLITHGOW
Loch House Caravan & Camping Park,
Loch House Farm, Linlithgow, Lothian (West), EH49 7RG
Tel: 01506 848283
Email: dotanddonj@btinternet.com
www.lochhousefarmcaravanpark
Pitches For ⬡ ⬡ ⬡ **Total** 0
Open Jan to Oct
Access Good **Site** Sloping
Facilities ⬡ ⬡ ⬡ ⬡ ⬡ ⬡ ⬡ ⬡
Nearest Town Linlithgow
Directions A706 Bo'ness road from Linlithgow High Street.
⚬ Linlithgow

MORAY
ABERLOUR
Speyside Camping & Caravanning Club Site, Speyside, Archiestown, Aberlour, Moray, AB38 9SL
Tel: 01340 810414
Email:
speyside.site@thefriendlyclub.co.uk
www.campingandcaravanningclub.co.uk/speyside
Pitches For ⬡ ⬡ ⬡ **Total** 75
Acreage 7 **Open** 25-Apr to 28-Oct
Access Good **Site** Level
Nearest Bus Stop (Miles) Outside
The surrounding area has historic castles, National Trust properties and gardens to visit. Salmon and Whisky are the specialities of this area of Scotland. STB 4 Star Graded and AA 3 Pennants. Non members welcome. You can also call us on 0845 130 7633.
Facilities ⬡ ⬡ ⬡ ⬡ ⬡ ⬡ ⬡ ⬡ ⬡ ⬡ ⬡ ⬡ ⬡ ⬡ ⬡ ⬡
Nearest Town Aberlour
Directions From the A9 at Carrbridge turn onto the A95 to Grantown-on-Spey then on to Aberlour. Take the A941 then turn left onto the B9102 signposted Archiestown, site is on the left after 3 miles.
⚬ Elgin

ELGIN
Riverside Caravan Park, West Road, Elgin, Moray, IV30 8UN
Tel: 01343 542813
Pitches For ⬡ ⬡ ⬡ **Total** 44
Open Apr to Oct
Access Good **Site** Level

Elgin is near to beaches and alongside the River Lossie. Ideal fun touring base. Fishing, golfing and plenty of shops, restaurants and entertainment for children nearby.
Facilities ⬡ ⬡ ⬡ ⬡ ⬡ ⬡ ⬡ ⬡ ⬡ ⬡ ⬡ ⬡ ⬡ ⬡ ⬡ ⬡ ⬡ ⬡
Nearest Town Elgin
Directions Situated off the A96 Aberdeen to Inverness road. On the western outskirts of Elgin, 3 minutes drive from the town centre.
⚬ Elgin

HOPEMAN
Station Caravan Park, Hopeman, Nr Elgin, Moray, IV30 5RU
Tel: 01343 830880
Email:
enquiries@stationcaravanpark.co.uk
www.stationcaravanpark.co.uk
Pitches For ⬡ ⬡ ⬡ **Total** 37
Acreage 13 **Open** Mar to Nov
Access Good **Site** Level
Nearest Bus Stop (Miles) ¼
On a beach on Moray Firth coast.
Facilities ⬡ ⬡ ⬡ ⬡ ⬡ ⬡ ⬡ ⬡ ⬡ ⬡ ⬡ ⬡ ⬡ ⬡ ⬡ ⬡ ⬡
Nearest Town Elgin
⚬ Elgin

PERTH & KINROSS
ABERFELDY
Scottish Canoe Assocation Grandtully Campsite, Lageonan Road, Grand Tully, Nr Aberfeldy, Perth & Kinross, PH9 0PL
Tel: 07760 117641
Email: sca.campsite@canoesscotland.org
www.canoesscotland.org
Pitches For ⬡ ⬡ ⬡ ⬡ **Total** 73
Open All year
Access Good
Nearest Bus Stop (Miles) ¼
Core route to Aberfeldy and Pitlochry, Grand tully rapids, canoeing, rafting and other outdoor activities.
Facilities ⬡ ⬡ ⬡ ⬡ ⬡ ⬡ ⬡ ⬡ ⬡
Nearest Town Aberfeldy
Directions From A9 at Ballinlvie, take the A827 to Aberfeldy, in Grand Tully village, turn left into Lageonan Road.
⚬ Pitlochry

ALYTH
Five Roads Caravan Park, Alyth, Blairgowrie, Perth & Kinross, PH11 8NB
Tel: 01828 632255
Email: steven.ewart@btopenworld.com
www.fiveroads-caravan-park.co.uk
Pitches For ⬡ ⬡ ⬡ ⬡ **Total** 28
Acreage 3 **Open** All Year
Access Good **Site** Level
Nearest Bus Stop (Miles) Outside
Three golf courses within a 1 mile radius.
Facilities ⬡ ⬡ ⬡ ⬡ ⬡ ⬡ ⬡ ⬡ ⬡ ⬡ ⬡ ⬡ ⬡ ⬡ ⬡ ⬡ ⬡
Nearest Town Alyth
Directions From Blairgowrie take the A926, after 4½ miles at the Blackbird Inn turn left.
⚬ Dundee

BLAIR ATHOLL
Blair Castle Caravan Park, Blair Atholl, Pitlochry, Perth & Kinross, PH18 5SR
Tel: 01796 481263
Email: mail@blaircastlecaravanpark.co.uk
www.blaircastlecaravanpark.co.uk
Pitches For ⬡ ⬡ ⬡ ⬡ **Total** 275
Acreage 35 **Open** Mar to Nov
Access Good **Site** Level
Nearest Bus Stop (Miles) ¼

Located within the grounds of Blair Castle, the Park is regularly visited by the native red squirrel, and enjoys easy access to Atholl Estates 40 mile network of way-marked trails and cycle tracks. Pony trekking nearby. Fishing available on Atholl

Facilities ⬛ symbols

Directions Follow A9 north past Pitlochry, after 6 miles turn off following signs to Blair Atholl. After 1 miles turn right into caravan park.

≠ Blair Atholl

BLAIRGOWRIE

Nether Craig Holiday Park, Alyth, Blairgowrie, Perth & Kinross, PH11 8HN
Tel: 01575 560204
Email: info@nethercraig.com
www.nethercraig.com
Pitches For 🛈 ⬛ ⬛ **Total** 50
Acreage 4 **Open** 15-Feb **to** 15-Jan
Access Good **Site** Level
Quiet, spacious location, away from major roads with picturesque views. Ideal base for touring, hill walking, fishing and golf.

Facilities ⬛ symbols

Nearest Town Blairgowrie
Directions At the roundabout south of Alyth, join the B954 signposted Glenisla. Follow caravan signs for 4 miles (DO NOT go into Alyth).

≠ Dundee

COMRIE

Twenty Shilling Wood Caravan Park, St Fillans Road, Comrie, Perth & Kinross, PH6 2JY
Tel: 01764 670411
Email: alowe20@aol.com
www.ukparks.co.uk/twentyshilling
Pitches For ⬛ ⬛ **Total** 10
Acreage 10¼ **Open** Late Mar **to** 20-Oct
Access Good **Site** Level
Nearest Bus Stop (Miles) Outside
Family run, spotless all season, peaceful, sheltered, sunny south facing park set in woodlands that are visited by deer and many woodland birds. Individual pitches. Sorry, NO tents. Pets permitted. David Bellamy Gold Award for Conservation. Booking essential.

Facilities ⬛ symbols

Nearest Town Crieff
Directions ½ mile west of Comrie on A85.

≠ Perth

COMRIE

West Lodge Caravan Park, Comrie, Crieff, Perthshire, PH6 2LS
Tel: 01764 670354
www.westlodgecaravanpark.co.uk
Pitches For 🛈 ⬛ ⬛ **Total** 20
Acreage 3 **Open** Apr **to** Oct
Access Good **Site** Level
Nearest Bus Stop (Miles) Outside
Sheltered friendly park, set in beautiful country area. Ideal for touring. Caravans for hire nightly or weekly.

Facilities ⬛ symbols

Nearest Town Comrie
Directions On A85, 5 miles from Crieff. 1 mile east of Comrie.

≠ Perth

DUNKELD

Inver Mill Farm Caravan Park, Inver, Dunkeld, Perth & Kinross, PH8 0JR
Tel: 01350 727477
Email: invermill@talk21.com
www.invermillfarm.com

Pitches For 🛈 ⬛ ⬛ **Total** 65
Acreage 5 **Open** End Mar **to** Mid/End Oct
Access Good **Site** Level
Nearest Bus Stop (Miles) ½
Riverside setting. 1 mile from Dunkeld which has many tourist attractions along with walking, fishing, golf and cycling.

Facilities ⬛ symbols

Nearest Town Dunkeld
Directions From the A9 turn onto the A822 signposted Crieff, turn immediately right following signs to Inver.

≠ Dunkeld

INCHTURE

Inchmartine Caravan Park, Dundee Road, Inchture, Perth & Kinross, PH14 9QQ
Tel: 01821 670212
Email: enquiries@perthshire-caravans.com
Pitches For ⬛ ⬛ **Total** 30
Acreage 8 **Open** End Mar **to** Oct
Access Good **Site** Level
Nearest Bus Stop (Miles) ¼
A rural setting.

Facilities ⬛ symbols

Nearest Town Inchure
Directions Situated just off the A90 northbound, 12 miles north of Perth and 10 miles south of Dundee.

≠ Dundee

KILLIN

Cruachan Farm Caravan & Camping Park, Killin, Perth & Kinross, FK21 8TY
Tel: 01567 820302
Email: enquiries@cruachanfarm.co.uk
www.cruachanfarm.co.uk
Pitches For ⬛ ⬛ **Total** 0
Open Mid Mar **to** Oct
Access Good **Site** level
Central location ideal for touring and hill walking.

Facilities ⬛ symbols

Nearest Town Killin
Directions 3 miles east on the A827, well signposted.

≠ Crianlarich

PERTH

Scone Camping & Caravanning Club Site, Scone Palace Caravan Park, Scone, Perth & Kinross, PH2 6BB
Tel: 01738 552323
Email: scone.site@thefriendlyclub.co.uk
www.campingandcaravanningclub.co.uk/scone
Pitches For 🛈 ⬛ ⬛ **Total** 120
Acreage 16 **Open** 01-Mar **to** 05-Nov
Site Lev/Slope
Nearest Bus Stop (Miles) ½
Trout and salmon fishing is available from the nearby River Tay. Just to the north of Perth. Ideal for touring central Scotland. STB 4 Star Graded, David Bellamy Gold Award and AA 3 Pennants. Non members welcome. You can also call us on 0845 130 7633.

Facilities ⬛ symbols

Nearest Town Perth
Directions From the Motorway follow signs for Scone Palace, after Scone Palace continue for 2 miles then turn left following camp site signs or signs for Stormontfield. After 1 mile turn left into Racecourse Road, site entrance is through the car park.

≠ Perth

PITLOCHRY

Milton of Fonab Caravan Site, Bridge Road, Pitlochry, Perth & Kinross, PH16 5NA
Tel: 01796 472882
Email: info@fonab.co.uk
www.fonab.co.uk
Pitches For 🛈 ⬛ ⬛ **Total** 154
Acreage 15 **Open** End Mar **to** Beg Oct
Access Good **Site** Level
Nearest Bus Stop (Miles) ¼
On the banks of the River Tummel. 5 minute walk to Pitlochry Festival Theatre and a 10 minute walk to Dam and Fish Ladder.

Facilities ⬛ symbols

Nearest Town Pitlochry
Directions ½ a mile south of Pitlochry, opposite Bells Distillery.

≠ Pitlochry

ST. FILLANS

Loch Earn Caravan Park, South Shore Road, St Fillans, Perth & Kinross, PH6 2NL
Tel: 01764 685270
Email: lochearn@btconnect.com
www.lochearn.com
Pitches For ⬛ ⬛ **Total** 300
Open 31-Mar **to** Oct
Access Good **Site** Lev/slope
Nearest Bus Stop (Miles) 1
Lochside park with fishing and boating.

Facilities ⬛ symbols

Nearest Town St Fillans
Directions From Perth take the A85 and turn off signed South Loch Earn. Before entering St. Fillans turn left over the hump back bridge, Park is 1 mile.

≠ Perth

TUMMEL BRIDGE

Tummel Valley Holiday Park - Parkdean, Tummel Bridge, Nr Pitlochry, Perth & Kinross, PH16 5SA
Tel: 0844 355 3740
Email: enquiries@parkdeanholidays.co.uk
www.parkdeantouring.com
Pitches For ⬛ ⬛ **Total** 26
Acreage 52 **Open** Mar **to** Nov
Access Good **Site** Lev/Slope
Nearest Bus Stop (Miles) Outside
Set on the banks of the River Tummel in the stunning Perthshire countryside.

Facilities ⬛ symbols

Nearest Town Pitlochry
Directions From A9 south turn left onto B8019 for Tummel Bridge, follow road for approx 1½ miles, turn left over Garry Bridge and follow road for 11 miles.

≠ Pitlochry

SCOTTISH BORDERS

ETTRICK

Honey Cottage Caravan Park, Hope House, Ettrick Valley, Selkirk, Borders, TD7 5HU
Tel: 01750 62246
www.honeycottagecaravanpark.co.uk
Pitches For 🛈 ⬛ ⬛ **Total** 0
Open All Year
Access Good **Site** Level
Alongside a river for fishing. Golf courses within easy reach. Ideal for walking, cycling or just relaxing in open countryside. Pub and restaurant 1 mile.

Facilities ⬛ symbols

Nearest Town Hawick/Selkirk

HAWICK

Riverside Caravan Park, Hornshole
Bridge, Hawick, Borders, TD9 8SY
Tel: 01450 373785
Email: info@bordercaravans.co.uk
www.riversidehawick.co.uk
Pitches For ▲ ⛺ ⛺ **Total** 40
Open Mar **to** Oct
Access Good **Site** Level
Nearest Bus Stop (Miles) Outside
On the banks of a river.
Facilities ⛳ ⨍ 🏠 🕀 🍴 🕀⊙🛒 ⚲ 🔲 🍸
🏠 🖩 🍴 🖃 💈 ✎ ⚘
Nearest Town Hawick
Directions 1 mile from Hawick on the A698.
⛺ Carlisle

JEDBURGH

**Jedburgh Camping & Caravanning Club
Site,** Elliot Park, Jedburgh, Borders, TD8
6EF
Tel: 01835 863393
Email: jedburgh.site@thefriendlyclub.co.uk
www.campingandcaravanningclub.co.uk/
jedburgh
Pitches For ▲ ⛺ ⛺ **Total** 50
Acreage 3 **Open** 21-Mar **to** 28-Oct
Access Good **Site** Level
Nearest Bus Stop (Miles) ¼
Quiet, secluded site bounded by the River
Jed. Ideal site for picturesque walks. STB 4
Star Graded and AA 3 Pennants. Non
members welcome. You can also call us on
0845 130 7633.
Facilities ⨍ 🏠 🕀 🍴 🕀⊙🛒 ⚲ 🔲 🍸
🖩 🖃 🛒 🍴 🖃 💈 ⚘
Nearest Town Jedburgh
Directions On the A68 Newcastle to
Edinburgh road, drive to the northern side of
Jedburgh and the entrance is opposite the
Edinburgh & Jedburgh Woollen Mills.
⛺ Berwick-upon-Tweed

JEDBURGH

**Lilliardsedge Holiday Park & Golf
Course,** Jedburgh, Scottish Borders, TD8
6TZ
Tel: 01835 830271
Email: info@bordercaravans.co.uk
www.lilliardsedgepark.co.uk
Pitches For ▲ ⛺ ⛺ **Total** 40
Open Mar **to** 06-Nov
Access Good **Site** Level
Nearest Bus Stop (Miles) Outside
On St Cuthberts Way with a 9 hole golf
course on site. Fishing available locally.
Small tents only
Facilities ⛳ ⨍ 🖃 🏠 🕀 🍴 🕀⊙🛒 ⚲ 🔲 🍸
💈 🏮 🖩 🍴 ✕ 🍷 🔟 ⚲ 🗻 ❀🖃 🖃 🖃 ⚘
⚲
Nearest Town Jedburgh
Directions 5 miles north of Jedburgh on the
A68.
⛺ Berwick

KELSO

Kirkfield Caravan Park, Grafton Road,
Yetholm, Kelso, Scottish Borders, TD5
8RU
Tel: 01573 420346
Email: fiona@frankgibsonatv.co.uk
www.kirkfieldcaravansite.co.uk
Pitches For ▲ ⛺ ⛺ **Total** 20
Open Apr **to** Oct
Access Good **Site** Level
Nearest Bus Stop (Miles) ¼
Situated at the end of Penine Way and on St
Cuthberts Walk. Near a river and the Cheviot
Hills.
Facilities ⨍ 🏠 🕀 🍴 🕀⊙ 🖩 🖃 🍴
Nearest Town Kelso

Directions From Kelso take the B6352 to
Yetholm
⛺ Berwick Upon Tweed

LAUDER

**Lauder Camping & Caravanning Club
Site,** Carfraemill, Oxton, Lauder, Borders,
TD2 6RA
Tel: 01578 750697
Email: lauder.site@thefriendlyclub.co.uk
www.campingandcaravanningclub.co.uk/
lauder
Pitches For ▲ ⛺ ⛺ **Total** 60
Acreage 5 **Open** 18-Apr **to** 28-Oct
Access Good **Site** Level
Nearest Bus Stop (Miles) Outside
Situated 24 miles south of the vibrant city of
Edinburgh. Close to Thirlestane Castle and
a good fishing area. Self catering chalets also
available to let. STB 4 Star Graded and AA 3
Pennants. Non members welcome. You can
also call us on 0845 130 7633.
Facilities ⛳ ⨍ 🏠 🕀 🍴 🕀⊙🛒 🔲 🍸
💈 🖩 🛒 🍴 🖃 🖃 ⚘
Nearest Town Edinburgh
Directions From Lauder, at the roundabout
turn right onto the A697, at the Lodge Hotel
turn left and the site is on the right behind
Carfraemill Hotel.
⛺ Edinburgh

MELROSE

Melrose Gibson Park Caravan Club Site,
High Street, Melrose, Borders, TD6 9RY
Tel: 01896 822969
www.caravanclub.co.uk
Pitches For ▲ ⛺ ⛺ **Total** 60
Acreage 3 **Open** All Year
Access Good **Site** Level
Nearest Bus Stop (Miles) 1
Peaceful site overlooked by the three hills
which gave rise to its Roman name of
Trimontium. Shops, playing fields and tennis
adjacent. Close to Melrose Abbey, Priorwood
Gardens and Abbotsford House. Non
members welcome. Booking essential.
Facilities ⛳ ⨍ 🖃 🏠 🕀 🍴 🛒 🔲 🍸 💈 🛒 ❀⚘
Nearest Town Melrose
Directions Turn left off the A68 at the
roundabout onto the A6091, at roundabout
in approx 3½ miles turn right onto the B6374
signposted Melrose. Site is on the right at
the petrol station and opposite Melrose
Rugby Club.

PEEBLES

Crossburn Caravan Park, Edinburgh Road,
Peebles, Scottish Borders, EH45 8ED
Tel: 01721 720501
Email:
enquiries@crossburncaravans.co.uk
www.crossburn-caravans.co.uk
Pitches For ▲ ⛺ ⛺ **Total** 50
Acreage 6 **Open** Apl/Easter **to** Oct
Access Good **Site** Level
Nearest Bus Stop (Miles) ¼
River nearby. Ideal touring base.
Facilities ⛳ ⨍ 🖃 🏠 🕀 🍴 🕀⊙🛒 ⚲ 🔲 🍸
🏠 🖩 🏮 🍴 🖃 ⚘
Nearest Town Peebles
Directions ½ mile north of Peebles on the
A703.
⛺ Edinburgh

SELKIRK

Victoria Park Caravan & Camping Site,
Victoria Park, Buccleuch Road, Selkirk,
Scottish Borders, TD7 5DN
Tel: 01750 20897
Pitches For ▲ **Total** 100
Open All Year
Access Good **Site** Level

Nearest Bus Stop (Miles) ¼
Next to the River Ettrick. Pleasant location
on the edge of the Historic Royal Burgh of
Selkirk. Ideal touring base for scenic Ettrick
and Yarrow or Walter Scott Country.
Facilities
Nearest Town Selkirk
Directions Convenient to both the A7 and
the A68 north and south routes.
⛺ Edinburgh

STIRLING

ABERFOYLE

Cobleland Caravan & Camping Site,
Station Road, Gartmore, Stirling, FK8 3RR
Tel: 02476 423008
Email:
enquiries@campingintheforest.co.uk
www.campingintheforest.co.uk
Pitches For ▲ ⛺ ⛺ **Total** 126
Open 20-Mar **to** 27-Oct
Access Good **Site** Lev/Slope
In the heart of the Trossachs. Queen
Elizabeth Forest Park offers a wealth of trails
and picnic sites, as well as cycling, fishing
and orienteering. Highland Boundary Fault
Trail.
Facilities ⛳ ⨍ 🏠 🕀 🍴 🕀⊙🛒 🔲 🏮 ❀⚲
Directions From Glasgow take the A81,
ignore 1st sign for Gartmore take next left
for Gartmore Cobleland site.
⛺ Stirling

BALMAHA

Cashel Camp Site, Rowardennan, Stirling,
G63 0AW
Tel: 02476 423008
Email:
enquiries@campingintheforest.co.uk
www.campingintheforest.co.uk
Pitches For ▲ ⛺ ⛺ **Total** 168
Open Mar **to** 27-Oct
Access Good **Site** Level
On the eastern shore of Loch Lomond.
Facilities ⛳ ⨍ 🏠 🕀 🍴 🕀⊙🔲 🍸
💈 🖩 🍴 ❀
Nearest Town Balloch
Directions Take the A811 to Drymen then
take the B837 to Balmaha Rowardennan,
please take care as its a bad road surface
and there is a sharp right hand corner. Cashel
is 3 miles after Balmaha on the left.

CALLANDER

Gart Caravan Park, Stirling Road,
Callander, Stirling, FK17 8LE
Tel: 01877 330002
Email: enquiries@theholidaypark.co.uk
www.theholidaypark.co.uk
Pitches For ⛺ ⛺ **Total** 131
Acreage 26 **Open** Apr **to** 15-Oct
Access Good **Site** Level
The ideal centre for walking, golf, fishing and
exceptional for off-road cycling. Or you can
simply relax and enjoy the scenery.
Facilities ⛳ ⨍ 🏠 🕀 🍴 🕀⊙🛒 ⚲ 🔲 🍸
🏮 🖩 🏮 🍴 🖃 🖃 ✎ ⚘
Nearest Town Callander
Directions Situated on the main A84, 1 mile
east of Callander.
⛺ Stirling

CALLANDER

Keltie Bridge Caravan Park, Callander,
Stirling, FK17 8LQ
Tel: 01877 330606
Email: stay@keltiebridge.co.uk
Pitches For ▲ ⛺ ⛺ ⛺ **Total** 75
Acreage 12 **Open** Apr **to** Oct

Access Good **Site** Level
Nearest Bus Stop (Miles) ¼
Well situated for exploring Loch Lomond and Trossachs National Park. Drive through motorhome service bay. Holiday homes for sale.
Facilities
Nearest Town Callander
Directions Well signposted just off the A84 from Doune towards Callander, 1 mile before Callander.
≠ Dunblane

DRYMEN

Milarrochy Bay Camping & Caravanning Club Site, Milarrochy Bay, Balmaha, Near Drymen, Stirling, G63 0AL
Tel: 01360 870236
Email:
milarrochy.bay.site@thefriendlyclub.co.uk
www.campingandcaravanningclub.co.uk/milarrochybay
Pitches For Å ⚌ ⚌ **Total** 150
Acreage 12 **Open** 21-Mar **to** 28-Oct
Access Good **Site** Level
On the east bank of Loch Lomond, in the heart of Rob Roy country. Near Queen Elizabeth Forest Park. Boat launching available on site. STB 4 Star Graded and AA 4 Pennants. Non members welcome. You can also call us on 0845 130 7633.
Facilities
Nearest Town Loch Lomond
Directions From the A811 Balloch to Stirling road, take the Drymen turnoff. In Drymen turn onto the B837 (junction is by the War Memorial) to Balmaha. After approx. 5 miles the road turns sharp right up a steep hill, the site is approx. 1½ miles.
≠ Balloch

FINTRY

Balgair Castle Holiday Park, Overglinns, Fintry, Stirling, G63 0LP
Tel: 01360 860399
Email: balgaircastle@holiday-parks.co.uk
www.holiday-parks.co.uk
Pitches For Å ⚌ ⚌ **Total** 33
Acreage 28 **Open** Apr **to** Oct
Access Good **Site** Level
On the banks of the River Endrick. Close to Blair Drummond Safari Park and Stirling Castle.
Facilities
Nearest Town Balfron
Directions From Stirling take the A811 west towards Drymen, then take the B822 south to Fintry. After Balgair Castle Holiday Park sign turn right and follow road down into Park reception, on right hand side as you enter.
≠ Stirling

KILLIN

Cruachan Caravan Park, Killin, Stirling, FK21 8TY
Tel: 01567 820302
Email: enquiries@cruachanfarm.co.uk
www.cruachanfarm.co.uk
Pitches For Å ⚌ ⚌ **Total** 55
Acreage 10 **Open** 15-Mar **to** Oct
Access Good **Site** Lev/Slope
Working farm set in countryside. Central location for touring, climbing, golf and fishing. Octolodges now available for rent.
Facilities
Nearest Town Killin
Directions 3 miles east of Killin on the A827.
≠ Crianlarich

KILLIN

High Creagan Caravan Park, Killin, Stirling, FK21 8TX
Tel: 01567 820449/07786880016
Pitches For ⚌ ⚌ **Total** 30
Acreage 7 **Open** Mar **to** Oct
Access Good **Site** Level
Nearest Bus Stop (Miles) Outside
Facilities
Directions 2½ miles east of Killin on the left of the A827.
≠ Crianlarich

KILLIN

Maragowan Caravan Club Site, Aberfeldy Road, Killin, Stirling, FK21 8TN
Tel: 01567 820245
www.caravanclub.co.uk
Pitches For ⚌ ⚌ **Total** 100
Acreage 8½ **Open** Mar **to** Nov
Access Good **Site** Level
Nearest Bus Stop (Miles) ½
On the banks of the River Lochay for salmon and trout fishing. Ideal for walkers and wildlife lovers. Close to Archray Forest, Scottish Wool Centre and two Visitor Centres. Non members welcome. Booking essential.
Facilities
Nearest Town Killin
Directions Just off the A827 just outside Killin Village.
≠ Killin

LOCHEARNHEAD

Balquhidder Braes Holiday Park, Balquhidder Station, Lochearnhead, Stirling, FK19 8NX
Tel: 01567 830293
Email: enquiries@balquhidderbraes.co.uk
www.balquhidderbraes.co.uk
Pitches For Å ⚌ ⚌ **Total** 4
Acreage 2 **Open** Mar **to** Oct
Access Good **Site** Level
Nearest Bus Stop (Miles) Outside
Nature trail on site.
Facilities
Nearest Town Lochearnhead
Directions From Stirling take the A84 and follow signs for Callander. 1 mile south of Lochearnhead.
≠ Stirling

STIRLING

Witches Craig Caravan & Camping Park, Blairlogie, Stirling, Stirling, FK9 5PX
Tel: 01786 474947
Email: info@witchescraig.co.uk
www.witchescraig.co.uk
Pitches For Å ⚌ ⚌ ⚌ **Total** 60
Acreage 5 **Open** Apr **to** Oct
Access Good **Site** Level
Nearest Bus Stop (Miles) ¼
Award winning park situated below the picturesque Oghil Hills.
Facilities
Nearest Town Stirling
Directions A91 Stirling to St Andrews road.
≠ Stirling

STRATHYRE

Immervoulin Caravan & Camping Park, Strathyre, Stirling, FK18 8NJ
Tel: 01877 384285
Email: immervoulin@freenetname.co.uk
www.immervoulin.com
Pitches For Å ⚌ ⚌ ⚌ **Total** 60
Acreage 8 **Open** Mar **to** Oct
Access Good **Site** Level

Nearest Bus Stop (Miles) ¼
Alongside the River Balvaig and 300 metres from Strathyre Village. Ideal for touring.
Facilities
Nearest Town Callander
Directions On the A84, 9 miles north of Callander.
≠ Stirling

WESTERN ISLES

HARRIS

Minch View Campsite 10 Drinishader, Isle of Harris, Western Isles, HS3 3DX
Tel: 01859 511207
Email: cath.macdonald@hebrides.net
Pitches For Å ⚌ ⚌ **Total** 8
Acreage 3 **Open** Apr **to** Sept
Access Good **Site** Level
Nearest Bus Stop (Miles) Outside
Friendly, family run site, situated between the sea and a fresh water loch. Beautiful beaches, excellent walking. Central for touring the Western Isles.
Facilities
Nearest Town Tarbert
Directions 5 miles south east of Tarbert Ferry Port. Turn off the A859 into Golden Road to Drinishader. Site is well signposted.

NORTH SHAWBOST

Eilean Fraoich Caravan & Camping Park, North Shawbost, Isle of Lewis, Western Isles, HS2 9BQ
Tel: 01851 710504
Email: eileanfraoich@btinternet.com
www.eileanfraoich.co.uk
Pitches For Å ⚌ ⚌ **Total** 25
Open May **to** Oct
Access Good **Site** Level
Nearest Bus Stop (Miles) Outside
Nera to beaches and historical sites. Ideal for hill walking.
Facilities
Nearest Town Stornoway
Directions From Stornoway take the A857 to Barvas, turn left onto the A858 for approx. 6 miles, turn left at Shawbost School.

STORNOWAY

Laxdale Holiday Park, 6 Laxdale Lane, Laxdale, Isle of Lewis, Western Isles, HS2 0DR
Tel: 01851 706966
Email: info@laxdaleholidaypark.com
www.laxdaleholidaypark.com
Pitches For Å ⚌ ⚌ ⚌ **Total** 43
Acreage 2 **Open** All year
Access Good **Site** Lev/Slope
Nearest Bus Stop (Miles) ¼
Peaceful, tree lined site. Centrally located for touring the isles of Lewis and Harris.
Facilities
Nearest Town Stornoway
Directions From Stornoway take the A857 for 1 mile, take the second turning on the left past the hospital.

NORTHERN IRELAND

ANTRIM

Six Mile Water Caravan Park, Lough Road, Antrim, Co. Antrim, BT41 4DG
Tel: 028 9446 4963
Email: sixmilewater@antrim.gov.uk
www.antrim.gov.uk/caravanpark
Pitches For 🏕 🚐 🚗 **Total** 67
Open 28-Feb **to** 02-Nov
Access Good **Site** Level
Nearest Bus Stop (Miles) 1
Tranquil, rural setting on the scenic shores of Lough Neagh and adjacent to Six Mile Water River. Slipway for boating. Within walking distance of Antrim town and Antrim Forum Leisure Complex. Also OPEN Weekends during February and November.
Facilities ⚿ ⏐ 🎠 💷 🌁 ⌂ ⊙ ↵ 🍴 🛒
🍴✕🎪🔥🐾🔌🛜
Nearest Town Antrim
Directions From the A26 Dublin road follow signs for Antrim Forum and Lough Shore Park. Turn off for Lough Road passing Antrim Forum (on the right), Park is at the end of the road.
🚃 Antrim

BELFAST

Dundonald Touring Caravan Park, Dundonald Leisure Park, 111 Old Dundonald Road, Belfast, BT16 0XT
Tel: 02890 809100/1
Email: sales@castlereagh.gov.uk
www.theicebowl.com
Pitches For 🏕 🚐 🚗 🚃 **Total** 22
Acreage 1½ **Open** 14-Mar **to** 02-Nov
Access Good **Site** Level
Nearest Bus Stop (Miles) Outside
Adjacent to The Ice Bowl with its ice rink, 10 pin bowling alley, adventure playground, pool tables, coffee bar and fast food restaurant. Closest park to Belfast city centre.
Facilities ⚿ ⏐ 🎠 💷 🌁 ⌂ ⊙ 🛒
🍴🐾🔌
Nearest Town Belfast
Directions From Belfast follow directions to City Airport on the M3, then take the A20 to Ulster, at the Hospital turn right and follow past traffic lights, turn right (Ice Bowl is left).

BALLYMONEY

Drumaheglis Marina & Caravan Park, 36 Glenstall Road, Ballymoney, Co. Antrim, BT53 7QN
Tel: 028 2766 0280/2766 0227
Email: drumaheglis@ballymoney.gov.uk
www.ballymoney.gov.uk
Pitches For 🏕 🚐 🚗 **Total** 65
Open 17-Mar **to** Oct
Situated on a boat park and 32 berth marina on the Causeway coastal route. Volley Ball, picnic areas, table tennis and nature walk on site.
Facilities
⏐ 💷 🌁 ⌂ ⊙ ↵ 🛒 🍴 🐠 🔥 🐾 🔌 🛜
Directions Off the A26 between Ballymoney and Coleraine. Turn left at Seacon crossroads and follow signs for Drumaheglis Marina.

BUSHMILLS

Ballyness Caravan Park, 40 Castlecatt Road, Bushmills, Co. Antrim, BT57 8TN
Tel: 028 2073 2393
Email: info@ballynesscaravanpark.com
www.ballynesscaravanpark.com
Pitches For 🚐 🚗 **Total** 48
Acreage 16 **Open** Mar **to** Oct
Access Good **Site** Lev/Slope

Multi award winning Park on the spectacular North Coast. Well maintained, quiet Park in a beautiful location. Close to Giants Causeway and Old Bushmills Distillery. AA 5 Pennants, 5 Stars and David Bellamy Gold Award.
Facilities ⚿ ⏐ 🎠 💷 🌁 ⌂ ⊙ ↵ 🛒 🍴
🍴🔥🛠🐠🌳🔌🔥🛜
Nearest Town Bushmills
Directions On the B66, ½ a mile south of Bushmills.
🚃 Coleraine

LARNE

Carnfunnock Country Park, Coast Road, Ballygally, Larne, Co. Antrim, BT40 2QG
Tel: 028 2827 0541/2826 0088
Email: carnfunnock@larne.gov.uk
www.carnfunnock.co.uk
Pitches For 🏕 🚐 🚗 **Total** 39
Open 14-Mar **to** 02-Nov
Set within a country park with a walled garden, a maze, family fun zone (mini golf, bouncy castle, bungee run, laser clay pigeon shooting and miniature railway), outdoor adventure playground, mini cars, trampolines and golfing activities, professional driving range and golf academy, Picnic and barbecue areas, gift and coffee shop. Regular weekend events. For tents open 23 April - 30 Sept.
Facilities ⚿ ⏐ 🎠 💷 🌁 ⌂ ⊙ 🛒
🐠✕🌳🐾🔌
Nearest Town Larne
Directions On the A2 Coast Road, 3½ miles north of Larne between Drains Bay and Ballygally.

LURGAN

Kinnego Marina Caravan Park, Kinnego Marina, Oxford Island, Lurgan, Co. Armagh, BT66 6WJ
Tel: 02838 32 7573
Email: kinnego.marina@craigavon.gov.uk
Pitches For 🏕 🚐 🚗 **Total** 20
Open Apr **to** Oct
Access Good **Site** Level
Nearest Bus Stop (Miles) ½
On the shores of Lough Neagh within the National Nature Reserve.
Facilities ⚿ ⏐ 💷 🌁 ⌂ ⊙ 🛒
🍴🐠🐾🔥🔌🛜
Nearest Town Lurgan
Directions Signposted Oxford Island from the M1 junction 10.
🚃 Lurgan

HILLSBOROUGH

Lakeside View Caravan & Camping Park, 71 Magheraconluce Road, Hillsborough, Co. Down, BT26 6PR
Tel: 028 9268 2098
Email: lakeside-view@hotmail.co.uk
www.lakeside-view.8m.com
Pitches For 🏕 🚐 🚗 **Total** 30
Open Easter **to** Oct
Quiet countryside park with views of lake and mountains. Half hours drive to Belfast. Caravans available for rent.
Facilities ⏐ 🎠 💷 🌁 ⌂ ⊙ 🛒 🐠 🌳 🐾
Directions From the M1 and A1 travel to Hillsborough Village. Take the B177 Ballynahinch road for 3 miles, signposted.

KILKEEL

Cranfield Caravan Park, 123 Cranfield Road, Kilkeel, Co. Down, BT34 4LJ
Tel: 028 4176 2572
Email: jimchestnut@btconnect.com
www.cranfieldcaravanpark.co.uk
Pitches For 🚐 🚗 **Total** 40
Open 17-Mar **to** Sept
Access Good **Site** Level
Nearest Bus Stop (Miles) Outside
Near the beach.
Facilities ⚿ ⏐ 🎠 💷 🌁 ⌂ ⊙ ↵ 🛒
🐠🐟✕🌳🐾🔌🛜
Nearest Town Kilkeel
Directions Signposted off the A2.
🚃 Newry

KILLYLEAGH

Delamont Country Park Camping & Caravanning Club Site, Delamont Country Park, Downpatrick Road, Killyleagh, Co. Down, BT30 9TZ
Tel: 028 4482 1833
Email:
delamont.site@thefriendlyclub.co.uk
www.campingandcaravanningclub.co.uk/delamont
Pitches For 🏕 🚐 🚗 🚃 **Total** 63
Acreage 4 **Open** 15-Mar **to** 11-Nov
Access Good **Site** Level
Nearest Bus Stop (Miles) ¼
On the shores of Strangford Lough within a country park (free entry for campers). Many walks, historical sites and cultural landmarks. David Bellamy Silver Award. Non members welcome. You can also call us on 0845 130 7633.
Facilities ⚿ ⏐ 🎠 💷 🌁 ⌂ ⊙ ↵ 🛒
🐠🔥🐾🔌
Nearest Town Downpatrick
Directions On the A22 1 mile south of Killyleagh and 4 miles north of Downpatrick.

NEWCASTLE

Murlough Cottage Caravan Park, 180-182 Dundrum Road, Newcastle, Co. Down, BT33 0LN
Tel: 028 4372 2906/4372 3184
Email: info@murloughcottage.com
www.murloughcottage.com
Pitches For 🚐 🚗 **Total** 26
Open Apr **to** Oct
Idyllic location in an area of outstanding natural beauty. A warm and friendly welcome awaits you!
Facilities ⏐ 🎠 💷 🌁 ⌂ ⊙ ↵ 🛒
🐠🔥🐟🐾🔥🔌🛜
Directions On the A24 2 miles north of Newcastle. Signposted.

LISNARICK

Castle Archdale Caravan Park, Lisnarick, Irvinestown, Co. Fermanagh, BT94 1PP
Tel: 028 6862 1333
Email: bookings@castlearchdale.com
www.castlearchdale.com
Pitches For 🏕 🚐 🚗 **Total** 158
Open Apr **to** Oct
Situated on the shores of Lough Erne and set amongst thousands of acres of forest park on a former WWII airbase. Close to Donegal and Sligo. Licensed restaurant, take-away, shop and play park. Seasonal opening times.
Facilities ⏐ 🎠 💷 🌁 ⌂ ⊙ ↵ 🛒
🐠🔥🐟✕🍷🌳🐾🔌🐟🔥🛜
Directions Signposted off the B82 Enniskillen to Kesh road, 10 miles north of Enniskillen.

LISNARICK

Drumhoney Caravan Park, Lisnarick, Irvinestown, Co. Fermanagh, BT94 1NB
Tel: 028 6862 1892
Email: info@drumhoneyholidaypark.com
www.drumhoneyholidaypark.com
Pitches For 🏕 ⛺ 🚐 🚗 **Total** 40
Acreage 30 **Open** Apr **to** Oct
Access Good **Site** Sloping
Nearest Bus Stop (Miles) ½
Millenium Forest walk beside Lough Erne ½ mile from site, ideal family base for childrens open farm train on park.
Facilities ⚿ 🗑 🚿 📞 ⊙ 🔁 🛒 🛍
🏪 🅿 ♨ 🎮 🍴 🎱 ⊞ ⛵ 🚲 ⚓ 🎿 🍸 ✆ 📶
Nearest Town Irvinestone
Directions Off the B82, 10 miles north of Enniskillen, signposted.

LONDONDERRY

BENONE

Benone Tourist Complex, 53 Benone Avenue, Limavady, Co. Londonderry, BT49 0LQ
Tel: 028 7775 0555
Email: benone.complex@limavady.gov.uk
www.limavady.gov.uk
Pitches For 🏕 ⛺ 🚐 🚗 **Total** 101
Acreage 11 **Open** Apr **to** Sept
Access Good **Site** Level
Nearest Bus Stop (Miles) ½
Two outside heated splash pools (seasonal), golf practice range, putting green, tennis courts, (admission fee per activity). Cafe (seasonal).Summer events programme.
Facilities ⚿ 🗑 🚿 📞 ⊙ 🔁 🛒 🛍
🏪 🅿 ♨ 🎮 🍴 ⚓ ⊞ ⛵ 🎿
Nearest Town Limavady
Directions On the A2 coast road, 12 miles from Limavady and 10 miles from Coleraine.
🚉 Castlerock

COLERAINE

Ballyleese Town & Country Caravan Park, 34 Agherton Road, Portstewart, Co. Londonderry, BT55 7PJ
Tel: 028 7083 3308
Email: bonalston@btconnect.com
www.bonalstoncaravans.com
Pitches For ⛺ 🚐 **Total** 16
Open Easter **to** Sept
Access Good **Site** Sloping
Nearest Bus Stop (Miles) ½
Quiet, rural setting on the edge of busy Portstewart. Ideal for enjoying all that the Causeway Coast has to offer.
Facilities 🗑 🚿 📞 🔁 ⊙ 🛒 🛍
🏪 🅿 ♨ 🎮 ⊞ 🍴 🎱
Nearest Town Portstewart
Directions Off the B185, turn left into Agherton Road (approx. 3 miles from Coleraine), Park is 700 metres on the right, signposted.
🚉 Coleraine

BOOKING IS ALWAYS
ADVISABLE IN THE
PEAK SEASON

PLEASE REMEMBER TO
MENTION CADE'S
WHEN REPLYING TO
OUR ADVERTISERS

REPUBLIC OF IRELAND

CLARE

COROFIN

Corofin Village, Main Street, Corofin, Co. Clare,
Tel: 0353 (0) 65 6837683
Email: info@corofincamping.com
www.corofincamping.com
Pitches For 🏕 ⛺ 🚐 **Total** 20
Acreage 1¼ **Open** Apr **to** Sept
Family run, sheltered site near to Burren and the Cliffs of Moher. 7 fishing lakes in the area, also good walking and cycling.
Facilities 🗑 🚿 📞 🅿 ⊙ 🛍 🎱 ⚓ 🍴 📶
Directions From Shannon Airport take the N18, N85 and R476.

DOOLIN

Nagles Doolin Camping & Caravan Park, Doolin, Co. Clare,
Tel: 0383 (0) 65 7074458
Email: ken@doolincamping.com
www.doolincamping.com
Pitches For 🏕 ⛺ 🚐 🚗 **Total** 99
Acreage 10 **Open** 11-Mar **to** Mid Oct
Situated on the edge of the Atlantic between the Cliffs of Moher and the Burren. Only 100 metres from Doolin Pier, ferry port for boats to Aran Islands. Shop only open from June BH weekend to the end of August. Lovely coastal walks and pot holing in the area.
Facilities 🗑 📞 🅿 ⊙ 🎱 ⚓ 🍴 📶
Directions From Lisdoonvarna go towards Cliffs of Moher, turn right for Doolin and follow signs to Doolin Pier. Park is situated 100m from Doolin Pier.

DOOLIN

O'Connors Riverside Camping & Caravan Park, Doolin, Co. Clare,
Tel: 0353 (0) 65 707 4498
Email: info@campingdoolin.com
www.campingdoolin.com
Pitches For 🏕 ⛺ 🚐 🚗 **Total** 100
Acreage 6¼ **Open** Apr **to** Sept
In the heart of Doolin in a unique setting overlooking the Aille River. Small and friendly family run Park on a farm. 3 Star Graded Park. Guesthouse on site (3 Stars).
Facilities 🗑 📞 🅿 ⊙ 🎱 ⚓ 🍴 📶
Directions From the N67 turn for Doolin, go straight across the main crossroads (Hotal Doolin on the right), go over the Aille River Bridge and the Park is on the left behind O'Connors Guesthouse.

KILKEE

Green Acres Caravan & Camping Park, Doonaha, Kilkee, Co. Clare,
Tel: 0353 (0) 65 905 7011
www.greenacrescamping.ie
Pitches For 🏕 ⛺ 🚐 🚗 **Total** 40
Acreage 12 **Open** Apr **to** Sept
Delightful setting on the shores of the River Shannon, with lovely beaches and spectacular coastal views. Dolphin watch at Carrigaholt (5 minutes drive).
Facilities 🗑 📞 🅿 ⊙ 🍴 ⚓
Directions From Kilrush take the N67 to Kilkee, then follow signs from the R487.

MOUNTSHANNON

Lakeside Holiday Park, Dooras, Mountshannon, Co. Clare,
Tel: 0353 (0) 61 927225
Email: lakesidecamping@gmail.com
www.lakesideireland.com

Pitches For 🏕 ⛺ 🚐 🚗 **Total** 45
Acreage 17¾ **Open** May **to** 01-Oct
Unique, spacious Park situated on the shores of Lough Derg, Irelands finest lake. Motor boats, rowing boats, kayaks, swimming, fishing, tennis, soccer and table tennis on site. NO dogs during July and August.
Facilities 🗑 📞 🅿 ⊙ 🎮 🎱 ⊞ ⚓ 📶
Directions On the R352, go through Mountshannon Village and take the first turn right (signposted).

CORK

BANTRY

Eagle Point Camping, Ballylickey, Bantry, West Cork, Co. Cork,
Tel: 0353 (0) 27 50630
Email: eaglepointcamping@eircom.net
www.eaglepointcamping.com
Pitches For 🏕 ⛺ 🚐 **Total** 125
Acreage 19¾ **Open** 19-Apr **to** 23-Sep
On a peninsula with a safe and sheltered coastline. Pebbled beaches suitable for watersports, swimming and fishing. Tennis on site. Shop and petrol station at park entrance. No commercial vehicles. Booking essential.
Facilities 🗑 📞 🅿 ⊙ 🎮 🎱 ⚓ 🍴 📶
Directions Take the N71 from Cork towards Bandon to Glengarriff, then take the R586 to Bantry. Opposite Cronins Petrol Station.

BLARNEY

Blarney Caravan & Camping Park, Stone View, Blarney, Co. Cork,
Tel: 0353 (0) 21 451 6519
Email: conquill@camping-ireland.ie
www.blarneycaravanpark.com
Pitches For 🏕 ⛺ 🚐 🚗 **Total** 40
Acreage 3 **Open** 25-Mar **to** 28-Oct
Award winning Park only 5 miles from the city of Cork. Sheltered, secluded and gently sloping family run park with views towards the famous Blarney Castle. 18 hole pitch 'n' putt on site. Plenty of attractions nearby. NO commercial vehicles.
Facilities 🗑 📞 🅿 ⊙ 🛍
🎱 ⊞ ⚓ 🍴 📶
Directions From the N25 take the N8 towards Cork. Turn onto the N20 and then turn right onto the R617.

CARRIGTWOHILL

Jasmine Villa Caravan & Camping Park, Carrigtwohill, Co. Cork,
Tel: 0353 (0) 21 488 3234
Email: conquill@campingireland.ie
www.blarneycaravanpark.com
Pitches For 🏕 ⛺ 🚐 **Total** 17
Acreage 1¼ **Open** All Year
Close to all amenities and beaches.
Facilities 🗑 📞 🅿 🍴 ⚓
Directions On the N25 Cork to Rosslare road, 1 mile from Carrigtwohill and 4 miles from Midleton.

CASTLETOWNBERE

Berehaven Camper & Amenity Park, Filane, Castletownbere, Co. Cork,
Tel: 0353 (0) 27 70700
Email: info@berehavengolf.com
www.berehavengolf.com
Pitches For 🏕 ⛺ 🚐 **Total** 22
Acreage 2½ **Open** All Year
Set amidst mountain scenery on the shores of Bantry Bay, breathtakingly beautiful. Ideal for fishing, hill walking, canoeing and golf. Very short walk to the ferry for Bere Island.
Facilities 🗑 📞 🅿 ⊙ 🍴 ⚓

CLONAKILTY

Desert House Caravan & Camping Park, Coast Road, Clonakilty, Co. Cork,
Tel: 0353 (0) 23 883 3331
Email: deserthouse@eircom.net
Pitches For Å ♠ ♨ ♒ ⌁ **Total** 36
Acreage 4 **Open** May to Sept
Small, family run Park on a dairy farm overlooking Clonakilty Bay. Sandy beaches and model railway village nearby. Take-away food available.
Facilities ⸋ ▥ ⌐ ⌂ ⫽ ⌸ ⚑ ⛽ ⊞ ⌁ ⚒ ⊁
Directions Take the N71 from Cork and follow signs.

FERMOY

Blackwater Valley Caravan & Camping Park, Mallow Road, Fermoy, Co. Cork,
Tel: 0353 (0) 25 32147
Email: blackwatervalleycaravanpark@gmail.com
www.fermoy.ie
Pitches For Å ♠ ♨ **Total** 30
Acreage 2 **Open** 15-Mar to Oct
Adjacent to Fermoy Town Park with its swimming pool and childrens play area. Fishing on site. No commercial vehicles.
Facilities ⸋ ▥ ⌐ ⌂ ⚑ ⌸ ⛽ ⊞ ⚒ ⊁ ✓
Directions From the M8/N8 take the R639 to Fermoy Town. Park is 100 metres from the town on the N72.

GLANDORE

The Meadow Camping Park, Glandore, Co. Cork,
Tel: 0353 (0) 28 33280
Email: meadowcamping@eircom.net
Pitches For Å ♠ ♨ ♒ ⌁ **Total** 19
Acreage 2½ **Open** Easter to 15-Sep
Family run park providing peace and tranquility, yet only 1 mile from the village. Three environmental awards. Near the beach. 10 minute drive to Union Hall for fresh fish, fishing or a whale watching trip.
Facilities ⸋ ▥ ⌐ ⌂ ⚑ ⌸ ⛽ ⊞ ⊁ ✓ ⚍
Directions From the N71 take the R597 to Glandore.

KINSALE

Garrettstown House Holiday Park, Kinsale, Co. Cork,
Tel: 0353 (0) 21 477 8156
Email: reception@garrettstownhouse.com
www.garrettstownhouse.com
Pitches For Å ♠ ♨ **Total** 60
Acreage 20 **Open** May to 06-Sep
Set within the grounds of an 18th Century Estate with top class facilities. Childrens Club and family discos. Crazy golf, snooker and tennis on site. Close to two Blue Flag beaches. Takeaway food available. Seal, dolphin and whale watching locally. 6 miles from Kinsale with its numerous attractions
Facilities ⸋ ▥ ⌐ ⌂ ⚑ ⌸ ⛽ ⊞
⚒ ⛽ ⊁ ⚑ ⚍ ⊁
Directions 6 miles from Kinsale on the R600.

ROSSCARBERY

O'Riordans Caravan Park, Owenahincha, Rosscarbery, Co. Cork,
Tel: 0353 (00 21 454 1825
Pitches For Å ♠ ♨ **Total** 16
Acreage 3¾ **Open** All Year
Family run Park beside a sandy beach. Adjacent to Castlefreke Woods. Modern mobile home available for hire.
Facilities ⸋ ▥ ⌐ ⌂ ⚑ ⛽ ⚒ ⊁
Directions Take the N71 to Clonakilty then to Rosscarbery.

SKIBBEREEN

Barleycove Holiday Park Crookhaven, Skibbereen, Co. Cork,
Tel: 0353 (0) 872277207
Email: barleycoveholidaypark@gmail.com
Pitches For Å ♠ **Total** 140
Acreage 9 **Open** June to Mid Sept
Situated in an area of outstanding natural beauty.
Facilities ⸋ ▥ ⌐ ⌂ ⚑ ⌸ ⛽ ⚒ ⛽ ⛽ ⚑ ⚒
Directions From Cork take N71 at Bandon take R589 towards Bantry just before Bantry follow signs to Crookhaven.

SKIBBEREEN

The Hideaway Camping & Caravan Park, Skibbereen, Co. Cork,
Tel: 0353 (0) 28 22254
Email: skibbereencamping@eircom.net
Pitches For Å ♠ ♨ **Total** 60
Acreage 5 **Open** Easter to 16-Sep
Rural setting, just a 10 minute walk to the market town of Skibbereen.
Facilities ⸋ ▥ ⌐ ⌂ ⚑ ⛽ ⊞ ⚑ ⊁ ⚍ ⚌
Directions ½ a mile from Skibbereen town centre on the R596 towards Castletownsend.

TIMOLEAGUE

Sexton's Caravan & Camping Park, R600 Clonakilty Road, Timoleague, Co. Cork,
Tel: 0353 88 46347/87 220 8088
Email: info.sextons@gmail.com
www.sextonscamping.com
Pitches For Å ♠ ♨ ♒ ⌁ **Total** 30
Acreage 4 **Open** Mid Mar to Mid Oct
Situated in countryside, yet only a 5 minute drive to beaches and family activities. Dog friendly site. Breakfast available. Free Wi-Fi. Groups welcome. Find us on Facebook.
Facilities ⛽ ⸋ ▥ ⌐ ⌂ ⌸ ⌸ ⛽
⚒ ⛽ ⊞ ⌸ ⚑ ⊁ ⚍
Directions From Cork take R600

DONEGAL
CARRIGART

Caseys Caravan Site, Downings, Letterkenny, Carrigart, Co. Donegal,
Tel: 0353 (0) 74 915 5376
Pitches For Å ♠ ♨ ♒ ⌁ **Total** 78
Acreage 20 **Open** Apr to Sept
On the edge of Sheephaven Bay in the fishing village of Downings. Bordered by a safe sandy beach. 200 yards from shops, pubs and a hotel. Two 18 hole links championship golf courses in ¼ mile. Interesting walks and drives.
Facilities ⸋ ▥ ⌐ ⌂ ⚑ ⌸ ⛽
⚒ ⛽ ✕ ⊞ ⚑ ⊁
Directions

DUBLIN
CLONDALKIN

Camac Valley Tourist Caravan & Camping Park, Green Isle Road, Clondalkin, Co. Dublin,
Tel: 0353 (0)1464 0644
Email: reservations@camacvalley.com
www.camacvalley.ie
Pitches For Å ♠ ♨ ♒ ⌁ **Total** 163
Acreage 37 **Open** All Year
Spacious premier park with top class facilities. Adjoining Corkagh Park with 300 acres of fishing lakes and playgrounds, and is ideal for walking.
Facilities ⸋ ▥ ⌐ ⌂ ⚑ ⌸ ⛽
⚒ ⛽ ✕ ⌸ ⌐ ⛽ ⊁ ⚍
Directions Off the N7 beside Corkagh Park near Clondalkin Village.

RUSH

North Beach Caravan & Camping Park, North Beach, Rush, Co. Dublin,
Tel: 0353 (0) 1843 7131
Email: info@northbeach.ie
www.northbeach.ie
Pitches For Å ♠ ♨ ♒ ⌁ **Total** 64
Acreage 4½ **Open** Apr to Sept
Plenty of amenities in the village. Ideal base for visiting Dublin. Twin axle caravans are not permitted on North Beach.
Facilities ⸋ ▥ ⌐ ⌂ ⚑ ⛽ ⚒ ⛽ ⚑
Directions Leave the M1 signposted Rush. Leave the R132 at the Esso, drive along Rush main street and at the third set of traffic lights turn left, after 100 metres turn right.

GALWAY
LEENANE CONNEMARA

Connemara Caravan & Camping Park, Lettergesh Renvyle, Leenane, Connemara, Co. Galway,
Tel: 0353 (0) 95 43406
Pitches For Å ♠ ♨ ♒ ⌁ **Total** 36
Acreage 5 **Open** May to Sept
Dolphins seen from the site. Sandy beaches. National Park & Adventure Centre and a diving centre close by.
Facilities ⸋ ▥ ⌐ ⌂ ⚑ ⛽ ⚒ ⛽ ⚑ ⊁
Directions 5 miles south of Leenane, turn right off the main Westport to Clifden road.

SALTHILL

Salthill Caravan Park, Salthill, Co. Galway,
Tel: 0353 (0) 91 523972
Email: info@salthillcaravanpark.com
www.salthillcaravanpark.com
Pitches For Å ♠ ♨ ♒ ⌁ **Total** 60
Acreage 13 **Open** 22-Mar to 28-Sep
Family run Park on the shores of Galway Bay with stunning views of of the Burren and Clare Hills. 1½ miles from Galway City. NO Commercial vehicles.
Facilities ⸋ ▥ ⌐ ⌂ ⚑ ⌸ ⛽ ⚒ ⛽ ⚑ ⊁ ⚍
Directions Approaching Galway on the N17, to avoid the city centre stay on the N6 which will take you to Dunnes Stores and onto Bodkin roundabout, turn right and continue straight on the N6 to Deane roundabout, just past at the traffic lights turn right onto the R337. Turn left after Joyces Supermarket and the Park is 200 metres on the right, signposted.

KERRY
ARDFERT

Sir Rogers Caravan Park, Banna, Ardfert, Tralee, Co. Kerry,
Tel: 0353 (0) 66 713 4730
Email: info@sirrogers.com.
www.sirrogerscaravanpark.com
Pitches For Å ♠ ♨ ♒ ⌁ **Total** 56
Acreage 3½ **Open** Feb to Dec
Modern family run park with state of the art childrens playground. Pleasant, safe and secure for families. 200 metres from the beach.
Facilities ⸋ ▥ ⌐ ⌂ ⚑ ⛽
⛽ ⊁ ⚑ ⌐ ⊁
Directions Approx 6 miles north west of Tralee on the R551.

CAHERDANIEL

Wave Crest Caravan & Camping Park, Caherdaniel, Co. Kerry,
Tel: 0353 (0) 66 947 5188
Email: wavecrest@eircom.net
www.wavecrestcamping.com
Pitches For Å ♠ ♨ ♒ ⌁ **Total** 100

Acreage 5½ **Open** All year
Elevated, landscaped Park with views of beaches, coves and the majestic mountains of the Beara Peninsula. Dolphins and basking sharks are familiar sights. A haven for outdoor enthusiasts. Takeaway food available. NO commercial vehicles.
Facilities

CAHIRCIVEEN
Mannix Point Camping & Caravan Park, Cahirciveen, Ring of Kerry Coast, Co. Kerry,
Tel: 0353 (0) 66 947 2806
Email: mortimer@campinginkerry.com
www.campinginkerry.com
Pitches For Å ⊕ ⊟ ⊟⁵ **Total** 42
Acreage 6¼ **Open** 15-Mar **to** 15-Oct
On the waterfront in the spectacular Gulf Stream coast of South West Kerry with wonderful views in every direction. 15 minute walk to the town and amenities. Ideal for hill, mountain and foreshore walks. Pre-booking is essential for the music festival and there is a minimum of a 3 night stay for that weekend (first weekend in August).
Facilities
Directions 300 metres from the N70, just west of Cahirciveen.

CASTLEGREGORY
Anchor Caravan Park, Castlegregory, Tralee, Co. Kerry,
Tel: 0353 (0) 66 713 9157
Email: anchorcaravanpark@eircom.net
www.anchorcaravanpark.com
Pitches For ⊕ ⊟ **Total** 30
Acreage 5 **Open** Easter **to** Sept
Sheltered Park with direct access to sandy beach for safe bathing. Ideal for the Dingle Peninsula, Tralee and the Ring of Kerry.
Facilities
Directions 12 miles from Tralee on the coast road to Dingle, signposted.

DINGLE
Campail Teach an Aragail, Gallarus, Baile na Gall, Dingle, Co. Kerry,
Tel: 0353 (0) 66 915 5143
Email: info@dingleactivities.com
www.dingleactivities.com
Pitches For Å ⊕ ⊟ **Total** 42
Acreage 3 **Open** Apr **to** 20-Sep
On the tranquil, pure and beautiful Dingle Peninsula, a Gaelic speaking area. Ideal for walking with the Way of the Saints to Mount Brandon, or the Dingle Way to visit the Blasket Islands. Pub and restaurant in the nearby village.
Facilities
Directions From Dingle (An Daingean) take the R559 to Baile an Fheirtearaigh and follow signs.

GLENBEIGH
Glenross Caravan & Camping Park, Glenbeigh Village, Ring of Kerry, Co. Kerry,
Tel: 0353 66 976 8451 (April -
Email: glenross@eircom.net
www.campingkerry.com
Pitches For Å ⊕ ⊟ ⊟⁵ **Total** 40
Acreage 4½ **Open** 29-Mar **to** 27-Sep
On the spectacular Ring of Kerry with fine views of Rossbeigh Strand. 5 minutes from the beach. Telephone number for Oct to April: 00 353 87 137 6865.

Facilities
Directions From Killarney take the N70, park is on the right just before the village.

KILLARNEY
Beech Grove Caravan & Camping Park, Fossa, Killarney, Co. Kerry,
Tel: 0353 (0) 64 663 1727
Email:
info@killarneybedandbreakfast.com
www.beechgrovecaravanandcamping.com
Pitches For Å ⊕ ⊟ **Total** 46
Acreage 3½ **Open** May **to** Sept
Family run site with a woodland background and panoramic views overllooking Killarneys lower lake.
Facilities
Directions On the N72, 3 miles west of Killarney, right after the Golden Nugget Pub.

KILLARNEY
Donoghues White Villa Farm Caravan & Camping Park, Lissivigeen, Killarney-Cork Road (N22, Killarney, Co. Kerry,
Tel: 0353 (0) 64 662 0671
Email: killarneycamping@eircom.net
www.killarneycaravanpark.com
Pitches For Å ⊕ ⊟ ⊟⁵ **Total** 24
Acreage 11 **Open** 06-May **to** Sept
Award winning, well landscaped, sheltered Park in the countryside, yet only minutes from Killarney town. The River Flesk runs through the farm for fishing. Coach trips from the Park. Self catering holiday apartments available for hire.
Facilities
Directions 2 miles east of Killarney on the N22, 300 metres from the N22/N72 roundabout.

KILLARNEY
Fleming's White Bridge Caravan & Camping Park, White Bridge, Ballycasheen Road, Killarney, Co. Kerry,
Tel: 0353 (0) 64 663 1590
Email: info@killarneycamping.com
www.killarneycamping.com
Pitches For Å ⊕ ⊟ ⊟⁵ **Total** 92
Acreage 24½ **Open** Mid Mar **to** 06-Oct
Multi award winning riverside Park, in a prime location away from all the busy road, yet only a short walk to the town. Coach trips from the site. Pool, gym and fitness centre nearby. Fishing and cycle hire on site.
Facilities
Directions 300 metres off the N22 south east of Killarney.

KILLARNEY
Fossa Caravan & Camping Park, Fossa, Killarney, Co. Kerry,
Tel: 0353 (0) 64 663 1497
Email: fossaholidays@eircom.net
www.fossacampingkillarney.com
Pitches For Å ⊕ ⊟ **Total** 120
Acreage 8 **Open** 28-Mar **to** Sept
Nearest Bus Stop (Miles) Outside
Beautiful wooded area overlooking the famous MacGillycuddy Reeks and only a 5 minute walk to Lough Leane. Ideal for touring the Kingdom of Kerry, and only 7 miles from Carrantuohill which is Irelands highest mountain. Tennis and takeaway food on site. Mobile homes available for hire.
Facilities
Directions On the N72 3 miles west of Killarney.

KILLARNEY
Killarney Flesk Caravan & Camping Park, Flesk, Muckross Road, Killarney, Co. Kerry,
Tel: 0353 (0) 64 31704
Email: killarneyfleskcamping.com
www.killarneyfleskcamping.com
Pitches For Å ⊕ ⊟ ⊟⁵ **Total** 72
Acreage 5 **Open** 15-Mar **to** Sept
Situated at the gateway to the National Park and lakes. At the start of the Kerry Walk for enjoying the magnificent woodlands and mountains, and our native deer! Entertainment in high season. Cycle hire and takeaway food available.
Facilities
Directions From Killarney take the N71, adjacent to Irelands National Events Centre.

LAURAGH
Creveen Lodge Caravan Park, Healy Pass Road, Lauragh Village, Co. Kerry,
Tel: 0353 (0) 64 668 3131
Email: info@creveenlodge.com
www.creveenlodge.com
Pitches For Å ⊕ ⊟ **Total** 20
Acreage 4 **Open** Easter **to** Oct
Small, well sheltered Park in the beautiful Ring of Beara with excellent amenities. The perfect place for a quiet holiday. Cottages and caravans available to hire.
Facilities
Directions From the R571 in Lauragh, take the R574 Healy Pass Road and look for signs.

TRALEE
Woodlands Park, Dan Spring Road, Tralee, Co. Kerry,
Tel: 0353 (0) 66 712 1235
Email: woodlandstralee@gmail.com
www.kingdomcamping.com
Pitches For Å ⊕ ⊟ ⊟⁵ **Total** 85
Acreage 15 **Open** Feb **to** Nov
Multi award winning Park situated in a quiet parkland setting at the gateway to Dingle Peninsula. Just a short walk through a rose garden to Tralee town centre. Close to a greyhound stadium, Aqua Dome, Aqua Golf, a museum, the National Folk Theatre and a cinema.
Facilities
Directions From the N21, N22 or N70, follow signs for Dingle N86.

KILKENNY
BENNETTSBRIDGE
Nore Valley Park, Annamult, Bennettsbridge, Kilkenny, Co. Kilkenny,
Tel: 0353 (0) 56 772 7229
Email: norevalleypark@eircom.net
www.norevalleypark.com
Pitches For Å ⊕ ⊟ ⊟⁵ **Total** 60
Acreage 5 **Open** Mar **to** Oct
Quiet, family run Park in a peaceful, rural setting on a farm where children can feed the animals. Lovely walks in the area. High standard of cleanliness. Delicious home baked food available. Fly fishing (extra charge), crazy golf, pedal go-karts, 3D maze, trailer rides and pool table on site.
Facilities
Directions From Kilkenny take the R700 to Bennettsbridge. Just before the bridge turn right at the sign, then after approx 3km turn left at the sign.

KILKENNY

Tree Grove Caravan & Camping Park,
Danville House, New Ross Road, Kilkenny,
Co. Kilkenny,
Tel: 0353 (0) 56 777 0302
Email: treecc@iol.ie
www.treegrovecamping.com
Pitches For 🏕 🚐 🚃 🚃 ⌇ **Total** 30
Acreage 4¼ **Open** Mar to Mid Nov
Perfectly situated for Medieval Kilkenny and
South East. 25 minute easy walk along a river
pathway to Kilkenny. Cycle hire on site. Also
open weekends from Nov to March by prior
arrangement only.
Facilities ⨍ 💷 ↑ 🏠 ▱ ◯ 🍽
🔥 🛠 ♣ 🅰 ⤳ 🛜
Directions Approx 1 mile from Kilkenny, after
the roundabout on the R700 in the direction
of New Ross.

LEITRIM
CARRICKONSHANNON

Battlebridge Caravan & Camping Park,
Leitrim Village, CarrickonShannon, Co.
Leitrim,
Tel: 0353 (0) 71 965 0824
Email:
camp@battlebridgecaravanandcamping.ie
www.battlebridgecaravanandcamping.ie
Pitches For 🏕 🚐 🚃 🚃 ⌇ **Total** 40
Acreage 3 **Open** 13 Jan 7FebDec
On the banks of the River Shannon with a
traditional Irish pub on site serving food. Cast
a fishing line from your pitch or enjoy our
private marina with slipway for boating. Miles
of forest and canal walks in the area, good
bird watching. Takeaway food available.
Facilities ⨍ 💷 ↑ 🏠 ▱ ◯ 🍽
🔥 ⛽ ♥ 🛒 🅰 ⤳ ✔ 🛜
Directions From CarrickonShannon take the
R280 to Leitrim, turn left onto the R284 to
Keadue, Park is ½ a mile.

MOHILL

Lough Rynn Caravan & Camping Park,
Lough Rynn, Mohill, Co. Leitrim,
Tel: 0353 (0) 86 825 4428
Email: infrastructure@leitrimcoco.ie
www.leitrimcoco.ie
Pitches For 🏕 🚐 🚃 🚃 ⌇ **Total** 20
Acreage 19 **Open** 29-Mar to Sept
On the shores of Lough Rynn and adjacent
to Lough Rynn House & Gardens. Host of
friendly pubs and restaurants and a childrens
play area close by.
Facilities ⨍ 💷 ↑ 🏠 ⌐ ▱ 🍽 ⤳
Directions 1¼ miles south of Mohill on the
road to Drumlish.

LIMERICK
ADARE

Adare Camping & Caravan Park, Adare,
Co. Limerick,
Tel: 0353 (0) 61 395376
Email: dohertycampingadare@eircom.net
www.adarecamping.com
Pitches For 🏕 🚐 🚃 🚃 ⌇ **Total** 28
Acreage 5 **Open** Apr to Oct
Family run Park with a high standard
throughout. Newly developed farm walk.
Outdoor hot tub on site.
Facilities ⨍ 💷 ↑ 🏠 ▱ ◯ 🍽 ◯ 🅰 ⤳ 🛜
Directions From Limerick take the N21 for
Tralee and continue through Adare, turn left
onto the R519 to Balingarry and follow signs.

LOUTH
DUNDALK

Gyles Quay Caravan Park, Riverstown,
Dundalk, Co. Louth,
Tel: 0353 (0) 42 937 6262
Pitches For 🏕 🚐 🚃 **Total** 139
Open 28-Mar **to** 01-Sep
Licensed pub on site with live entertainment.
Facilities ⨍ 💷 ↑ 🏠 ▱ ◯ 🍽
🔥 ⛽ ♣ 🅰 ⤳
Directions From the M1 take the R173 for
Dundalk. Follow signs for Carlingford for
approx 7 miles then turn right for Gyles Quay.
The Park is towards the end of the road on
the right.

MAYO
ACHILL ISLAND

**Keel Sandybanks Caravan & Camping
Park,** Achill Island, Keel, Co. Mayo,
Tel: 0353 (0) 98 43211
Email: info@achillcamping.com
www.achillcamping.com
Pitches For 🏕 🚐 🚃 🚃 ⌇ **Total** 100
Acreage 15 **Open** 28-Mar **to** 10-Sep
Set spectacularly between Slievemore
Mountain, the Minaun Cliffs and Keel beach
on Achill Island. Plenty of activities locally.
Tennis on site.
Facilities ⨍ 💷 ↑ 🏠 ▱ ◯ 🍽
🔥 ♣ 🅰 ⤳ 🛒 🛜

BALLINA

Belleek Park Caravan & Camping,
Belleek, Ballina, Co. Mayo,
Tel: 0353 (0) 96 71533
Email: lenahan@belleekpark.com
www.belleekpark.com
Pitches For 🏕 🚐 🚃 🚃 ⌇ **Total** 58
Acreage 9¾ **Open** Mar to 01-Nov
Award winning park in a tranquil and
sheltered location with excellent facilities and
high standards. Close to the town and the
River Moy (one of Europes most prolific
salmon rivers). Ten minute walk to a forest
park and riverside walks.
Facilities ⨍ 💷 ↑ 🏠 ▱ ◯ 🍽
🔥 ⛽ 🛠 ◯ 🅇 🔥 🅰 ⌖ 🛒 🛜
Directions Take the R314 from Ballina
towards Ballycastle, Park is just outside the
town boundary, look for signs to Belleek on
your right, turn right and the Park entrance
is 300 metres on the right.

CASTLEBAR

Carra Caravan & Camping Park,
Belcarra, Castlebar, Co. Mayo,
Tel: 0353 (0) 94 903 2054
Email: post@mayoholidays.com
www.horsedrawncaravan.com
Pitches For 🏕 🚐 🚃 **Total** 20
Acreage 1¾ **Open** 19-Jan to 23-Nov
Village centre site. Horsedrawn holidays and
country walks are a speciality from this site.
Close to all amenities and attractions.
Facilities ⨍ 💷 ↑ 🏠 ▱ ◯ 🍽 🔥 ◯ 🛒 ⤳
Directions Take the N84 from Castlebar
towards Ballinrobe, immediately turn left for
Ballycarra (Belcarra).

CASTLEBAR

Carrowkeel Camping & Caravan Park,
Ballyvary, Castlebar, Co. Mayo,
Tel: 0353 (0) 94 903 1264
Email: mail@carrowkeelpark.ie
www.carrowkeelpark.ie
Pitches For 🏕 🚐 🚃 **Total** 58
Acreage 5 **Open** 26-Mar **to** 01-Oct
Well maintained Park in the heart of Mayo.
Clubhouse with live entertainment in high

season. Small shop with basic food supplies.
Takeaway food available. Just a few miles
from the famous River Moy for salmon
fishing.
Facilities ⨍ 💷 ↑ 🏠 ▱ ◯ 🍽
🔥 ⛽ ◯ 🛠 🅇 🔥 🅰 ⤳ 🛜
Directions 5 miles from Castlebar, just off
the N5.

CASTLEBAR

Lough Lannagh Caravan Park, Castlebar,
Co. Mayo,
Tel: 0353 (0) 94 902 7111
Email: info@loughlannagh.ie
www.loughlannagh.ie
Pitches For 🏕 🚐 🚃 **Total** 20
Acreage 2½ **Open** 22-Mar **to** 01-Sep
Lakeside setting just a 10 minute walk from
Castlebar. Kids activities July and August.
Breakfast caf, B&B, tennis and table tennis
on site. Also for the over 18's, gym, sauna
and steam rooms.
Facilities ⨍ 💷 ↑ 🏠 ▱ ◯ 🍽 🅇 🔥 🛒 🛜
Directions On the N5 at the edge of
Castlebar going towards Westport, straight
over two roundabouts, at the third take the
second exit then turn immediately left.

CONG

Cong Caravan & Camping Park,
Lisloughrey, Quay Road, Cong, Co. Mayo,
Tel: 0353 (0) 94 954 6089
Email: info@quietman-cong.com
www.quietman-cong.com
Pitches For 🏕 🚐 🚃 🚃 ⌇ **Total** 40
Acreage 3 **Open** All Year
Situated between Lough Mask and Lough
Corrib, 1 mile from the fascinating Cong
Village. Fisherman and boatsmans paradise!
Lakeside and forest walks. Bike and boat
rental on site.
Facilities ⨍ 💷 ↑ 🏠 ▱ ◯ 🍽
🔥 🍴 ◯ 🛠 🅰 ⤳ 🛒 🛜
Directions From Cong head out on the
Galway road, go past Ashford Castle
entrance and take the next turn right, the
Park is on your right after the cemetary.

KNOCK

Knock Caravan & Camping Park, Main
Street, Knock, Co. Mayo,
Tel: 0353 (0) 94 938 8100
Email: caravanpark@knockshrine.ie
www.knockshrine.ie
Pitches For 🏕 🚐 🚃 **Total** 39
Acreage 7¼ **Open** Mar to Oct
Sheltered, landscaped park. 5 minute walk
from Our Lady's Shrine and Knock Museum.
Ideal base for touring Mayo and the West of
Ireland. Mobile homes for hire.
Facilities ⨍ 💷 ↑ 🏠 ▱ ◯ 🍽
🔥 ◯ ♣ 🅰 ⤳ 🛒
Directions At Knock roundabout take Main
Street for 1 mile, Park is on the left.

WESTPORT

**Westport House Parkland Caravan &
Camping Park,** Westport House &
Adventure Pk, Westport, Co. Mayo,
Tel: 0353 (0) 98 27766/98 2778
Email: camping@westporthouse.ie
www.westporthouse.ie
Pitches For 🚐 🚃 🚃 ⌇ **Total** 95
Acreage 10 **Open** Various dates
Situated in the grounds of Westport House
& Gardens with tennis, pitch n putt, fishing,
swan pedaloes, mini railway, log flume ride,
bouncy castle, Pirate Queen Ships Galleon,
and indoor Jungle World (soft play). Easy
drive to beaches.

Facilities ⓕ ⓦ ⌖ ⌂ ◲ 🍴
🍴 🍷 ⓣ ♨ ♨ ⓔ ✚ ⓦ
Directions On the R335 2 miles from Westport, turn right at Westport Quay.

ROSCOMMON

BOYLE

Lough Key Forest & Activity Park,
Caravan & Camping Dept., Boyle, Co. Roscommon,
Tel: 000 353 71 966 2212
www.loughkey.ie
Pitches For ⓐ ⓓ ⓔ **Total** 72
Acreage 13½
Situated in Lough Key Forest Park with a legendary backdrop of water, parkland and forest encompassing a landmark cluster of unique attractions offering gentle pursuits or energetic activities. Boda Borg Technology House and Adventure Play Kingdom.
Facilities ⓕ ⓦ ⌖ ⌂ ◲ 🍴 ✚
Directions On the N4, approx 2½ miles east of Boyle.

GAILEY BAY

Gailey Bay Caravan & Camping Park,
Gailey Bay, Knockcroghery, Co. Roscommon,
Tel: 0353 (0) 90 666 1058
Email: gaileybay@hotmail.com
www.gaileybay.com
Pitches For ⓐ ⓓ ⓔ **Total** 27
Acreage 2¾ **Open** Mid April **to** Oct
Fishing tackle and boat hire on site.
Facilities ⓕ ⓦ ⌖ ⌂ ◲ ⓣ ♨ ♨ ✚
Directions Take the N61 from Roscommon towards Athlone. After Knockcroghery Village turn right the immediately left after the railway crossing, at first crossroads turn right.

BOYLE

Lough Arrow Touring Park, Ballynarry, Riverstown, Boyle, Co. Sligo,
Tel: 0353 (0) 71 966 6018
Email: latp@eircom.net
www.lougharrowcaravanpaek.com
Pitches For ⓐ ⓓ ⓔ ⓔ **Total** 30
Acreage 8½ **Open** Mid Mar **to** Oct
Award winning, landscaped site in a conservation area of stunning natural beauty overlooking Lough Arrow. Boules pitch, golf practice nets and boat hire on site.
Facilities ⓕ ⓗ ⓦ ⌖ ◲ 🍴 ⓢⓩ ⓔ ♨ ✚
Directions Take the N4 north, pass Boyle and turn first right sp Ballyfarnon and follow signs.

SLIGO

ENNISCRONE

Atlantic Caravan Park Atlantic Caravan Park, Enniscrone, Co Sligo,
Tel: 0353 (0) 96 36132
Email: atlanticcaravanpk@eir.net
www.atlanticcaravanpark.com
Pitches For ⓐ ⓓ ⓔ **Total** 25
Acreage 40 **Open** 29 Apl **to** 10-Sep
Atlantic Coast Caravan Park is situated overlooking Killala Bay with it's many facilities.
Facilities ⓕ ⓦ ⌖ ◲ 🍴 ⓢⓩ ⓔ ♨ ⓔ
Directions From Dublin take N4 to Collooney then N59 to Culleens then R297 to Enniscrone

ROSSES POINT

Greenlands Caravan & Camping Park, Rosses Point, Co. Sligo,
Tel: 0353 (0) 71 917 7113
Email: rossespointcvp@eircom.net
www.sligocaravanandcamping.ie
Pitches For ⓐ ⓓ ⓔ ⓔ **Total** 100
Acreage 6¼ **Open** 27-Mar **to** 15-Sep
Overlooking the Atlantic Ocean with magnificent views of Coney Island, Oyster Island, Blackrock Lighthouse and Benbulben and Knocknarea Mountains. Two bathing beaches. Adjacent to s golf club.
Facilities & ⓕ ⓦ ⌖ ⌂ ◲ 🍴
ⓐ ⓣ ♨ ♨ ✚ ⓔ
Directions On the R29, 5 miles west of Sligo.

STRANDHILL

Strandhill Caravan & Camping Park, Strandhill, Co. Sligo,
Tel: 0353 (0) 71 916 8111
Email: strandhillcvp@eircom.net
www.sligocaravanandcamping.ie
Pitches For ⓐ ⓓ ⓔ ⓔ **Total** 100
Acreage 15 **Open** 27-Mar **to** 29-Sep
Beside Strandhill beach.
Facilities & ⓕ ⓦ ⌖ ⌂ ◲ 🍴
ⓐ ⓣ ♨ ✚ ⓔ
Directions 5 miles west of Sligo City on the R292, on Airport Road.

TIPPERARY

AHERLOW

Ballinacourty House Caravan & Camping Park, Glen of Aherlow, Co. Tipperary,
Tel: 0353 (0) 62 56559
Email: info@camping.ie
www.camping.ie
Pitches For ⓐ ⓓ ⓔ **Total** 50
Acreage 5 **Open** Apr **to** Oct
Quiet and unique family run Park set in the beautiful Glen of Aherlow in the grounds of an 18th Century estate with the restored stable block as our main building. Wonderful views of the Galtee Mountains and the Sliebh na Much Hills. Tennis on site.
Facilities ⓕ ⓦ ⌖ ⌂ ◲ 🍴 ♨ ✚
ⓢⓩ ⓔ 🍴 ⓣ ♨ ♨ ✚ ⓔ
Directions Take the N24 from Cahir roundabout towards Tipperary, after 4 miles turn left to Glen of Aherlow Scenic Route, turn next right over the railway crossing and follow road through Rossadrehid Village, after approx 8½ miles turn right and follow signs to the Park.

CAHIR

The Apple Camping & Caravan Park, Moorstown, Cahir, Co. Tipperary,
Tel: 0353 (0) 52 744 1459
Email: con@theapplefarm.com
www.theapplefarm.com
Pitches For ⓐ ⓓ ⓔ ⓔ **Total** 32
Acreage 3½ **Open** May **to** Sept
Well maintained, nicely landscaped, unique park on a fruit farm. Succession of fruits to try all summer from strawberries and raspberries to apples and plums. Tennis on site.
Facilities ⓕ ⓦ ⌖ ⌂ ☺ ◲ 🍴
ⓐ ♨ ⓔ ⓔ
Directions On the N24 between Cahir and Clonmel.

CLOGHEEN

Parson's Green, Clogheen, Co. Tipperary,
Tel: 0353 (0) 52 65290
Email: kathleen_noonan@eircom.net
www.clogheen.com

Pitches For ⓐ ⓓ ⓔ **Total** 40
Acreage 27 **Open** All Year
Small family run Park with excellent facilities including coffee shop and takeaway, farm museum, indoor and outdoor playgrounds, pet field, pony and pony n trap rides, boat rides and tennis court. Garden and river walks. Close to many places of interest.
Facilities ⓕ ⓦ ⌖ ⌂ ◲ 🍴
🍴 🍷 ⓣ ♨ ♨ ✚ ✚
Directions From Cahir take the R668.

ROSCREA

Streamstown Caravan & Camping Park, Roscrea, Co. Tipperary,
Tel: 0353 (0) 50 521519
Email: info@tipperarycaravanpark.com
www.tipperarycaravanpark.com
Pitches For ⓐ ⓓ ⓔ ⓔ **Total** 30
Acreage 2½ **Open** Easter **to** Sept
Beautifully landscaped family run Park on a dairy farm in quiet surroundings. Ideal for walking the Slieve Bloom Mountains. Mobile homes for hire.
Facilities ⓕ ⓦ ⌖ ⌂ ◲ 🍴 ⓣ ♨ ♨ ✚ ⓔ
Directions Just off the N7. From Roscrea take the R491 to Shinrone for 1½ miles, signposted.

WATERFORD

DUNGARVAN

Bayview Caravan & Camping Park, Gold Coast Golf Resort, Dungarvan, Co. Waterford,
Tel: 0353 (0) 58 45100/58 4505
Email: info@bayviewcaravancamping.com
www.bayviewcaravancamping.com
Pitches For ⓐ ⓓ ⓔ **Total** 32
Acreage 5 **Open** MidFeb **to** Early Nov
Award winning Park adjacent to The Gold Coast Golf Hotel & Leisure Centre with its 18 hole golf course which overlooks Dungarvan Bay. Bike hire and ten pin bowling. 1 mile from Clonea Beach.
Facilities ⓕ ⓦ ⌖ ⌂ ◲ 🍴
🍴 🍷 ♨ 🎱 ♨ ✚ ⓔ
Directions Turn south off the N25 or the R675 onto the Gold Coast road and follow signs.

DUNGARVAN

Casey's Caravan & Camping Park, Clonea, Dungarvan, Co. Waterford,
Tel: 0353 (0) 58 41919
Pitches For ⓐ ⓓ ⓔ **Total** 284
Acreage 19¾ **Open** Various dates
Award winning Park with direct access to a golden sands beach. Crazy golf on site. Wet World Kids Club during July and August. Hotel with leisure centre adjacent. Whilst here why not visit the famous Waterford Crystal Factory.
Facilities ⓕ ⓦ ⌖ ⌂ ◲ 🍴
ⓐ ⓣ ♨ ✚ ⓔ
Directions From Waterford take the N25 towards Dungarvan, turn left after the Clonea Strand & Gold Coast Amenity sign. Pass Dungarvan Golf Club and turn first left, go straight over crossroads and roundabout onto Clonea.

TRAMORE

Newtown Cove Caravan & Camping Park, Newtown Road, Tramore, Co. Waterford,
Tel: 0353 (0) 51 381979/51 381
Email: info@newtowncove.com
www.newtowncove.com
Pitches For ⓐ ⓓ ⓔ **Total** 40

Acreage 5½ **Open** Various dates
Superbly kept, multi award winning, family run Park in a peaceful setting. Short distance from Tramore with its sandy beach, and just a 5 minute walk from the picturesque cove of Newtown. Plenty of attractions nearby. Mobile homes for hire. No commercial vehicles. Booking is advisable.
Facilities ✦ 🆖 🖉 ſ 🔌 ⊡ 📶
🏊 🖪 🔟 🔥 🗘 ⊞ 📶

WEXFORD
FETHARDONSEA
Ocean Island, FethardonSea, New Ross, Co. Wexford,
Tel: 0353 (0) 51 397148
Email: oceanisland@eircom.net
www.oceanislandcaravanpark.com
Pitches For Å 🚐 🚙 **Total** 42
Acreage 3 **Open** Easter **to** Sept
1¼ miles to the beach.
Facilities ✦ 🆖 🖉 ſ 🔌 ⊡ 📶 🏊 🖪 🔥 🗘
Directions From Wexford take the R733 to Duncannon Road roundabout and turn left sp Wellington Bridge. Follow signs for FethardonSea.

KILMUCKRIDGE
Morriscastle Strand Caravan & Camping Park, Morriscastle, Kilmuckridge, Co. Wexford,
Tel: 0353 (0) 53 913 0124
Email: info@morriscastlestrand.com
www.morriscastlestrand.com
Pitches For Å 🚐 🚙 🚙 **Total** 120
Acreage 40 **Open** 08-Mar **to** 29-Sep
Beside the soft sand dunes with 12 miles of Blue Flag beach. Close to many attractions.
Facilities ⚬ ✦ 🆖 🖉 ſ 🔌 ⊡ 📶
🏊 🖪 ✕ 🍴 🔥 🗘 🗘 ⊞ 📶
Directions From Wexford take the R741 and follow signs for Kilmuckridge Village. Park is clearly signposted.

ROSSLARE
St Margarets Beach, Lady's Island, Rosslare Harbour, Co. Wexford,
Tel: 0353 (0) 53 913 1169
Email: info@campingstmargarets.ie
www.campingstmargarets.ie
Pitches For Å 🚐 🚙 **Total** 38
Acreage 5 **Open** Mid Mar **to** Oct
Quiet, rural park in an area of natural beauty. 500 metres from a sandy beach. 15 minutes from Rosslare Ferry Port.
Facilities ✦ 🆖 🖉 ſ 🔌 ⊡ 📶 🏊 🖪 🗘 ⊞ 📶
Directions From Rosslare take the N25, approaching Tagoat, turn left just after the roundabout towards Lady's Island and Carne. Continue past Butlers Bar on the left and turn next left. Signposted from the N25.

WEXFORD
Ferrybank Caravan & Camping, Ferrybank, Wexford, Co. Wexford,
Tel: 0353 (0) 53 918 5256
Email: info@wexfordswimmingpool.ie
www.wexfordswimmingpool.ie
Pitches For Å 🚐 🚙 **Total** 97
Acreage 10 **Open** All Year
Overlooking Wexford Harbour. Within 9 miles of Blue Flag beaches, heritage sites and nature reserves. Booking essential for May and September.
Facilities ✦ 🆖 🖉 ſ 🔌 ⊡ 📶
🏊 🔥 🔥 ⟍ 🗘 📶
Directions ½ a mile east of Wexford Town on the R741 (over the bridge).

WEXFORD
The Trading Post, Ballaghkeen, Co. Wexford,
Tel: 0353 (0) 53 912 7368
Email: info@wexfordcamping.com
www.wexfordcamping.com
Pitches For Å 🚐 🚙 🚙 **Total** 21
Acreage 3 **Open** Apr **to** Sept
4 Star family run Park. Beside a traditional thatched pub, a shop and a service station (open 24 hours for fuel). 5km from the beach and only 25km from Rosslarf Ferry Port.
Facilities ⚬ ✦ 🆖 🖉 ſ 🔌 ⊡ 🏊 🖪 🔟 🔥 🗘 ⊞ 📶
Directions From Enniscorthy take the Blackwater/Oulart road for approx 4km then turn right onto the R744. Go through Ballaghkeen and at the R741 intersection turn right, Park is approx 2km beside the Emo petrol station. ENTRANCE FROM THE FORECOURT.

WICKLOW
DONARD
Moat Farm Caravan & Camping Park, Donard, Co. Wicklow,
Tel: 0353 (0) 45 404727
Email: moatfarmdonard@gmail.com
Pitches For Å 🚐 🚙 🚙 **Total** 40
Acreage 2½ **Open** Mid Mar **to** Mid Sept
Small, quiet and secluded family run Park set in a tranquil, rural area in the foothills of Wicklow Mountains. Short stroll to Donard Village. Painters, walkers and photographers paradise. No commercial vehicles.
Facilities ✦ 🆖 🖉 ſ 🔌 ⊡ 📶 ⊛ 🔟 🗘
Directions From the N81 in Doinard, turn at The Old Toll House Pub and follow signs.

RATHDRUM
Hidden Valley Caravan & Camping Park, Rathdrum, Co. Wicklow,
Tel: 0353 (0) 86 727 2872
Email: info@irelandholidaypark.com
www.irelandholidaypark.com
Pitches For Å 🚐 🚙 🚙 **Total** 80
Acreage 18 **Open** Various dates
Serene haven of tranquility and relaxation. Set in a beautiful valley overlooking the cascading waters of the Avonmore River and our very own lake for fishing, swimming, kayaking and rowboats. Abundance of wildlife. NEW fun park on site. 10 minute walk to Rathdrum and its amenities. Numerous walks in the Wicklow Mountains and Clara Vale National Park.
Facilities ✦ 🆖 🖉 ſ 🔌 ⊡ 🔟 🔥 🗘 🗘 ⊞ 🗘 📶
Directions From Dublin take the N11/M50 South to the R752 exit and go into Rathnew. Follow signs to Rathdrum and on passing Glanbia (on the left) take the next right turn.

REDCROSS
River Valley Caravan Park, Redcross, Co. Wicklow,
Tel: 000 353 404 41647
Email: info@rivervalleypark.ie
www.rivervalleypark.ie
Pitches For Å 🚐 🚙 🚙 **Total** 190
Acreage 60 **Open** 15-Mar **to** 04-Nov
Access Good **Site** Level
Nearest Bus Stop (Miles) 2
Beautiful gardens like Powerscourt, Avondale and Mount Usher close by.
Facilities ⚬ ✦ 🆖 🆖 🖉 ſ ☺ 🔌 ⊡ 📶
🔟 ✕ 🔟 🔥 🔥 🗘 🗘 ⊞ ☼ 📶
Nearest Town Wicklow
Directions From N11 (Wicklow) turn right at Lil Doyles Pub to Redcross village, Park on left past Mickey Finns Pub.
🚇 Wicklow

INDEX TO PARKS OPEN ALL YEAR
Look for the County in which you wish to stay, then choose the Town, the park name is shown alongside. Then simply refer to the main section of the guide to find out more about the park you have selected.

ENGLAND

BRISTOL (COUNTY OF)
BRISTOL, Baltic Wharf C C Site

BUCKINGHAMSHIRE
MILTON KEYNES, Old Dairy Farm C & C Site

CAMBRIDGESHIRE
CAMBRIDGE, Appleacre Park
CAMBRIDGE, Cambridge Cherry Hinton C C Site
CAMBRIDGE, Roseberry Tourist Park
ELY, Riverside C & C Park
HUNTINGDON, Burliegh Hill Farm
HUNTINGDON, Stroud Hill Park
HUNTINGDON, The Willows Caravan Park
PETERBOROUGH, Ferry Meadows C C Site
WISBECH, Virginia Lake Caravan Park

CHESHIRE
CHESTER, Chester Fairoaks C C Site
CHESTER, Manor Wood Country Caravan Park
NORTHWICH, Delamere Forest C & C Club Site

CORNWALL
BODMIN, Ruthern Valley Holidays
BUDE, Budemeadows Touring Park
BUDE, Woodview C & C Park,
HAYLE, Lavender Fields Touring Park
LANDS END, Cardinney C & C Park
LOOE, Bay View Farm
LOOE, Camping Caradon Touring Park
LOOE, Polborder House C & C Park
LOOE, Tencreek Holiday Park
NEWQUAY, Carvynick Country Club,
NEWQUAY, Trekenning Tourist Park
PADSTOW, Old MacDonalds Farm
PADSTOW, Padstow Touring Park
PENZANCE, Bone Valley C & C Park
PORTSCATHO, Treloan Coastal Holidays
REDRUTH, Globe Vale Holiday Park
REDRUTH, Lakeside Camping
SALTASH, Dolbeare Park
ST. JUST, Kelynack C & C Park
TORPOINT, Whitsand Bay Holiday Park
TRURO, Carnon Downs C & C Park
TRURO, Killiwerris Touring Park

CUMBRIA
APPLEBY, Hawkrigg Farm
APPLEBY, Silverband Park
ARNSIDE/SILVERDALE, Silverdale C Park
CONISTON, Coniston Park Coppice C C Site
DENT, Ewegales Farm
GRANGEOVERSANDS, Meathop Fell C C Site
KIRKBY LONSDALE, New House Caravan Park
LONGTOWN, High Gaitle Caravan Park
SILLOTH, Stanwix Park Holiday Centre
ULLSWATER, Sykeside Camping Park
ULLSWATER, The Quiet Site
ULVERSTON, Bardsea Leisure

DERBYSHIRE
BAKEWELL, Chatsworth Park C C Site
BAKEWELL, The Grouse & Claret
BUXTON, Beech Croft Farm
CASTLETON, Castleton C C Site
CHESTERFIELD, Millfield C & Touring Park
DOVERIDGE, Cavendish Caravan Site
EDALE, Fieldhead Campsite
HOPE, Hardhurst Farm
MATLOCK, Lickpenny Caravan Park
MATLOCK, Packhorse Farm Bungalow
SWADLINCOTE, Conkers C & C Club Site

DEVON
BUCKFASTLEIGH, Beara Farm Camping Site
BUCKFASTLEIGH, Bowden Farm Campsite
CHAGFORD, Woodland Springs Adult T p
COMBE MARTIN, Stowford Farm Meadows
DAWLISH, Cofton Country Holidays
EXETER, Kennford International Caravan Park
HOLSWORTHY, Noteworthy C & Campsite
KINGSBRIDGE, Parkland
NEWTON ABBOT, Lemonford Caravan Park
OKEHAMPTON, Bundu C & C Park
PLYMOUTH, Riverside Caravan Park
SOUTH MOLTON, Riverside C & C Park
SOUTH MOLTON, Riverside C & C Park.,
TAVISTOCK, Tavistock C & C Club Site
TIVERTON, West Middlewick Farm Caravans & C

DORSET
BOURNEMOUTH, Charris C & C Park
CHARMOUTH, Manor Farm Holiday Centre
CHRISTCHURCH, Longfield Caravan Park

CHRISTCHURCH, Mount Pleasant Touring Park
SHAFTESBURY, Blackmore Vale C & C Park
SIXPENNY HANDLEY, Church Farm C & C Park
WAREHAM, Birchwood Tourist Park
WAREHAM, Manor Farm C & C Park
WAREHAM, Wareham Forest Tourist Park
WEYMOUTH, Bagwell Farm Touring Park

DURHAM
DURHAM, Durham Grange C C Site
DURHAM, Finchale Abbey Caravan Park

GLOUCESTERSHIRE
CHELTENHAM, Briarfields Motel & Touring Park
CIRENCESTER, Mayfield Touring Park
DURSLEY, Hogsdown Farm C & C
GLOUCESTER, The Red Lion Inn C & C Park
MORETON IN MARSH, MoretonInMarsh C C Site
SLIMBRIDGE, Tudor Caravanning & C Park
TEWKESBURY, Sunset View Park

HAMPSHIRE
FAREHAM, Dibles Park
NEW MILTON, Setthorns C & C Site
SOUTHSEA, Southsea Leisure Park

HEREFORDSHIRE
HEREFORD, Cuckoos Corner
PETERCHURCH, Poston Mill Park

HERTFORDSHIRE
HERTFORD, Hertford C & C Club Site

ISLE OF WIGHT
COWES, Waverley Park Holiday Centre
SANDOWN, Village Way C & C Park

KENT
ASHFORD, Broadhembury C & C Park
CANTERBURY, Canterbury C & C Club Site
FOLKESTONE, Black Horse Farm C C Site
MARDEN, Tanner Farm Touring C & C Park
RAMSGATE, Nethercourt Touring Park

LANCASHIRE
BLACKPOOL, Mossview Caravan Park
LANCASTER, Wyreside Lakes Fishery
MORECAMBE, Venture Caravan Park

LEICESTERSHIRE
CASTLE DONINGTON, Donington Park F/house
LEICESTER, Hill Top Caravan Park
MARKET BOSWORTH, Bosworth Water Trust

LINCOLNSHIRE
BOSTON, Orchard Park

BOSTON, Pilgrims Way C & C Park
LINCOLN, Oakhill Leisure
LINCOLN, Shortferry Caravan Park
MARKET DEEPING, The Deepings Caravan Park
MARKET RASEN, Lincolnshire Lanes C & C Site
MARKET RASEN, Walesby Woodland CC P
MARKET RASEN, Wolds View touring Park,
SPILSBY, Meadowlands

LONDON
ABBEY WOOD, Abbey Wood C C Site
CRYSTAL PALACE, Crystal Palace C C Site

MANCHESTER
LITTLEBOROUGH, Hollingworth Lake C P

NORFOLK
BURGH ST. PETER, Waveney River Centre
CLIPPESBY, Clippesby Hall
FAKENHAM, Crossways C & C Park
GREAT HOCKHAM, Thetford Forest C & C Club
Site
GREAT YARMOUTH, Rose Farm T & C Park
KINGS LYNN, Kings Lynn C & C Park
SANDRINGHAM, The Sandringham Estate C C
STANHOE, The Rickels C & C Park
SWAFFHAM, Breckland Meadows Touring Park
THETFORD, Lowe Caravan Park
WYMONDHAM, Rose Cottage Caravan Site,

NORTHAMPTONSHIRE
KETTERING, Kestrel Caravans

NORTHUMBERLAND
ALNWICK, Railway Inn Caravan Park
BERWICKUPONTWEED, Ord House CP

NOTTINGHAMSHIRE
MANSFIELD, Tall Trees Park
NEWARK, Milestone Caravan Park
NEWARK, Robin Hood Retreat
NOTTINGHAM, Manor Farm Caravan Site
NOTTINGHAM, Thorntons Holt Camping Park
OLLERTON, Shannon C & C Park
WORKSOP, Clumber Park C C Site
WORKSOP, Riverside Caravan Park

OXFORDSHIRE
BANBURY, Barnstones C & C Site
BLETCHINGDON, Diamond C & C Park
BLETCHINGDON, Greenhill LP
BURFORD, Wysdom TP
OXFORD, C & C Club Site

RUTLAND
OAKHAM, Rutland C & C

WALES

ANGLESEY
RHOSNEIGR, Tyn Llidiart Camping Site

CONWY
BETWS-Y-COED, Rynys Farm Camping Site
BETWS-Y-COED, Y Giler Arms
COLWYN BAY, Bron-Y-Wendon T C P

GWYNEDD
ARTHOG, Garthyfog Camping Site
BEDDGELERT, Beddgelert C & C Site
DOLGELLAU, Tanyfron C & C Park
DOLGELLAU, Tyddyn Farm
TYWYN, Dol Einion

NEWPORT
NEWPORT, Pentre-Tai Farm
NEWPORT, Tredegar House Country Park

PEMBROKESHIRE
NEWPORT, Tycanol Farm Camp Site

POWYS
BALA, Henstent Park
BRECON, Anchorage Caravan Park
LLANDRINDOD WELLS, Bryncrach Farm
NEW RADNOR, Old Station Caravan Park
WELSHPOOL, Rhyd-Y-Groes T C P
WELSHPOOL, Riverbend Caravan Park

SWANSEA
RHOSSILI, Pitton Cross C & C Park

WREXHAM
WREXHAM, Plassey Leisure Park

SCOTLAND

ABERDEENSHIRE
ABERDEEN, Deeside Holiday Park
CRUDEN BAY, Craighead C & C Park
KINTORE, Hillhead Caravan Park

ANGUS
KIRRIEMUIR, Drumshademuir Caravan Park

AYRSHIRE (NORTH)
LARGS, South Whittlieburn Farm

AYRSHIRE (SOUTH)
TURNBERRY, Balkenna Caravan Park

CLACKMANNAN
ALLOA, The Woods Caravan Park

DUMFRIES & GALLOWAY
CROCKETFORD, Park of Brandedleys
DALBEATTIE, Glenearly Caravan Park
ECCLEFECHAN, Cressfield Caravan Park
GRETNA, Braids Caravan Park
KIPPFORD, Kippford Holiday Park
KIRKPATRICK FLEMING, King Robert the
Bruces Cave Caravan & Camping Site
LANGHOLM, Whitshiels Caravan Park
MOFFAT, Moffat C 7 C Site
STRANRAER, Aird Donald Caravan Park

DUNBARTONSHIRE (WEST)
BALLOCH, Lomond Woods Holiday Park

EDINBURGH (CITY)
EDINBURGH, Drum Mohr Caravan Park
EDINBURGH, Edinburgh Caravan Club Site
EDINBURGH, Mortonhall C & C Park

HIGHLANDS
AVIEMORE, Dalraddy Holiday Park
AVIEMORE, Glenmore Caravan & Camping Park
DUNBEATH, Inver Caravan Park
DUNDONNELL, Badrallach Bothy & Campsite
GLENCOE, Invercoe Caravan & Camping Park
GLENCOE, Red Squirrel Campsite
UIG, Uig Bay Camping & Caravan Site

LOTHIAN (EAST)
ABERLADY, Aberlady Caravan Park
NORTH BERWICK, Station Park Caravan Site,

LOTHIAN (WEST)
BLACKBURN, Mosshall Farm Caravan Park
LINLITHGOW, Beecraigs C & C Site
PERTH & KINROSS
ABERFELDY, Scottish Canoe Assocation
Grandtully Campsite
ALYTH, Five Roads Caravan Park

SCOTTISH BORDERS
ETTRICK, Honey Cottage Caravan Park
MELROSE, Melrose Gibson Park C C Site
SELKIRK, Victoria Park Caravan & Camping Site

WESTERN ISLES
STORNOWAY, Laxdale Holiday Park
ETTRICK, Honey Cottage Caravan Park
MELROSE, Melrose Gibson Park C C Site
SELKIRK, Victoria Park Caravan & Camping Site

SUFFOLK
SHOTLEY, Shotley Caravan Park
WOODBRIDGE, Moat Barn T C P

SUSSEX (EAST)
HORAM, Woodland View Touring Park

WARWICKSHIRE
SPA, Lairhillock Touring Park,

WEST MIDLANDS
MERIDEN, Somers Wood Caravan Park

WILTSHIRE
CHIPPENHAM, Plough Lane Caravan Site

WORCESTERSHIRE
STOURPORT-ON-SEVERN, Lincomb Lock C P

YORKSHIRE (EAST)
BRIDLINGTON, Old Mill Caravan Park

YORKSHIRE (NORTH)
HELMSLEY, Foxholme TT C & C Park
PICKERING, Overbrook Caravan Park
YORK, Moorside Caravan Park
YORK, Willow House Caravan Park

YORKSHIRE (WEST)
LEEDS, Moor Lodge Caravan Park

WALES
CARMARTHENSHIRE
CARMARTHEN, Pant Farm C & C P

CONWY
PENMAENMAWR, Tyddyn Du Touring Park

DENBIGHSHIRE
RUTHIN, Dyffryn Ial Caravan Site

GWYNEDD
ABERSOCH, Trem Y Mor
CAERNARFON, Silver Birches Camping

PEMBROKESHIRE
FISHGUARD, Rosebush C & C P
HERMON, The Lamb Inn Touring Caravan Park
TENBY, Red House Farm

POWYS
CRICKHOWELL, Riverside C & C P
LLANDRINDOD WELLS, Dalmore Caravan Park
WELSHPOOL, Rhyd-Y-Groes Touring C & C Park

SCOTLAND
FIFE
LEVEN, Monturpie Caravan Park,,

HIGHLANDS
INVERGARRY, Faichemard Farm C & C P

INDEX TO PARKS WITH FISHING ON SITE
Look for the County in which you wish to stay, then choose the Town, the park name is shown alongside. Then simply refer to the main section of the guide to find out more about the park you have selected.

ENGLAND
CAMBRIDGESHIRE
EARITH, Westview Marina
HUNTINGDON, Houghton Mill Caravan Club Site
HUNTINGDON, Huntingdon Boathaven & C P
HUNTINGDON, Quiet Waters Caravan Park
HUNTINGDON, Stroud Hill Park
ST. NEOTS, Camping & Caravanning Club Site
WISBECH, Virginia Lake Caravan Park

CHESHIRE
CHESTER, Manor Wood Country Caravan Park
CHESTER, Netherwood Touring Site
MACCLESFIELD, Strawberry Wood C P

CORNWALL
BODMIN, South Penquite Farm
BUDE, Wooda Farm Holiday Park

CRANTOCK, Treago Farm C & C Site
FOWEY, Penmarlam Caravan & Camping Park
HAYLE, Beachside Holiday Park
NEWQUAY, Trencreek Holiday Park
NEWQUAY, Trethiggey Touring Park
NEWQUAY, Trevornick Holiday Park
PADSTOW, Mother Ivey's Bay Holiday Park
PERRANPORTH, Perran Springs Holiday Park
PORTSCATHO, Treloan Coastal Holidays
ST. AUSTELL, Meadow Lakes
ST. AUSTELL, Pensagillas Park
ST. IVES, St Ives Bay Holiday Park
WADEBRIDGE, Trewince Farm Holiday Park

CUMBRIA
BASSENTHWAITE, Herdwick Croft Caravan Park
CARLISLE, Dalston Hall Caravan Park
CONISTON, Coniston Hall Camping Site

CONISTON, Pier Cottage Caravan Park
DENT, Ewegales Farm
EGREMONT, Tarnside Caravan Park
KENDAL, Waters Edge Caravan Park
KESWICK, Burns Farm Caravan Site
PENRITH, Cross Dormont Camp Site
PENRITH, Lowther Holiday Park
PENRITH, Park Foot Caravan & Camping Park
PENRITH, Waterside House Campsite
ULLSWATER, Waterfoot Caravan Park
ULVERSTON, Bardsea Leisure
WINDERMERE, Hill of Oaks Caravan Estate

DERBYSHIRE
ASHBOURNE, Callow Top Holiday Park
ASHBOURNE, Rivendale Caravan & L P
BAMFORD, Swallowholme C & C Park
BUXTON, Shallow Grange

DEVON
ASHBURTON, River Dart Country Park
BUDLEIGH SALTERTON, Ladram Bay H P
COMBE MARTIN, Newberry Valley Park
CROYDE BAY, Ruda Holiday Park
DAWLISH, Cofton Country Holidays
EXETER, Springfield Holiday Park
ILFRACOMBE, Watermouth Cove Holiday Park
MORTEHOE, Twitchen House Holiday Village
MORTEHOE, Warcombe Farm Camping Park
PUTSBOROUGH, Putsborough Sands C P
SOUTH MOLTON, Riverside C & C Park
SOUTH MOLTON, Riverside C & C Park.,
UMBERLEIGH, Umberleigh C & C Club Site
WOOLACOMBE, Golden Coast Holiday Village
WOOLACOMBE, Woolacombe Bay H Village

DORSET
BRIDPORT, Britt Valley Campground
BRIDPORT, Freshwater Beach Holiday Park
CHARMOUTH, Manor Farm Holiday Centre
CHIDEOCK, Golden Cap Holiday Park
CHRISTCHURCH, Meadowbank Holidays
SHAFTESBURY, Blackmore Vale C & C Park
ST. LEONARDS, Back-of-Beyond Touring Park
THREE LEGGED CROSS, Woolsbridge Manor
Farm Caravan Park
WAREHAM, East Creech C & C Site

DURHAM
DURHAM, Finchale Abbey Caravan Park
MIDDLETON-IN-TEESDALE, Mickleton Mill C P

ESSEX
HARWICH, Dovercourt Caravan Park
MERSEA ISLAND, Waldegraves H & L Park

SOUTHEND ON SEA, Riverside Village H P
ST. OSYTH, Hutleys Touring Park

GLOUCESTERSHIRE
CIRENCESTER, Second Chance Caravan Park
GLOUCESTER, The Red Lion Inn C & C Park
TEWKESBURY, Croft Farm Leisure & Water Park
TEWKESBURY, Mill Avon Holiday Park
TEWKESBURY, Winchcombe C & c Club Site

HAMPSHIRE
BRANSGORE, Harrow Wood Farm Caravan Park
FORDINGBRIDGE, Hill Cottage Farm C & C Park
RINGWOOD, Oakdene Forest Park

HEREFORDSHIRE
BROMYARD, Boyce Caravan Park
LEOMINSTER, Arrow Bank Holiday Park
LEOMINSTER, Nicholson Farm
LEOMINSTER, Pearl Lake Leisure Park
PETERCHURCH, Poston Mill Park
ROSS-ON-WYE, Broadmeadow Caravan Park

HERTFORDSHIRE
HODDESDON, Lee Valley Caravan Park,

ISLE OF WIGHT
SANDOWN, Adgestone C & C Club Site
SANDOWN, Village Way C & C Park
SHANKLIN, Ninham Country Holidays

KENT
MARDEN, Tanner Farm T C P

LANCASHIRE
BENTHAM, Riverside Caravan Park
GARSTANG, Claylands Caravan Park
GARSTANG, Fell View Park,
GARSTANG, Six Arches Caravan Park
KIRKHAM, Whitmore Fisheries & Caravan Park
LANCASTER, Wyreside Lakes Fishery

LEICESTERSHIRE
MARKET BOSWORTH, Bosworth Water Trust

LINCOLNSHIRE
BOSTON, Orchard Park
BOSTON, Walnut Lake Lodges & Camping
HORNCASTLE, Ashby Park
HUTTOFT, Jolly Common Adult Only C P
INGOLDMELLS, Hardy's Touring Site
LINCOLN, Oakhill Leisure
LINCOLN, Shortferry Caravan Park
MARKET DEEPING, The Deepings Caravan Park
SKEGNESS, Pine Trees Leisure Park
SKEGNESS, Skegness Water Leisure Park

SPALDING, Ashleigh C P
TATTERSHALL, Willow Holt C & C Park

NORFOLK
BURGH ST. PETER, Waveney River Centre
DISS, The Willows C & C Park
DOWNHAM MARKET, Grange Farm TT P
FAKENHAM, The Old Brick Kilns
GREAT HOCKHAM, Thetford Forest CC & C
HARLESTON, Little Lakeland CP
HEMSBY, Long Beach C P
HOLT, Kelling Heath H P
HORSEY, Waxham Sands H P
MUNDESLEY, Sandy Gulls Cliff Top Touring Park
NORWICH, Norwich C C C Site
REEDHAM, Reedham Ferry
SHERINGHAM, Beeston Regis C P
WYMONDHAM, Rose Cottage Caravan Site,

NORTHUMBERLAND
HALTWHISTLE, Haltwhistle C & C Club Site
HALTWHISTLE, Seldom Seen

NOTTINGHAMSHIRE
MANSFIELD, Tall Trees Park
NEWARK, Milestone C P
TUXFORD, Marnham Meadows

OXFORDSHIRE
BLETCHINGDON, Greenhill L P
WALLINGFORD, Bridge Villa C & C Park
WITNEY, Hardwick Parks

SHROPSHIRE
BISHOPS CASTLE, The Green Caravan Park
BRIDGNORTH, The Riverside CP
BRIDGNORTH, Woodend Farm
ELLESMERE, Fernwood C P
LUDLOW, Westbrook Park
SHREWSBURY, Beaconsfield Farm Holiday Park
SHREWSBURY, Severn House
TELFORD, Pool View C P
WHITCHURCH, Roden View Caravan & Camping

SOMERSET
BREAN SANDS, Holiday Resort Unity
BREAN SANDS, Warren Farm Holiday Centre
BRUTON, Batcombe Vale C & C Park
BURNHAM-ON-SEA, Diamond Farm C & T P
DULVERTON, Exebridge Lakeside C C Site
EXFORD, Westermill Farm
GLASTONBURY, The Old Oaks Touring Park
LANGPORT, Thorney Lakes Caravan Site
TAUNTON, Waterrow Touring Park
WELLINGTON, Gamlins Farm Caravan Park
WILLITON, Home Farm Holiday Centre

STAFFORDSHIRE
CHEADLE, Hales Hall Caravan & Camping Park
LEEK, Glencote Caravan Park

SUFFOLK
BUNGAY, Outney Meadow Caravan Park
EYE, Honeypot Caravan & Camping Park
LOWESTOFT, Heathland Beach Holiday Park
NAYLAND, Rushbanks Farm
SAXMUNDHAM, Mill Hill Farm C & C Park.,
SAXMUNDHAM, Whitearch Touring Park
SUFFOLK SUDBURY, Willowmere Caravan Park

SURREY
CHERTSEY, Chertsey C & C Club Site

SUSSEX (EAST)
BATTLE, Brakes Coppice Park
EASTBOURNE, Fairfields Farm C & C Park
ROBERTSBRIDGE, Park Farm Camp Site
UCKFIELD, Heaven Farm
UCKFIELD, Honeys Green Caravan Park

SUSSEX (WEST)
HORSHAM, Sumners Ponds Fishery & Campsite

WARWICKSHIRE
STRATFORD-UPON-AVON, Island Meadow C P
WOLVEY, Wolvey Caravan & Camping Park

WILTSHIRE
CALNE, Blackland Lakes
SALISBURY, Green Hill Farm C & C Park
TROWBRIDGE, Stowford Manor Farm
WESTBURY, Brokerswood Country Park

WORCESTERSHIRE
BEWDLEY, Bank Farm Holiday Parks Ltd.
MALVERN, Kingsgreen Caravan Park
STOURPORT-ON-SEVERN, Lickhill Manor C P
STOURPORT-ON-SEVERN, Lincomb Lock C P
WORCESTER, Ketch Caravan Park

YORKSHIRE (EAST)
BRIDLINGTON, Thornwick & Sea Farm
BRIDLINGTON, Thorpe Hall C & C Site
STAMFORD BRIDGE, Weir Caravan Park
WITHERNSEA, Willows Holiday Park

YORKSHIRE (NORTH)
BENTHAM, Riverside Caravan Park
BOROUGHBRIDGE, Boroughbridge C & C C Site
ELVINGTON, Elvington Lake Caravan Park
FILEY, Orchard Farm Holiday Village
HARROGATE, High Moor Farm Caravan Park
KNARESBOROUGH, Kingfisher C & C Park

HIGHLANDS
ACHARACLE, Resipole Holiday Park
ARISAIG, Portnardoran Caravan Site
AVIEMORE, Dalraddy Holiday Park
DUNDONNELL, Badrallach Bothy & Campsite
DURNESS, Sango Sands C & C Site
EDINBANE, Skye C & C Club Site
GLENCOE, Invercoe Caravan & Camping Park
ISLE OF SKYE, Glen Brittle Camp Site,
LOCHINVER, Clachtoll Campsite
ROY BRIDGE, Bunroy C & C Site
SPEAN BRIDGE, Gairlochy Holiday Park
STRATHPEFFER, Riverside C & C Park
UIG, Uig Bay Camping & Caravan Site
ULLAPOOL, Broomfield Holiday Park

LOTHIAN (WEST)
LINLITHGOW, Beecraigs C & C Site

MORAY
ABERLOUR, Aberlour Gardens Caravan Park
ELGIN, Riverside Caravan Park

PERTH & KINROSS
BLAIRGOWRIE, Nether Craig Holiday Park
DUNKELD, Inver Mill Farm Caravan Park
PITLOCHRY, Milton of Fonab Caravan Site
ST. FILLANS, Loch Earn Caravan Park
TUMMEL BRIDGE, Tummel Valley Holiday Park

SCOTTISH BORDERS
ETTRICK, Honey Cottage Caravan Park
HAWICK, Riverside Caravan Park

STIRLING
ABERFOYLE, Cobleland C & C Site
BALMAHA, Cashel Camp Site
SCALLANDER, Gart Caravan Park
CALLANDER, Keltie Bridge Caravan Park
FINTRY, Balgair Castle Holiday Park
KILLIN, Maragowan Caravan Club Site
STRATHYRE, Immervoulin C 7 C Park

WESTERN ISLES
HARRIS, Minch View Campsite,

Please take a moment to visit Cade's Facebook Page and 'Like It'. We can then keep you up to date with any news and events that we think may be of interest.

www.facebook.com/cadesguides

or scan the QR code.

Cosy but deadly

The carbon monoxide from a badly adjusted camping light or stove can kill.

Barbecues in enclosed spaces are lethal, too.

Make sure your camping light and stove are clean and properly adjusted. Never take a portable barbecue – or lit charcoal – into an enclosed space like a tent or caravan.

Make sure exhaust from generators is properly vented away from occupied areas

Carbon Monoxide (CO) is a colourless, odourless, highly poisonous gas that can kill in minutes. Carbon Monoxide poisoning can be caused by ANY fuel that burns or smoulders.

Watch out for the symptoms – • Mild headache • Dizziness • Nausea • Vomiting • Fatigue • Drowsiness •

CFOA
Chief Fire Officers Association

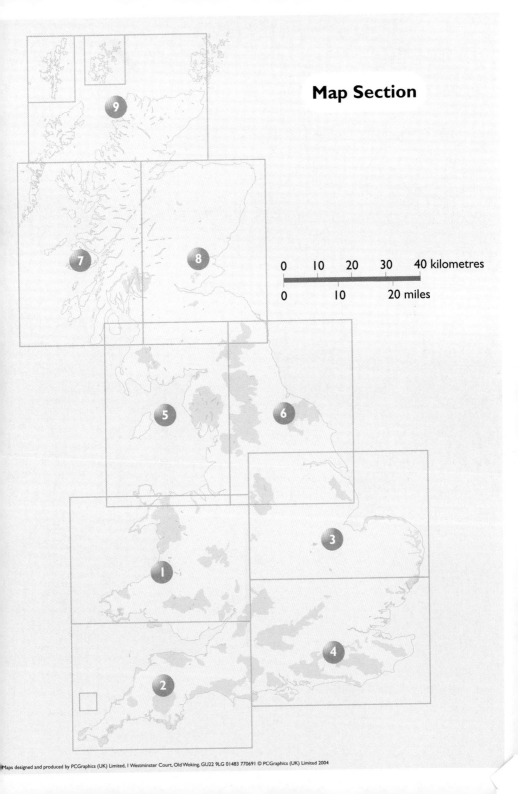

Map Section

0   10   20   30   40 kilometres

0   10   20 miles

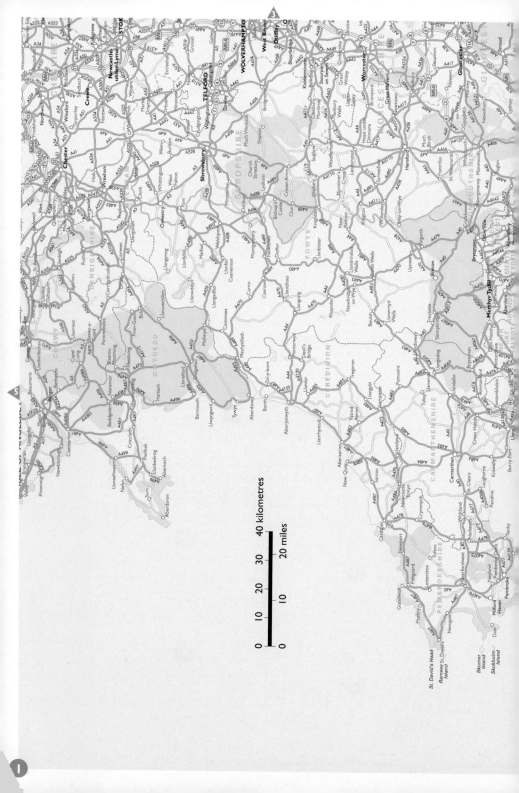

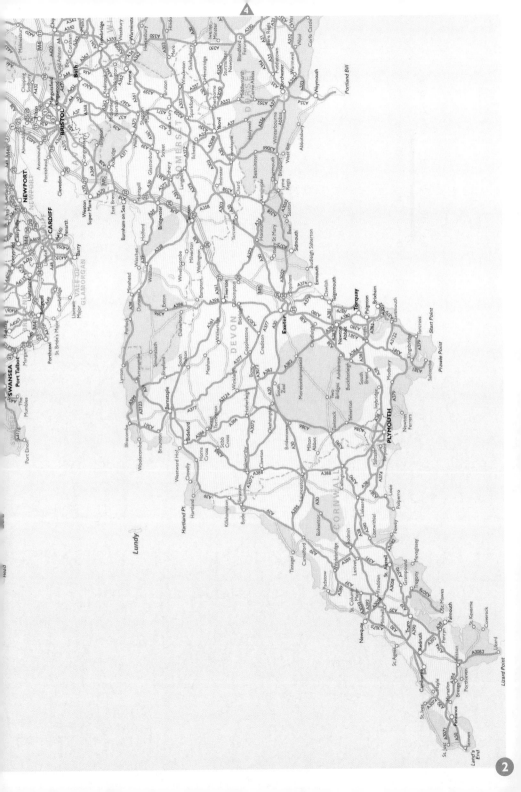

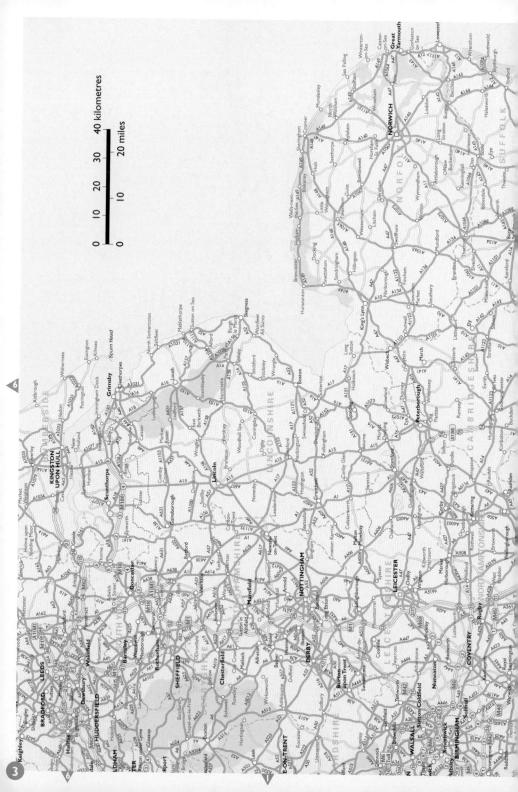

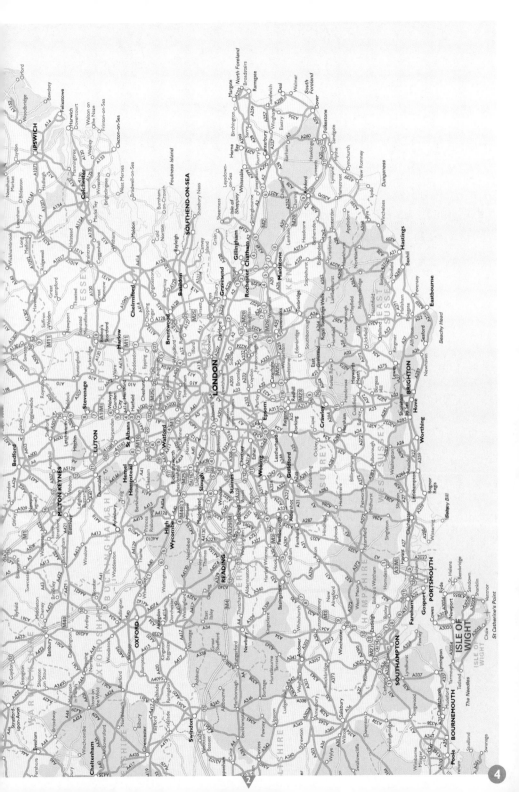

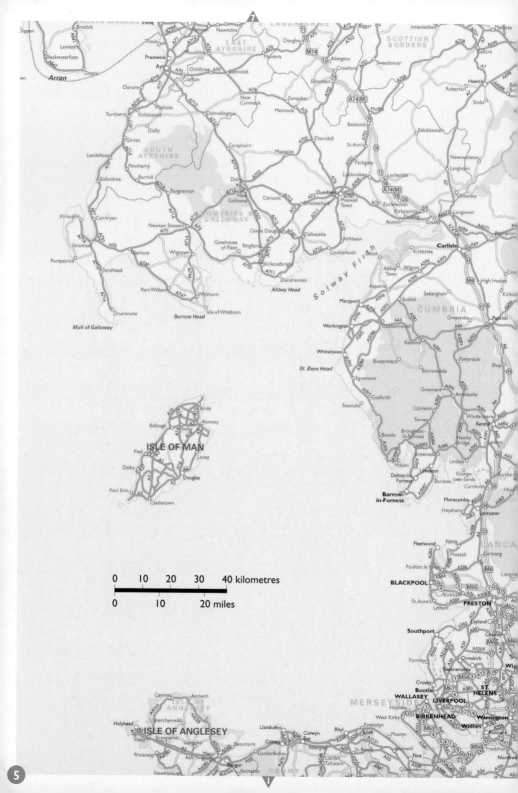

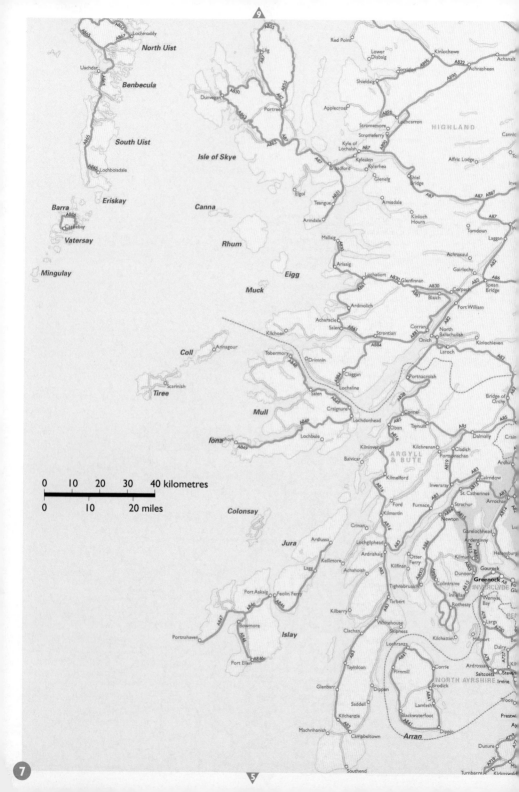

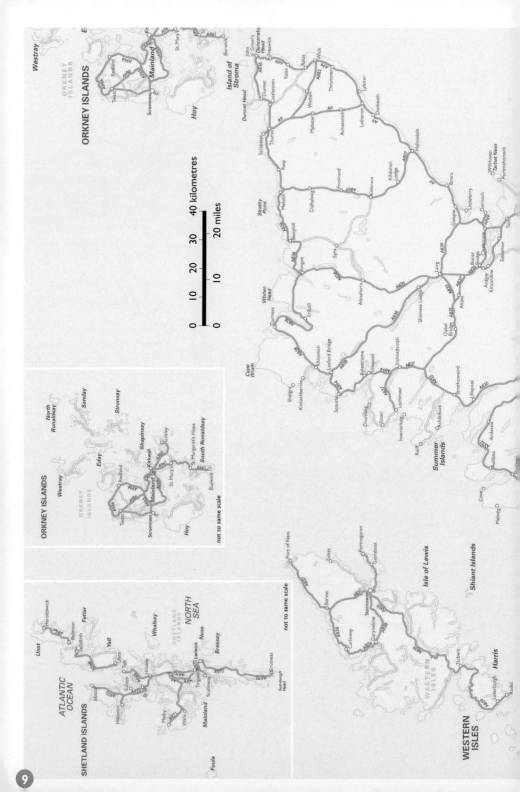

| CADE'S | ONE POUND | CADE'S | ONE POUND |

CAMPING, TOURING & MOTOR CARAVAN SITE GUIDE 2017

PRESENT THIS VOUCHER TO THE SITE OPERATOR WHEN PAYING TO RECEIVE ONE POUND DISCOUNT PER VOUCHER, PER NIGHT. SEE CONDITIONS OVERLEAF. VALID UNTIL 31-12-17

CAMPING, TOURING & MOTOR CARAVAN SITE GUIDE 2017

PRESENT THIS VOUCHER TO THE SITE OPERATOR WHEN PAYING TO RECEIVE ONE POUND DISCOUNT PER VOUCHER, PER NIGHT. SEE CONDITIONS OVERLEAF. VALID UNTIL 31-12-17

| CADE'S | ONE POUND | CADE'S | ONE POUND |

CAMPING, TOURING & MOTOR CARAVAN SITE GUIDE 2017

PRESENT THIS VOUCHER TO THE SITE OPERATOR WHEN PAYING TO RECEIVE ONE POUND DISCOUNT PER VOUCHER, PER NIGHT. SEE CONDITIONS OVERLEAF. VALID UNTIL 31-12-17

CAMPING, TOURING & MOTOR CARAVAN SITE GUIDE 2017

PRESENT THIS VOUCHER TO THE SITE OPERATOR WHEN PAYING TO RECEIVE ONE POUND DISCOUNT PER VOUCHER, PER NIGHT. SEE CONDITIONS OVERLEAF. VALID UNTIL 31-12-17

| CADE'S | ONE POUND | CADE'S | ONE POUND |

CAMPING, TOURING & MOTOR CARAVAN SITE GUIDE 2017

PRESENT THIS VOUCHER TO THE SITE OPERATOR WHEN PAYING TO RECEIVE ONE POUND DISCOUNT PER VOUCHER, PER NIGHT. SEE CONDITIONS OVERLEAF. VALID UNTIL 31-12-17

CAMPING, TOURING & MOTOR CARAVAN SITE GUIDE 2017

PRESENT THIS VOUCHER TO THE SITE OPERATOR WHEN PAYING TO RECEIVE ONE POUND DISCOUNT PER VOUCHER, PER NIGHT. SEE CONDITIONS OVERLEAF. VALID UNTIL 31-12-17

| CADE'S | ONE POUND | CADE'S | ONE POUND |

CAMPING, TOURING & MOTOR CARAVAN SITE GUIDE 2017

PRESENT THIS VOUCHER TO THE SITE OPERATOR WHEN PAYING TO RECEIVE ONE POUND DISCOUNT PER VOUCHER, PER NIGHT. SEE CONDITIONS OVERLEAF. VALID UNTIL 31-12-17

CAMPING, TOURING & MOTOR CARAVAN SITE GUIDE 2017

PRESENT THIS VOUCHER TO THE SITE OPERATOR WHEN PAYING TO RECEIVE ONE POUND DISCOUNT PER VOUCHER, PER NIGHT. SEE CONDITIONS OVERLEAF. VALID UNTIL 31-12-17

| CADE'S | ONE POUND | CADE'S | ONE POUND |

CAMPING, TOURING & MOTOR CARAVAN SITE GUIDE 2017

PRESENT THIS VOUCHER TO THE SITE OPERATOR WHEN PAYING TO RECEIVE ONE POUND DISCOUNT PER VOUCHER, PER NIGHT. SEE CONDITIONS OVERLEAF. VALID UNTIL 31-12-17

CAMPING, TOURING & MOTOR CARAVAN SITE GUIDE 2017

PRESENT THIS VOUCHER TO THE SITE OPERATOR WHEN PAYING TO RECEIVE ONE POUND DISCOUNT PER VOUCHER, PER NIGHT. SEE CONDITIONS OVERLEAF. VALID UNTIL 31-12-17

PITCH FEE DISCOUNT VOUCHERS

CONDITIONS OF USE

Vouchers will only be redeemed by those sites featuring a ⬛ symbol in the *facilities* line of their County entry. Presentation of this voucher to the Site Operator at the time of paying your balance will entitle you to a one pound discount per voucher, per night. (Only one voucher per night). Vouchers may be used in multiples i.e. five vouchers presented for a five night stay will entitle you to a discount of £5.00.

A **CADE'S CAMPING, TOURING & MOTOR CARAVAN SITE GUIDE 2017 EDITION** must be presented at the time of payment. Vouchers are valid for accommodation only. Vouchers may not be exchanged for cash. Not to be used with any other offer. Valid until 31-12-17.

CONDITIONS OF USE

Vouchers will only be redeemed by those sites featuring a ⬛ symbol in the *facilities* line of their County entry. Presentation of this voucher to the Site Operator at the time of paying your balance will entitle you to a one pound discount per voucher, per night. (Only one voucher per night). Vouchers may be used in multiples i.e. five vouchers presented for a five night stay will entitle you to a discount of £5.00.

A **CADE'S CAMPING, TOURING & MOTOR CARAVAN SITE GUIDE 2017 EDITION** must be presented at the time of payment. Vouchers are valid for accommodation only. Vouchers may not be exchanged for cash. Not to be used with any other offer. Valid until 31-12-17.

CONDITIONS OF USE

Vouchers will only be redeemed by those sites featuring a ⬛ symbol in the *facilities* line of their County entry. Presentation of this voucher to the Site Operator at the time of paying your balance will entitle you to a one pound discount per voucher, per night. (Only one voucher per night). Vouchers may be used in multiples i.e. five vouchers presented for a five night stay will entitle you to a discount of £5.00.

A **CADE'S CAMPING, TOURING & MOTOR CARAVAN SITE GUIDE 2017 EDITION** must be presented at the time of payment. Vouchers are valid for accommodation only. Vouchers may not be exchanged for cash. Not to be used with any other offer. Valid until 31-12-17.

CONDITIONS OF USE

Vouchers will only be redeemed by those sites featuring a ⬛ symbol in the *facilities* line of their County entry. Presentation of this voucher to the Site Operator at the time of paying your balance will entitle you to a one pound discount per voucher, per night. (Only one voucher per night). Vouchers may be used in multiples i.e. five vouchers presented for a five night stay will entitle you to a discount of £5.00.

A **CADE'S CAMPING, TOURING & MOTOR CARAVAN SITE GUIDE 2017 EDITION** must be presented at the time of payment. Vouchers are valid for accommodation only. Vouchers may not be exchanged for cash. Not to be used with any other offer. Valid until 31-12-17.

CONDITIONS OF USE

Vouchers will only be redeemed by those sites featuring a ⬛ symbol in the *facilities* line of their County entry. Presentation of this voucher to the Site Operator at the time of paying your balance will entitle you to a one pound discount per voucher, per night. (Only one voucher per night). Vouchers may be used in multiples i.e. five vouchers presented for a five night stay will entitle you to a discount of £5.00.

A **CADE'S CAMPING, TOURING & MOTOR CARAVAN SITE GUIDE 2017 EDITION** must be presented at the time of payment. Vouchers are valid for accommodation only. Vouchers may not be exchanged for cash. Not to be used with any other offer. Valid until 31-12-17.

CONDITIONS OF USE

Vouchers will only be redeemed by those sites featuring a ⬛ symbol in the *facilities* line of their County entry. Presentation of this voucher to the Site Operator at the time of paying your balance will entitle you to a one pound discount per voucher, per night. (Only one voucher per night). Vouchers may be used in multiples i.e. five vouchers presented for a five night stay will entitle you to a discount of £5.00.

A **CADE'S CAMPING, TOURING & MOTOR CARAVAN SITE GUIDE 2017 EDITION** must be presented at the time of payment. Vouchers are valid for accommodation only. Vouchers may not be exchanged for cash. Not to be used with any other offer. Valid until 31-12-17.

CONDITIONS OF USE

Vouchers will only be redeemed by those sites featuring a ⬛ symbol in the *facilities* line of their County entry. Presentation of this voucher to the Site Operator at the time of paying your balance will entitle you to a one pound discount per voucher, per night. (Only one voucher per night). Vouchers may be used in multiples i.e. five vouchers presented for a five night stay will entitle you to a discount of £5.00.

A **CADE'S CAMPING, TOURING & MOTOR CARAVAN SITE GUIDE 2017 EDITION** must be presented at the time of payment. Vouchers are valid for accommodation only. Vouchers may not be exchanged for cash. Not to be used with any other offer. Valid until 31-12-17.

CONDITIONS OF USE

Vouchers will only be redeemed by those sites featuring a ⬛ symbol in the *facilities* line of their County entry. Presentation of this voucher to the Site Operator at the time of paying your balance will entitle you to a one pound discount per voucher, per night. (Only one voucher per night). Vouchers may be used in multiples i.e. five vouchers presented for a five night stay will entitle you to a discount of £5.00.

A **CADE'S CAMPING, TOURING & MOTOR CARAVAN SITE GUIDE 2017 EDITION** must be presented at the time of payment. Vouchers are valid for accommodation only. Vouchers may not be exchanged for cash. Not to be used with any other offer. Valid until 31-12-17.

CONDITIONS OF USE

Vouchers will only be redeemed by those sites featuring a ⬛ symbol in the *facilities* line of their County entry. Presentation of this voucher to the Site Operator at the time of paying your balance will entitle you to a one pound discount per voucher, per night. (Only one voucher per night). Vouchers may be used in multiples i.e. five vouchers presented for a five night stay will entitle you to a discount of £5.00.

A **CADE'S CAMPING, TOURING & MOTOR CARAVAN SITE GUIDE 2017 EDITION** must be presented at the time of payment. Vouchers are valid for accommodation only. Vouchers may not be exchanged for cash. Not to be used with any other offer. Valid until 31-12-17.

CONDITIONS OF USE

Vouchers will only be redeemed by those sites featuring a ⬛ symbol in the *facilities* line of their County entry. Presentation of this voucher to the Site Operator at the time of paying your balance will entitle you to a one pound discount per voucher, per night. (Only one voucher per night). Vouchers may be used in multiples i.e. five vouchers presented for a five night stay will entitle you to a discount of £5.00.

A **CADE'S CAMPING, TOURING & MOTOR CARAVAN SITE GUIDE 2017 EDITION** must be presented at the time of payment. Vouchers are valid for accommodation only. Vouchers may not be exchanged for cash. Not to be used with any other offer. Valid until 31-12-17.

CADE'S — ONE POUND	CADE'S — ONE POUND
CAMPING, TOURING & MOTOR CARAVAN SITE GUIDE 2017 PRESENT THIS VOUCHER TO THE SITE OPERATOR WHEN PAYING TO RECEIVE ONE POUND DISCOUNT PER VOUCHER, PER NIGHT. SEE CONDITIONS OVERLEAF. VALID UNTIL 31-12-17	**CAMPING, TOURING & MOTOR CARAVAN SITE GUIDE 2017** PRESENT THIS VOUCHER TO THE SITE OPERATOR WHEN PAYING TO RECEIVE ONE POUND DISCOUNT PER VOUCHER, PER NIGHT. SEE CONDITIONS OVERLEAF. VALID UNTIL 31-12-17
CAMPING, TOURING & MOTOR CARAVAN SITE GUIDE 2017 PRESENT THIS VOUCHER TO THE SITE OPERATOR WHEN PAYING TO RECEIVE ONE POUND DISCOUNT PER VOUCHER, PER NIGHT. SEE CONDITIONS OVERLEAF. VALID UNTIL 31-12-17	**CAMPING, TOURING & MOTOR CARAVAN SITE GUIDE 2017** PRESENT THIS VOUCHER TO THE SITE OPERATOR WHEN PAYING TO RECEIVE ONE POUND DISCOUNT PER VOUCHER, PER NIGHT. SEE CONDITIONS OVERLEAF. VALID UNTIL 31-12-17
CAMPING, TOURING & MOTOR CARAVAN SITE GUIDE 2017 PRESENT THIS VOUCHER TO THE SITE OPERATOR WHEN PAYING TO RECEIVE ONE POUND DISCOUNT PER VOUCHER, PER NIGHT. SEE CONDITIONS OVERLEAF. VALID UNTIL 31-12-17	**CAMPING, TOURING & MOTOR CARAVAN SITE GUIDE 2017** PRESENT THIS VOUCHER TO THE SITE OPERATOR WHEN PAYING TO RECEIVE ONE POUND DISCOUNT PER VOUCHER, PER NIGHT. SEE CONDITIONS OVERLEAF. VALID UNTIL 31-12-17
CAMPING, TOURING & MOTOR CARAVAN SITE GUIDE 2017 PRESENT THIS VOUCHER TO THE SITE OPERATOR WHEN PAYING TO RECEIVE ONE POUND DISCOUNT PER VOUCHER, PER NIGHT. SEE CONDITIONS OVERLEAF. VALID UNTIL 31-12-17	**CAMPING, TOURING & MOTOR CARAVAN SITE GUIDE 2017** PRESENT THIS VOUCHER TO THE SITE OPERATOR WHEN PAYING TO RECEIVE ONE POUND DISCOUNT PER VOUCHER, PER NIGHT. SEE CONDITIONS OVERLEAF. VALID UNTIL 31-12-17
CAMPING, TOURING & MOTOR CARAVAN SITE GUIDE 2017 PRESENT THIS VOUCHER TO THE SITE OPERATOR WHEN PAYING TO RECEIVE ONE POUND DISCOUNT PER VOUCHER, PER NIGHT. SEE CONDITIONS OVERLEAF. VALID UNTIL 31-12-17	**CAMPING, TOURING & MOTOR CARAVAN SITE GUIDE 2017** PRESENT THIS VOUCHER TO THE SITE OPERATOR WHEN PAYING TO RECEIVE ONE POUND DISCOUNT PER VOUCHER, PER NIGHT. SEE CONDITIONS OVERLEAF. VALID UNTIL 31-12-17

CONDITIONS OF USE

Vouchers will only be redeemed by those sites featuring a ▣ symbol in the *facilities* line of their County entry. Presentation of this voucher to the Site Operator at the time of paying your balance will entitle you to a one pound discount per voucher, per night. (Only one voucher per night). Vouchers may be used in multiples i.e. five vouchers presented for a five night stay will entitle you to a discount of £5.00.

A **CADE'S CAMPING, TOURING & MOTOR CARAVAN SITE GUIDE 2017 EDITION** must be presented at the time of payment. Vouchers are valid for accommodation only. Vouchers may not be exchanged for cash. Not to be used with any other offer. Valid until 31-12-17.

CONDITIONS OF USE

Vouchers will only be redeemed by those sites featuring a ▣ symbol in the *facilities* line of their County entry. Presentation of this voucher to the Site Operator at the time of paying your balance will entitle you to a one pound discount per voucher, per night. (Only one voucher per night). Vouchers may be used in multiples i.e. five vouchers presented for a five night stay will entitle you to a discount of £5.00.

A **CADE'S CAMPING, TOURING & MOTOR CARAVAN SITE GUIDE 2017 EDITION** must be presented at the time of payment. Vouchers are valid for accommodation only. Vouchers may not be exchanged for cash. Not to be used with any other offer. Valid until 31-12-17.

CONDITIONS OF USE

Vouchers will only be redeemed by those sites featuring a ▣ symbol in the *facilities* line of their County entry. Presentation of this voucher to the Site Operator at the time of paying your balance will entitle you to a one pound discount per voucher, per night. (Only one voucher per night). Vouchers may be used in multiples i.e. five vouchers presented for a five night stay will entitle you to a discount of £5.00.

A **CADE'S CAMPING, TOURING & MOTOR CARAVAN SITE GUIDE 2017 EDITION** must be presented at the time of payment. Vouchers are valid for accommodation only. Vouchers may not be exchanged for cash. Not to be used with any other offer. Valid until 31-12-17.

CONDITIONS OF USE

Vouchers will only be redeemed by those sites featuring a ▣ symbol in the *facilities* line of their County entry. Presentation of this voucher to the Site Operator at the time of paying your balance will entitle you to a one pound discount per voucher, per night. (Only one voucher per night). Vouchers may be used in multiples i.e. five vouchers presented for a five night stay will entitle you to a discount of £5.00.

A **CADE'S CAMPING, TOURING & MOTOR CARAVAN SITE GUIDE 2017 EDITION** must be presented at the time of payment. Vouchers are valid for accommodation only. Vouchers may not be exchanged for cash. Not to be used with any other offer. Valid until 31-12-17.

CONDITIONS OF USE

Vouchers will only be redeemed by those sites featuring a ▣ symbol in the *facilities* line of their County entry. Presentation of this voucher to the Site Operator at the time of paying your balance will entitle you to a one pound discount per voucher, per night. (Only one voucher per night). Vouchers may be used in multiples i.e. five vouchers presented for a five night stay will entitle you to a discount of £5.00.

A **CADE'S CAMPING, TOURING & MOTOR CARAVAN SITE GUIDE 2017 EDITION** must be presented at the time of payment. Vouchers are valid for accommodation only. Vouchers may not be exchanged for cash. Not to be used with any other offer. Valid until 31-12-17.

CONDITIONS OF USE

Vouchers will only be redeemed by those sites featuring a ▣ symbol in the *facilities* line of their County entry. Presentation of this voucher to the Site Operator at the time of paying your balance will entitle you to a one pound discount per voucher, per night. (Only one voucher per night). Vouchers may be used in multiples i.e. five vouchers presented for a five night stay will entitle you to a discount of £5.00.

A **CADE'S CAMPING, TOURING & MOTOR CARAVAN SITE GUIDE 2017 EDITION** must be presented at the time of payment. Vouchers are valid for accommodation only. Vouchers may not be exchanged for cash. Not to be used with any other offer. Valid until 31-12-17.

CONDITIONS OF USE

Vouchers will only be redeemed by those sites featuring a ▣ symbol in the *facilities* line of their County entry. Presentation of this voucher to the Site Operator at the time of paying your balance will entitle you to a one pound discount per voucher, per night. (Only one voucher per night). Vouchers may be used in multiples i.e. five vouchers presented for a five night stay will entitle you to a discount of £5.00.

A **CADE'S CAMPING, TOURING & MOTOR CARAVAN SITE GUIDE 2017 EDITION** must be presented at the time of payment. Vouchers are valid for accommodation only. Vouchers may not be exchanged for cash. Not to be used with any other offer. Valid until 31-12-17.

CONDITIONS OF USE

Vouchers will only be redeemed by those sites featuring a ▣ symbol in the *facilities* line of their County entry. Presentation of this voucher to the Site Operator at the time of paying your balance will entitle you to a one pound discount per voucher, per night. (Only one voucher per night). Vouchers may be used in multiples i.e. five vouchers presented for a five night stay will entitle you to a discount of £5.00.

A **CADE'S CAMPING, TOURING & MOTOR CARAVAN SITE GUIDE 2017 EDITION** must be presented at the time of payment. Vouchers are valid for accommodation only. Vouchers may not be exchanged for cash. Not to be used with any other offer. Valid until 31-12-17.

CONDITIONS OF USE

Vouchers will only be redeemed by those sites featuring a ▣ symbol in the *facilities* line of their County entry. Presentation of this voucher to the Site Operator at the time of paying your balance will entitle you to a one pound discount per voucher, per night. (Only one voucher per night). Vouchers may be used in multiples i.e. five vouchers presented for a five night stay will entitle you to a discount of £5.00.

A **CADE'S CAMPING, TOURING & MOTOR CARAVAN SITE GUIDE 2017 EDITION** must be presented at the time of payment. Vouchers are valid for accommodation only. Vouchers may not be exchanged for cash. Not to be used with any other offer. Valid until 31-12-17.

CONDITIONS OF USE

Vouchers will only be redeemed by those sites featuring a ▣ symbol in the *facilities* line of their County entry. Presentation of this voucher to the Site Operator at the time of paying your balance will entitle you to a one pound discount per voucher, per night. (Only one voucher per night). Vouchers may be used in multiples i.e. five vouchers presented for a five night stay will entitle you to a discount of £5.00.

A **CADE'S CAMPING, TOURING & MOTOR CARAVAN SITE GUIDE 2017 EDITION** must be presented at the time of payment. Vouchers are valid for accommodation only. Vouchers may not be exchanged for cash. Not to be used with any other offer. Valid until 31-12-17.

CADE'S   ONE POUND

CAMPING, TOURING & MOTOR CARAVAN SITE GUIDE 2017

PRESENT THIS VOUCHER TO THE SITE OPERATOR WHEN
PAYING TO RECEIVE ONE POUND DISCOUNT PER
VOUCHER, PER NIGHT. SEE CONDITIONS OVERLEAF.
VALID UNTIL 31-12-17

CADE'S   ONE POUND

CAMPING, TOURING & MOTOR CARAVAN SITE GUIDE 2017

PRESENT THIS VOUCHER TO THE SITE OPERATOR WHEN
PAYING TO RECEIVE ONE POUND DISCOUNT PER
VOUCHER, PER NIGHT. SEE CONDITIONS OVERLEAF.
VALID UNTIL 31-12-17

CADE'S   ONE POUND

CAMPING, TOURING & MOTOR CARAVAN SITE GUIDE 2017

PRESENT THIS VOUCHER TO THE SITE OPERATOR WHEN
PAYING TO RECEIVE ONE POUND DISCOUNT PER
VOUCHER, PER NIGHT. SEE CONDITIONS OVERLEAF.
VALID UNTIL 31-12-17

CADE'S   ONE POUND

CAMPING, TOURING & MOTOR CARAVAN SITE GUIDE 2017

PRESENT THIS VOUCHER TO THE SITE OPERATOR WHEN
PAYING TO RECEIVE ONE POUND DISCOUNT PER
VOUCHER, PER NIGHT. SEE CONDITIONS OVERLEAF.
VALID UNTIL 31-12-17

CADE'S   ONE POUND

CAMPING, TOURING & MOTOR CARAVAN SITE GUIDE 2017

PRESENT THIS VOUCHER TO THE SITE OPERATOR WHEN
PAYING TO RECEIVE ONE POUND DISCOUNT PER
VOUCHER, PER NIGHT. SEE CONDITIONS OVERLEAF.
VALID UNTIL 31-12-17

CADE'S   ONE POUND

CAMPING, TOURING & MOTOR CARAVAN SITE GUIDE 2017

PRESENT THIS VOUCHER TO THE SITE OPERATOR WHEN
PAYING TO RECEIVE ONE POUND DISCOUNT PER
VOUCHER, PER NIGHT. SEE CONDITIONS OVERLEAF.
VALID UNTIL 31-12-17

CADE'S   ONE POUND

CAMPING, TOURING & MOTOR CARAVAN SITE GUIDE 2017

PRESENT THIS VOUCHER TO THE SITE OPERATOR WHEN
PAYING TO RECEIVE ONE POUND DISCOUNT PER
VOUCHER, PER NIGHT. SEE CONDITIONS OVERLEAF.
VALID UNTIL 31-12-17

CADE'S   ONE POUND

CAMPING, TOURING & MOTOR CARAVAN SITE GUIDE 2017

PRESENT THIS VOUCHER TO THE SITE OPERATOR WHEN
PAYING TO RECEIVE ONE POUND DISCOUNT PER
VOUCHER, PER NIGHT. SEE CONDITIONS OVERLEAF.
VALID UNTIL 31-12-17

CADE'S   ONE POUND

CAMPING, TOURING & MOTOR CARAVAN SITE GUIDE 2017

PRESENT THIS VOUCHER TO THE SITE OPERATOR WHEN
PAYING TO RECEIVE ONE POUND DISCOUNT PER
VOUCHER, PER NIGHT. SEE CONDITIONS OVERLEAF.
VALID UNTIL 31-12-17

CADE'S   ONE POUND

CAMPING, TOURING & MOTOR CARAVAN SITE GUIDE 2017

PRESENT THIS VOUCHER TO THE SITE OPERATOR WHEN
PAYING TO RECEIVE ONE POUND DISCOUNT PER
VOUCHER, PER NIGHT. SEE CONDITIONS OVERLEAF.
VALID UNTIL 31-12-17

CONDITIONS OF USE

Vouchers will only be redeemed by those sites featuring a ◪ symbol in the *facilities* line of their County entry. Presentation of this voucher to the Site Operator at the time of paying your balance will entitle you to a one pound discount per voucher, per night. (Only one voucher per night). Vouchers may be used in multiples i.e. five vouchers presented for a five night stay will entitle you to a discount of £5.00.

A **CADE'S CAMPING, TOURING & MOTOR CARAVAN SITE GUIDE 2017 EDITION** must be presented at the time of payment. Vouchers are valid for accommodation only. Vouchers may not be exchanged for cash. Not to be used with any other offer. Valid until 31-12-17.

CONDITIONS OF USE

Vouchers will only be redeemed by those sites featuring a ◪ symbol in the *facilities* line of their County entry. Presentation of this voucher to the Site Operator at the time of paying your balance will entitle you to a one pound discount per voucher, per night. (Only one voucher per night). Vouchers may be used in multiples i.e. five vouchers presented for a five night stay will entitle you to a discount of £5.00.

A **CADE'S CAMPING, TOURING & MOTOR CARAVAN SITE GUIDE 2017 EDITION** must be presented at the time of payment. Vouchers are valid for accommodation only. Vouchers may not be exchanged for cash. Not to be used with any other offer. Valid until 31-12-17.

CONDITIONS OF USE

Vouchers will only be redeemed by those sites featuring a ◪ symbol in the *facilities* line of their County entry. Presentation of this voucher to the Site Operator at the time of paying your balance will entitle you to a one pound discount per voucher, per night. (Only one voucher per night). Vouchers may be used in multiples i.e. five vouchers presented for a five night stay will entitle you to a discount of £5.00.

A **CADE'S CAMPING, TOURING & MOTOR CARAVAN SITE GUIDE 2017 EDITION** must be presented at the time of payment. Vouchers are valid for accommodation only. Vouchers may not be exchanged for cash. Not to be used with any other offer. Valid until 31-12-17.

CONDITIONS OF USE

Vouchers will only be redeemed by those sites featuring a ◪ symbol in the *facilities* line of their County entry. Presentation of this voucher to the Site Operator at the time of paying your balance will entitle you to a one pound discount per voucher, per night. (Only one voucher per night). Vouchers may be used in multiples i.e. five vouchers presented for a five night stay will entitle you to a discount of £5.00.

A **CADE'S CAMPING, TOURING & MOTOR CARAVAN SITE GUIDE 2017 EDITION** must be presented at the time of payment. Vouchers are valid for accommodation only. Vouchers may not be exchanged for cash. Not to be used with any other offer. Valid until 31-12-17.

CONDITIONS OF USE

Vouchers will only be redeemed by those sites featuring a ◪ symbol in the *facilities* line of their County entry. Presentation of this voucher to the Site Operator at the time of paying your balance will entitle you to a one pound discount per voucher, per night. (Only one voucher per night). Vouchers may be used in multiples i.e. five vouchers presented for a five night stay will entitle you to a discount of £5.00.

A **CADE'S CAMPING, TOURING & MOTOR CARAVAN SITE GUIDE 2017 EDITION** must be presented at the time of payment. Vouchers are valid for accommodation only. Vouchers may not be exchanged for cash. Not to be used with any other offer. Valid until 31-12-17.

CONDITIONS OF USE

Vouchers will only be redeemed by those sites featuring a ◪ symbol in the *facilities* line of their County entry. Presentation of this voucher to the Site Operator at the time of paying your balance will entitle you to a one pound discount per voucher, per night. (Only one voucher per night). Vouchers may be used in multiples i.e. five vouchers presented for a five night stay will entitle you to a discount of £5.00.

A **CADE'S CAMPING, TOURING & MOTOR CARAVAN SITE GUIDE 2017 EDITION** must be presented at the time of payment. Vouchers are valid for accommodation only. Vouchers may not be exchanged for cash. Not to be used with any other offer. Valid until 31-12-17.

CONDITIONS OF USE

Vouchers will only be redeemed by those sites featuring a ◪ symbol in the *facilities* line of their County entry. Presentation of this voucher to the Site Operator at the time of paying your balance will entitle you to a one pound discount per voucher, per night. (Only one voucher per night). Vouchers may be used in multiples i.e. five vouchers presented for a five night stay will entitle you to a discount of £5.00.

A **CADE'S CAMPING, TOURING & MOTOR CARAVAN SITE GUIDE 2017 EDITION** must be presented at the time of payment. Vouchers are valid for accommodation only. Vouchers may not be exchanged for cash. Not to be used with any other offer. Valid until 31-12-17.

CONDITIONS OF USE

Vouchers will only be redeemed by those sites featuring a ◪ symbol in the *facilities* line of their County entry. Presentation of this voucher to the Site Operator at the time of paying your balance will entitle you to a one pound discount per voucher, per night. (Only one voucher per night). Vouchers may be used in multiples i.e. five vouchers presented for a five night stay will entitle you to a discount of £5.00.

A **CADE'S CAMPING, TOURING & MOTOR CARAVAN SITE GUIDE 2017 EDITION** must be presented at the time of payment. Vouchers are valid for accommodation only. Vouchers may not be exchanged for cash. Not to be used with any other offer. Valid until 31-12-17.

CONDITIONS OF USE

Vouchers will only be redeemed by those sites featuring a ◪ symbol in the *facilities* line of their County entry. Presentation of this voucher to the Site Operator at the time of paying your balance will entitle you to a one pound discount per voucher, per night. (Only one voucher per night). Vouchers may be used in multiples i.e. five vouchers presented for a five night stay will entitle you to a discount of £5.00.

A **CADE'S CAMPING, TOURING & MOTOR CARAVAN SITE GUIDE 2017 EDITION** must be presented at the time of payment. Vouchers are valid for accommodation only. Vouchers may not be exchanged for cash. Not to be used with any other offer. Valid until 31-12-17.

CONDITIONS OF USE

Vouchers will only be redeemed by those sites featuring a ◪ symbol in the *facilities* line of their County entry. Presentation of this voucher to the Site Operator at the time of paying your balance will entitle you to a one pound discount per voucher, per night. (Only one voucher per night). Vouchers may be used in multiples i.e. five vouchers presented for a five night stay will entitle you to a discount of £5.00.

A **CADE'S CAMPING, TOURING & MOTOR CARAVAN SITE GUIDE 2017 EDITION** must be presented at the time of payment. Vouchers are valid for accommodation only. Vouchers may not be exchanged for cash. Not to be used with any other offer. Valid until 31-12-17.

Family Fun
for everyone!

Billing Aquadrome is set in over 235 acres of beautiful Northamptonshire countryside located in the heart of England. The park offers an abundance of activities with cycling, country walks, fishing, fun fair, crazy golf and events throughout the year.

Facilities available include a modern leisure complex with bars and restaurants, arcade, indoor pool with splash zone, water flume, Jacuzzi and soft play area.

ISBN 978-1-905963-19-5

9 781905 963195

10799

UK RETAIL PRICE £7.99

Tent Pitches
from £16 per night

Camping Pods
from £42 per night

Touring Pitches
from £16 per night

Call us 01604 408181   *or Visit* billingaquadrome.com

BILLING AQUADROME, CROW LANE, NORTHAMPTON NN3 9DA